CONCEPT OF SOIL SCIENCE

Dr. S.G. RAJPUT
M.Sc. (JRF), NET, Ph.D.
Gold Medalist (JAU, Gujarat)
Department of Soil Science & Agricultural Chemistry
Brahmanand Post Graduate College, Rath (Hamirpur) U.P.- 210 431
A Premier Agriculture College of Bundelkhand University, Jhansi 284128 (INDIA)

KALYANI PUBLISHERS
LUDHIANA • NEW DELHI • NOIDA (U.P.) • HYDERABAD • CHENNAI
KOLKATA • CUTTACK • GUWAHATI • KOCHI • BENGALURU

KALYANI PUBLISHERS

Head Office

B-1/1292, Rajinder Nagar, **Ludhiana**-141 008 • Ph : 0161-2760031, 2745756
E-mail : kalyanibooks@yahoo.co.in **Website :** www.kalyanipublishers.co.in

Administration Office

4779/23, Ansari Road, Daryaganj, **New Delhi**-110 002 • Ph : 011-23271469, 23274393
E-mail : kalyani_delhi@yahoo.co.in, kalyani_delhi@kalyanipublishers.in

Works

B-16, Sector-8, **NOIDA** (U.P.)

Branches

1, Mahalakshmi Street, T. Nagar, **Chennai**-600 017 • Ph : 044-24344684
Gopabandhu Lane, Behind Govt. Bus Stand, Badambadi, **Cuttack**-753 012 (Odisha) • Ph : 0671-2311391
4-3-65/2/A, Behind HVS Public School, Raghunath Bagh
Sultan Bazar, **Hyderabad**-500 095 • Ph : 040-24750368
10/2B, Ramanath Mazumdar Street, **Kolkata**-700 009 • Ph : 033-22416024
Arunalaya, 1st Floor, Saraswati Road, Pan Bazar, **Guwahati**-781 001 • Ph : 0361-2731274
Koratti Parambil House, Convent Road, **Kochi**-682 035 • Ph : 0484-2367189
No. 24 & 25, 1st Floor, Hameed Shah Complex, Cubbonpet Main Road, **Bengaluru**-560 002

16 + 612 = 628 Pages 28" x 40" 39.25 Formes

KPP R 33260 05

Second Revised and Enlarged Edition, 2021

Typesetting at
Times Printographic

ISBN 978-93-272-2605-8

PRINTED IN INDIA

at Diamond Agencies Pvt. Ltd., B-125, Sec. 63, NOIDA

ACKNOWLEDGEMENT

The availability of information of information on Soil Science is scare in India for the student to prepare for competitive examinations such as ARS/NET/SRF/JRF/UPSC/PCS & SAUs Exams and UG, PG courses.

I acknowledge with thanks to Dr. J.V. Veshampayan, Hon'ble Vice-Chancellor, Bundelkhand University, Jhansi; Dr. I.P. Singh, President of the College Managing Committee; for providing necessary amenities, who are the source of inspiration, which enable me to write to this text book.

I express my great sentiments of regards and indebtedness my Dr. RD Mahan, Ex-Principal & HOD; Dr. Neelam Kumar Singh, Principal, Dr. Kailash, Ex Principal & HOD Physics, Dr. Surendra Singh, Ex-Principal & HOD GPB, Dr. Balwant Singh, Prof. Halkey Prasad, Dr. NK Singh, Dr. VK Singh, Dr. BK Pandey, Dr. RS Singh, K. Ram and RP Singh, of the Brahmanand PG College, Rath (Hamirpur) U.P. and Dr. K.B. Polara, Professor, and Dr. N.B. Babaria, Professor & Head, Deptt. of Agril. Chem. & Soil Science, J.A.U. Junagadh (Gujarat), Dr. DD Tiwari Ex-Professor & Head, Dr. AK Sachan, Professor, Deptt. of Agril. Chem. & Soil Science, C.S. Azad University of Agric. & Tech., Kanpur for their constant attention and guidance completion of text book.

I would like to express special thanks to Dr. Kripa Shankar, Ex-Registrar & HOD Entomology, Dr. Dhoom Singh, Director, Dr. Haresh Pratap Singh, Registrar of the C.S. Azad University of Agric. & Tech., Kanpur, Dr. S.K. Uttam, Dr. Musnish Kumar, Dr. RP Singh, Dr. Sarvesh Kumar Deptt. of Soil Cons. & Water Mgnt., C.S. Azad University of Agric. & Tech., Kanpur; Dr. P.K. Rajput, Janta College, Bakewar and my nearest Dr. Dashrath Singh, Dr. Sarju Narain from Brahmanand PG College, Rath (Hamirpur) U.P., Dr. Vishnu Rajput, Scientist, Russia for his support and guidelines completion of text book without which my task could not have been accomplished.

I fully acknowledge the most willing help, unending love and co-operation from my friends cum brothers Dr. Shailendra, Dr. Jitendra; Dr. AN Shukla; Dr. Umesh Chandra; Dr. UC Tripathi; Dr. Umakant; Dr. UC Mishra; Dr. Rajendra Kumar, Dr. Sheela Singh, Dr. Kamlesh Rajput, Dr. Arun Kumar, OS, Shri Dharam Pal Singh, Shri Brajesh, Shri Veerendra, Shri Shailendra from the Brahmanand PG College, Rath (Hamirpur) U.P; and my nearest friend always with me Dr. Ravi, Asstt. Prof. (Dhampur), Pradeep (FSO), Dr. Somraj (Bank Manager), Umesh (PCS-DHO), Dr. Yogesh (AP), Dr. Hemant (MI), Raj Yadav (MI); Dr. Sunil Yadav (ARS), Prem (Bank Manager), Kalyan (TA), Gendan, Pavan Maurya (Bank Manager), Ravendra (TA), and Manoj Rajput (Bank Manager) their unending help during the writing text book, for their timely help.

At last but foremost, I express deepest sense of gratitude to my beloved parents Mr. P.S. Rajput and Mr. Yadram Rajput, Smt. Kusumlata, and my brothers Mahendra, Vinod, and my Bhabhi Kunti, Vimla with lovely nice nephews Soni, Mona, Ram Ji, Syam Ji & Satyam whose selfless love, filial affection, constant encouragement, obstinate sacrifices, sincere prayers, expectations and blessings have always been vital source of inspiration in my life.

I heartily thank my wife Vijay Laxmi Rajput and son Divya Pratap Singh & Daughter Divyanshi who was always with me in my mind and heart and continuously inspired me for the completion of this text book.

There are number of well wishers whom I cannot forget and I thank to one and all associated with me directly and indirectly.

Last but not least I am very sincerely thankful to my beloved Swami Brahmanand Ji Maharaj whose grace is always to motivate and inspiring to me for every moment of my work.

2021 **S.G. RAJPUT**

Dedicated

to

Most Spiritual

Swami Brahmanand Ji Maharaj

And

My Late Mother

लाखन सिंह राजपूत
राज्य मंत्री
कृषि, कृषि शिक्षा एवं अनुसंधान विभाग
उत्तर प्रदेश

सं० 354 /वी.आई.पी./रा.म.कृ./कृ.शि./20
उत्तर प्रदेश सचिवालय,
F1/2, बापू भवन, पंचम तल,
लखनऊ
दूरभाष : 0522-2235342(का०)
दिनांक : 07/12/20

Foreword Second Edition

Despite the connections between soils and human health, there has not been a great amount of attention focused on this area when compared to many other fields of scientific study. The agriculture education or research is dynamic nature in term of content, practices, resources, knowledge etc. Soils and Human Health brings together authors from diverse fields with an interest in soils and human health, including soil science, geology, geography, biology, and anthropology to investigate this issue from a number of perspectives. Among the basic assets of agriculture, soil is vital component. Unfortunately, integrated knowledge of various aspects of Soil Pedology, Soil Physics, Soil Chemistry, Soil Fertility, Soil Conservation etc. is not very common. Consequently, we see extensive abuse of the soil in our country. It may takes a century to make one centimeter of top soil but all this work of nature can be destroyed in no time either due to erosion arising from improper management or other human activities like removing good soil for making bricks. The care and maintenance of soil health is, therefore, upmost important for safeguarding future of agriculture.

In a scientific world where the trend has often been ever-increasing specialization and increasingly difficult communication between fields and subfields, the interdisciplinary nature of soils and human health studies presents a significant challenge going forward. Fields with an interest in soils and human health need to have increased cross-disciplinary communication and cooperation. This book is a step in the direction of accessibility and innovation, elucidating the state of knowledge in the meeting of soil and health sciences, and identifying places where more work is needed.

The book "CONCEPT OF SOIL SCIENCE" second edition includes four primer chapter covers different aspects of soil science with suitable illustrations using from Indian data. The interpretation of subject matter has been made carefully and systematically in each chapter making its book useful for competitive examinations and for the curriculum of graduate, post graduate and research in respect to agriculture and allied disciplines.

I hope that this book would be great value for the students and all of these interested in soil science. I complement the author for giving all the usable information on the subject at is place.

04.12.2020

Advo. Lakhan Singh Rajput
State Agriculture Minister (Agriculture, Agriculture Education & Research)
Government of Uttar Pradesh, Lucknow

FOREWORD

FIRST EDITION

Among the basic assets of agriculture, soil is vital component. Unfortunately, integrated knowledge of various aspects of Soil Pedology, Soil Physics, Soil Chemistry, Soil Fertility, Soil Conservation etc. is not very common. Consequently, we see extensive abuse of the soil in our country. It may takes a century to make one centimeter of top soil but all this work of nature can be destroyed in no time either due to erosion arising from improper management or other human activities like removing good soil for making bricks. The care and maintenance of soil health is, therefore, upmost important for safeguarding future of agriculture.

The text book "CONCEPT OF SOIL SCIENCE" comprising of thirty chapters covers different aspects of soil science with suitable illustrations using from Indian data. The interpretation of subject matter has been made carefully and systematically in each chapter making its book useful for competitive examinations like ARS, NET, SRF, JRF, UPSC, PCS, SAUs exam etc.

I hope that this book would be great value for the students and all of these interested in soil science. I complement the author for giving all the usable information on the subject at is place.

G.C. Tiwari
Vice-Chancellor
C.S. Azad University of Agric. & Tech.,
Kanpur-208 002 (INDIA)

PREFACE

SECOND EDITION

It is great feeling for us to write the preface for the second edition of CONCEPT OF SOIL SCIENCE. The first edition received overwhelming support and was appreciated by both the teachers and students. We feel greatly satisfied by the positive response of the academic community. But we do realize that it has been now over almost eight year since the first edition appeared in 2012, and a revision had become overdue.

The book has covered the syllabus prescribed by ICAR as per recommendation of Fifth Deans' Committee on Higher Agricultureal Education in India *w.e.f.* 2016-17 for under-graduate courses in Agriculture, Forestry, Horticulture, Engineering, Animal Husbandry & Dairying and Sericulture curriculum as Fundamental of Soil Sciences, Soil Manure, Fertilizer and Soil Fertility Management, and Problematic Soil and their Management, etc, incorporated; and the availability of information on soil science is scare in India for the student to prepare for competitive examinations such as ARS/NET/SRF/JRF/UPSC/PCS & SAUs Exams, and guiding post graduate and doctoral research in soil science.

We are very happy that we are able to offer an extensively revised, updated and expanded version of the book, which contains considerable amount of new material in four chapters like and as information in form of appendices. We do hope that the revised edition will be more useful to the readers and would enjoy similar support from them as did the first edition.

The book Concept of Soil Science comprises of thirty four chapters including Multiple Choice Question. In second edition four new chapters included as Chemistry of Plant Nutrition, Soil Amendment, Problematic Soils in Different Ecosystems and MCQs. A separate chapter on Multiple Choice Question and the answer has been included to help the students to evaluate themselves. The subject matter is both narrative and critical. Elastration have been added to make the subject matter all the more clear. Citations are avoided in the text so that the reader is not destructed. The other does not claim perfection but at the same time, he in all humility, has made all possible efforts to make this text book up to date and useful to students from all point of view. This book highlighted in Soil Pedology, Soil Physics, Soil Chemistry, Soil Fertility, Soil Conservation and concept's up to Soil Science.

It is felt that this text book meets a long felt need of soil science students and also may be useful for teachers of soil science and agricultural chemistry of different Indian agricultural universities. I welcome any suggestions for improvement of this book. Suggestions will receive the greatest consideration.

2021 **S.G. RAJPUT**

PREFACE

FIRST EDITION

The availability of information on soil science is scare in India for the student to prepare for competitive examinations such as ARS/NET/SRF/JRF/UPSC/PCS & SAUs Exams, and guiding post graduate and doctoral research in soil science.

The book **Concept of Soil Science** comprises of thirty chapters. This book has been written by following the syllabi in the under graduate and post graduate studies of soil science of different agricultural universities of India and also it is intended to soil scientist, plant nutritionists and other who are concerned with the studies of soils, plants and fertilizers etc. this present text book is written to satisfy the various course requirements in soil science. The subject matter is both narrative and critical. Elastration have been added to make the subject matter all the more clear. Citations are avoided in the text so that the reader is not destructed. The other does not claim perfection but at the same time, he in all humility, has made all possible efforts to make this text book up to date and useful to students from all point of view. This book highlighted in Soil Pedology, Soil Physics, Soil Chemistry, Soil Fertility, Soil Conservation and concept's up to Soil Science.

It is felt that this text book meets a long felt need of soil science students and also may be useful for teachers of soil science and agricultural chemistry of different Indian agricultural universities. I welcome any suggestions for improvement of this book. Suggestions will receive the greatest consideration.

S.G. RAJPUT

CONTENTS

S. No.	Chapters	Pages
1.	What is Soils ?	1–8
	SOIL PEDOLOGY	
2.	Rocks and Minerals	9–29
3.	Soil Weathering and Formation	30–39
4.	Soil Morphology	40–46
5.	Soil Classification and Taxonomy	47–59
6.	Soils of India	60–67
7.	Soils of Uttar Pradesh	68–77
	SOIL PHYSICS	
8.	Soil Physical Properties	78–93
9.	Soils Air	94–99
10.	Soils Temperature	100–105
11.	Soil Water	106–121
12.	Dynamic Soil Properties	122–128
	SOIL CHEMISTRY	
13.	Soil Colloid and Ion Exchange	129–154
14.	Soil Reaction and Buffering	155–161
15.	Salt Affected Soils	162–191
16.	Acid and Acid Sulphate Soils	192–203
17.	Quality of Irrigation Water	204–216
18.	Soil Pollution	217–243

SOIL FERTILITY

19. Plant Nutrition 244—257

20. Chemistry of Plant Nutrients 258—287

21. Manure and Fertilizer 288—324

22. Soil Amendment 325—333

23. Soil Organism and Biofertilizer 334—346

24. Soil Organic Matter and Humus 347—362

25. Soil Health and Soil Quality 363—400

SOIL AND WATER CONSERVATION

26. Soil Erosion and Conservation 401—425

27. Soil Survey and Land Use Planning 426—431

28. Water Management 432—451

29. Soil Management 452—465

30. Problematic Soils in Different Ecosystems 466—481

CONCEPTS UP TO SOIL SCIENCE

31. Practical's and Analytical Chemistry 482—520

32. Modern Perspective in Soil Science 521—532

Soil Science Terminology (Lexicon) 533—544

Multiple Choice Questions 545—589

Appendices **590—612**

Appendix–I 590—598

Appendix–II 599—600

Appendix–III 601—609

Appendix–IV 610—610

Appendix–V 611—612

CHAPTER 1

What Is Soil?

ORIGIN OF THE EARTH

The earth's crust and its composition

Classically there are three divisions of earth's sphere corresponding to the **solid, liquid** and **gas**, which constitute the Earth.

Biosphere. The part of the Earth's environment in which living organisms are found, and with which they interact to produce a steady-state system, effectively a whole planet ecosystem.

Hydrosphere. The total body of water that exists on or close to the surface of the Earth.

Lithosphere. The upper (oceanic and continental) layer of the solid Earth, comprising all crustal rocks and the brittle part of the uppermost mantle.

Composition of earth crust

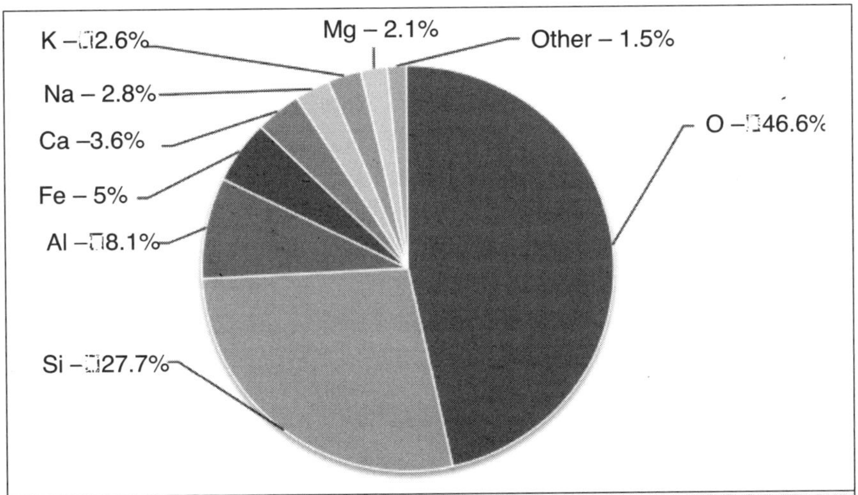

Fig. 1.1. Composition of Earth Crust

- Out of 118 elements known, 8 are sufficiently abundant as to constitute 98.6 per cent (by weight) of the earth's crust (up to 16 km).
- The two elements occurring in greatest abundance are non metallic (oxygen and silicon) and comprise nearly three-fourth (75%) of the total composition of the crust.
- Most of the hard, naturally formed substance of the earth is referred to as rock. Rock is composed of elements.
- The materials of the earth's crust fall into two principal categories, namely minerals and rocks.

What is Earth System ?

1. Earth Energy Budget. This module focuses on the analysis of environmental/earth systems phenomena partially as a problem of the transformation and flow of energy within organized systems. Potential areas of application include: global climate change; ecosystem energetic; energy flow and material cycles of carbon, hydrogen, nitrogen and phosphorus; human energy infrastructure; ocean dynamics; and planetary formation and evolution. Soils strongly impact global environmental change, ecosystem energetic, and energy flow and material cycles.

2. Atmospheric Ozone. The atmosphere is the air surrounding the Earth. It extends up to 200 km into the atmosphere and its composition changes over time. The atmosphere layer at 15-30 km altitude has an ozone concentration of 1-10 parts per million. The ozone layer limits the amount of ultraviolet radiation reaching the ground surface. Ultraviolet radiation can cause damage to certain plant cells and affect the biotic activity in the pedosphere.

3. Hydrological Cycle. This module focuses on the global hydrological cycle, local hydrological cycle, and human consumption of water. Key systems concepts include equilibrium, feedback, closed versus open systems, residence times and the nature of transient responses to perturbations. The local hydrological cycle is strongly controlled by soil and landscape properties.

4. The Biosphere. The biosphere is the whole region of the Earth's surface, the ocean and the air that is inhabited by living organisms. The key emphases for this module are: putting the biosphere into a time perspective - considering how organisms and the earth evolved together through interchanges of energy and pressure; and putting the biosphere into a spatial perspective by examining the effect of the atmosphere, hydrosphere, lithosphere and pedosphere on the distribution of biomes and ecosystems within the earth.

5. Biogeochemical Cycles. The global carbon cycle is a key element of the Earth System and plays an important role in determining Earth's climate. It is interconnected with the global hydrologic cycle and the planetary energy cycle to determine climate. It is also inter connected with the global cycles for elements such as nitrogen, phosphorus, sulfur, and heavy metals. The pedosphere supports life in terrestrial ecosystems and impacts the cycling of elements and energy flow of the Earth System.

6. Soil Processes, Land Use, and Land Cover Change. This module focuses on: soils and their function in terrestrial ecosystems; the linkage between soils and the biosphere; the different time scales in which soils regenerate and humans degrade soils; the impact of land use practices; and the long-term economic, ecological, and human consequences of good and poor soil management.

7. Economics, Sustainability and Natural Resources. This module focuses on analyses of linkages between economics and environmental change on local, regional and global scales and addresses the role of economic analysis in the design and implementation of environmental policy. The sustainable use of renewable natural resources (soil, air, water, microbes, plants and animals) in the context of non-renewable resources (oil, natural gas, natural forests) is a major environmental issue facing human society at local, regional and global levels.

8. The Antarctic. This module focuses on Antarctica, illustrating the interdisciplinary processes of glaciology, geology, biology, and chemistry, which influence Earth phenomena and human activities in an international context.

9. El Nino - Southern Oscillation. El Nino is a disruption of the ocean-atmosphere system in the tropical Pacific having important consequences for weather around the globe. Among these consequences is increased rainfall across the southern tier of the US and in Peru, which has caused destructive flooding, and drought in the West Pacific, sometimes associated with devastating brush fires in Australia. The change in weather patterns impacts water storage and plant growth in terrestrial ecosystems.

10. Observing Systems and Remote Sensing. The use of radars, sensors, spectroscopy, air borne and satellite photography allows for the gathering of information without actual physical contact with what is being observed. Passive satellite remote sensing involves the measurement of electromagnetic radiation (i.e. light, heat) upwelling to a satellite instrument. By examining the electromagnetic spectrum of radiation emitted from the sun, or emitted from the Earth system, as it interacts with the Earth system, one may discover signal information for different processes or changes in the atmosphere, oceans, or on Earth's surface. Some applications connected to soil and landscape processes include land use, land cover change, water pollution and flooding.

11. Human Population - Environment Interactions. This module focuses on issues of human population and environmental interaction and addresses issues such as the dynamics of human population, the consumption of natural resources, social dimensions, and industrial ecology. Integration of these issues could lead to assessment of the human impact on the environment.

12. Health and Climate Change. This module focuses on the impact of climate change on human health. Climate change affects the moisture and temperature regimes, the intensity of ultraviolet radiation on the Earth's surface and other processes which may affect ecosystem health. These in turn could impact human health.

13. Earth System History. This module provides an overview of the scales and development of solid earth, oceans, atmosphere and life with focus on events or trends that are particularly important to present-day earth system components and processes. It emphasizes the inter relatedness of life and earth processes. Human induced climate changes will be superimposed on the background of natural variability and variations of temporal, spatial, and energy scales of processes in all aspects of the Earth systems.

14. System Concepts and the Earth System. This module focuses on the applicability of systems theory to the real world, systems concepts and terminology, and an introduction to integrative systems modeling. Systems theory focuses on the arrangement of and relations between the parts which connect them to the whole. Mathematical systems theory is applied to problems in such diverse fields as engineering, computing, ecology, and management.

Why Study Soils?

Many thousands of students and professionals find that some knowledge of soil is essential for success in their careers. What does one gain from studying soils? Some reasons for studying soil are described in this lesson.

1. Soil is an integral part of the ecosystem. Air, water and soil comprise the various ecosystems of the earth. A biome is a complex system of soil, climate and organisms. Soil is susceptible to pollution. We pollute soil by exposing it to human sewage, industrial waste products, agricultural and milling wastes, and natural contaminants.

2. Soil is the domain of Archeology. Soils can reveal information about ancient climates, geology and peoples. Archeologist study ancient habitats, dwellings, and other cultural factors by examining soil. Often buried topsoil holds a rich archeological find.

3. Soil properties affect engineering projects. To an engineer soil is earthy material that can be excavated with a shovel. Soil is construction material and typically is the natural foundation that supports the man-made foundation of a building. Soil properties limit engineering uses for a parcel of land. Soils may or may not be suitable for such uses as road beds, septic tank drain fields, dwellings with basements, or recreation facilities.

4. Soil is the primary resource for food Production. A subsistence diet requires about 400 lb (181 kg) of grain per person per year. This amount of grain production requires about 0.11 acres (0.045 hectares).

5. Soils profoundly affect human history. Farmers in Mesopotamia were irrigating 5500 years ago. Their fields were more productive then than they are now. Irrigated agriculture is rarely sustainable because it tends to raise water tables and increase soil salinity. In Egypt, where farming was successful and sustainable, civilization thrived. The plow was invented there some 6000 years ago. One observer theorized that the pyramids were built because of the large unemployed workforce-unemployed because agriculture was so successful that not all citizens had to be involved in food production. In North America modern settlers caused the erosion of about one-half of our original endowment of topsoil in only about 150 years of myopic farming.

6. The study of soils is a science of inherent value to mankind. Soil science includes two main divisions: Edaphology and Pedology. Edaphology is the study of soils as habitat for plants and other organisms. Xenophon, Cato, was early edaphologists. Van Helmont (1577 - 1644) performed a famous willow experiment, concluding that because the only thing he gave a growing willow was water, willows are made of water. He was partly correct but did not realize that the dry matter came mostly from invisible carbon dioxide in the air. Scientific advances accelerated in the 1700s and 1800s. Pedology is the study of soil as a geologic entity. Pedology was born in Russia in the late 1800s. The USDA systematic approach to Pedology is based loosely on the Russian approach.

The Approaches of Soil Study

(*i*) **Pedological approach.** The origin of the soil, its classification, and its description are examined in pedology (from the Greek word *pedon*, which means soil or earth).

(*ii*) **Edaphological approach.** Edaphology (from the Greek word *edaphos*, which means soil or ground) is the study of soil from the standpoint of higher plants.

Soil Science has six well defined and developed disciplines

Soil Pedology	:	Dealing with the genesis, survey and classification
Soil Physics	:	Involves the study of physical properties
Soil Conservation	:	Dealing with protection of soil against physical loss by erosion or against chemical deterioration i.e. excessive loss of nutrients either natural or artificial means.
Soil Chemistry	:	Chemical constituents, chemical properties and the chemical reactions
Soil Fertility	:	Nutrient supplying properties of soil
Soil Microbiology	:	Deals with micro organisms, its population, classification, its role in transformations

Views on Soil (Science)

The term SOIL was derived from the Latin Word "SOLUM" Means FLOOR

- For a Layman soil is dirt or debris
- For an Agriculturist soil is a habitat for plant growth (to grow crops)
- For a Mining Engineer soil is a debris covering the Rocks
- For a Civil Engineer soil is a material on which road bed or house bed is formed
- For a Home Owner soil is a mellow or loamy or hard material

Definitions

Generally soil refers to the loose surface of the earth as identified from the original rocks and minerals from which it is derived through weathering process.

Whitney (1892). Soil is a nutrient bin which supplies all the nutrients required for plant growth

Hilgard (1892). Soil is more or less a loose and friable material in which plants, by means of their roots, find a foothold for nourishment as well as for other conditions of growth"

Dokuchaiev (1900). Russian scientist - Father of soil science - Soil is a natural body composed of mineral and organic constituents, having a definite genesis and a distinct nature of its own.

Joffe (1936). "Soil is a natural body of mineral and organic constituents differentiated into horizons - usually unconsolidated - of variable depth which differs among themselves as well as from the underlying parent material in morphology, physical makeup, chemical properties and composition and biological characteristics".

Jenny (1941). Soil is a naturally occurring body that has been formed due to combined influence of climate and living organisms acting on parent material as conditioned by relief over a period of time.

Ruffin and Simonson (1968). Soil is a mixture of Earth's uppermost mantle of weathered rock and organic matter.

Buckman and Brady (1969). Soil is a dynamic natural body on the surface of the earth in which plants grow, composed of mineral and organic materials and living forms

Soil Science Society of America (1970)

(*i*) Soil is the unconsolidated mineral matter on the surface of the earth that has been subjected to and influenced by genetic and environmental factors of parent material, climate (including moisture and temperature effects), macro and microorganisms and topography, all affecting over a period of time and producing a product, that is "SOIL" that differs from the material from which it is derived in many, physical, chemical, biological and morphological properties and characteristics.

(*ii*) The unconsolidated mineral material on the immediate surface of the earth that serves as a natural medium for the growth of land plants.

As soil provides nutrients, water, air and anchorage and supports life on Earth, it can be called as **Soil of Infinite Life (SOIL)**

Soil as a three dimensional body

Soil is a three dimensional body having length, breadth and depth. They form a continuation over the land surface and differ in properties from place to place. Its upper boundary is air or water and lower boundary is the rock lithosphere.

Composition of soil on volume basis (Soil components)

Mineral matter	:	45%
Organic matter	:	5%
Soil water	:	25%
Soil air	:	25%

Soil can be compared to various systems of animals

Digestive system	:	Organic matter decomposition
Respiratory system	:	Air circulation & exchange of gases
Circulatory system (blood)	:	Water movement within the soil
Excretory system	:	Leaching out of excess salts
Brain	:	Soil clay
Colour	:	Soil colour
Height	:	Soil depth

Field view of soil

In a field, above bedrock some unconsolidated debris is present almost universally. This material is known as regolith, which may be negligibly shallow, or hundreds of meters in thickness. It may be material, which has weathered from the underlying rock, or it may have been transported by the action of wind, water or ice and deposited upon the bedrock. The regolith tends to vary in composition from place to place.

Difference between surface soil and sub-soil

Surface Soil	Sub Soil
1. It is completely weathered.	1. It is partially weathered.
2. Surface soil is dominated by finer particles like silicate clay.	2. Sub-soil is dominated by quartz particles and other coarse fragments of minerals.
3. Surface soil porous and friable.	3. The sub-soil is more massive and compact.
4. Aeration status of surface soil is good and exchange of gases between atmosphere and soil air takes place.	4. Aeration status of sub-soil is very poor and hence exchange of gases is very much limited.
5. The number and activity of soil micro-organisms is very high.	5. The microbial population and their activity is very low.
6. Relatively higher organic matter content due to presence of higher biomass on the soil surface.	6. Due to lack in plant & animal residues in the sub-soil, the amount of o. m. is very low.
7. Due to presence of higher organic matter content the colour of the surface soil is deep brown or dark.	7. The colour of sub-soil is light & some times may be light yellowish colour depending on the nature and kinds of unweathered materials.
8. It is fertile. Most of the essential plant nutrients are present.	8. It is less fertile; very few essential plant nutrients are present.
9. Surface soil has no hard pan.	9. Sub-soil sometimes has hardpan.
10. It has good physical management condition because of surface soil.	10. It has poor physical condition.
11. CEC is very high.	11. CEC is low.

SOME IMPORTANT CONCEPT, CONTRIBUTOR AND DISCOVERIES

- Father of Soil Science and Soil Pedology — **V.V. Dokuchaiev (1886)**
- Father of Indian Soil Science — **J.W. Leather**
- Father of Soil Physics — **Hillel**
- Father of Soil Chemistry — **J. Thamus**
- Father of Agricultural Chemistry — **Van Liebig**
- Father of Soil Conservation — **H.N. Bunett**
- Father of Soil Conservation (UP) — **Azidulla Khan**
- Father of Soil Testing Programme — **G.S. Troug**
- 'A' value — **Fried and Dean**
- 'E' value — **Russell**
- 'Y' or 'L' value — **Larsen**
- pH concept — **Sorenson**

- pE concept — **Silen**
- Law of limiting factor — **Blakman**
- Law of minimum/Law of limiting nutrient — **Lievig**
- Water – essential for plant — **Van Helment**
- Water – transpiration — **Woodward**
- Salt index — **Puri**
- DRIS concept — **Beaufils**
- Q/I concept — **Beckett**
- DTPA/Extractable micronutrients — **Lindsey and Norvell**
- Polyphenol theory of organic matter — **Stevenson**
- Phenomenon of radioactivity — **Becquerel**
- Soil catena — **Milne**
- Integrated soil test approach — **Colwell**
- CEC — **Thampson and Way**
- Nutrient sufficiency concept — **Baule**
- Lignin theory — **Waksman**
- Ultra micronutrient concept — **Nicholas**
- Per cent yield concept — **Baule**
- Root CEC — **Devaux**
- Target yield concept — **Ramamoorthi *et al.***
- Electrochemical theory of nutrient — **Lundegardh**
- Theory of relativity — **Lundegardh**
- Nutrient mobility and per cent sufficiency concept — **Bray**
- Benchmark soils of India — **Murthi *et al.***
- Biogas — **S.V. Desai and S.C. Biswas**
- Electroultrafilteration theory — **Lundergardh**
- Soil as an inexhaustible source of nutrients — **Cameroon**
- CEC is next to photosynthesis — **Marshall**
- Root exchange contact — **Jenny & Overstreet**

❑❑❑

CHAPTER 2

Rocks and Minerals

"Mineral is defined as the natural substance generally inorganic nature having a definite chemical composition, and a definite molecular arrangement"

More or less 2000 minerals are involved in soil formation.

LIST OF IMPORTANT MINERALS

Primary minerals			
Orthoclase	$KAlSi_3O_8$	Quartz	SiO_2
Albite	$NaAlSi_3O_8$	Muscovite	$KAl_3Si_3O_{10}$ $(OH)_2$
Anorthite	$CaAlSi_2O_8$	Biotite	K $Al_3(Mg\ Fe)_3Si_3O_{10}(OH)_2$
Sodalime feldspar	$CaNaAlSi_3O_8$	Olivine	$(Mg\ Fe)_2SiO_4$
Hornbland	$Ca_2Al_2Mg_2Fe_3Si_3O_8$	Tourmaline	$NaFeAl_4B_2Si_4\ O_{19}(OH)$
Augite	$Ca_2(Al\ Mg_4)MgFe_4Si_6O_{24}$		
Secondary minerals			
Calcite	$CaCO_3$	Oxiapetite	$Ca[Ca_3(PO_4)_3]_3$
Dolomite	$CaCO_3MgCO_3/CaMg.(CO_3)_2$	Carbonate apatite	$CaCO_3[Ca_3(PO_4)_2]_2$
Quick lime	CaO	Kaolinte	$Al_4Si_4O_{10}(OH)_8$
Hydrated lime	$Ca(OH)_2$	Montmorillonite	$Al_4Si_8O_{20}(OH)_4$
Gypsum	$CaSO_4.2H_2O$	Illite	$2Al_2Si_4O_4O_{10}(OH)_2K$
Pyrite	FeS_2	Chlorite	$Si_6AlMg_6O_{20}(OH)_4$
Chalcopyrite	$CuFeS_2$	Vivinite	$Fe_3(PO_4)_2.8H_2O$
Hematite	Fe_2O_3	Talc	$H_2Mg_3(SiO_3)_4$
Limonite	$Fe_2O_3.3H_2O$	Rutile	TiO_2
Magnettite	Fe_3O_4 or $FeOFe_2O_3$	Ilmite	$FeTiO_3$ or $FeOTiO_2$

Magnetite	$Mg CO_3$	Zircon	$4 ZrSiO_4$
Siderite	$Mg CO_3FeO_3$	Titanite	$CaTiSiO_5$
Apetite	$Ca_4[Ca_3(PO_4)_3]$	Bauxite	$CaTiSiO_5$
Florapetite	$CaFCa_4(PO_4)_2$	Serpentine	$Mg_3Si_2.2H_2O$
Chlorapetite	$CaCl.Ca(PO_4)_2$	Galina	PbS

Physical Properties of Minerals

Hardness. Hardness is the ability of one substance to scratch another substance. Geologists use Moh's hardness scale, which is an arbitrary scale that ranks minerals based on hardness, on a scale from 1 to 10. The average pocket knife has a hardness of about 5.5, a copper penny 3.5 and a human fingernail about 2.5. A field geologist has such tools in his pocket. Hardness above 7 is called Gemstone hardness (can not be scratched by quartz). Some minerals are softer in a certain direction only. Some example given as below:

Hardness (Moh's Scale)	*Minerals*	*Nature*
1	Talc	Softest in nature
2	Gypsum	↓
3	Calcite	
4	Fluorite	
5	Apatite	
6	Feldspar	
7	Quartz	
8	Topaz	
9	Corundum	
10	Diamond	Hardest naturally occurring substance

Density. Density of a mineral is an important natural property, although not easily tested in the field. Heaviest are the gold and platinum metals (density close to 20). Silicates weigh in between 2.5 and 3.5, ores between 4 and 8.

Cleavage. Cleavage of a mineral refers to how it breaks. Depending on the crystal structure, some minerals break in a regular, predictable manner, whereas others don't. If a mineral breaks in such a way that it leaves smooth, shiny surfaces, then it is said to have cleavage, and those surfaces are called cleavage surfaces. Cleavage can be perfect, good or merely incipient. The more perfect cleavage is, the thinner the sheets are that can be split off. Among the thinnest are flakes of mica.

Fracture. When a mineral is shattered or broken open, fracture surfaces are formed that may not have good cleavage. The appearance of such fracture surfaces is judged conchoidal (rounded), smooth, splintery, hackly, fibrous, even or uneven.

Twinning. Twinning can be defined by the appearance of fine parallel lines, called striations, on the cleavage planes of some minerals. Twinning occurs when a mineral repeatedly changes the direction in which it is growing.

Transparency. According to its transparency to visible light, a mineral is called water-clear, transparent, translucent or opaque. Between these are innumerable intermediate stages. Minerals may be translucent at their edges only.

Lustre. Lustre refers to the way a mineral reflects light. It is independent of colour and can occur in various qualities. If a mineral reflects light in a similar way as a metal, it is said to have metallic lustre. Other types of lustre are: glassy (vitreous), pearly, silky, resinous, greasy, waxy and earthy. The degree of lustre is described as splendent, shining, glistening, glimmering, matt, dull.

Colour. Variety of colour is the most striking characteristic of minerals, and in many cases it is their natural colour (yellow sulphur, red cinnabar, green malachite, blue azurite, etc). But alien atoms in small quantities can cause changes in the natural colours of crystals. Some minerals occur in an amazing variation of hues (fluorspar is transparent, white, wine-yellow, honey-yellow to green, blue and violet).

Special light effects. Light is reflected and diffracted by regularly intercalated foreign substances, by fine fractures or by twinning. **Labradorescence** is a magnificent play of colours like in the blue labradorite. **Opalescence** is the reflection of light as bright rainbow colours when an opal is turned.

Streak. The colour of a powdered mineral on a white underlay, like pyrite crystals having greenish-black powder on their naturally yellow crystals.

CLASSIFICATION OF COMMON MINERALS

A mineral is an inorganic, natural solid which is found in nature. Its atoms are arranged in definite patterns (an ordered internal structure) and it has a specific chemical composition that may vary within certain limits. A rock is an aggregate of one or more minerals.

1. **Native elements.** Minerals consisting of a single element.

- **Platinum (Pt).** density 21.46, hardness 4-4.5. Found as granules in sand form some igneous rocks, and noble metals.
- **Gold (Au).** Density 19.3, hardness 2.5-3. Often found in association with pyrite, chalco pyrite and arsenopyrite in quartz veins. When found in streams, the gold is in small flat particles of varying sizes. It is very ductile (heat and electricity) and mineable. Used for ornaments because of its malleability.
- **Silver (Ag).** Density 10-11, harnesses 2.5-3.
- **Copper (Cu).** Density 8.95, hardness 2.5-3. First used for making tools, later mixed with tin to make bronze.
- **Sulfur (S).** Density 2.07, hardness 1.5-2.5.
- **Graphite (C).** Density 2.09-2.21, hardness 1-2. Found in compact masses, large deposits. Its high melting point and electrical conductivity makes it suitable for high temperature electrodes. It is used as a dry lubricant in high temperature applications.
- **Diamond (C).** Density 3.50, hardness 10. Lustrous, transparent, colourless, yellow or green. Brittle and hard.
- Also **Mercury (Hg)**—density 13.59, **Arsenic (As)**—density 5.63, hardness 3.5, **Antimony (Sb)**—density 6.61, hardness 3-3.5.

2. Oxides (–O). Oxides are common in geochemical environments poor in silica. Silicates form easily from a magma, so if silica is used up in a magma chamber, then the oxides remain to be formed. Their structure is complex : octahedral crystals and very stable against weathering, but dissolving slowly in hydrochloric acid (HCl).

- **Magnetite Fe_3O_4.** Density 5.17, hardness 6. It is magnetic iron oxide. Large deposits are segregated from igneous magmas at high temperatures and are mined near the surface as iron ores. Can contain chromium or manganese.
- **Maghemite Fe_2O_3.** Iron sesquioxide, Magnetic.
- **Hematite Fe_2O_3.** Iron sesquioxide, ferric iron oxide. Non-magnetic.
- **Ilmenite** group $ATiO_3$:
  - **Ilmenite $FeTiO_3$**, titanic iron ore, black sand containing 36.8% iron and 31.6% titanium, is the principle ore for titanium, but is hard to melt. Ilmenite is part of basic igneous rocks such as gabbro and norite.
  - **Perovskite $CaTiO_3$**, stibiconite $SbSb_2(O,OH,H_2O)_7$, betafite,
- **Hydrous oxides of iron, limonites**
  - **Limonite.** $FeO[OH].nH_2O$. Density 5.26, hardness 5-6. Rust. Non-magnetic. Oxidized iron minerals. It is an important iron ore, found in many shapes and colours, from ochre to blood red.
  - **Goethite.** $HFeO_2$. Non-magnetic
- **Aluminium oxides**
  - **Alumina Al_2O_3.** Aluminum sesquioxide,
  - **Bauxite.** A mixture of various oxides such as boehmite, diaspore, hydrargillite, alumogel, etc., mixed with iron hydroxides which impart the red colour.
  - **Corundum Al_2O_3.** Aluminum oxide. Density 4-4.1, hardness 9. An important mineral, used as precious stone (red ruby and blue sapphire), and its greyish variety as emeri for abrasive and refractory products.
- **Spinel group AB_2O_4**
  - **Spinel.** Magnesium-aluminum oxide. $MgAl_2O_4$. Density 3.55, hardness 7.5-8.
  - Also : **hercynite, galaxite, gahnite, chrysoberyl, franklinite, trevorite, alexandrite**.
- **Cuprite.** Cu_2O. Density 6.14, haardness 3.5-4. Copper ore. Octahedral crystals, dark red.
- Also : Tenorite (CuO), rutile (TiO_2), Cassiterite (SnO_2), Pyrolusite (MnO_2) Psilomelane $(Ba,H_2O)Mn_5O_{10}$, Manganite (MnO(OH), anatase (octahedrite), brookite, wolframite $(Mn,Fe)WO_4$, columbite, euxenite, uraninite (UO_2), curite, gummite,brucite $(Mg(OH)_2$

3. Hydroxides (—OH)

- **Gibbsite.** Aluminium hydroxide. $Al(OH)_3$. Found in aluminium ore.
- **Brucite.** Magnesium hydroxide. $Mg(OH)_2$. One of magnesium's ores.

4. Carbonates (—CO_3) metal-ion solid solutions. Usually medium or low hardness. Soluble in hydrochloric acid (HCl)

❒ **Calcite.** Density 2.71, hardness 3. Most common, most abundant of all minerals. It has many forms of crystallisation (up to 700 forms). Fine-grained, dissolves easily in rainwater, especially when loaded with carbon dioxide in the form of carbonic acid (H_2CO_3).

- **Limestone.** $CaCO_3$.
- **Marble.** (metamorphic). $CaCO_3$. Limestone in a metamorphic crystalline (or granular) state, and capable of taking a polish. Used in sculpture and architecture.
- **Aragonite** $CaCO_3$. Orthorhombic crystals.

❒ **Dolomite.** Calcium Magnesium carbonate. $CaMg(CO_3)_2$. It is the chief source of magnesium. Used for agricultural fertiliser, steel manufacturing, and as a filler in paint, putty and rubber. Marble composed of dolomite has beautiful colours.

❒ **Ankerite** $CaFe(CO_3)_2$.

❒ Also : Magnesite ($MgCO_3$), breunerite, mesitite, smithsonite ($ZnCO_3$), siderite ($FeCO_3$), sphaerocobaltite ($COCO_3$), rhodochrosite/ dialogite ($MnCO_3$), strontianite ($SrCO_3$), cerussite ($PbCO_3$), Azurite ($Cu_3(CO_3)_2(OH)_2$, Malachite $Cu_2CO_3(OH)_2$, rosasite, aurichalite.

5. Sulfides (—S)

❒ **Pyrite** (Fool's Gold). FeS_2. A yellow lustrus form of irondisulphide.

❒ **Galena.** Lead sulfide. PbS.

❒ **Cinnabar.** Mercury sulfide. HgS.

❒ Also : Chalcocite, covellite, bornite, argentite, sphalerite, marmatite, wutzite, chalcopyrite, tetrahydrite, tennantite, pyrrhotite, niccolite, metacinnabarite, stibnite, bismuthinite, marcasite, hauerite, cobaltite, ullmanite, arsenopyrite, molybdenite, skutterudite, proustite, pyrargyrite, bournonite, cannizarite, sartorite, realgar, orpiment.

6. Sulfates (—SO_4)

❒ **Gypsum $CaSO_4.2H_2O$.** Density 2.31, hardness 2. A hydrated form of calcium sulphate, occurring naturally and used in the building industry and to make plaster of Paris. Easily identified because it can be scratched by fingernail and is light. Also: selenite, sericolite, alabaster.

❒ **Barite.** Barium sulfate. $BaSO_4$.

❒ Also: Thenardite Na_2SO_4, Celestine $SrSO_4$, anglesite $PbSO_4$, jarosite $KFe_3(SO_4)_2(OH)_6$, brochantite, linarite, leadhillite, lanarkite Pb_2SO_5, alunite $KAl_3(SO_4)_2(OH)_6$, hanksite, chalcanthite, melanterite, goslarite, epsomite $MgSO_4$, morenosite $NiSO_4$, pickeringite, halotrichite, coquimbite, alunogen $Al_2(SO_4)_3.16H_2O$, copiapite, soda-alum, potash-alum, ammonia-alum, urano-pilite, zippeite, johannite.

7. Phosphates (—PO_4)

❒ **Apatite.** $Ca_5F(PO_4)_3$. Density 3.1, hardness 5. A naturally occurring crystalline mineral of calcium phosphate and fluoride, used in the manufacture of fertilisers. A fairly common mineral found in pegmatites, metamorphic and igneous rock, and in ore veins.

- Also : lithiophilite Li,$MnFePO_4$, xenotime YPO_4, monazite $CePO_4$, linbethenite $Cu_2(OH)PO_4$, olivenite $Cu_2(OH)AsO_4$, adamite $Zn_2(OH)AsO_4$, cornetite $Cu_3(OH)_3PO_4$, descloizite, brazilianite, crandallite.

8. Halides (—Cl, —F)

- **Chlorites (—Cl)**
  - **Halite** (Salt). NaCl. Rock-salt.
  - **Sylvite.** KCl. Potassium salt, occurs in compact masses.
  - **Karnallite.** $KMgCl_3.6H_2O$. milk white or reddish granular masses.
- **Fluorides**
  - **Fluorite.** Calcium fluoride. CaF_2. Density 3.18, hardness 4, isometric crystals. Very wide range of colours.
  - Also: cryolite, atacamite, cotunnite, nadorite.

9. Silicates (SiO_2) (—SiO_4) (—Si_3O_8) (—SiO_3). Arranged by heavy element content (the *Bowen* series)

- **Olivine.** Density 3.27-3.37, hardness 6.5-7. Ultrabasic. (Fe, Mg, Mn) silicates in solid solution. Olivine = forsterite + fayalite. Density 3.3-4.4. Tetrahedral structure. Green. Resistant to weathering but susceptible to metamorphism. Much of the Earth is made out of this mineral, and it is a major component of the mantles of other terrestrial planets. It is usually a greenish crystal, often found as inclusions in basaltic lavas. Large crystals are called chrysolite and are used for jewellery.
  - **Foresterite Mg_2SiO_4.** Light-green.
  - **Fayalite Fe_2SiO_4.** Dark-green or black.
- **Inosilicates**
  - **Pyroxene.** Ultrabasic. (Ca, Fe, Mg, Na, Al, Ti) silicates in solid solution. White. Density 2.8-3.7. Common in meteorites. 10% of crust. Single chain tetrahedral structure. Moderately resistant to weathering.
  - **Diopside.** (Ca, Mg)SiO_3 = wollastonite + enstatite in solid solution
    - **Wollastonite** (metamorphic). $CaSiO_3$
    - **Enstatite**. $MgSiO_3$
  - **Augite.** A complex calcium magnesium aluminous silicate occurring in many igneous rocks. (Fassaite, bronzite, capholite)
  - **Hypersthene.** A rock-forming greenish mineral of magnesium iron silicate, harder than hornblende.
  - Also: hedenbergite $CaFeSi_2O_6$, Johannsenite $CaMnSi_2O_6$, spodumene $LiAlSi_2O_6$. (triphane, kunzite, hiddenite),
  - **Amphibole.** Basic. $(Ca, Mg, Fe, Al, Na)_{7-8}(Si,Al)_8O_{22}(OH, F, O)_2$. Density 2.8-3.7. Double chain tetrahedral structure. 7% of crust.
    - **Horneblende.** $(Ca, Na, K)_{2-3}(Mg, Fe, Al)_5(Si, Al)_9O_{22}(OH, F)_2$

- Also: tremolite $Ca_2Mg_5Si_8O_{22}(OH)_2$, actinolite, glaucophane, crocidolite, riebeckite.

❒ **Tectosilicates**

- **Feldspar.** (Aluminum silicates). Ultrabasic to intermediate. (K,Na,Ca,Al) silicates in solid solution. Density 2.6-2.8, 60% of crust. Framewòrk-tetrahedral structure. Hard. Glassy or pearly looking, light colour. Moderately resistant to weathering and metamorphism.
- **Plagioclase feldspars**
  - **Anorthite $CaAl_2Si_2O_8$.** Plagioclase calcium feldspar. Ultrabasic. White to medium gray with striations.
  - **Albite $NaAlSi_3O_8$.** Plagioclase sodium feldspar. Intermediate white.
  - Also: danburite, sodalite, haueyinite, lazurite (lapis lazuli), scapolite, wernerite.
- **Othoclase feldspars**
  - **K-feldspar $KAlSi_3O_8$.** Orthoclase (Microcline) potassium feldspar. Density 2.56. Hardness 6. Light cream to salmon pink. Used in ceramics and glass making.
  - Also: Adularia, Sanidine, Microcline.
- **Feldspathoid group:** Nepheline (Na,K) $AlSiO_4$, analcitè $NaAlSi_2O_6.H_2O$, leucite $KAlSi_2O_6$.
- **Zeolites:** Natrolite, scolecite, thomsonite, mesolite, dachiardite, forestite, laumontite, mordenite, arduinite, ferrierite, heulandite, stilbite, and many more.

❒ **Mica.** Basic to acidic. (K,Mg,Fe,Al) silicates. Black. Density 2.76-3.2. Common in igneous rocks. 4% of crust. It is a sheet silicate with properties of talcum for mica. Any of a group of silicate minerals with a layered structure.

- **Biotite.** Basic $K(Mg,Fe)_3(AlSi_3O_{10})(OH)_2$. A black, dark brown or green micaceous mineral occurring as a constituent of metamorphic and igneous rocks.
- **Muscovite.** Acidic. $KAl_3Si_3O_{10}(OH)_2$. A silver-grey form of mica ('white mica') with a sheetlike crystalline structure, giving a pearly luster, used in the manufacture of electrical equipment, etc. Also: fuchsite, alurgite.
- Also: paragonite, phlogopite, lepidolite, chrysocolla $CuSiO_3.2H_2O$.

❒ **Chlorite group.** Are similar to the micas, dark green or blue green.

- **Serpentine $Mg_3Si_2O_5(OH)_4$.** A soft rock mainly of hydrated magnesium silicate, usually dark green (a chlorite) and sometimed mottled or spotted like a serpent's skin, taking a high polish and used as a decorative material.
- **Chrysotile.** Asbestos serpentine with exceptionally long fibres. Colour white, greenish, silky lustre. Used for buildings, insulation and high temperature applications.
- Also: kaemmererite, penninite, clinochlore, antigorite.

❒ **Zircon $Zr(SiO_4)$.** Density 4.6-4.7. Hardness 7.5. Trigonal crystal, prismatic pyramid. Glassy or milky in colour, but may be coloured (rock quartz, smoky quartz, morion quartz, citrine, amethyst). Most abundant and widest disseminated mineral. Essential constituent of volcanic, metamorphic and sedimentary rock.

❒ **Quartz SiO_2.** Ionic co-valent bond. Density 2.6. Hard mineral, virtually insoluble in water. Translucent. One of the most important components of granite. Opal, jasper, agate, chalcedony, flint. Tetrahedral structure. Also: Chalcedony, agate, onyx, jasper, tridymite, opal.

❒ **Garnet $A_3B_2(SiO_4)_3$.** Density 3.3-3.5. Tetrahedral structure. A vitreous silicate mineral, especially a transparent deep-red kind used as a gem.

- **Almandine $Fe_3Al_2(SiO_4)_3$.** Wine-red. Density 4.25.
- Also: Pyrope. $Mg_3Al_2(SiO_4)_3$, spessartite. $Mn_3Al_2(SiO_4)_3$, grossularite. $Ca_3Al_2(SiO_4)$, andradite $Ca_3Fe_2(SiO_4)_3$, uvarovite. $Ca_3Cr_2(SiO_4)_3$.

❒ **Clay.** Minerals (hydrous aluminium silicates) are the end products of weathering. All clay minerals are sheet silicates, each clay type owing its distinctive character to the cations such as sodium (Na^+), potassium (K^+), magnesium (Mg^{++}) or calcium (Ca^{++}), which occupy positions in and between the sheets.

- **Fibrous, open clays, palygorskite.** Open and well hydrated clays, not common in soils but are important in lake deposits which have salt-lagoon characteristics.
- Sepiolite and attapulgite.
- **Two-layer clays.** (1:1 clay; Si-Al lattice) fixed distance hydrogen-bonded (–O–OH–) between the silica and alumina sheets. Formed through rapid leaching of silica in volcanic soils (allitic weathering). Consist of tetrahedral silica and an octahedral alumina layer. These are rich in alumina, have poor cation-exchange capacity, stable structure and swell very little when moistened. Tropical climates, high rainfall, acidic conditions.
  - ◆ **Kaolinite $Al_4Si_4O_{10}(OH)_8$.** Absorbs little water but is just right for pottery and ceramics. Fine soft white clay produced by the decomposition of other clays of feldspar, used especially for making porcelain (pipe clay), and in medicines. Also called china clay. The word *kaolin* means *high hill* in Chinese.
    - Also: **nacrite, dickite.**
    - **Hydrated 1:1 clays**: **Hallosite $Al_2Si_2O_5(OH)_4.2H_2O$.** High alumina clay, which has slender tube crystals, and is white coloured. Used for making high quality 'bone' china porcelain and industrial ceramics.
- **Three-layer clays, smectite.** (2:1 clays; Si-Al-Si lattice) variable distance (–O–O–) bonded. Formed by slow leaching of silica, consisting of one octahedral alumina layer sandwiched between two tetrahedral silica layers. Have high cation-exchange capacity (CEC), but lower than amorphous clays. Weak structure, low water permeability and swells when moistened. Temperate climates, low rainfall, neutral to alkaline soils, especially under grasslands.
  - ◆ **Expanding lattice clays**
    - **Montmorillonite $(Al,Mg)_8(Si_4O_{10})_3(OH)_{10}.12H_2O$** or **$Al_4(Si_4O_{10})_2(OH)_4.xH_2O$.** Holds and absorbs large amounts of water. 20% in clay from volcanic weathering.
    - **Bentonite:** a soft plastic light-coloured clay formed by chemical alteration of

volcanic ash. It is composed essentially of montmorillonite and related smectite minerals.

  - Also: **beidelite**

- ◆ **hydrous micas**
  - **Chlorite $Mg_{10}Al_2(Si_6A_{12})O_{20}(OH)_{16}$.** Absorbs large amounts of water. A green flaky mineral, decomposition product of dark micas and is found in many altered rocks such as schists. (Note this mineral bears no relationship to the element chloride Cl, but its name relates to its green colour)
  - **Illite (muscovite). $K_2Al_4(Si_6A_{12})O_{20}(OH)_4$.**
  - **Vermiculite:**
    - ❍ **Amorphous clays.** Formed from easily weatherable materials such as volcanic ashes, lava or basalt. Have high cation-exchange capability. Low density, permeable to water and air. Decay of organic matter is slow and humus content high. Tropical climates.
    - ❍ **Nontronite.** Absorbs and holds large amounts of water. 50% in clay from volcanic weathering.
    - ❍ **Pelagic clays ('red clay').** Aluminium silicates. Any combination of montmorillonite, kaolinite, chlorite with an admixture of silt and clay sized grains of quartz, feldspar and other minerals. The chlorite crystal can be modified into an iron rich form. Deep sea sediments commonly contain this iron-rich form, from which it derives its name 'red clay'.

❒ **Subsaturite**

- **Kyanite** (metamorphic). A blue crystalline mineral of aluminium silicate.
- **Topaz $Al_2SiO_4(OH,F)_2$.** Density 3.6, hardness 8. A transparent or translucent aluminium silicate mineral, usually yellow, used as a gem.
- **Staurolite $(Fe,Mg)_4Al_{18}Si_8O_{46}(OH)_2$.** Density 3.65-3.77, hardness 7-7.5. Crystals cross shaped, dark grey to reddish brown.
- **Sillimanite Al_2SiO_5.** An aluminium silicate occurring in orthorhombic crystals or fibrous masses. Aillimanite, Andalusite, Kyanite or Dysthene.
- Also : humite, titanclinohumite, braunite, titanite $CaTiSiO_5$, datolite, dumortierite, howlite.

❒ **Sorosilicates**

- Also : gehlenite $Ca_2Al_2SiO_7$, cuspidine $Ca_4Si_2O_7(F,OH)_2$, ilvaite, hemimorphite, epidote $Ca_2(Al,Fe)_3Si_3O_{12}OH$, piedmontite, zoisite, clinozoisite, allanite, orthite, idocrase/ vesuvianite.

❒ **Cyclosilicates**

- Also : Benitoite $BaTiSi_3O_9$, eudialyte, taramellite, axinite, beryl $Be_3A_{12}Si_6O_{18}$ (emerald, aquamarine, heliodor, morganite), cordierite, tourmaline, dioptase.

❒ **Phyllosilicates**

- **Talc $Mg_3Si_4O_{10}(OH)_2$.** Any crystalline form of magnesium silicate that occurs in soft flat plates, usually white or pale green in colour and used as a lubricator.
- Also: Apophyllite, pyrophillite $A_{12}Si_4O_{10}(OH)_2$, agalmatolite.

TABLE 2.1. Chemical composition and physical characteristics of important minerals

Sr. No.	Mineral	Chemical composition	Colour	Streak	Luster	Opacity	Hardness	Sp. gr.
I. ELEMENTS								
1.	Graphite	C	Steel grey	Dark shining	Metallic	Opaque	1	2.2
2.	Sulphur	S	Yellow	Yellow or white	Resineous	Translucent	1-2	2.07
II. OXIDES								
3.	Rock crystal (Quartz)	SiO_2	Various	White	Vitreous	Transparent	7	2.6-2.7
4.	Amethyst	SiO_2	Purple	White	Vitreous	Translucent	7	2.65
5.	Milkquartz	SiO_2	Milk white	White	Vitreous	Translucent	7	2.65
6.	Chalcedony	SiO_2	Variously colourcd	White	Resineous	Opaque	7	2.6
7.	Brucite	$Mg(OH)_2$	Greenish white	White	Pearly to vitreous	Translucent	2.5	2.39
8.	Carnelian	SiO_2	Yellow red	White	Resinous to waxy	Translucent	7	2.6
9.	Gibbsite	$Al(OH)_3$	Greenish grey	White	Pearly to vitreous	Transparent	2.5	2.39
10.	Agate	SiO_2	Variegated colours	White	Resineous waxy	Translucent	7	2.6
11.	Goethite	$FO_3.H_2O$ or $FeO(OH)$	Blackish brown yellow	Brownish	Adamantine	Transparent	5.5-5	3.3-4.3
12.	Flint	SiO_2	Smoky brown bluish	White	Resineous waxy	Translucent	7	2.6
13.	Jaspar	SiO_2	Dull red, brown yellow	White	Dull (earthy)	Opaque	7	3.6
14.	Opal	SiO_2	All coloured white, yellow,brown, grey etc.	White	Sub vitreous	Translucent	5.5-6.5	1.9-2.3
15.	Haematite	Fe_2O_3	Steel grey	Rcd	Earthy to metallic	Opaque	5-6.5	4.9-5.2
16.	limenite	$FeTiO_3$	Black	Black	Metallic	Opaque	5-6	4.72
17.	Limonite	$2(Fe_2O_3).3H_2O$ $FeO(OH)_2nH_2O$	Yellowish	Brownish	Earthy	Opaque	5-5.5	3.6-4.0
18.	Magnetite	Fe_3O_4	Black	Black	Dull metallic	Opaque	5.5-6.5	4.9-5.2
19.	Pyrolusite	MnO_2	Dark grey to black	Black	Metallic	Opaque	6-6.5	5.06
20.	Corundum	Al_2O_3	Red, brown, black	White	Vitreous	Opaque	9	4

III. SILICATES								
21.	Plagioclase feldspar	Na($AlSi_3O_8$) + Ca ($Al_2Si_2O_8$)	White greenish and reddish	White	Pearly	Translucent	6-6.5	2.6-2.76
22.	Albite	NaAl Si_3O_8	Greyish white	White	Sub vitreous	Translucent	6	2.6-2.76
23.	Anorthite.	$CaAl_2Si_3O_8$	Greyish white	White	Sub vitreous	Translucent	6	2.6-2.76
24.	Oligoclase	$Na_2CaAl_2Si_6O_{17}$	Greyish white	White	Sub vitreous	Translucent	6	2.6-2.76
25.	Orthoclase Feldspar	$KAlSi_3O_8$	Colourless to pinkish white	White	Vitreous-pearly	Translucent	6	2.56
26.	Microcline	$KalSi_3O_8$	Creamy to pinkish white	White	Vitreous to pearly	Translucent	6	2.56
27.	Zeolite	Ca.K.Na.Al. silicates	White	White	Vitreous to pearly	Translucent	6	2.8
28.	Stilbite	$CaAl_2Si_7O_{18}7H_2O$	Creamy to pinkish white	White	Vitreousto pearly	Opaque	4	2.1-2.2
29.	Kaolinite	$Al_4Si_4O_{10}(OH)_8$	Whitish grey	White	Pearly	Opaque	1	2.6
30.	Montmorillonite	$Al_2Si_4O_{10}(OH)_2\,xH_2O$	Greyish yellow	White	Dull	Opaque	2-2.5	2.6
31.	Pyrophyllite	$Al_2Si_4O_{10}(OH)_2$	Yellowish white	White	Pearly	Opaque	1-1.5	2.84
32.	Serpentine	$Mg_6Si_4O_{10}(OH)_8$	Greenish yellow to greyish white	White	Waxy to silky	Opaque	4-6	2.5-2.6
33.	Muscovite-mica	$KAl_2(AlSi_3O_{10})(OH)_2$	Colourless to white	White	Pearly to vitreous	Translucent	2.5	2.8-2.31
34.	Galuconite	$K(Fe,Mg,Al)_2(Si_4O_{10})(OH)_2$	Green to brown	Greenish grey	Earthy	Opaque	2-3	2.5-2.8
35.	Apophyllite	$KCa_4(Si_4O_{10})_2F.8H_2O$	Pinkish white	White	Pearly to vitreous	Translucent	5	2.35
36.	Chorite	$Mg_{10}Al_2(Si_6Al_2)O_{22}(OH)_{16}$	Brownish green	Greenish white	Earthy to pearly	Translucent	1.5-2.5	2.6-3.3
37.	Hornblende	$NaCa(Mg,Fe,Al)_5(Si,Al)_8O_{22}(OH)_2$	Dark green to brown or black	Greyish	Vitreous	Opaque	5.5-6.0	3.0-3.4
38.	Augite	$Ca(Mg,Fe,Al)(Al,Si)_2O_3$	Dark green	Whitish grey	Vitreous	Opaque	6	3.2-3.5
39.	Enstatite	$MgSiO_3$	Light green	White	Vitreous	Opaque	6	3.2-3.9
40.	Epidote	$Ca_2(Al, Fe)_3Si_3O_{12}(OH)$	Brownish	Greyish white	Vitreous	Opaque	7	3.3-3.6

41.	Talc	$Mg_3Si_4O_{10}(OH)_2$	Greyish white	White	Pearly	Translucent	1	2.82
42.	Vermiculite	$Mg_3Si_4O_{16}(OH)_2xH_2O$	Yellow	White	Pearly	Opaque	1.5	2.4
43.	Actinolite	$Ca_2(Mg,Fe)_5Si_3O_{22}(OH)_2$	Green	Greenish white	Vitreous	Opaque	5.5	3.35
44.	Olivine	$MgFeSiO_4$	Olive green to dark green	Whitish grey	Vitreous	Opaque	6.5	3.2-4.3
45.	Zircon	$ZrSiO_4$	Various colour	white	Vitreous	Opaque	7.5	—
46.	Tourmaline	$Na(Mg,Fe)_3Al_6(BO_3)_3(Si_6O_{18})(OH)_4$	Blackish brown to dark blue	White	Vitreous	Opaque	7.5	3.0-3.2
IV. CARBONATES								
47.	Calcite	$CaCO_3$	Colourless to white	White	Vitreous	Translucent	3	2.71
48.	Magnesite	$MgCO_3$	Brownish	Brown	Dull metallic	Opaque	5.5	—
49.	Dolomite	$CaCO_3$ $MgCO_3$	White	White	Vitreous to pearly	Translucent	3.5-4.0	2.85
V. SULPHATES								
50.	Anhydrite	$CaSO_4$	White	Grayish white	Vitreous	Translucent	3.5	2.96
51.	Baryte	$BaSO_4$	White	White	Vitreous	Translucent	3-3.5	4.48
52.	Gypsum	$CaSO_4.2H_2O$	Colourless or white	White	Vitreous to pearly	Translucent	2	2.32
VI. SULPHIDE								
53.	Iron pyrite	FeS_2	Brass yellow	Greenish black	Metallic	Opaque	6-6.5	5.01
54.	Copper pyrite	$CuFeS_2$	Brass yellow	Greenish black	Vitreous	Opaque	3.4	3.1
55.	Galena	Pbs	Grey	Grey black	Metallic	Opaque	4-5	3.2
VII. PHOSPHATES								
56.	Apatite	$Ca_3(P0_4)_2(F,Cl,OH)$	Pink to yellow	White	Vitreous	Transparent to Opaque	5	3.1-3.2
VIII. HALIDES								
57.	Fluorite (Fluorspar)	CaF_2	Violet blue	Colourless	Vitreuse	Opaque	4.0	3.1
58.	Halite (rock salt)	NaCl	Bluish white	Colourless	Vitreous	Opaque	2.5	2.1

STUDY OF ROCKS

"Rocks may be defined as a mixture of one or more minerals. So their physical and chemical composition vary with the properties of mineral, and rocks are mostly solid in nature and varying in hardness."

"**Petrology** *is the science of rock which formed the unit of the earth's crust.*"

"**Petrography** *which deals with the description of rocks.*"

"**Petrogenesis** *which is the study of the origin of rocks.*"

CLASSIFICATION OF ROCKS

On the basis of origin and structure, rocks are classified into three groups

1. Igneous rocks 2. Sedimentary rocks 3. Metamorphic rocks

Rocks

- **Igneous rocks**
  (Latin word, *Ingis = Fire*)
  Or
  Primary rocks
  Or
  Layerless rocks
  Or
  Massive rocks
  Or
  Crystline rocks
  e.g., Grenite, Rhiolite, Pichstone, Obsidiun, Synite, Trachyte, Diorite, Andesite, Basalt, Gabbro, Dacite, Tanolite
- **Sedimentary rocks**
  (L,; *Sedimentum= Settling*)
  Or
  Straitified rocks
  Or
  Aquas rocks
  e.g., Sand stone, Clay Stone, Slat Stone, Conglomarate, Grevals, Lime Stone, Dolomite, Bauxite, Anhydrite, Halite, Silvite, Cornalite, Gypsum, Shale, Morl, Anthrasite, Diatomite, Peat, Coal
- **Metamorphic rocks**
  (Means = changed form)
  e.g., Marbal, Gneiss, Quartzite, Schist, Graphite.

1. Igneous rocks

"Igneous rocks are formed by the cooling and crystallization of molten material-magma on or beneath the surface of the earth."

Classification of igneous rocks :

On the basis of silica content :

Igneous Rocks

- **Acidic Igneous Rocks**
  (65-75% silica)
  - These rocks formed by orthoclase quartz mica.
  - Low in potassium
  - Sandy in nature due to particle of quartz mineral

  e.g., Granite, Rhiolite, Pitchstone, Obsidian (Non Crystalline Nature)
- **Intermediate Igneous Rocks**
  (55-65% Silica)
  - Sub-acidic
    (60-65% silica)
    e.g.,
    Synite, Tracite
  - Sub-basic
    (55-60% silica)
    e.g.,
    Diorite, andesite
- **Basic Igneous rocks**
  (45-55% silica)
  It formed by plagioclase, augite, magnetite mineral

On the basis of origin :

Igneous Rocks

Intrusive rocks *Or* Plutonic rocks	Extrusive rocks *Or* Volcanic rocks *Or* Effusive rocks
• Slowly cooled inside of the crust • Large crystals ***e.g.,*** Granite, Syanite, Diorite Granite, Quartz, Granodiorite, Diorite, Gabbro, Peridotite	• cooled rapidly at the surface • small crystals ***e.g.,*** Rhyolite, Andesite, Basalt, Dacite, Andesite, Gabbro, Peridotite. ***Pyroclastic rocks*** : debris ejected by volcanoes • **Tuff** is made of compacted debris from old volcanic ash showers. • **Ignimbrites** are sheets of coalesced fine particles which once flowed at high speed, extremely hot, fluid avalanches.

Sedimentary Rocks

"Sedimentary rocks are formed by consolidation of sediment derived from breaking down of pre-existing of rocks. Sediments are transported in new places by air or water activity and deposited in new arrangements to sedimentary rocks."

- These rocks are formed always in layer form, so they are called *Stratified* rocks.
- These rocks are mostly formed by water action, so they are called *Aqueous* rocks.
- In India, *Tarai* areas of Himalaya mountain are formed by sedimentary rocks.
- In India sand stone, lime stone, dolomite and shale sedimentary rock are generally found.

These rocks formed by four processes;

(*i*) Weathering (*ii*) Transportation

(*iii*) Deposition (*iv*) Cementation

Weathering; the igneous rocks (primary) and other rocks disintegrate owing to physical, chemical and biological weathering. The percolating water having carbonic and humic acid decomposed the rocks and minerals, increase to quartz and other secondary minerals, solute substances, like calcium, magnesium, iron and salt:

$$2KAlSi_3O_8 + H_2CO_3 + H_2O = Al_2Si_2(OH)_4 + K_2CO_3 + 4Si_2$$

Transportation; the disintegrated material is transport by the agencies, such as water, winds, glacier, runoff and gravity.

Deposition or sedimentation; the detrital materials, comprising materials and rocks fragments, are deposited when carrying agent has no longer energy enough to move it further.

Diagenesis; (Cementation and Compaction); the weight of upper incumbent layers thousand of meter thick causes compression of the lower layer of deposits.

Cementation; the most common material that serves as cementing agents are: lime, silica and iron oxide. Water that percolates carries the binding mineral/material in solution, these in the voids of the loose sediments and binds the sediments together on deccation.

Classification of sedimentary rocks:

(i) On the basis of origin :

Sedimentary Rocks

- Mechanically formed rocks *Or* Fragmental rocks *Or* Clastic rocks *Or* Dentrial rocks (Formed by deposition and cementation of erosive products of igneous rocks, and vary in texture and structure)
  e.g., Sand Stone, Clay Stone, Slaty Stone, Conglomerate, Gravels
- Chemically formed rocks
  - Inorganically
    - (A) Formed by precipitation and flocculation
      e.g., Lime stone, dolomite, bauxite.
    - (B) Formed by evaporation
      e.g., Anhydrite, Halite, Sylvite, Varnalite, Gypsum, Shale
  - Organically (Formed by accumulation of partial decomposed OM under anaerobic condition)
    e.g., Lignite, Morl, Anthrite, Ditomite

(ii) On the basis of properties :

Sedimentary Rocks

- Transported Mechanically and deposited
  - Arenacious (Sandy in nature, composited in selaceous material)
    - Loose — ***e.g.,*** Lime stone
    - Consolidated — ***e.g.,*** Sand stone, Conglomerate, Bracia
  - Argillaceous (clayey in nature, composited of hydrated silicate of alumina)
    - Loose — ***e.g.,*** Pipe clay, Fire clay, Keolinite
    - Consolidated — ***e.g.,*** Shale, Laterites
- Transported in solution and precipitation
  - Chemically precipitate
    - Loose of CO_2 and insoluble in sea water — ***e.g.,*** Lime stone, dolomite, chalk
    - Evaporation — ***e.g.,*** Gypsum, Rock phosphate
  - Organic precipitate
    - Carbonaceous (formed deposition of vegetation under anaerobic condition) — ***e.g.,*** Lignite, Peat, Anthrite
    - Selaceous (formed from minute part of plant and animals and deposited and fresh water) — ***e.g.,*** Chert, Kiese diatomaceous

3. Metamorphic rocks

"Metamorphic rocks have been chemically altered by heat, pressure and deformation, while buried deep in the earth's crust. These rocks show changes in mineral composition or texture or both. This type of rock classification is highly specialized and complex."

There are three classes are metamorphism :

(*i*) Thermo-metamorphism

(*ii*) Dyno-metamorphism (pressure + heat)

(*iii*) Hydro-metamorphism

- These rocks are very hard, weather easily and crystalline in nature.
- Texture and chemical composition of igneous and sedimentary rocks have been changed.

Classification of metamorphic rocks :

On the basis of texture and composition

Metamorphic Rocks

Foliated rocks
Or
Flocky rocks
Or
Layerless rocks

- Foliated in nature
- Plate like mineral and arrengement in horizontal and pressure matamorphism.

e.g., Slate, Quartzite and Schist.

Unfoliated rocks
Or
Unflocky rocks
Or
Unlayered rocks

- Unfloculated in nature
- Equidimentional form

e.g., Marbal, Gniess

Properties of metamorphic rocks

- **Slates** are foliated rocks representing low-grade metamorphic alteration of shales (laminated clay).
- **Argillite** is a mudstone, much hardened by pressure.
- **Schists** are foliated medium-grade metamorphic rock with parallel layers, vertical to the direction of compaction.
- **Gneiss** is banded rocks consisting of alternating layers of quartz and feldspar, of high metamorphic grade.
- **Quartzites** represent metamorphosed sandstone.
- **Greywacke** is severely hardened sandstone with mica and feldspar, sometimes containing fossils.
- **Chert** is a siliceous rock deposited chemically, often common among greywacke.
- **Marble** is metamorphosed limestone, just recrystallised.

TABLE 2.2. Importance of Rocks: Their Characteristics and Mineralogical Composition

S. No.	Name of Rocks	General Appearnance	Mineralogical composition	Classification	Remarks
IGNEOUS ROCKS					
1.	Granite	Light coloured, mixture of pink and white or black and white with shining medium granied hard rocks	Orthoclase feldspar, quartz and mica with or without hornblende	Igneous plutonic, acid rock	High silica content. sp. gr. 2.64 g/cc.
2.	Syenite	Light coloured pale grey to pink, medium grained hard rocks	Little or absence of quartz, orthoclase feldspar, horn-blende, sometimes little plagioclase feldspar.	Igneous plutonic sub acidic rock	Intermediate silica sp. gr. is 2.80
3.	Diorite	Greenish black, medium grained hard rocks	Plagioclase feldspar, horn-blende, biotite and augite.	Igneous plutonic sub basic rocks	Sp. gr. is 2.80
4.	Basalt	Dark coloured very compact and fine grained rocks with micro crystalline structure	Plagioclase feldspar, Augite, Magnetite.	Igneous volcanic basic rocks	Av. sp. gr. is 3.0, high content of basic ions and smooth surface
5.	Trap (Amygdaloidal)	Medium coloured fine grained compact rocks with cavities filled with zeolite.	Plagioclase feldspar, Augite and magnetite	Igneous volcanic basic rocks	—
6.	Trap (vesicular)	Medium coloured rock with greenish spots, grained with long vesicles.	Plagioclase feldspar, fine Augite and mgnetite.	Igneous volcanic basic rocks	—
7.	Trap (concretionary)	Medium coloured, fine grained, concretionary soft rock.	Plagioclase feldspar Augite, Magnetite	Igneous volcanic basic rocks	Irregular rounded mass
8.	Trap (Buff or red)	Buff coloured, fine grained, fairly compact rock, with unfilled cavities.	Plagioclase fieldspar, horn-blende, magnetite	Igneous volcanic basic rocks	—
SEDIMENTARY OR AQUEOUS ROCKS					
9.	Shingle	Light red coloured loose mass composed of large rounded pebbles.	Mainly quartz	Loose, arenaceous sedimen-tary rock	Layers are compressed

10.	Grit	Composed of sharp and angular sand with grey colour.	Mainly quartz	Loose, arenaceous, sedimentary rocks	Layer can not be distinguished
11.	Conglomerate	Variously coloured consists of large rounded pebbles with elastic texture present	Mainly quartz but pebble of other minerals are also	Consolidated arenaceous sedimentary rock	Hardly any layers are seen.
12.	Breccia	Variously coloured coarse-grained rock composed of angular fragments fixed in the matrix of fine sand.	Mainly Quartz with other minerals	Consolidated arenaceous sedimentary	Layer can not be seen
13.	Sand stone (white)	Dirty white colour) granular mass made up of consolidated sand. Not so hard and compact.	Mainly quartz	-do-	Rough to feel no layers
14.	Sandstone (Badami)	Slightly reddish colour, granular and rough to feel, medium hard rock	Mainly quartz	-do-	No Layers
15.	Sand Stone with Layers	Slightly red or red and layers grey coloured layers fine grain medium hard layered rock	Mainly quartz	-do-	Distinct layers
16.	Sand stone black	Grey black some times with metallic iron luster. coarse grained medium hard rock	Quartz with hydrated oxide of iron and aluminum as cementing material	-do-	Very few layer to be seen
17.	Laterite	Brown red with yellow spots, vesicular medium hard rock, rough to feel hills	Mixture of hydrated oxids of iron and alumina	Consolidated argillaceous loose sedimentary	It becomes hard when opened.
18.	Shale (White)	White coloured soft rock easily crumbling in hand extremely fine grained with definite layers	Mainly clay	Consolidated argillaceous Sedimentary rocks	—
19.	Shale (Red) or (Pink)	Scarlet red coloured fine grain porous soft rocks with definite layers	Mainly clay	-do-	—
20.	Shale (Yellow)	Porous light yellow coloured soft rocks with layers	Mainly clay	-do-	—

S. No.	Name of Rocks	General Appearance	Mineralogical composition	Classification	Remarks
21.	Lime stone	Light yellowish green colour with layer quite visible quick effervescence with acid	Mainly $CaCO_3$	Consolidated calcareous, Sedimentary rocks	Layers are quite distinct
22.	Lime stone	Black colour with layers gives effervescence with acid	-do-	-do-	Distinguished from black marble by layer
23.	Lime stone do	White granular mass with rough surface and gives effervescence with acid.	-do-	-do-	No layers
24.	Lime stone	Dirty white granular porous, some times cellular fairly soft	-do-	-do-	—
25.	Limestone	Red coloured hard, gives effervescence with acid	-do-	-do-	No layer
26.	Coal	Black shining colour with layers	Carbon	Carbonaceous sedimentary rock	—
METAMORPHIC ROCKS					
27.	Quartzite	Fine granular mass rather rough to feel dull whitish grey colour without layer	Entirely quartz	Hydro-metamorphic rocks	—
28.	Hematite quartzite	Alternate layer of hematite and quartzite, yellowish brown coloured hard rock	Hematite and quartz	Gokak and Kandala	—
29.	Granite gneiss	White and pink colour with layers arranged in a parallel manner but are compact	Quartz, orthoclase feldspar hornblende and mica	-do-	Layers are not distinct, can not be separated
30.	Granite Schist	Light coloured and white or pink with layers	-do-	Dynamo-metamorphic rock (foliated)	Layers can be easily separated
31.	Mica schist	Various colour like light green, pink, white or black, shining foliated soft rocks	Mica and few crystals of quartz	-do-	-do-

32.	Quartz mica schist	Light coloured rocks with mica forming thin layer	Quartz is abundant mica is also an imp. constituent	-do-	—
33.	Chlorite schist.	Green coloured foliated rocks	Mainly chlorite with quartz, feldspar, mica	-do-	-do-
34.	Hornblende schist	Dark green coloured fairly soft rocks with elongated crystals	Mainly hornblende	-do-	—
35.	Talc schist	Greenish white mass soft and soapy to feel layers are seen	Chiefly talc	-do-	Very soft rocks
36.	Slate	Grey to black colour compacted and uniform texture, foliated structure	Mainly clays (formed from shale)	-do-	-do-
37.	Marble (white)	White shining and crystalline appearance readily gives efferve-scence with acid, hard rock	$CaCO_3$ (Recrystalize)	Thermo-metamorphic rocks	No layer
38.	Marble (green)	Green coloured shining and crystalline appearance, readily gives effervescence with acid, hard rock	-do-	-do-	-do-

Metamorphic rock may be of sedimentary origin or stem from igneous rocks. Rocks formed under high temperatures (basalt, gabbro) are less sensitive to metamorphosis than those so.

- Pressure from continental collision and consequent folding and overthrusting of the crust (dynamometamorphism).
- Temperature from sinking deeper, into warmer layers of the crust (metamorphism).
- Temperature from igneous hot lava running nearby, either overhead or from intrusions (contact or thermal metamorphism).
- Temperature from steam escaping from hot vents.
- Repetitive metamorphism (polymetamorphism).

CHAPTER 3

Soil Weathering and Formation

"The breaking down of rocks and minerals by chemical, physical and biological agencies are called weathering of rocks and minerals"

Weathering of rocks and minerals are three types :

1. Mechanical weathering or physical weathering (Disintegration)
2. Chemical weathering (Decomposition)
3. Biological weathering (Both)

1. Mechanical weathering

(*i*) Mechanical weathering by the physical agent like water, wind, ice, hail, storm, temperature, frost and glacier etc.

(*ii*) Consolidated massive rocks converted into smaller part without any 'chemical changes'.

(*iii*) In physical weathering size, shape of rocks and minerals may be change.

- Animals and Plants
- Temperature Variation
- Crystallization
- Unloading and Exfoliation

2. Chemical weathering

(*i*) Subsequent chemical weathering is not possible in the absent of water.

(*ii*) Chemical weathering takes place mainly at surface of the rocks and produces secondary products.

3. Biological weathering

Biological agent or living agent which are responsible for disintegration and decomposition of rocks and minerals.

PROCESSES OF CHEMICAL WEATHERING

Following chemical agent help in chemical weathering some extent.

(a) Solution

Some substance present in rock is directly dissolved in water and dissolved substances removed by continuous action of water resulting consolidated massive rock are converted into smaller parts.

$$NaCl + H_2O \longrightarrow \underset{\text{(Solution)}}{Na^+ + Cl^- + H_2O}$$

(b) Hydration

Hydration means chemical combination of water molecules with a mineral to a form new mineral. Many anhydrous minerals undergo hydration when they come in contact with water. Hydration reactions occur in primarily on the surface edge of mineral grains, but may pervade the entire structure in simple salts.

$$\underset{\text{Hematite (Red)}}{2FeO_3 + 3HOH} \longrightarrow \underset{\text{Limonite (yellow)}}{2FeO_3.3H_2O} \quad ...(1)$$

$$\underset{\text{(Anhydrate)}}{CaSO_4 + 2H_2O} \longrightarrow \underset{\text{(Gypsum)}}{CaSO_4.2H_2O} \quad ...(2)$$

- Hydration means chemical combination of molecule with a particular mineral.
- Hydration process is more effective under moist areas then dry areas.

(c) Hydrolysis

Hydrolysis one of the most important process in chemical weathering and results in complete degradation or drastic modification (structure and composition) of the weatherable primary minerals. Hydrolysis involved the partial dissociation of water into H^+ and OH^- ions. The pure water undergoes very limited dissociation, but the presence of dissolved carbon dioxide, minerals and organic acids in it, the concentration of H ions increases, resulting in an accelerated hydrolytic action of water.

$$KAlSi_3O_8 + H_2O \xrightarrow{\text{Hydrolysis}} HAlSi_3O_8 + KOH$$

(d) Oxidation

Oxidation means addition of oxygen to mineral, minerals containing iron : Mn & SO_4 are more subjective to oxidate.

$$\underset{\text{(Ferrous oxide)}}{4FeO + O_2} \longrightarrow \underset{\text{Hematite (Ferric oxide)}}{2Fe_2O_3}$$

(e) Reduction

Reduction means removal of oxygen to compound, under the condition of excess water (less or no oxygen) due to poor drainage takes place reduction.

$$2Fe_2 O_3 \longrightarrow 4FeO$$

(f) Carbonation

Carbonic acid (H_2CO_3), although a weak acid of carbon dioxide, is very important in the chemical weathering of the minerals.

WEATHERING RATE OF IMPORTANT MINERALS

Primary	Secondary	Formula	Weathering Rate
	Goethite	FeOOH	Slowest
	Hematite	Fe_2O_3	↓
	Gibbsite	$Al(OH)_3$	
Quartz		SiO_2	
Clay Minerals		Al silicates	
Muscovite		$KAl_3Si_3O_{10}(OH)_2$	
Microcline		$KAlSi_3O_8$	
Orthoclase		$KAlSi_3O_8$	
Biotite		$KAl(Mg,Fe)_3Si_3O_{10}(OH)_2$	
Albite		$NaAlSi_3O_8$	
Hornblende		$Ca_2Al_2Mg_2Fe_3Si_6O_{22}(OH)_2$	Fast
Augite		$Ca_2(Al,Fe)_4(Mg,Fe)_4Si_6O_{24}$	↓
Anorthite		$CaAl_2Si_2O_8$	
Olivine		$(Mg,Fe)_2SiO_4$	
	Dolomite	$CaMg(CO_3)_2$	
	Calcite	$CaCO_3$	
	Gypsum	$CaSO_4 \cdot 2H_2O$	Fastest

SOIL FORMATION

"Soil formation is the process of weathering of rock and mineral into regolith and consequent regolith is transformed to soil."

Factor of soil formation

According to **Dockuchaiev** (1889) five soil forming factors:

$$S = f(Cl, o, r, p, t)$$

According to Hens Jenny, (1941)

$$S = f(Cl, b, r, p, t \ \ldots)$$

$S = f(Cl)\ b, r, p, t \ \ldots)$ – Climofuction or Climosequence

$S = f(Cl_R)\ b, r, p, t \ \ldots)$ – Hydrofunction or Hydrosequence

$S = f(Cl_T), b, r, p, t \ \ldots)$ – Thermofunction or Thermosequence

$S = f(b)\ Cl, r, p, t \ \ldots)$ – Biofunction or Biosequence

$S = f(r)Cl, b, p, t \ \ldots)$ – Topofunction or Toposequence

$S = f(p)Cl, b, r, t \ \ldots)$ – Lithofunction or Lithosequence

$S = f(t)Cl, b, r, p, \ \ldots)$ – Chronofunction or Chronosequence

where, S = Soil forming factors f = Function of

Cl = Climate b = Biosphere

r = Relief or topography p = Parent material
t = Time (Age)   . . . = fire, water, ice

According to J.S. Joffe (1949), soil forming factor are divided in to follows

A. Active soil forming factors

(*i*) Climate

(*ii*) Vegetation and organisms (biosphere)

B. Passive soil forming factors

(*i*) Parent material

(*ii*) Relief or topography

(*iii*) Time (also known as *Neutral* factor)

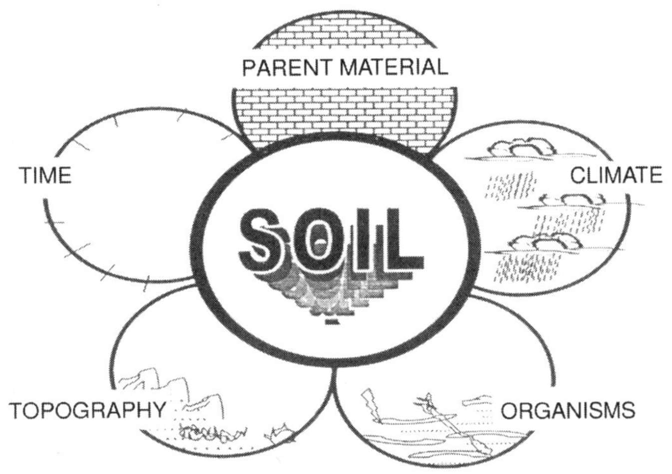

Fig. 3.1. Soil—the end product of soil forming factors

Climate. The climate is the dominant factor in soil formation. The rainfall, temperature, wind, evaporation, transpiration are the different components of climate. The influence of climate in soil formation is both direct and indirect. Directly, it supply water and heat to react upon parent material (rainfall and temperature). Indirectly the climate governs the flora and fauna which forms the source of energy in the shape of organic matter.

Temperature is another component of climate. The rate of chemical reaction becomes approximately double for every 10°C rise in temperature. It also controls the type of vegetation, evapotranspiration, humidity and biological activity. Evaporation, transpiration and humidity modify the effect of precipitation by either reducing or increasing the quantity of water available for percolation and reaction.

The soil properties which are affected by climatic conditions are pH, base saturation, organic matter content, clay mineralogical composition and amount and nature of clay. In general with increase in rainfall, there is decrease in pH, base saturation, content of carbonates and soluble salts but increase in that of clay.

Soils formed from the same parent material under low and high rainfall area vary in morphology and physico-chemical properties. Soils formed in low rainfall area are very dark grayish brown to black in colour, alkaline, high CEC and some time calcareous. While soils formed in high rainfall area are yellow to red in colour, acidic, low CEC and devoid of lime. Lateritic acid soil are formed under high temperature and moderate to high rainfall (Arid and Semi arid areas). Podzols and forest soils are formed under humid and cool condition (temperate climatic condition).

Organisms/Biotic factor. This is usually referred to as biotic factor. Vegetation, microbes, animals and man all greatly influence the soil formation processes. This can be presented as S = f (O) cl, r, p, t

Effect of vegetations

1. Direct effects. It adds organic matter into the soil.

2. Indirect effect. Rainfall interception, generation of microclimate and recycling of nutrient, profile mixing, structural stability etc. Micro organisms add N in soil through symbiotic and asymbiotic way. The micro-organism plays a vital role in decomposition of organic matter and mineralization of nutrient. Insects, burrowing animals, rodents earthworms etc interfere the weathering process which lead to distinct horizon differentiation. Man through his land use activity causes both deleterious and beneficial effects on the soil-cultivation of virgin land, growing of crop, removal of natural vegetation accelerate erosion through burning, shifting, grazing and cultivation, management practices like, drainage, use of manures and fertilizers, puddling, irrigation, leveling, reclamation.

Relief or Topography. The condition of land surface is described in relief or topography. It is the elevation or inequalities of the land surface considered collectively e.g. level, flat, undulating, hilly etc. Topography (relief) influences soil formation primarily through its effect on drainage run off, soil erosion and microclimate.

Soil properties affected by relief

1. Depth of solum
2. Thickness and OM content of A horizon
3. Colour of the profile
4. Degree of horizon differentiation
5. Kind and degree of 'Pan' development
6. Soil reaction
7. Soluble salt content
8. Temperature
9. Relative wetness of the profile
10. Characterstics of the parent material

The profile development is more in flat topography while in undulating topography it varies with situation – shallow profile in upper region and deeper in low lying area. Steep slope at hill side have thinner A and B horizon due to high erosion and less leaching. Gently slopping area has thick horizons, tall vegetation and high O.M. content in soil. Upland area have light colour, less soluble salts, kaolinite clay and red colour soil (laterite soil). While in low land area have dark deep soil with high salts montmorillonite clay and black in colour (black soil).

PARENT MATERIAL

"C horizon refer as parent material"

Parent material is that mass (alluvium, colluviums, aeolian/loess, glacial-till) from which the soil has formed. The parent materials transported from their place of origin are named according to the main force responsible for the transport and redeposition. The material transported and deposited by water is ***alluvium***, found along major stream courses, at the bottom of slopes of mountains, and along small streams flowing out of drainage basins, ***Colluvium*** is used for poorly sorted materials near the base of strong slopes transported by the action of gravity. ***Lacustrine*** consists of materials that have settled out of the quiet water of lakes. ***Glacial*** consist of all the materials picked up, mixed, disintegrated, transported and deposited through the action of glacial ice or of water resulting primarily from melting of glaciers. The wind blown materials are termed ***loess*** when the texture is silty and ***eolian*** sand when these are primarily sand. The materials deposited by the melting glaciers vary widely in particle size called as ***till*** or ***moraine***. If the parent material is transported by water and fine sediments deposited at the bottom of the sea and get exposed at the surface due to change in sea level named as ***marine***. The soils developed on such transported parent materials bear the name of the parent material, viz. alluvial soils from alluvium, colluvial soils from colluviums (Fig. 3.2).

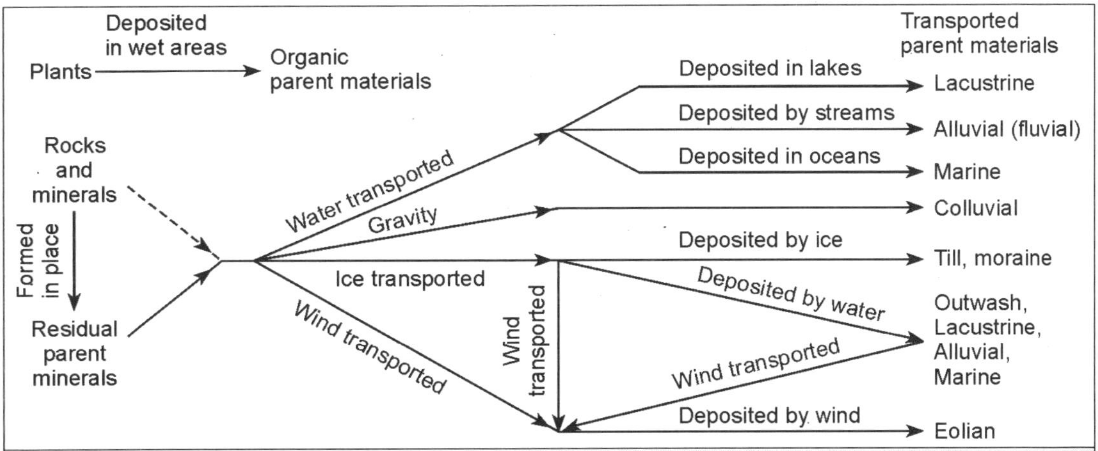

Fig. 3.2. How various kinds of parent material are formed, transported and deposited.

Time (Age): The actual length of time for weathering of parent material plays a significant role in soil formation. The length of time required for a soil to develop horizons depends upon many factors such as climatic, nature of parent material, burrowing animals and relief. A horizon tends to develop faster under cool, humid, forested conditions.

Certain soils are termed mature or immature which give some idea of the time factor. Hence the age of soil is measured in terms of state of maturity rather than years. A mature soil has well developed profile.

Mohr and Van Baren (1959), recognized the following five stage of soil development:

1. Initial. Unweathered parent material.

2. Juvenile. Weathering started/initiation, but much of original material still unweathered.

3. Senile. Easily weatherable minerals fairly decomposed, clay content has increased, slowly weatherable minerals still appreciable.

4. Virile. Decomposition arrives at a final stage, only most resistant minerals survive.

5. Final. Soil development completed under prevailing conditions and parent material are completely weathered.

SOIL FORMING PROCESS

The interaction of soil forming factors may be expressed by a series of physical chemical and biological reactions collectively they represent soil forming processes which leads to the moulding of soil body. The soil formation in each area is the result of a specific pedogenic process. The ultimate result of soil formation is profile development. These are as under :

Soil forming process

Basic or fundamental soil forming processes

1. Eluviation
2. Illuviation
3. Humification
4. Horizinization

Specific soil forming process

Zonal process

1. Podolization (Silication)
2. Laterization (Desilication)
3. Calcification and Gypsification
4. Decalcification

Intrazontal process

1. Argillation
2. Gleization
3. Pedoturbation
4. Lessivage
5. Alkalinization

Some Important Process of Pedogenesis

Term	Brief Description
Eluviation	Eluviation is the mobilization and translocation of certain constituents namely clay, Fe_2O_3, Al_2O_3, SiO_2, humus, $CaCO_3$ and other soluble salts etc. from one area of the soil body to the other area.
Illuviation	Illuviation is the immobilization and accumulation of the eluviated constituents at a depth below the soil surface.
Horizonation	Horizonation, differentiation of soil in different horizons along the depth of the soil body.
Argillation	Argillation is a process by which the dispersed clay particles are migrated from upper to the lower soil horizons resulting a textural horizon. As a result of this process argillic horizon is formed.
Leaching (deplition)	General term for washing out or eluviating soluble materials from the solum.
Enrichment	Genral term for addition of material to a soil body.
Erosion, Surfacial	Removal of material from the surface layer of a soil body.
Cumulization	Aeolian, hydrologic and made additions of mineral particle to the surface of a soil solum.
Calcification	Process including accumulating of calcium carbonate in Cca and possibly other horizons of a soil results in formation of a soil calcic horizon.
Decalcification	Calcification and Gypsification are the soil forming processes in arid and semi-arid regions and refer to the formation and accumulation of calcium carbonate and gypsum respectively. Calcareous and gypsyferous soils are formed.
Salinization	Salinization is the process of accumulation of soluble salts in soil. Such as SO_4^{2-}, Cl^- of Ca^{2+}, Mg^{2+}, Na^+ and K^+ in salty horizons. The accumulation of soluble salts is due to local condition. It is common in arid and semi-arid regions. The soils formed are known as saline soils.
Desalinization	The removal of soluble salts from salic soil horizons
Alkalinization (solinization)	The process involves the accumulation of sodium ions on the exchange complex of the clay, resulting in the formation of sodic soils (***solonetz***).
Dealkalinization (solodization)	The leaching of sodium ions on the exchange site in a soil.

Lessivage	Lessivage is the hydration and adsorption of ions on exchange complex.
Pedoturbation (ferrization, allization)	Biological, physical (freez-thaw and wet-dry cycle) churning and cycling of soil materials, thereby horizonizing the solum in varying degree.
Podzolization	The chemical migration of aluminum and iron and/or organic matter, resulting in the concentration of silica (*i.e.* silication) in the layer eluviated.
Desilication (ferrallization)	The chemical migration of silica out of soil solum and thus the concentration of sesquioxide in the solum (goethite, gibbsite etc.) with or without formation of ironstone (leterite : hardent plinthite) and concretion.
Laterization	Removal of silica from upper layers leaving sesquivoxides (chiefly Fe&Al oxide) to concentrate in the solum.
Resilication	Formation of Keolinite from Gibbsite in presence of excess $Si(OH)_4$ in solution or formation of smectite from Keolinite in the presence of large amount of $Si(OH)_4$ at higher pH value.
Decomposition	The breakdown of mineral and organic materials.
Synthesis	The formation of new particles of mineral and organic material.
Malanization	The darking of light-colour initial, undecomposed materials by the mixture of organic matter (as in a dark Al or molic or umbric horizons).
Leucinization	The paling of horizons by disappearance of dark organic material either through transformation of light colour ones or through removal from the horizons.
Littering	The accumulation of organic matter and associated humus on the mineral soil surface to depth of less then 30 cm.
Humification	Humification is the process of decomposition of organic matter and synthesis of new organic substances.
Paludilization	Another process that may be operative in soils is pedoturbation. It is the process of mixing of the soil. For example argilli pedoturbation is observed in deep black soils.
Ripening	Chemical, biological and physical changes in organic soil after air penitrates previously waterlogged material.
Mineralizaion	Decomposition of organic matter and subsiquent release of oxide solides.
Braunification/ Rubification	Release of iron from primary minerals and the dispersed particles of iron oxide in increasing amounts; their progressive oxidation or hydration, giving the soil ash brownish, reddish brown or red colours, respectively.
Ferrugination	Iron sesquioxdes adher firmly to sand soil particles and gravel giving them red colour resulting produced cemented Fe layer.
Gliezation	The reduction of iron under anaerobic "water logged" soil conditions, with the production of bluish to grayish matrix colour, with or without yellowish brown, brown and black mottles and ferric and magniferrous concentration.
Loosening	Increase the volume of void by activity of plants, animal and human by freezing thawing or other physical process and by removal of material by leaching.
Hardening	Decrease in volume of voids by colapse and compaction and by filling of some voids with fine earth, carbonates, silica and other materials.

Eluviation

When salt, humus, small clay particle etc. are dissolved in water, or conside in water or suspense and goes down in lower layer by percolation, from the upper surface layer and upper horizons the process is called eluviation. *Eluvial* word is derived from E- out, lov means washed. Thus eluvial denotes wash out. This process occurs following four processes:

(*i*) **Salvation.** Element from the minerals by simple process dissolving in water and goes down to upper layer by percolation.

(*ii*) **Suspension.** Humus, colloid and small clay particle make suspension and goes down to upper layer to percolation.

(*iii*) **Reduction.** Generally Fe and Mn after reduction goes down in lower layer by percolation.

(*iv*) **Cheluviation.** Generally Fe and Al make complex compound with humus and goes down in lower layer by percolation.

Podzolization (Silication)

Podzol word is derived from Russian language word *i.e.* Podzola, *pod* = under, *zola* = ash *i.e.* 'A' ash like horizon.

"Humus sesquive oxide and clay particle goes down in 'B' horizon by percolation from 'A' horizon, resulting the ratio of silica and sesquive oxide (more then 2) in 'A' horizon and accumulation humus sesquivoxide and small clay particle 'B' horizon the process is called podzolization and soil so formed is called Podzol soil."

Properties

(*i*) This process opposite of laterization.

(*ii*) This process is a type of eluviation.

(*iii*) This process occurs in humid temperate regions or cold humid regions as well as high rainfall area and having high content of organic matter and less bases in parent material.

(*iv*) Fertility status of these soils are low and acidic in nature.

(*v*) Dominant in Illite type of clay minerals.

(*vi*) Spodic epipedon is found in 200 cm soil depth of mineral soil.

Laterization

Laterite word derived from latin language word *later* means brick like brittle and hard.

"When mobile silica is deposited in 'B' horizon and residual sesquivoxide remains on 'A' horizon, resulting decreases the silica sesquive oxide (<2) in 'A' horizons and 'A' horizon as brick like red and hard due to hemetite, the process is called laterization and soil so formed laterite soil."

A useful index of to determine the degree of laterization is the SiO_2: AlO_3 ratio. If the ratio is a genuine laterite the (*Oxisols*) and if the ratio is between 1-2, then the soils are lateritic (*Ultisols*).

Properties

(*i*) This process is occurs in tropical and subtropical and/or hot humid tropics as well as high rainfall area and temperature.

(*ii*) Dominantly keolinite type of clay minerals in soils.

(*iii*) This soils formed by basic parent material.

(*iv*) These soils are generally granular in nature and good drainage condition.

(*v*) These soils are deep.

(*vi*) These soil deficient in N, P, K, Ca, Mg, low in CEC (4.2 Cmol(p^+/kg)), OM, soluble salt and less clay content.

(*vii*) These soils are suitable for growing of Tea, Coffee, Rubber and Cinchona.

Location

These soils found in top of hill of Rajasthan, and plane part of Orissa, Maharashtra and Assam.

❑ ❑ ❑

CHAPTER 4

Soil Morphology

Soil Morphology

"It is the constitution of the soil including the texture, structure, consistence, colour and other physical, chemical and biological properties of the various soil horizons that make up the soil profile. The morphology of a soil is best evaluated from the in-situ examination of the soil profile."

Soil Profile

"A vertical cut of soil from the surface, down to the hard rock from which the soil is formed is known as soil profile. The profile consists of different layers or horizons."

Or

"The development of soil profile is constructive processes where in disintegrated material resulted from weathering of rocks and minerals get converted into a soil body."

Soil Horizon

"A soil horizon is a layer of soil, approximately parallel to the soil surface, with characteristics produced by soil-forming processes".

Theoretical soil Profile

"A theoretical soil profile showing different horizons or layers are shown in the following figure."

Organic Horizons. The 'O' group is the organic horizon which is formed at the very surface of the mineral soil resulting from the decayed plant and animal products. This horizon is commonly found in forest areas where sufficient plants are present. It can be divided into three specific horizons as follows :

O_1 or Oi — In this first layer of organic horizons, the original forms of plants and animals can be easily recognized or identified by the naked eye.

O_2 or Oe — In this specific layer of organic horizons, the original forms of plants and animals cannot be recognized visually.

O_3 or Oa.—In this layer of organic horizons, the organic matter completely decomposed and cannot identified by naked eye.

'A' horizons [eluvial (outer) horizons]. This 'A' horizon is present at or near the surface and it is characterized as zones of 'washing out' or maximum leaching. These horizons can be divided into three specific horizons as follows :

A_1 or A— It is the uppermost mineral soil horizon rich in organic matter which imparts darker colour as compared to the lower horizons.

A_2 or E— It is the horizon of washing out or eluviation of clay, iron and aluminium oxides and corresponding accumulation or resistant minerals, such as quartz. It imparts light colour than that of the upper horizon (A_1).

A_3 or AB/EB — It is transition horizon between A and B having properties more available those of A_1 or A_2 than that of B horizons. Sometimes it may be absent.

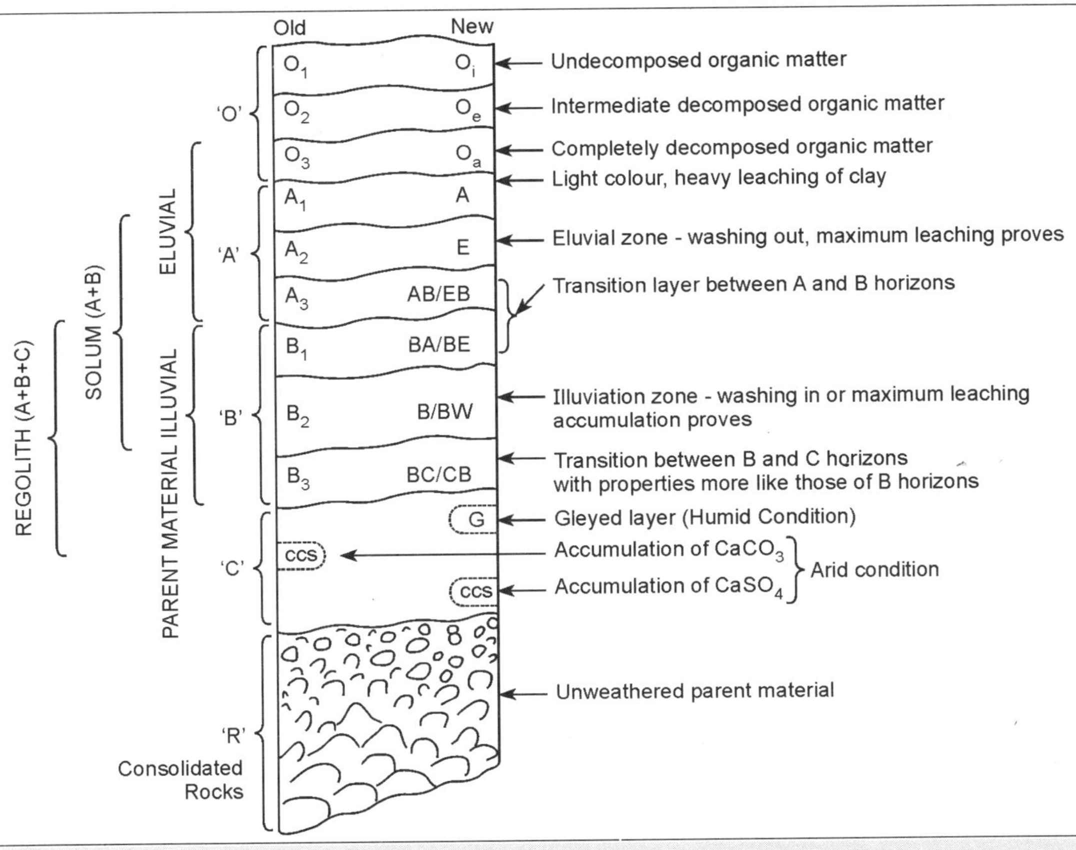

Fig. 4.1. A well developed hypothetical imaginary soil profile.

'B' [*illuvial* (inner) horizons]. This horizons are the zone of 'washing in' or accumulation of materials such as iron and aluminum oxides and silicate clays, from the above horizons or even from the below horizons in arid conditions as calcium carbonate, calcium sulphate and other salts during evaporation. These horizons sometimes are referred to as the 'Sub soil' where it may not be considered as the plough layer. It can be divided into three specific horizons as follows :

B_1 or BA/BE — It is a transition horizon between A and B having properties more nearly like B than A. It may be sometimes absent.

B_2 or B/BW — This horizon considered as the zone of maximum accumulation of clays and hydrous oxides. In this horizon organic matter content is generally higher than that of A_2 horizon. Developments of blocky or prismatic structure are found.

B_3 or BC/CB — It is the transition horizon between B and C having properties more like those of B than horizon.

'C' Horizon. It is the unconsolidated material underlying the Solum (A plus B horizon). It may or may not be the same as the parent material from which the Solum formed. This horizon also considers as outside the zones of major biological activities and is very little affected by Solum forming processes. The upper portion of the C horizon may sometimes be considered as the Solum since continually weathering and erosion are going on.

R layer. It is the consolidated rocks below the C horizons. If 'C' is absent it is below B horizons.

Solum. Both A and B horizons collectively called solum (Mineral soil). O + A + B (Organic soil).

Regolith. Solum plus parent material (A+B+C) is referred to as regolith. (Organic soil O + A + B + C).

Rules governing use of symbols

(1) The capital letter symbols : O, A, B, C and R is used to designate the different horizons. Horizon A, B and C are called *master horizons*.

(2) The subdivision is indicated by placing arabic number after the capital letter, such as O_1, O_2, O_3, A_1, A_2, A_3, B_1, B_2, etc.

(3) Further sub division within same horizon is indicated as A_{11}, A_{12}, B_{21}, B_{22}, or B_{23} as needed.

(4) Major change in horizon is indicated by putting suffixes in master horizon. A_2g or B_3Ca, Bt or Ap, A_{21}g, A_{22}g, C_1Ca, C_2Ca

(5) Lithological discontinuities are indicated by prefixing Roman number to master horizon. ***e.g.*** The sequence may be : A_2, B_1, II B_2, B_3, II C_1, III C_2. The first or upper most material is not numbered for that Roman I is understood.

Sub horizon symbols

To indicate certain additional characters a few suffixes are used with the appropriate horizon designation.

Master horizons	*Suffix*	*Descriptions*	*Symbol*
'O'	i	Slightly decomposed O.M. and it can be easily identified by naked eye.	Oi
	e	Intermediate decomposed O.M. and it can be identified by naked eye.	Oe
	a	Completely decomposed O.M. and it can not be easily identified by naked eye.	Oa
'A'	b	Buried genetic soil horizon.	Ab
	f	Frozen soil	Af
	p	Disturbed due to plowing or by other means *e.g.* Ap, Ap_2.	Ap
'B'	c	Accumulation of concretion.	Bc
	h	Accumulation of illuvial humus *e.g.* Bh or B_2h.	Bh
	k	Ca accumulation of carbonate	Bk
	n	Accumulation of sesquioxides *e.g.* B_2cn.	Bn
	o	Residual accumulation of sesquioxide	Bo
	q	Accumulation of silica	Bq
	s	Accumulation of $CaSO_4$ in crystalline forms *e.g.* Ccs.	Bs
	t	Accumulation of translocated silicate clay *i.e.* argillic horizon *e.g.* Blt.	Bt
	w	Accumulation of clay silica	Bw
	v	Plinthite character (high iron, poor humus, rich sesquioxide found in *oxisols*)	Bv
	x	Fragipan character—high bulk density, brittle when moist and very hard when dry.	Bx
	z	Accumulation of salts in more soluble then gypsum.	Bz
'C'	g	Gleying *i.e.* intense reduction of iron *e.g.* Cg, $A_{21}g$.	Cg
	m	Cementation or indurations	Cm
	r	Weathered of soft bedrock	Cr
	y	Accumulation of gypsum	Cy
	d	Unconsolidated material	d
	j	Jerosite (yellow)	j
	jj	Frost churning	jj

SOIL MORPHOLOGICAL FEATURE/SOIL TAXONOMICAL

- Smallest unit to study the soil pedon.
- The concept of pedon was given by Simension.
- The size of pedon is 1-10 m^2 (Generally m^2).
- The shape of pedon is hexagonal.
- Pedon is a three dimensional natural body.
- Two or three pedons together in single soil unit series is called polypedon.

Diagnostic Horizons. The horizons which are of special type other than master horizon A, B, C and used in classification are the diagnostic horizons. These diagnostic horizons may be on the surface or sub surface.

Diagnostic Surface Horizons. The surface diagnostic horizons are called epipedons. (Greek *epi*-over and *pedon*-soil). The epipedon is the upper part of the soil darkened by organic matter.

The characteristic of epipedon are :

(*i*) They form on or near the surface.
(*ii*) They are darkened by o.m. or eluviated in some case or both.
(*iii*) They may be illuvated partly.
(*iv*) They may include Ap or whole A horizon or it may include part of B horizon also.

Epidedons : MUOHAP GMF

Mollic, Ochric, Umbric, Histic, Anthropic, Plaggic, Grassarenic, Melenic, Foliastic

@ ***Mollic, Ochric, Umbric*** are commonly found in India.

Diagnostic surface horizons (epipedon) and their characteristic

Mollic (L. *mollis* = soft). Epipedons (surface horizons) strong soil structure, thick, dark coloured, 50% or more base saturation, organic carbon not less than 0.6%, less than 250 ppm 1% citric acid soluble phosphate.

Umbric (L. *Umbra* = shade/dark). Same as mollic epipedon except for base saturation (< 50%).

Ochric (Gk. *Ochros* = pale, light coloured). Light coloured, low organic carbon content, may be hard and massive when dry.

Histic (Gk. *Hoistos* = tissue). Very high in organic carbon content, usually found in very poorly drained mineral soils that are close to organic soils.

Anthropic (Gk. *Anthropos* = man). Formed due to long term effect of human use of the soil for residence purposes, more citric acid soluble P_2O_5 and all other characteristics are same as mollic epipedons except moisture status.

Plaggen (Ger. *Plaggen* = sod). Formed due to long continued manuring where sod was used as bedding for animals in stables and burns and subsequently was deposited on other soils. Thickness 50 cm or more.

Grassarenic (L. *Grossus*, thick = *Arena* = sand). Sandy in horizon, 100 cm or more thickness found above argillic endopedon.

Melanic (Gr, *Melas* = melan-black). Thick black colour horizon and containing at or near with in 30 cm, high in O.M. content (6% O.M. or more in all layers), found commonly in volcanic ash soil.

Foliastic. Comprises organic material that remains saturated in one month.

Sub Surface Diagnostic Horizons

The sub-surface diagnostic horizons are called *endopedons*. (Gr. endo-lower/under and peden-soil).They are mostly B horizons but under certain condition it may be lower part of 'A' depending upon soil morphological characters.

ENDOPEDON:

CAF	GAS	SOC	DAS	PPP	NSKG
Calcic	**Gypsic**	Spodic	Duric	Petrocalcic	Natric
Albic	Agric	**Oxic**	**Argillic**	Petrogypsic	Sulphuric
Fragipan	**Salic**	**Cambic**	Sombric	Placic	**Knadic**
*Ortstien (new added)					Glosic

Calcic (L, *calyx*, *Calc* = lime). This layer has secondary accumulation of carbonatos of Ca or Mg thickness >15 cm, 15% or more $CaCO_3$ equivalent at least 5% more $CaCO_3$ underlying layer.

Albic (L, *Albus* = white). Without sesquivoxie, light colour, clay Fe and Al are mostly removed, strongly E horizons.

Fragipan (L, *Fragilis* = brittle). Low silica content and low temperature. Britle hard and high BD, low permeability.

Gypsic. It is a horizon of calcium sulphate enrichment, 15 cm or more thick, and at least 5% or more gypsum than under laying layer.

Agric (L. *Ager* = field). Organic and clay accumulation just below the plough layer, C:N ratio in the agric horizon is low (usually < 8), pH is close to neutrality (6-6.5), illuvial materials (humus and clay) accumulate as lamellac directly below the very surface horizon.

Salic. It is a horizon of accumulation of soluble salts which are soluble than $CaSO_4$, 15 cm or more thickness and 2% or more soluble salts.

Spodic (Gr, *spodus* = wood ash). Accumulation of organic matter, Fe, Al oxide, occurs in temperate region with high rainfall area, acidic in nature, low fertile, found commonly in spodosols.

Oxic (*Oxic*-modified for oxide). The oxic horizon is a sub-surface horizon at least 30 cm thick consisting of a mixture of hydrated oxides of iron or aluminium, or both, with variable amount of kaolinite and accessory highly insoluble minerals such as quartz sand.

Cambic (L, cambriare = change). Change in physical condition in soil or colour by biological reaction, weakly wreathed 'B' horizon found commonly in inceptisols order.

Duripan (L, *durus* = Hardpan). Hard layer like cement due to excess amount of silica content, arid region check the penetration of roots and water.

Argillic (L. *Argilla* = white clay). Silicate clay accumulation, an argillic horizon should be at least one-tenth as thick as the sum of the thickness of all overlying horizon formation of argillic horizon is slow, it is not genetically young.

Sombric (sp. *Sombra* = shade). Accumulation of organic matter, a acidic in nature.

Petrocalcic (Gr, *Petra* = rochs, *Calx* = chalk). This is a special kind of calcic horizon. It is more indurated, does not disperse in water and can not be penetrated by spade when dry.

Petrogypsic (Gr, *Petra* = rock; *calx* = chlk). Strong gypsum horizon, check the root penitation and water movment.

Placic (Gr, *Base of plax* = flate ston; meaning a thin cemented pan). Fe and Mn, check the root penetration and water movement. It is a kind of Fe or Fe + Mn or Fe + Mn + O.M. accumulation pan, thin 2-10 mm, dark brown to reddish in colour.

Natric (NL. *Natrium* = sodium). It is special kind of argillic horizon, high in sodium (Sodium adsorption ratio, SAR ⊕ 13), more exchangeable magnesium plus sodium than calcium plus exchange acidity (at pH 8.2), Columnar or prismatic structure.

Sulfuric (L, *sulphur*). Very high acidic horizon, jerosite, mottle, yellow sulphur mineral, more amount of sulphur.

Kandic (*Kand modified from kandite*). Accumulation of slightly clay.

Glossic (Gr, *Glossa* = tounguae). 5 cm or more thickness, formed in eluvial and illuvial part.

***Ortstien (Gr, *Ort* = front edge; *stein* = ston).** It is the 25 cm more thick, consisting spodic materials and in a layer which is 50% or more cemented.

Other Macropedogenic Features

These features are usually used as diagnostic criteria at a some what lower level in the classification.

Plinthite. This is a humus-poor sesquivoxide rich horizon. It becomes hard like iron stone or aggregates with repeated wetting and drying, reddish brown in colour (leterite soil).

Lithic contact. This is a boundary between soil and continuous coherent, underlying material that has hardness >3 Moh's.

Paralithic contact. This is a boundary between soil and underlying coherent material, with a hardness <3 moh's.

Permafrost. This is a continuous frozen layer.

Gilgai relief. The micro relief of soil produced by moisture. Found in soils that contain large amounts of clay that swells and shrinks considerably with wetting and drying.

Slickensides. When soil peds press against each other during soil wetting. It is usually present in soils that contain appreciable quantities of expanding layer lattice silicates. A slickenside is a smoothed surface with parallel striae and grooves.

Dignostic organic horizons

Fabric. Fibrus material >2/3 of the mass (slightly decomposed of organic matter).

Humic. Fibrus material <1/3-2/3 of the mass (intermediate decomposition).

Sapric. Fibrous material <1/3 mass (High decomposition).

Humiluvic. Illuvial humus accumulates in continuous cultivated field under acidic organic soil.

Limnic. Organic or inorganic materials deposited in water by action of quick micro organism. e.g. morl, sedimentary peat (caprogenous).

***20th endopedon,** new added.

For detail information on :

http://www.pedosphere.com/resources/sg_usa/,
http://clic.cses.vt.edu/forum/,
http://soils.usda.gov/technical/classification/taxonomy/
http://soils.usda.gov/

❑❑❑

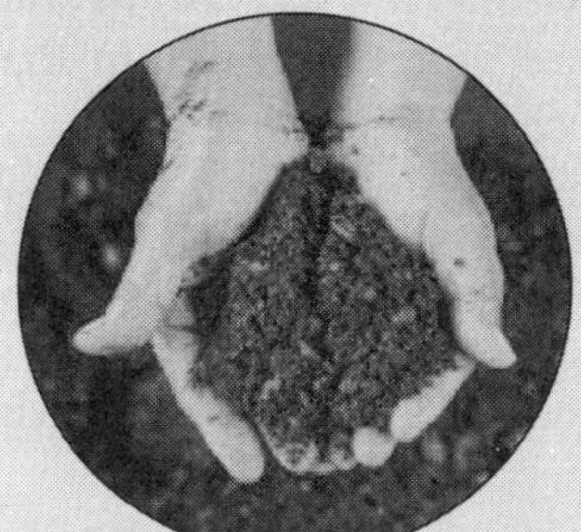

CHAPTER 5

Soil Classification and Taxonomy

"Soil classification is a systematic arrangement of soil individuals into various groups based on their properties with certain objectives."

EARLY SYSTEMS OF SOIL CLASSIFICATION

Early systems of soil classification were very simple and practical.

1. **Economic classification.** It was adopted by the Revenue Department for grouping the soils according to their productivity was for purpose of taxation.
2. **Physical classification.** It was based of on soil texture property associated soil productivity. This system is good enough for agricultural purposes but does not meet the requirement of soil science.
3. **Chemical classification.** Based on chemical composition—Calcareous soils, Acid soils, sodic soils etc. But these characteristics do not permit to classify all kinds of soils occurring in nature.
4. **Geological classification.** Based on underlying parent material. Residual or sedentary soil, transported soils. The other factors of soil formation—climate and vegetation which dominate over the influence of parent material were not considered and there by upset the geological classification.
5. **Physiographic classification.** Based on physiographic condition of soil on the landscape—Level soils, Basin soils, Terrace soils, Mountain soils, Hilly soils, Upland soils, Low land soils. This has limited value as two or more soil groups with different properties may by classified in one group.
6. **Genetic classification.** Recently in the later part of the 19th century and early part of 20th century Dokuchaiv (1900), Coffey (1912), Marbut (1935) classified the soils on the basis of zonality. The basis of this classification depends on the genesis or origin of the soil and its subsequent development. These classification systems are based upon the study of the soil profile, which is the ultimate product and reflection of all

the soil forming factors and processes. **Marbut's morphogenetic** soil classification system was revised and elalaborated by Balwin, Kellogg and Thorp (1938) of USDA. The whole system was categories into order, sub order, great group and sub group at higher level and families, series types and phase at lower category level.

Serious problem were found when some soil series did not fit in any of the existing great soil group, whereas others could be placed equally well in two great soil groups. Realizing this problem the soil classification of Baldwin *et al.* (1938) was modified by Thorp and Smith (1949).

After modification, the soils can be grouped into three orders namely, Zonal, Intrazonal and Azonal based on the Zonality concept developed by Russian Soil Geologist **Dokuchaiev**.

Zonal Soils. Zonal soils were groups of soils developed under similar climatic conditions and distributed in a climatic belt. Soils in this group possess well developed profiles reflecting the influence of climate and vegetation. The only differences due to the parent material are rendered subordinate by dominating climate influences. Example, laterite soil, podzol soil, chernozem soil etc.

Intrazonal Soils. The soils occur within a zone, but reflect the influence of some local conditions, such as topography and/or the parent material. Under these conditions, the characteristics of soils imparted by the local conditions are dominant *viz*. excess of water, salt, calcium carbonate etc. example; saline, sodic and saline sodic soil etc.

Azonal Soils. The soils have poorly developed profiles because of time as a limiting factor. The group included young soils without horizon differentiation so the soils could not be grouped in any one of these two order (Zonal and Intrazonal) and was placed in a separate order known as Azonal soils, Example; Alluvial soils.

These three orders were further divided into nine (9) suborders on the basis of specific climatic and vegetative regions. Each of the sub-order, in turn was divided into great soil groups having expressions of more specific conditions. The great soil groups were further sub-divided into numerous soil series and soil types.

Limitations/Draw backs in Genetic system of soil classification

(1) The two highest categories are defined in genetic terms and not on the basis of soil properties.

(2) The definitions and concepts of the highest category (order) in relation to soil properties are not clear.

(3) At great group are defined on the basis of only environmental factor and not on the basis of soil properties.

(4) Same properties were used at different level of classification.

(5) More emphasis has been given to soil colour and vegetation than that of soil properties.

(6) Nomenclature is not informative.

NEW COMPREHENSIVE SYSTEM OF SOIL CLASSIFICATION/SOIL TAXONOMY/ CLASSIFICATION ACCORDING TO 7TH APPROXIMATION

In order to overcome different anomalies in earlier system of soil classification a new comprehensive system has been developed. Initially started in 1951, several approximations were made after taking critical suggestions from pedologists of different countries. The *7th Approximation* was published in 1960 with supplements in 1964, 1967, 1975, 1999, 2000, 2005 and 2009. *Soil Taxonomy A Basic System of Soil Classification for Making and Interpreting Soil Surveys* was published in 1975. The 7th Approximation lays more stress on the morphology of soils themselves rather than on the environmental factors.

Characteristics of Soil Classification—7th Approximation

1. It is a natural classification of soil.
2. The classification is based on properties of the soils.
3. The properties selected should be observable or measurable. Properties which can be measured quantitatively should be preferred.
4. The properties selected should be those that either affect soil genesis or result from soil genesis.
5. The properties with the greater significance to plant growth should be selected for the higher category.
6. The classification system is flexible.

CATEGORIES

There are six categories of classification in *Soil Taxonomy*

(*i*) **Order** .... Highest category

(*ii*) **Sub-order**

(*iii*) **Great group** .... Basic category

(*iv*) **Sub-group**

(*v*) **Family**

(*vi*) **Series** .... Lowest category

ORDER

The order is based on soil forming process. In a given order, soil properties are similar in their genesis. For example, soils that developed under grassland vegetation and is characterized by a thick, dark surface horizon with high metallic cations. Soils with these properties are included in the order, Mollisols. There are following eleven soil orders in soil taxonomy.

CONCEPT

Condition	Yes →
Soils that have *permafrost* with in 100 cm or gelic material with permanent frost within 200 cm of surface.	Gelisols
Soils that do not have andic soil properties, but have >30% organic matter to a depth of 40 cm.	Histosols
Soils that have andic soil properties in 60% or more of the thickness between the soil surface and 60 cm or lithic or paralithic contact.	Spodosols
Highly weathered soils with an oxic horizon with in 150 cm, but have no kandic horizon, or contain > 40 % clay in the surface 18 cm soils and have a kandic horizon with in 100 cm of the surface overlaying the oxic horizon.	Andisols
Soils swell-shrink type, clay, having 30% or more clay up to 50 cm depth or to lithic/paralithic contact, deep cracks that open and close periodically, at 50 cm of the surface overlying the oxic horizons.	Oxisols
Swell with swell-shrink type, clay having 30% or more up to 50 cm depth or to lithic/paralithic contact, deep cracks that open and close periodically, at 50 cm and have slikensides or wedge-shaped aggregates.	Vertisols
Dry soils that have an ochric, or anthropic epipedon, and either have a salic orizons and solution with water within or calcic, gypsic/cambic patrocalcic, or a duripan, or have an argillic/natric horizon and an aridic soil moisture regime, and have on sulphuric horizon within 150 cm.	Aridisols
Low base saturation soils that have an argillic or candic but no fragipan and a base saturation by sum of cations of <35% at 180 cm depth below the surface.	Ultisols
Dark-coloured base-rich (>50%) soils are grassland vegetation with a *mollic* epipedon this is not both hard and massive when dry.	Molisols
High base status (>35%) soils of the humid and subhumid regions with a mollic epipedon that is not both hard and massive when dry.	Alfisols
Soils have that no spodic, argillic, natric, oxic, petrocalcic, plinthite, but have an altered or cambic-B horizon, or an umbric and plaggen epipedon or have a sulphuric horizon with in 150 cm of the surface.	Inceptisols
Other recent soils no diagnostic horizon other than an ochric or anthropic epipedon.	Entisols

KEYS TO SOIL TAXONOMY : ORDERS

Sr. No.	Name	Description
1.	**Gelisols**	Soils that have : 1. Permafrost within 100 cm of the soil surface; *or* 2. Gelic materials within 100 cm of the soil surface and permafrost within 200 cm of the soil surface.
2.	**Histosols**	Other soils that : 1. Do not have andic soil properties in 60 percent or more of the thickness between the soil surface and either a depth of 60 cm or a densic, lithic, or paralithic contact or duripan if shallower; *and* 2. Have organic soil materials that meet *one or more* of the following: (*a*) Overlie cindery, fragmental, or pumiceous materials and/or fill their interstices and directly below these materials, have a densic, lithic, or paralithic contact; *or* (*b*) When added with the underlying cindery, fragmental, or pumiceous materials, total 40 cm or more between the soil surface and a depth of 50 cm; *or* (*c*) Constitute two-thirds or more of the total thickness of the soil to a densic, lithic, or paralithic contact and have no mineral horizons or have mineral horizons with a total thickness of 10 cm or less; *or* (*d*) Are saturated with water for 30 days or more per year in normal years (or are artificially drained), have an upper boundary within 40 cm of the soil surface, and have a total thickness of *either :* 1. 60 cm or more if three-fourths or more of their volume consists of moss fibers or if their bulk density, moist, is less than 0.1 g/cm^3; *or* 2. 40 cm or more if they consist either of sapric or hemic materials, or of fibric materials with less than three-fourths (by volume) moss fibers and a bulk density, moist, of 0.1 g/cm^3 or more.
3.	**Spodosols**	Other soils that do not have a plaggen epipedon or an argillic or kandic horizon above a spodic horizon, *and* have *one or more* of the following : 1. A spodic horizon, an albic horizon in 50 per cent or more of each pedon, and a cryic soil temperature regime; *or* 2. An Ap horizon containing 85 per cent or more spodic materials; *or* 3. A spodic horizon with *all* of the following characteristics: (*a*) *One or more* of the following : 1. A thickness of 10 cm or more; *or* 2. An overlying Ap horizon; *or* 3. Cementation in 50 per cent or more of each pedon; *or* 4. A coarse-loamy, loamy-skeletal, or finer particle-size class and a frigid temperature regime in the soil; *or* 5. A cryic temperature regime in the soil; *and* (*b*) An upper boundary within the following depths from the mineral soil surface: *either* 1. Less than 50 cm; *or* 2. Less than 200 cm if the soil has a sandy particle-size class in at least some part between the mineral soil surface and the spodic horizon; *and*

(*c*) A lower boundary as follows:

1. *Either* at a depth of 25 cm or more below the mineral soil surface or at the top of a duripan or fragipan or at a densic, lithic, paralithic, or petroferric contact, whichever is shallowest; *or*
2. At any depth,
   (*a*) If the spodic horizon has a coarse-loamy, loamy-skeletal, or finer particle-size class and the soil has a frigid temperature regime; *or*
   (*b*) If the soil has a cryic temperature regime.
3. A directly overlying albic horizon in 50 percent or more of each pedon; *or*
4. No andic soil properties in 60 per cent or more of the thickness *either:*
   (*a*) Within 60 cm either of the mineral soil surface or of the top of an organic layer with andic soil properties, whichever is shallower, if there is no densic, lithic, or paralithic contact, duripan, or petrocalcic horizon within that depth; *or*
   (*b*) Between either the mineral soil surface or the top of an organic layer with andic soil properties, whichever is shallower, and a densic, lithic, or paralithic contact, a duripan, or a petrocalcic horizon.

4. Andisols Other soils that have andic soil properties in 60 per cent or more of the thickness *either:*

1. Within 60 cm either of the mineral soil surface or of the top of an organic layer with andic soil properties, whichever is shallower, if there is no densic, lithic, or paralithic contact, duripan, or petrocalcic horizon within that depth; *or*
2. Between either the mineral soil surface or the top of an organic layer with andic soil properties, whichever is shallower, and a densic, lithic, or paralithic contact, a duripan, or a petrocalcic horizon.

5. Oxisol Other soils that have *either:*

1. An oxic horizon that has its upper boundary within 150 cm of the mineral soil surface and no kandic horizon that has its upper boundary within that depth; *or*
2. 40 percent or more (by weight) clay in the fine-earth fraction between the mineral soil surface and a depth of 18 cm (after mixing) *and* a kandic horizon that has the weatherable-mineral properties of an oxic horizon and has its upper boundary within 100 cm of the mineral soil surface.

6. Vertisols Other soils that have :

1. A layer 25 cm or more thick, with an upper boundary within 100 cm of the mineral soil surface, that has *either* slickensides *or* wedge-shaped peds that have their long axes tilted 10 to 60 degrees from the horizontal; *and*
2. A weighted average of 30 per cent or more clay in the fine-earth fraction either between the mineral soil surface and a depth of 18 cm or in an Ap horizon, whichever is thicker, *and* 30 per cent or more clay in the fine-earth fraction of all horizons between a depth of 18 cm and either a depth of 50 cm or a densic, lithic, or paralithic contact, a duripan, or a petrocalcic horizon if shallower; *and*
3. Cracks that open and close periodically.

7. Aridisols Other soils that :

1. Have :
   (*a*) An aridic soil moisture regime; *and*

(*b*) An ochric or anthropic epipedon; *and*

(*c*) *One or more* of the following with the upper boundary within 100 cm of the soil surface: a cambic horizon with a lower depth of 25 cm or more; a cryic temperature regime and a cambic horizon; a calcic, gypsic, petrocalcic, petrogypsic, or salic horizon; or a duripan; *or*

(*d*) An argillic or natric horizon; *or*

2. Have a salic horizon; *and*

(*a*) Saturation with water in one or more layers within 100 cm of the soil surface for 1 month or more during a normal year; *and*

(*b*) A moisture control section that is dry in some or all parts at some time during normal years; *and*

(*c*) No sulfuric horizon that has its upper boundary within 150 cm of the mineral soil surface.

8. Ultisols Other soils that have *either :*

1. An argillic or kandic horizon, but no fragipan, and a base saturation (by sum of cations) of less than 35 per cent at one of the following depths :

(*a*) If the epipedon has a sandy or sandy-skeletal particle-size class throughout, *either:*

1. 125 cm below the upper boundary of the argillic horizon (but no deeper than 200 cm below the mineral soil surface) or 180 cm below the mineral soil surface, whichever is deeper; *or*
2. At a densic, lithic, paralithic, or petroferric contact if shallower; *or*

(*b*) The shallowest of the following depths :

1. 125 cm below the upper boundary of the argillic or kandic horizon; *or*
2. 180 cm below the mineral soil surface; *or*
3. At a densic, lithic, paralithic, or petroferric contact; *or*

2. A fragipan and *both* of the following :

(*a*) Either an argillic or a kandic horizon above, within, or below it or clay films 1 mm or more thick in one or more of its subhorizons; *and*

(*b*) A base saturation (by sum of cations) of less than 35 per cent at the shallowest of the following depths :

1. 75 cm below the upper boundary of the fragipan; *or*
2. 200 cm below the mineral soil surface; *or*
3. At a densic, lithic, paralithic, or petroferric contact.

9. Mollisols Other soils that have *both* of the following:

1. *Either :*

(*a*) A mollic epipedon; *or*

(*b*) *Both* a surface horizon that meets all the requirements for a mollic epipedon except thickness after the soil has been mixed to a depth of 18 cm *and* a subhorizon more than 7.5 cm thick, within the upper part of an argillic, kandic, or natric horizon, that meets the color, organic-carbon content, base saturation, and structure requirements of a mollic epipedon but is separated from the surface horizon by an albic horizon; *and*

2. A base saturation of 50 per cent or more (by NH_4OAc) in all horizons *either* between the upper boundary of any argillic, kandic, or natric horizon and a depth of 125 cm below that boundary, *or* between the mineral soil surface and a depth of 180 cm, *or* between the mineral soil surface and a densic, lithic, or paralithic contact, whichever depth is shallowest.

10. Alfisols Other soils that do not have a plaggen epipedon and that have *either:*

1. An argillic, kandic, or natric horizon; *or*
2. A fragipan that has clay films 1 mm or more thick in some part.

11. Inceptisols Other soils that have *either :*

1. *One or more* of the following:
   - (*a*) A cambic horizon with its upper boundary within 100 cm of the mineral soil surface and its lower boundary at a depth of 25 cm or more below the mineral soil surface; *or*
   - (*b*) A calcic, petrocalcic, gypsic, petrogypsic, or placic horizon or a duripan with an upper boundary within a depth of 100 cm of the mineral soil surface; *or*
   - (*c*) A fragipan or an oxic, sombric, or spodic horizon with an upper boundary within 200 cm of the mineral soil surface; *or*
   - (*d*) A sulfuric horizon that has its upper boundary within 150 cm of the mineral soil surface; *or*
   - (*e*) A cryic temperature regime and a cambic horizon; *or*
2. No sulfidic materials within 50 cm of the mineral soil surface; *and both:*
   - (*a*) In one or more horizons between 20 and 50 cm below the mineral soil surface, either an *n* value of 0.7 or less or less than 8 percent clay in the fine-earth fraction; *and*
   - (*b*) *One or both* of the following:
     1. A salic horizon or a histic, mollic, plaggen, or umbric epipedon; *or*
     2. In 50 per cent or more of the layers between the mineral soil surface and a depth of 50 cm, an exchangeable sodium percentage of 15 or more (or a sodium adsorption ratio of 13 or more), which decreases with increasing depth below 50 cm, *and* also ground water within 100 cm of the mineral soil surface at some time during the year when the soil is not frozen in any part.

12. Entisols Other soils.

TABLE 5.1. Soil orders of 7th Approximation

Sr. No.	*Order*	*Equivalent soil groups of earlier system*
1.	Entisols	Azonal soils, *Alluvial soils, Regosols*
2.	Vertisols	*Grumosols* (Regurs or black cotton soil in India), black earth (Indonesia)
3.	Inceptisols	*Andosols, Brown forest*
4.	Aridisols	*Desert soils,* Reddish Desert, Brown and Reddish-Brown soils.
5.	Mollisols	Chestnut, Chernozem, Rendzina, some Brown soils.
6.	Spodosols	*Podsols,* Brown podsolic soils, ground water podsols.
7.	Alfisols	*Grey-Brown podsolic soils, Non-calcic soils,* Grey Wooded soils, Degraded chernozem, some Half-Bog soils.
8.	Ultisols	Red yellow podsolic soils. Reddish-Brown Lateritic soils (U.S.A.), some Half-Bog soils.
9.	Andisol	Volcanic ejection, volcanic ash.
10.	Oxisols	*Latosols* and *Laterite soils*
11.	Histosols	*Organic soils,* Bog soils
12.	Gelisols	Don't recommendation of particular soil.

Gelisols

- Vegetation : lichens, moss, liverwort, sedges, grass
- Climate : pergelic
- Soil moisture regime : variety of soil moisture regimes
- Major soil property : accumulation of organic matter, special features formed by cryoturbation
- Diagnostic horizons :
- Epipedon : histic
- Major processes : cryoturbation
- Characteristics : soils that contain within 200 cm of the ground surface permafrost (permanently frozen ground)

SUB-ORDER

The sub-orders are sub-divisions of orders. The sub-order indicates genetic homogeneity. Climatic environment, vegetation and wetness help in determining the genetic processes. Fifty seven sub-orders have been recognized.

TABLE 5.2. Definition of soil moisture regimes

Soil moisture regime	*Characteristics*
Aridic	Soil moisture content less than the amount retained at 15 atmospheres of tension (1500 kPa - permanent wilting point). 'In most years' - 6 out of 10 years
Xeric	Soils of temperate areas that experience moist winters and dry summers (i.e. mediterranean climates)
Torric	Soils are dry more than half the time (in arid climatic zone)
Perudic	In most years precipitation exceeds evapotranspiration every month of the year
Udic	In most years soils are not dry more than 90 consecutive days
Ustic	In most years soils are dry for 90 consecutive days and moist in some part for half the days the soil temperature is above 5°C (i.e., during potential growing season)
Aquic	Soils that are sufficiently saturated, reducing conditions occur. They usually have low chroma mottles or have gleyed subsoils

TABLE 5.3. Definitions and features of soil temperature regimes

Temperature regime	*MAT in root zone [°C]*	*Characteristics and some locations*
Pergelic	< 0	Permafrost (i.e. the depth of freezing in winter exceed the depth of thawing in summer, as a consequence, a layer of permanently frozen soil of grounds develop) and ice edges common. Tundra of northern Alaska and Canada and high elevations of the Rocky Mountains.
Cryic	0-8	Cool to cold soils of the Northern Great Plains of the U.S., forested regions of eastern Canada.

Frigid	< 8	A soil with a frigid regime is warmer in summer than a soil with cryic regime. The difference between mean summer and mean winter soil temperatures is more that 5°C.
Mesic	8-15	Midwestern and Great Plains regions where corn and winter wheat are common crops.
Thermic	15-22	Coastal Plain of southeastern U.S. where temperatures are warm enough for cotton.
Hypothermic	> 22	Citrus areas of Florida peninsula, southern California. Tropical climates and crops.

If the name of a soil temperature regime has the prefix iso, the mean summer and mean winter soil temperatures for June, July, and August and for December, January, and February differ less than 5°C at a depth of 50 cm.

TABLE 5.4. Soil orders its formative elements and their Major Characteristics

S. No.	*Name*	*Formative element*	*Sub order*	*Short name of sub-group*	*Major Characteristics*
1.	Entisols	ent	5	*Aqu, Ar, Orth, Flue, Psamm*	Little profile development, Ochric epipedon common
2.	Inceptisols	ept	6	*Aqu, Umber, Ochr, And, Plagy, Trap*	Embryonic soils with few diagnostic features, Ochric or umbric epipedon; Cambic horizon.
3.	Mollisols	oll	7	*Aqua, Xer, Ud, Ust, Bor, Alb, Rend*	Mollic epipedon, high base saturation, dark soils, some with argillic or nitric horizons.
4.	Alfisols	alf	5	*Aque, Xer, Ud, Ust, Bar*	Argillic or nitric horizon; high to medium base saturation.
5.	Ultisols	ult	5	*Aqu, Xer, Ud, Ast, Ham*	Argillic (clay) horizon, low base saturation.
6.	Oxisols	ox	5	*Aqu, Per, Ud, Ust, Torr*	Oxic horizon, no argillic horizon, highly weathered.
7.	Vertisols	ert	4	*Xer, Ud, Ust, Torr*	High in swelling clays, deep cracks when soil dry, dark colour.
8.	Aridisols	id	2	*Arg, Orth*	Dry soil, ochric epipedon, sometimes argillic or nitric horizon.
9.	Spodosols	od	4	*Aqu, Hum, Ferr, Orth*	Spodic horizon commonly with Fe, Al, and humus accumulation, forest.
10.	Histosols	ist	4	*Fibre, Hem, Sopr, Fal*	Peat or bog; more than 30% organic matter (organic soil).
11.	Andisols*	and	7	*Aqu, Xer, Ud, Ust, Torr, Vitr, Cry*	From volcanic ejects, dominated by allophane or Al-humic complexes.
12.	Gelisols*	el	2	*Hist, Orth*	Frost churning

*Recently added as a soil order.

SUBORDERS : FORMATIVE ELEMENTS

TABLE 5.5. Suborder names in Soil Taxonomy—formative elements and meaning

Formative element	*Derivation*	*Meaning or Connotation*
alb	L. *albus*, white	Presence of an albic horizon
aqu	L. *aqua*, water	Characteristics associated with wetness
ar	L. *arare*, to plow	Mixed horizon
arg	L. *argilla*, white clay	Presence of an argillic horizon
bor	Gr. *boreas*, northern	Cool climate
calc	L. *calcis*, lime	Presence of a calcic horizon
camb	L. *cambiare*, to exchange	Presence of a cambic horizon
cry	Gr. *kryos*, cold	Cold climate
dur	L. *duras*, hard	Presence of a duripan
fibr	L. *fibra*, fiber	Least decomposed stage
fluv	L. *fluvius*, river	Flood plains
fol	L. *folia*, leaf	Mass of leaves
gyps	L. *gypsum*, gypsum	Presence of a gypsic horizon
hem	Gr. *hemi*, half	Intermediate state of decomposition
hist	Gr. *histos*, tissue	Organic soil material
hum	L. *humus*, earth	Presence of organic matter
ochr	Gr. base of *ochros*, pale	Presence of an ochric epipedon
plagg	Ger. *Plaggen*, sod	Presence of plaggen epipedons
per	L. *perennis*, all year	Perudic soil moisture regime
psamm	Gr. *psammos*, sand	Sand textures
rend	Polish *Rendzina*, limestone soil	Rendzinalike
sal	L. *sal*, salt	Presence of a salic horizon
sapr	Gr. *sapros*, rotten	Most decomposed stage
stat	Gr. *statiskos*, stationary	No congelli-pedoturbation
torr	Gr. *torridus*, hot, dry	Torric soil moisture regime
trop	Gr. *tropikos*, of the solstice	Continually warm
turb	L. *turbidus*, disturbed	Active congelli-pedoturbation
ud	L. *udus*, humid	Udic soil moisture regime
umbr	L. *umbra*, shade	Presence of an umbric epipedon
ust	L. *ustus*, burnt	Ustic soil moisture regime
vitr	L. *vitrum*, glass	Presence of glass
xer	Gr. *xeros*, dry	Xeric soil moisture regime
orth-	Gr. *orthos*, true	The common ones

GREAT GROUP

It is subdivision of suborder 254 great-groups are recognized till now on the basis of diagnostic horizons, base status, soil temperature and moisture content.

SUB-GROUP

The sub-groups are sub-divisions of the great groups. There are more than 1200 sub-groups has been recognized.

FAMILY

The family is differentiated on the basis of texture, mineralogy, and temperature and soil depth (15 cm). About 6600 families are recognized.

SERIES

The series is a sub-division of the family and is the most specific unit of classification. Differentiating characteristics are primarily based on the kind arrangement of horizons. About 16,800 soils series are recognized.

NOMENCLATURE IN SOIL TAXONOMY

1. **Order:** ends with—Sol e.g. Aridisol
2. **Sub-order:** It is composed of—Formative element of order + any differentiating character like temperature, moisture, drainage, diagnostic horizon etc +S. (S, except Oxisol)

   e.g. Aquolls — Wet soil – Mollisols (oll)

   Aquents — Wet soil – Entisols (ent)

   Argid — Dry soil – Aridisols (id)

3. **Great group:** It is composed of order, + sub-order + one or more specific characters which modify the sub-order.

   e.g. Argiaqoll — Mollisol - order

   Aqoll - sub-order wetness

   Arg - argillic horizon

4. **Sub-group:** It is identified with a binomial nomenclature.

e.g. A 'Typic' adjective is used when sub-group represent a 'Central concept' of the great group.

e.g. Typic Agriaqoll.

There are integrated between different sub-groups or between great groups in the same order.

5. **Family:** In nomenclature of family-we have textural class, mineralogy, temperature regime and some time reaction, drainage class and topography.

e.g. Fine-clay/Very fine clayey, mixed montmorillonitic, calcareous, hyperthermic, Typic Chromustert.

6. Series: Name of the series is given on the basis where it is first described. e.g. Jalalpur series, Eru series etc.

Soil Series	Sub-group	Great group	Sub-order	Order
Bodali	Verti Ustorthents	Ustorthents	Orthents	Entisols
Onjal-II	Typic Ustipsamments	Ustipsamments	Psamments	Entisols
Balota	Typic Ustifluvents	Ustifluvents	Fluvents	Entisols
Eru	Typic Chromusterts	Chromusterts	Usterts	Vertisols
Mulad	Udic Chromusterts	Chromusterts	Usterts	Vertisols
Ilav	Typic Ustochrepts	Ustochrepts	Ochrepts	Inseptisoil
Baldha	Lithic Ustochrepts	Ustochrepts	Ochrepts	Inseptisoil
Jalalpur	Vertic Ustochrepts	Ustochrepts	Ochrepts	Inseptisoil
Amalsad	Fluventic Ustocherpts	Ustochrepts	Ochrepts	Inseptisoil
Dandi	Typic Halaquepts	Halaquepts	Aquepts	Inseptisoil
Nargol	Vertic Halaquepts	Halaquepts	Aquepts	Inseptisoil

❑❑❑

CHAPTER 6

Soils of India

India, situated between the latitudes of 08°4′ to 37°06′ N and longitudes of 68°07′ to 97°25′ E, has a geographical area of 329 mha. Physiologically, it can be divided into the three broad regions, viz., Peninsula (a triangular plateau in Deccan and south of the Vindhyas), Extra-Peninsula (mountain region of the Himalayas), and the Indo-Gangetic separating the two above-mentioned regions.

Soils of India have been divided into the following eleven major groups :

(1) Red soils. Red colour in red soils is due to the presence of various oxides of iron. They are either formed *in-situ* or from the products of decomposition of rocks washed to a lower level. They include soil locally known as *red sandy soil and red alluvium*. They are mostly formed under sub-humid climate from a number of rock formations like granite, shales etc. Their main features are a light texture, porous structure, absence of lime, and low soluble salts. They are generally poor in fertility constituents such as N, P, K and lime and are highly deficient in organic matter. They have a low base exchange capacity. They are slightly acidic to neutral in reaction, the pH ranging from 6.0 to 7.5. The characteristic clay mineral is kaolinite. Area of red soils are whole of Chennai and Mysore, part of A.P., M.P., Orissa and Bihar (Chhotanagpur), Birbhumi (W. Bengal), Santhal Pargana (Bihar), Mirzapur, Jhansi and Hamirpur districts of U.P. and eastern half of Rajasthan. The most of the red soils have been classed in the order Alfisols.

(2) Lateritic soils. They are found mostly in areas of high rainfall. They are light in texture and have an open free-draining structure. There is no retention of water. There is practically no horizon differentiation in the soil profile. They are deficient in lime and are slightly to moderately acid in reaction. The pH varies from 5.0 to 6.0. They are low in base exchange capacity. Laterite soils formed at high levels have a pale red colour are highly gravely and are poor in all fertility constituents. These formed at low levels have a darker colour probably due to a great accumulation of humus, a slightly finer texture and are quite well-drained. These soils are found all along the west coast of Maharashtra, Mysore and Kerala, on tops of hills in the Deccan, Madhya Pradesh and in Orissa along the Eastern Ghat.

(3) Black soils. The black soil developed from Basaltic rock under semi-arid conditions. The soils are black or dark brown in colour. They include soils locally known as ***regur*** or black cotton soil, deep black soil, medium black soil. The colour varies considerably, alluvium soil of Narbada and Tapti are blackish-brown. Their texture ranges from sandy loam to heavy clay. Some black soils may be porous and others may be compact and impervious. One of the characteristic features of black soil is that it swells on wetting during the rainy season and shrinks and cracks in summer. The base exchange capacity of deep black soil is quite high. The pH varies from 7.5 to 8.5. The soils are on the whole low in fertility. The soils are deficient in nitrogen and phosphorus. They are rich in potash and lime. They black soils are found in parts of Maharashtra, Gujarat, M.P., Rajasthan, U.P., A.P., Chennai and Mysore.

(4) Alluvial soils. They are characterized by extreme depth and grey or grayish-brown colour. Their texture varies from sandy loam to clay loam. The structure is also variable, loose and free-draining in the case of sandy soils, and compact and impervious in clayey soils. These soils are most fertile; they are deficient in nitrogen, phosphorus and humus but are well supplied with lime. Their base exchange capacity is comparatively low. The pH varies from 7.0 to 8.0. They are very extensive in area and cover large parts of Rajasthan, Punjab, U.P., Bihar and West Bengal and extend even into west Assam and north Gujarat. The soils developed in the western parts of the Indo-Gangetic plains are, however, markedly different from those in the eastern region.

(5) Desert soils. They have developed in arid regions mostly under the influence of physical weathering. They are mainly sandy. They contain large amounts of soluble salts and varying proportions of lime. They have a high pH and are very poor in fertility constituents. Desert soils are found in large parts of Rajasthan, south Punjab and in the range of Kutch. The temperature regime is very high throughout the year. The rainfall ranges from 50 cm to less than 10 cm.

(6) Saline and alkaline soils. These soils are developed in arid and semi-arid regions. Basin shaped topography (poor drainage) is also responsible for their development. They are mainly found in the black soil region in the south and west, in the Indo-Gangetic alluvium in the north, and in the deltaic and coastal regions all along the west and east coast.

(7) Peaty and marshy soils. They are formed in depression under submerged conditions and have acquired a blue colour due to the presence of ferrous iron. Peaty soils are found scattered in Kerala, north Bihar and north Uttar Pradesh and have developed in humid regions as a result of the accumulation of large quantities of organic matter.

(8) Tarai soils. Tarai soils have a wet regime and high water table conditions for most part of the year. Tarai soils are foothill soils and extend in strips of varying widths at the foot of the Himalayas in Jammu and Kashmir, U.P., Bihar and West Bengal. Soils under the natural conditions are thickly vegetated and swampy. The soils were derived from the materials washed down by the erosion of mountains. The parent materials are of alluvial sediments and consist of hard clay.

(9) Brown hill soils. These soils are formed on the hills under forests. They are mainly found in the Himalayas on sandstones and shales. The surface soils are dark brown loam to silty clay in texture, acidic to neutral in reaction. These soils may be classified in order Alfisols.

(10) Sub-mountain soils. These soils are formed in high rainfall regions of sub-

Himalayan under coniferous forests. The soils are acidic in reaction. The organic matter accumulation is high and there is absence of free lime.

(11) Mountain meadow soils. These soils occur at high elevation in the Himalayas. The soils are shallow with grass vegetation.

Major soil group	Soil taxonomy orders
Alluvial soil	Entisol, Inceptisol, Alfisol
Black soil	Vertisol, Inceptisol, Entisol
Red soil	Alfisol, Inceptisol, Ultisol

Major soil group	Soil taxonomy orders
Laterite soil	Alfisol, Ultisol, Oxisol
Desert soil	Entisol, Aridisol

DIFFERENT SPECIFIC TYPE OF SOILS IN INDIA

- **Chalka Soil**
  - (*i*) These soil found in Andhra Pradesh.
  - (*ii*) Sandy texture and red in colour. (Red sandy clay loam)
  - (*iii*) These soils developed on sites and foot hills.
  - (*iv*) These soils suitable for growing of sorghum, maize, caster, groundnut and gram.
- **Chhattisgarh Basin**
  - (*i*) **Red Bhata Soils.** Poorest soils fill of stones and gravel, without consistency.
  - (*ii*) **Yellow Matasi soils.** Clay loam textured famous for rice cultivation.
  - (*iii*) **Kanhar soils.** Clay texture in nature, dark brown to black in colour, suitable for *rabi* session crops.
  - (*iv*) **Mellow Soils.** A soil is easily penetrated with tillage tools are called as mellow soils.
- **Thermogenic soil.** Dominants soil formation factor is high temperature and development in sub-tropical region.
- **Wood land.** Vegetation dominated by tree.
- **Marse land.** Waterlogged ground with large mineral.
- **Swamp land.** An area saturated with water more time in which soil surface is not deeply submerged.
- **Teast soil.** Excess molybdenum in soils.
- **Ectodynamorphic soil.** Soils whose dominated by parent material.
- **Endodynamorphic soil.** Soils whose dominated mainly though effect of climate and vegetation, and natural vegetation soil profile are developed.

TABLE 6.1. Major Soil Types of India

Properties	*Alluvial Soil*	*Black Cotton Soil*	*Red Soil*	*Laterite Soil*	*Desert Soil*
1. Location and Distribution	Rajasthan, Haryana, Punjab, Uttar Pradesh, in velley of Krishna Kavery, Narmada, Brahmputra, Godavary, Tapti and Surma rivers. These soil are devided into two groups (*i*) New alluvial soil of recent alluvial soil or Khadar soil (*ii*) Old alluvial soil or Bhangar soil	These soil are also known as *Rangur* (Telgu) soil or Nullahregadi soil or Black clay or Black soil or Noon soil or Late soil etc. These soils in part of M.P. Gujarat, Maharashtra, West of A.P., Plateau of Deccan and T.N. Black cotton soil are devided in three group on the basis of depth : (*i*) Shallow 30 cm or less (*ii*) Medium 30-100 cm (*iii*) Deep-100-300 cm or more	Red soil is also known as early soil. Whole part of Madras and Mysore, in part of U.P. (Mirzapur, Hamirpur and Jhansi), Jharkhand (Chhota-nagpur), Bihar (Santhal), W.B. (Singhbhumi), East part of Rajasthan, M.P., A.P. and Orissa	Hills of south, Hill of Rajasthan, plain part of Orissa and Maharastra, Central India	North west part of India surrounding by desert soil *i.e.,* in between Sindhu river and Aravali mountain, P.B. RJ., Kathiyawarh (Saurastra) and west district of U.P.
2. Order	New alluvial soil–*Entisols* Old alluvial soil–*Inceptisols*	*Vertisols* *Mollisols*	*Alfisols*	*Oxisols*	*Aridisols*
3. Climate and Rainfall	On the basis of rainfall alluvial soils devided into four type (*i*) Lahour to Delhi– 350-650 mm (*ii*) Delhi–east U.P.– 650-1000 mm (*iii*) East U.P.-Bihar– 1000-1350 mm (*iv*) Bihar-Bay of Bengal– 1350-1700 mm	Semi-arid to humid Semi-arid to sub-humid	Sub-humid	Tropical and sub-tropical region with high rainfall area	Arid climate

4. Area Old	150 mha 15 lac km^2, 43%	75 mha	5.1 mha	25 mha	29 mha
5. Main crop and vegetation	All crops (approx)	Cotton dominant, Sorghum, Bajra, Maiz, Wheat, Ragi and other millet crops	Cotton, Bajra, Maiz, Wheat, Pulses	In upland Tea Coffee, Sincona, paddy, Kaju in low land	Sorghum, Bajra, Pulses
6. Other Properties	1. Sandy loam to clay loam in texture in nature 2. Soil colour in light brown-brawn 3. Soil pH between 7-8 4. Deficiency to N, P, humus and Zn, mod.-high in K and excess in lime 5. Dominated by illitic mineral 6. Low base exchange capacity then other soils 7. Some time cankar layer is found in 'B' horizon 8. These soil generally in friable in nature	1. Highly clayey in nature with clay content in with between 30-80 % 2. Soil colour is black 3. Soil pH 7.8-8.7 in calcareous soil but in sodic soil upto 9.5 4. Deferent in N, P, O.M. and rich in K, Fe, Al, $CaCO_3$ $MgCO_3$. 5. These soil dominated of montmorillonite type of clay minerals 6. CEC is 30-60 Cmol (P^+) kg^{-1} 7. These soil developed from basaltic rocks 8. These soil do not have eluviation and illuvia-tion process due to churning and floccu-lation	1. Loamy sand – clayey texture 2. Soil colour is red 3. Soil neutral to slightly acidic reaction 4. Soil deficient in NPK and low in O.M. 5. Generally lime is absent 6. CEC is <20 7. Silica sesquioxide ratio 2 8. These soil are formed crystalline rock in which Granite, Gniess and Schist 9. Soil have high porosity as well rapid leaching and infiltration	1. High clay content in nature 2. Soil colour is brick like red and hard soil are acidic in nature i.e. pH 5-6 3. Essential plant nutrient generally low some time P and humus excess, P is combining with Fe become unavailable to plant 4. CEC is <16 5. Silica sesqiuoxide ratio 1-1.25 6. There is practically no horizon differ-entiation. 7. Soil characteristics by compact, honey combed and vesi-cular sub soil mass Plinthite present	1. Sandy-loamy fine sand soil with clay content between 3 to 5-<10% 2. Soil colour light brown to brown 3. Soils slightly –moderate alkaline in nature i.e. pH 7.8-9.2 3. Poor soil fertility status especially in NPK, Zn and S 4. Poor water hold-ing capacity

Properties	Tarai Soil	Saline-Sodic Soil	Organic Soil	Forest & Mountain Soil	Podzol Soil	Skeletal Soil
1. Location and Distribution	Tarai area of Punjab, UP, Bihar, WB and Himalaya. These soils are formed by accumulation and sedimentation of residue of sediment imported by various river from Himalaya mountain Dry Tarai soil also known as Bhangar	Saline soil – Rajasthan, Punjab, UP, Bihar, W.B. Sodic Soil –Haryana, Gujarat, Maharashtra, Tamil Nadu	Tarai part of Himalaya mountain, middle part of Bihar, north east part of UP, surrounding in WB, Kerala and Kochi	Jammu and Kasmir, Himachal Pradesh, Uttarakhand, UP, Bihar, MP, AP and Kerala	Himalaya mountain, in some part of south India	Laddak area of Himalaya mountain, Vindhyan region of middle area which is formed by silty rocks. Physical weathering is dominated then chemical
2. Order	*Mollisols*	*Aridisols*	*Histosols*	Deciduous forest– *Histosol* Evergreen– *Spodosols*	*Spodosols*	*Entisols*
3. Climate and Rainfall	Wet regime with high ground water	Arid and semi-arid region	Humid region with low temperature	Any climate	Humid temperate region with high residues	Cold climate
4. Area Old	5.7 mha	7 mha	2720 km^2 Peat–150 km^2 Muck–2570 km^2	60 mha	Very less in India	24 mha or 7915 km^2
5. Main Crop & Vegetation	Several grass and in lower area paddy	Paddy crop dominated	Paddy crop dominated	Apple, Peach, Alucha	–	–
6. Other Properties	1. Silty loam dark grey black colour, soil pH is 4.7-5.8. 2. Under water logged condition poor soil fertility status, under drained soil good soil fertility 3. In lower layer stones and gravels are dominated	1. Poor soil physical properties, mostly soil structure and water drainage. 2. Saline soil colour is white-brown. 3. Sodic soil colour is Black and soil pH always >7.4.	1. Course medium and fine texture in nature. 2. Soil colour is blue due to presence of Fe as ferrous form other wise black colour due to high amount of OM is found between 15-50% and some time 80% organic matter content. 3. CEC is 50-100, soil are high fertile. 4. 'O' horizon are clear and mature, and soil have less B.D. and P.D.	1. Sandy loam, loam clay loam and clayey texture and excess O.M. and N content 2. In lower layer Fe, Al and humus are accumulate 3. These soil are formed by accumulation of organic matter which residue plant and vegetation	1. Soil colour wood ash like 2. Soil pH of upper most surface soil is less but increases with increasing soil depth. 3. CEC of 'A' is less then 'A2' 'A3' horizon due to presence of organic matter and again increases in 'B' horizon. 4. Silica is dominant and aluminum is less in vice-versa, high fe and Al.	1. Silty loam – loam textured in nature 2. Soil colour is light brown- yellowish brown high proportion of coarse material and low inorganic matter, unfertile soil. 3. Very shallow soils i.e. 6-15 cm depth, very difficult to get agriculture production. 4. These are mineral soil in which neutral, soil profile and horizon are absent

- **Ferrellite soil.** Good drained soils formed basic igneous rocks it consisting mainly hydrated oxide of Fe and Al and low in silicon content.
- **Eutrophic soil.** High nutritive soils are called Eutrophic or high soils fertility is called Eutrophic soil.
- **Dystrophic soil.** Poor soils fertility is called dystrophic soil.
- **Embryonic soil.** Beginning stage of soil formation, and occurring in humid region.
- **Desertification.** Transformation of productive land to desert land is called desertification.
- **Hydrophilic soils.** Soils developed by dominated wet regime and fulvic acid is dominated.
- **Halomorphic soil.** Soils are developed in presence of excess salt under arid and semi-arid regime.
- **Calcimorphic soil.** Salt are developed in the presence of lime in P.M.

MAJOR SOILS TYPES OF INDIA [ACCORDING: INDIAN COUNCIL OF AGRICULTURAL RESEARCH (ICAR)]

Loose material and uppermost layer of earth's crust. Important natural resource. Formed due to weathering of rocks. Provides nutrients and water to plants. Factors affecting soil formation : Climate, Vegetation, Age of rock, Relief and Parent rocks.

Eight major types according to Indian Council of Agricultural Research (ICAR). Alluvial soils, Black soils, Red soils, Laterite soils, Desert soils, Mountain soils, Saline and Alkaline soils, Peaty and Marshy soils

Alluvial Soil. Alluvial soil formed by deposition of alluvium by rivers. Occupies 15 Lakh sq km area in India. Contribute greatly in agricultural development. Two types : Khadar and Bhangar. Khadar: Newer alluvium. Sandy, pale brown composition. Found in lower areas. Flooded every year.

Alluvial soil Bangar soils are older alluvium, clayey and dark in colour, coarse in nature, contains Kankar (lime nodules), pebbles and Gravels. represents riverine alluvium of Himalayan rivers.

Alluvial soil characteristics: Transported soils, coarser in upper section and finest in delta. Light to dark in colour. Rich in Potash and Humus. Poor in Phosphorous and Nitrogen. Highly fertile, good for all crops (kharif and rabi). Crops : Rice, Wheat, Sugarcane, Cotton, Jute. Areas: Punjab, Haryana, U.P, Bihar, W.B, Assam, Parts of Orissa, delta regions of South India.

Black Soil. Black soil also known as Regur or Black Cotton soil. Dark grey to black in colour, high clay content, highly moist retentive, develops cracks in summer. Covers 5.4 lakh sq km. Highly suitable for cotton. Rich in iron, lime, calcium, Magnesium, carbonates, and alumina.

Black soil poor in phosphorous, nitrogen and organic matter. Areas: Deccan Trap which includes: Maharastra, Gujarat, M.P, Parts of A.P, Karnataka, Parts of T.N and Rajasthan. Crops : Cotton, Sugarcane, Groundnut, Millets, Rice, Wheat, Oilseeds.

Red Soil. Red soil formed due to weathering of old crystalline rocks. More sandy and less clayey, Rich in iron, small amount of humus, poor in phosphorus, nitrogen and lime. Slightly acidic and do not retain moisture, 3.5 lakhs sq km area. Porous and Friable in nature.

Red soils are dominated in Tamil Nadu, Southern Karnataka, parts of Madhya Pradesh, Maharashtra, West Bengal, Eastern Rajasthan, North Eastern States. Crops : Ragi, Groundnut, millet, Tobacco, Potato, Rice, Wheat, Sugarcane.

Laterite Soil. Laterite soil Latin word meaning *brick*. Formed under high temperature and rainfall with wet and dry spell. Silica is leached due to high rainfall, remnants of iron and aluminum oxides left behind is know as Laterite. Brown to yellowish colour, becomes hard when exposed to atmosphere used as building material.

Laterite Soil. Laterite soil rich in Iron, poor in Lime, Potash and Magnesium. It occupies 2.4 Lakh sq km. Areas: Parts of Assam, Karnataka, T.N., A.P., M.P., Kerala, Crops : Tea, Coffee, Cashew, Rubber and Coconut.

Desert Soil. Desert soil contains soluble salts, originated by Mechanical disintegration and wind deposit. Porous and coarse. 90% sand and 5% clay. Rich in Nitrates and Phosphates. Poor in Nitrogen and Humus. friable, sandy and low moist content. Area: 1.4 lakh sq km.

Desert soil areas are arid and Semi arid regions of Rajasthan, south-north Haryana, Punjab, North Gujarat. Crops : Drought resistant crops like millets and barley.

Mountain Soil. Mountain soil found in hill slopes. Formed by deposition of organic matter from forest. rich in humus, poor in Potash and Lime. Areas: Assam, Kashmir, Sikkim and Arunachal Pradesh. Crops : Tea, Coffee, Spices and Tropical Fruits.

Saline and Alkaline Soil. Saline and alkaline soil contains salts like Sodium, Magnesium, Calcium. Infertile, unfit for cultivation, sandy to loamy in texture. Areas : Parts of Gujarat, Rajasthan, Punjab, Haryana, U.P and Maharashtra.

Peaty and Marshy Soil. Peaty and Marshy soil occur in Humid region. Formed by accumulation of organic matter, black in colour, highly acidic and heavy. Areas : Kottayam and Alleppey in Kerala, Coastal Orissa, Sundarbans of W.B.

❑❑❑

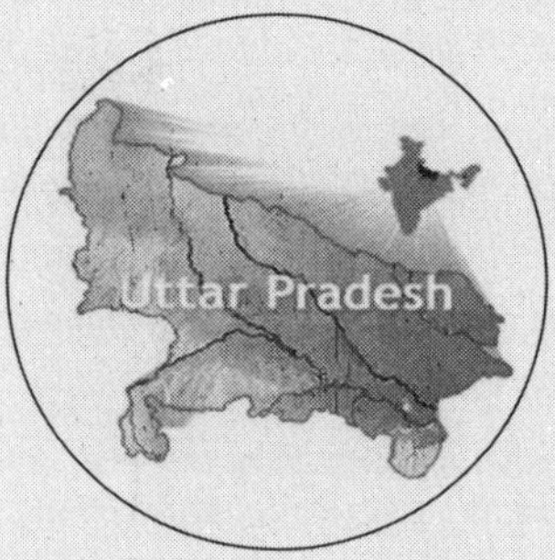

CHAPTER 7

Soils of Uttar Pradesh

The state of Uttar Pradesh is one of the large state of the country and divisible into three physiographic regions *viz*. the Himalayas the Ganga plain and Vindhyan hills and plateau. The climate varies from temperate to arid type and soils from young to mature developed from a wide variety of rocks and minerals.

GEOGRAPHY

It is lying between 23°52′-30°25′ N latitude and 77°04′-84°39′ E longitude, the state of Uttar Pradesh is a land locked state occupying total geographical area of 29.4 mha comprising of 7.33 per cent of the total area of the country. It is running along with the state of Bihar in east, Madhya Pradesh in south, Rajasthan in south-west, Delhi and Haryana in west and Uttarakhand and Himachal Pradesh in the north-west.

PHYSIOGRAPHY

The state is subdivided into three distinct physiographic regions from north to south *viz*. The Himalayas, the Gangetic plain and the Vindhyan hills and plateau.

(*i*) The Himalayas

The Himalayas rise in three longitudinal zones differing in distinct orographical features and consist of :

(*i*) the sub Himalayas or Sivalik zone, 300-600 meters high,

(*ii*) the lesser Himalayas 2000-3000 meters high and

(*iii*) the greater Himalayas or Himadri, 7000-9000 meters high above mean sea level.

(*ii*) The Gangetic plain

Between Himalayas in the north and Vindhyan hills and plateau in the south lies the great Gangetic plain sprawling in almost three-fourth area of the state. It is a very deep and almost level land sloping gently from north-west to south-east. Physiographically, it can be divided between older alluvium (Banger) occupying relatively higher elevations and the new alluvium (Khadar) occupying lower areas along the main rivers and their distributaries.

(*iii*) The Vindhyan hills and plateau

Located south of the Gangetic plain, this region forms part of the foreland of Deccan peninsula and is bound in the north by river Yamuna and partly by the river Ganga. It has been divided into following sub-divisions consisting of (*i*) Bundelkhand plateau, (*ii*) Vindhyan hills (*iii*) Vindhyan scarp land and (*iv*) Vindhyan plateau.

CLIMATE

Climate in general is humid temperate in Himalayan region. Summers are short and cool while winters record frost and snow at higher altitude. The annual rainfall ranges between 1400 to 2000 mm. The climate of Gangetic plain varies from semiarid to sub-humid. The summers are very hot. The winters are cool and dry. The mean annual rainfall ranges from 650 mm (south west corner of the state *i.e.* Agra and Mathura districts) to 1000 mm (eastern and south eastern parts of the state). The climate of Vindhyan hills and plateau is subtropical with mean annual rainfall between 1000-1200 mm received mostly during the monsoon season extending from July to September.

VEGETATION

In Himalayan region, forests of rododendrons (Rhododendron sp) and bhojpatra (Betula utilis) occupy the snowline of Himalayas at the highest elevation and are succeeded down by the forests of Silver fir (*Abies pindrow*), Spruce (*Picea smithiana*), deodar (*Cedrus deodara*), Pine (*Pinus roxburghii*) and Oak (*Quercuy incana*). The foot hills are covered by Sal (*Shorea robusta*) forests. In the Gangetic plain, natural vegetation consists of a variety of deciduous trees, shrubs and grasses. The common natural flora consists of dhak (*Butea monosperma*), babul (*Acacia nilotica*), Karer (*Capparis aphylla*), Khor usar (*Sporobolus arabicus*), bhurbhuri (*Sporobolus coromandelinus*) and munja (*Sachharum munja*) grasses.

In the Vindhyan hills and plateau, the natural flora of the region comprises of dhak (*Butea monosperma*) mahuwa (*Madhuka latifolia*) bakla (*Anoqueissus latifolia*); Salai (*Boswellia serrata*), teak (*Tectona grandis*) tendu (*Diospyros melanoxylon*) and a wide variety of xerophytic shrubs and grasses.

SOILS OF UTTAR PRADESH

The soils of Uttar Pradesh have been classified in seven broad soil groups as shown in figure 7.1. These are (*i*) Hill soils (*ii*) Bhabar soils (*iii*) Tarai soils (*iv*) Alluvial soils (*v*) Vindhyan soils (*vi*) Bundelkhand soils (*vii*) Aravali soils.

1. Hill Soils

These soils constitute nearly 14 per cent of the total area of the state in the northern most part of the state. They have developed from biotite, schists and phyllitic material under a cool and moist climate. Four soil association types have been recognised in this tract comprising of (*i*) red loams (*ii*) brown forest (*iii*) podsolic and (*iv*) meadow soils.

At great group level, the hill soils have now been classified as Fragudalfs, Hapludalfs, Haplustalfs, Dystrochrepts, Eutrochrepts, Haplumbrepts, Palehumults Ustorthents and Argiudolls.

They are brown to greyish brown and dark grey in colour having neutral to slightly acidic soil reaction. Moderately acidic soils occur only at higher elevations where leaching of bases with percolating rain waters is a common occurrence.

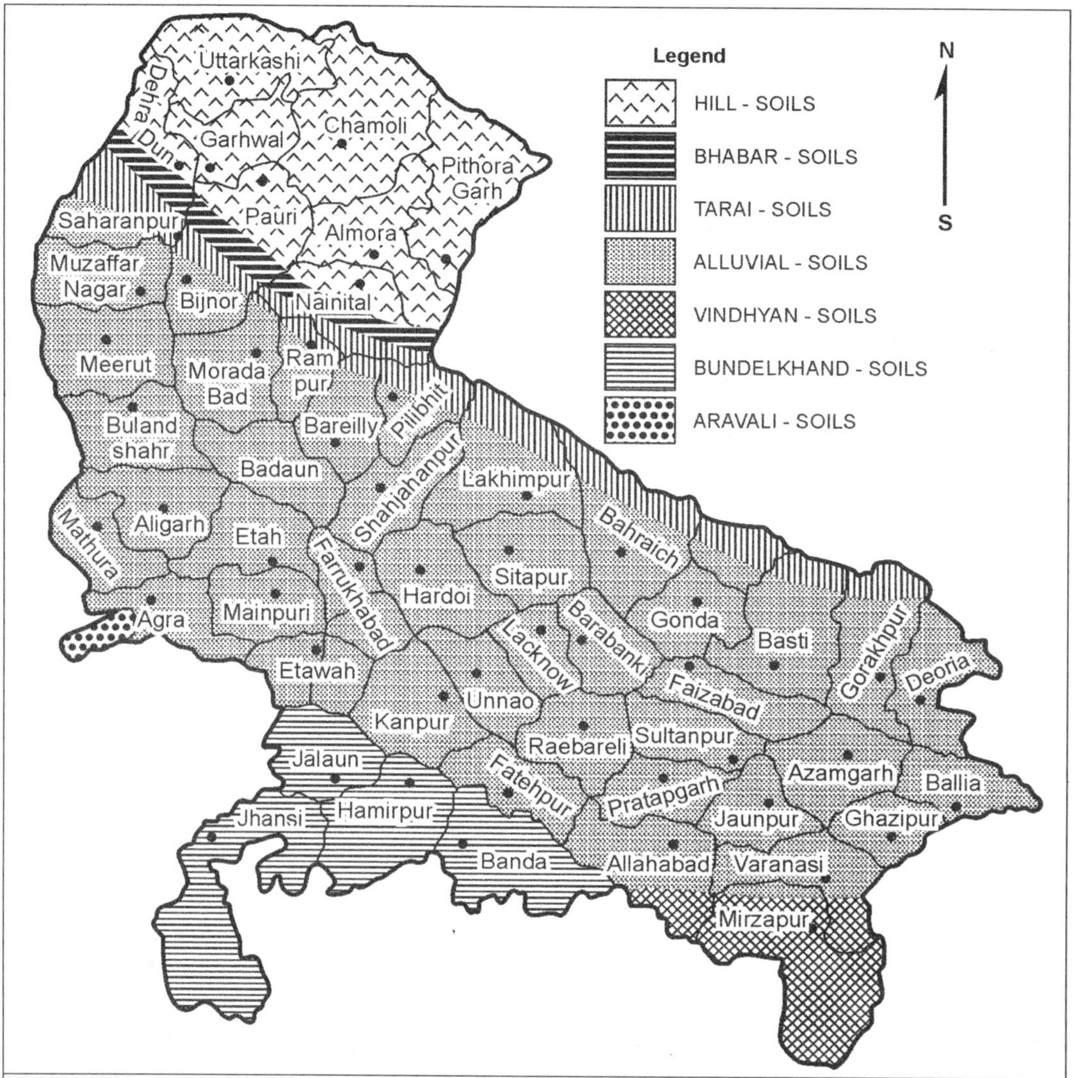

Fig. 7.1. Soil of Uttar Pradesh with Uttarakhand

2. Bhabar Soils

Immediately adjoining the outer spurs of Himalayas there is a narrow belt of alluvial fan, termed as Bhabar, running from west to east in the foot hill region. These soils constitute nearly two per cent of the total area of the state. They have developed from the mechanically transported alluviums from the adjoining Siwalik and Himalayan ranges comprising of micaceous sandstones and conglomerates inter stratified with boulders along with purple shales and clays. At great group level, these soils have been classified as Ustochrepts, Ustorthents and Haplustolls.

They are coarse gravelly to fine silty, calcareous, dark grey soils, rich in plant nutrients. The nutrients are drained due to the presence of boulders in the substratum leading to acute scarcity of moisture for normal crop growth.

3. Tarai Soils

The term tarai means the moist or wet area. Tarai soils are alluvial soils occuring as a narrow belt to the south of Bhabar soils in the valleys of sub-mountain region of Uttar Pradesh stretching from Dehradun to the extreme north-east portion of the state and occupying nearly 5.7 per cent of the total area of the state.

The tarai belt is divided into two distinct parts, *viz*.,

(*a*) north western tarai extending from Dehradun to Lakhimpur Kheri and

(*b*) north-eastern tarai extending from Baharaich to Deoria district up to the eastern most border of the state.

The soil association recognised in the north western tarai include (*i*) tarai sand, (*ii*) tarai loams highly calcareous, (*iii*) tarai loams-slightly calcareous, (*iv*) tarai loams non-calcareous, (*v*) tarai clay loam-highly calcareous and (*vi*) tarai clay loam non-calcareous.

The recognised soil associations in north eastern tarai include

(*i*) Gandak recent alluviums-calcium soils with a large reserve of soft-lime,

(*ii*) Gandak flat-leached calcium soils with a layer of nodular calci-carbonate ($CaCO_3$) accumulation and

(*iii*) Gandak uplands-degraded calcium soils. The soils of the north-western tarai region have now been classified as Hapludolls, Haplaquolls, Ustorthents and Ustochrepts at the sub-group level.

These are grey to dark grey soils varying in texture from sand to clay loam and have high content of organic matter. Water table is high and the soils remain saturated or fairly moist during the major part of the year.

4. Alluvial Soils

These soils are most important in this state occupying nearly 61.8 per cent of the total area of Uttar Pradesh. They were excessively deep soils and have developed from the alluvium deposited by the two major rivers of the state the Ganga and the Yamuna and their tributaries, The alluvial material deposited by the Ganga and its tributaries is derived from the soft dolomitic rocks of Himalayas and that deposited by the Yamuna and its tributaries owes its origin to the basaltic rock of central Indian hills.

The soils developed on Gangetic alluvium are neutral to moderately alkaline and calcareous especially at lower depth.

Based on topographical features, the soil associations recognized in these soils are (*i*) Khadar or the recent alluviums, (*ii*) soils of flat land; (*iii*) uplands soils and (*iv*) lowland soils.

Texturally, they vary from, coarse sands to fine clays, The alluvial soils developed from Yamuna alluvium are quite dissimilar to Gangetic alluvial soils. They are dark to very dark grey, fine textured, calcareous soils showing remarkable swelling and shrinking on wetting and drying. The alluvium laid down by the river Gandak and Ghaghra in north-eastern part of Uttar Pradesh is highly calcareous. The general slope of the Gangetic plain being from north-west to south-east, the finer fraction increases from western to eastern parts of the state due to gravimetric assorting of soil particles during the course of their deposition. At great group level, these soils are classified as Hapludalfs, Paludalfs, Haplustalfs, Ochraqualfs, Eutrochrepts, Ustochrepts, Ustipsarnment, Psammaquents, Ustifluvents, Ustorthents and Calciorthents.

These soils are generally poor in phosphorus (P_2O_5) nitrogen (N) and organic matter.

5. Bundelkhand Soils

These soils lying in the Bundelkhand region of the state constitute nearly 10.9 per cent of the total area of the state. They have developed from Vindhyan rocks abounding in gneiss and granites of the Deccan trap with highly ferruginous beds and often soft lime stone.

The soils can be divided into two broad groups (*a*) red soils and (*b*) black soils. These two are again divided into four-soils associations. Four soil association have been recognized in the area which include

(*i*) Bundelkhand-coarse grained reddish brown soils,

(*ii*) Bundelkhand-coarse grained grey to greyish brown soils,

(*iii*) Bundelkhand-clay loam black soils and

(*iv*) Bundelkhand-fine clayey black soils. Locally these soils are termed as Rakar, Parwa, Kabar and Mar respectively.

The red soils Rakar and Parwa belong to the order Ultisols, Alfisols and Inceptisols and the black soils are grouped under the great groups, Pellusterts, Chromusterts and Ustochrepts.

The Rakar soils are residual slightly acidic, coarse grained, shallow and excessively permeable soils occupying higher elevations.

The Parwa soils are alluvial, mildly alkaline, very deep soils with free calcium carbonate ($CaCO_3$) accumulation at lower depths.

The black soils Mar and Kabar are very deep soils confined to lowlying land scapes having fine texture and the remarkable property of shrinkage and swelling on wetting and drying.

6. Vindhyan Soils

These soils lying south of the Ganga in the south-east comer of Uttar Pradesh occupying nearly 5.1 per cent of the total area of the state. They have developed on Vindhyan rocks comprising of Vindyan and Kaimur sandstones, shales, mixed conglomerates, calcarious and hematitic slates schists, gneiss, carboniferous rocks and to some extent the lime-stones.

Five types of soil association have been recognised in the area and termed as Vindhyan type 1 to type 5. Vindhyan type 1 and 2 occupy the uplands. Vindhyan type 3 lies on flats while Vindhyan type 4 and type 5 rests on the lowlands. The upland soils belong to great groups Haplustults, Rhodostults and Rhodostulfs. The flat lands and lowland soils generally fall within the great group Haplustalfs, Ochraqualfs, Eutrochrepts, Ustochrepts and Ustitluvents.

Vindhyan type 1 and 2 are brown to dark brown, coarse textured, shallow to moderately deep slightly acidic and excessively drained soils. Vindhyan type 3 soils are very deep, yellowish grey, loam to clay loam with somewhat restricted drainage. Vindhian type 4 and 5 are fine textured grey to dark grey, poorly drained soils underlain by a calcic horizon.

7. Aravali Soils

These soils, lying in the south west corner of Agra district, occupy only 0.21 per cent of the total area of the state. They have developed from various formations of Vindhyan sandstones including Kaimur group as the lowest and Bhander group as the highest member in the outer spurs of central India hills of Bharatpur and Dholpur.

PROBLEMS OF SOILS

Besides, the above soils group, some problem soils are found in the state of Uttar Pradesh. The problem soils include saline and alkali soils; eroded soils shallow and excessively permeable soils and waterlogged soils.

1. Saline and Alkali Soils

These soils occupy an area of about 1.28 mha mostly in alluvial tract. The worst affected districts include Manipur, Aligarh, Etah, Farrukhabad, Etawah, Auraiya, Kanpur (Rural), Kanpur, Unnao, Fetahpur, Allahabad, Rae Bareli, Lucknow, Pratapgarh and Hardoi. There is also a stretch of these soils in the sub humid parts of the state comprising of the districts of Azamgarh, western parts of Ballia, northern parts of Ghazipur and Bhadohi tehsil of Varanasi. The saline soils occupying western districts of Agra and Mathura are quite different in morphology and chemical composition from the alkali soils found in the rest of the state. Degraded alkali soils-solodi have been found in small lowlying pockets of Azamgarh districts and parts of Lucknow and Hardoi districts developed under continued rice cultivation.

2. Eroded Soils

Nearly 5.5 mha area is affected by soil erosion. Area affected by wind erosion is estimated to be 0.9 mha, 0.15 mha by glacial erosion; 2.94 mha by sheet and rill erosion and 1.53 mha area is under gullies.

Wind erosion assumes serious dimensions in the south west parts of Agra and Mathura districts bordering Rajasthan. Ravine control and reclamation is a major problem along the banks of the Yamuna, Chambal and Betwa.

3. Shallow and excessively permeable soils

These soils are found in the hill districts and uplands of Bundelkhand and Vindhya regions of the state. Shallow depth and excessive permeability along with low inherent fertility limit crop production in these soils.

4. Waterlogged soils

The problem of waterlogged soils is much evident in eastern parts of Uttar Pradesh. Karail soils occurring in the lower basins of the Ganga below the point of confluence of the Yamuna with the Ganga in the districts of Allahabad, Mirzapur, Varanasi, Ghazipur and

Ballia represent the typical hydromorphic soils of the state. The high water table and very slow surface drainage pose a serious problem of water logging in major parts of eastern Uttar Pradesh. In some parts of the state, problem has been accentuated by canal irrigation.

LAND CAPABILITY CLASSIFICATION

Land capability classification of the soils mentioned above has been given in the following table 7.1.

TABLE 7.1. Land Use Capability Classes of Soils with their Limitations

S. No.	Soils	Class	Limitations
1.	Hill soils (less area)	III, IV	Soil erosion and root zone limitation
	(more area)	IV, VIII	
2.	Bhabar soils (more area)	VI, VII	Low moisture holding capacity and root zone
	(limited area)	III	limitation
3.	Tarai soils	II, IV	Wetness, overflows and erosion
4.	Alluvial soils (more area)	I, IV	Erosion, alkalinity and wetness
	(less area)	VI, VII	
5.	Bundelkhand soils	II, V	Root zone limitation, excess permeable
	Rakar soils		
6.	Parwa soils	II, VI	Erosion
7.	Mar and Kabar soils	II, IV	Erosion
8.	Vindhyan soils Type 1 and 2	III, IV	Root zone limitation and soil erosion
9.	Type-3	II, IV	Erosion and wetness
10.	Type 4 and 5	II, III	Wetness
11.	Aravali soils	III, VI	Climate and wind erosion

FERTILIZER MANAGEMENT

Fertilizer management depends upon the soil fertility status.

1. Nitrogen

Seventy seven districts out of 88 districts of Uttar Pradesh and Uttarakhand have low nitrogen and the rest districts as Almora, Banda, Chamoli, Dehradun, Nainital, Pilibhit, Pithoragarh, Tehri Garhwal and Uttar Kashi have medium nitrogen.

2. Phosphorus

The soils of Uttar Pradesh are deficient in available phosphorus content. On the whole, 41 districts are low and 14 are medium in available phosphorus content. Soils of districts-Bareilly, Rampur, Shahjahanpur, Badaun, Moradabad, Bijnore, Farrukhabad, Faizabad, Baharaich, Gonda, Hardoi, Lakhimpur, Sitapur have medium available phosphorus.

3. Potassium

Out of 50 districts, 29 districts are low in potassium, 17 medium and only 4 high in available potassium.

4. Sulphur

Total sulphur content varied from 84 to 168 ppm. The average value of non-sulphate, organic, total water soluble and sulphate-sulphur are 56.6, 45.2, 14.2 and 9.5 ppm respectively in the 0-30 cm layer.

The available sulphur content of the surface soils representing various soils associations of district Kanpur *viz*. recent alluvium, Ganga flats, Ganga uplands, Central lowland and Yamuna uplands varied from 15 to 37.5,15 to 35.0 15 to 15.5 to 47.5,15 to 38.8 and 20 to 27.5 ppm respectively.

5. Zinc

The available zinc status of soils of Uttar Pradesh varied considerably. The available zinc content (dithizone extractable) of soils from six eastern districts of the state *viz*. Basti, Deoria, Azamgarh, Balia, Ghazipur and Kanpur ranged from 0.02 to 1.82 ppm with more than 97 per cent samples showing deficiency. Rice, wheat and other crops grown on these soils showed zinc deficiency symptoms associated with some fungal and viral diseases which seemed to be secondary in nature. The Tarai soils of Ghazipur, Jaunpur, Varanasi, Deorea and Gorakhpur have found to be adequate in zinc.

Bulandshahr, Meerut, Muzaffarnagar, Hamirpur and Banda districts, respectively are severely deficient in zinc while Jalaun soils contained adequate zinc.

6. Iron

The Iron deficiency is found in Hardoi, Unnao, Kanpur and Farrukhabad while the Hamirpur district contained sufficient Iron. The order of iron availability is found to be Hill > Alluvial > Vindhyan > Bundelkhand > Tarai soils.

7. Copper

Copper deficiency is observed only in Unnao (13%), Hardoi (7%) and Farrukhabad (2%) and available copper status of soils in Kanpur and Hamirpur districts is adequate.

8. Molybdenum

Molybdenum (Mo) contents in surface soils of Tarai, Kanpur, Varanasi and Bundelkhand regions are in the ranges of 1.89-2.09, 1.56-1.73, 1.60-2.32, 1.49-1.67 and 1.52-1.73 ppm respectively. Soils of tarai, Kanpur, Varansai and Bundelkhand regions are adequate in available molybdenum content ranging from 0.087-0.112, 0.113-0.186, 0.112-0.199 and 0.102-0.121 ppm respectively.

9. Manganese

Magnitude of manganese deficiency ranging from 0.043-0.044 ppm, 2 per cent in Farrukhabad district to 9 per cent in Kanpur district. Manganese deficiency in Hardoi, Unnao and Hamirpur is 7, 3 and 4 per cent, respectively.

10. Boron

Total boron is high ranging from 49-630 ppm in alluvial soils, 122 to 586 ppm in Bhabhar soils, 201 to 630 ppm in Bundelkhand soils and 58 to 467 ppm in Vindhyan soils.

Available boron varied between 0.10 and 1.55 ppm in normal soils and 0.82 and 10.05 ppm in saline alkali soils. An average content of boron is 0.58 ppm in alkali soils and 0.31 ppm in normal soils.

GENERAL FERTILIZER RECOMMENDATION

The fertilizer recommendations for important crops have been presented in table 7.2.

TABLE 7.2. General Fertilizer Recommendations for HYV of Different Crops in Uttar Pradesh

S. No.	*Crop*	*Fertilizer recommendation (kg/ha)*			*Time of application*
		N	*P_2O_5*	*K_2O*	
1.	Wheat	120	60	40	Full P_2O_5, K and 1/3 N at sowing and rest N equal proportion at 1st and 2nd irrigation
2.	Barley	40	20	—	Full P and $\frac{1}{2}$ N at sowing and rest half N at 1st irrigation
3.	Indian mustard	80-120	40	40	Full P, K and $\frac{1}{2}$ N at sowing and rest half at 1st irrigation
4.	Gram	10-15	40	—	Full N and P at sowing
5.	Maize	120	60	60	Full P, K and $\frac{1}{2}$ N at sowing and rest half N in equal proportion at knee high and tasseling states
6.	Pearl millet	80-100	40	40	Full P, K and $\frac{1}{2}$ N at sowing and rest half N after one month sowing
7.	Rice	120	60	60	Full P, K and $\frac{1}{2}$ N at sowing $\frac{1}{4}$ N at tillering and $\frac{1}{4}$ N at panicle initiation stages
8.	Red gram	10-15	40	—	Full N and P at sowing
9.	Groundnut	15	30	45	Full N, P and K at sowing
10.	Soyabean	20	80	40	Full N, P and K at sowing
11.	Potato	180	60	60	—
12.	Sugarcane	200	80	60	—

TECHNIQUES FOR EFFICIENT FERTILIZER USE

The techniques for efficient fertilizer use are mentioned here.

1. Nitrogen

Crop response to fertilizer N depends upon the varieties grown, HYVs of cereals being more responsive compared with indigenous varieties. Sowing dates have very pronounced effect on nitrogen use efficiency, response to added N decreases with delay in sowing transplanting of wheat and rice. Ammonium sulphate and urea are superior to calcium ammonium nitrate for rice. In saline and alkali soils, ammonium sulphate proved to be better than calcium ammonium nitrate.

Application of nitrogen in 2-3 splits has been found more effective. Nitrogen efficiency is increased when it is applied with phosphorous. Efficacy of urea super granule is significantly higher compared with that of prilled ureas.

2. Phosphorus

The most important factor influencing crop response to added phosphorus is the initial phosphorus status of the soil. Among phosphatic fertilizers, superphosphate proved to be better than rock phosphate and other phosphatic fertilizers in neutral and saline-alkali soils. In maize-wheat and rice-wheat cropping systems increased efficiency of rock phosphate when it is mixed with pyrites and single superphosphate.

3. Potassium

Crop responses to applied potassium depend upon crop varieties, rate, time and method of application, type of soil, climate including temperature, moisture, etc;

In coarse textured soils and under heavy rainfall, split application of potassium may be preferred to basal dressing in order to avoid leaching losses and to ensure better utilization of added potassium when potassium is applied sufficiently at tillering stage, rice plants become resistant to Akagare disease.

❑❑❑

SOIL PHYSICS

CHAPTER 8

Soil Physical Properties

Physical properties of a soil greatly influence its use and behavior towards plant growth. The plant support root penetration, drainage, aeration, retention of moisture and plant nutrients are linked with the physical conditions of the soil. Physical properties also influence the chemical and biological behavior of all soils.

Importance of physical properties of soils

1. How soils can should be used.
2. Determination the stability for the production of different crop plants.
3. To determine the soils suitability for a foundation for building of a bed.
4. To know the soil-water-air relationship and water management through soils.
5. To exert considerable control over the deterioration of the soils itself by erosion.

The physical properties of a soil depend on the amount, size, shape, arrangement and mineral composition of its particles. The physical properties also depend on organic matter content and pore spaces. The important physical properties of soils are (1) Soil Texture (2) Soil Structure (3) Soil Density (4) Soil Porosity and (5) Soil Colour.

PARTICLE SIZE ANALYSIS (MECHANICAL ANALYSIS)

The mineral component constitutes the soil mass. This mineral portion consists of particles of various sizes. According to the size, the soil particles are grouped into gravels, sands, silts and clays which are termed as ***soil separates***. The process of determining the amounts of individual soil separates below 2 mm in diameter is called ***mechanical analysis***. It is based on Stoke's law (1851).

Stoke's Law

Stoke's law may be defined as the settling velocity of a particle falling in a fluid (still) medium will be proportional to the square of its radius. It is expression an equation

$$V = K \cdot r^2$$

where, V = Velocity of particles
r = Radius of particles
K = Constant

Stoke's law (1851), stated that the resistance offered by the liquid to the fall of the particles varied with the radius of the sphere and not with the surface, which mathematically formula :

$$V = \frac{2}{9} \times \frac{g\,(ds - dw)\,r^2}{\eta}$$

where, V = velocity of settling particle (cm/sec)
g = acceleration due to gravity (981 cm/sec^2)
ds = density of soil particle (2.65 g/cc)
η = coefficient of viscosity (0.0015 at 4°C)
dw = density of water (1.0 g/cc)
r = radius of spherical particle (cm)

Assumption in the Stoke's Law :

- No Brownian movement
- Particle smooth and regid sphere
- No effect of wall pressure
- No slipping between particles and liquid
- Critical velocity of fall
- Lower viscosity resistance

To make a mechanical analysis, a sample of soil is crushed lightly in a wooden mortar. The material passed through the sieve is taken for mechanical analysis. The organic matter and other binding materials are removed from the soil before the mechanical separation.

There are several methods of mechanical analysis *viz.*, sieve method, sedimentation method, centrifugal method, International pipette method and hydrometer method. Pipette method is universally employed for carrying out mechanical analysis of soil.

(1) SOIL TEXTURE

Soil texture refers to the relative proportion of particles of various sizes in a given soil or it refers to the relative percentage of sand, silt and clay in a soil.

Classification of soil separates

There are a number of systems of naming soil separates. They are :

(*a*) System of the International Society of Soil Science (ISSS),
(*b*) System developed by United State Department of Agriculture (USDA)
(*c*) British Standard Institution (BSI) System, and
(*d*) Mohr's Ten fraction System.

The international system is more accurate and standard which is commonly followed in India. All systems of the world are presented in Table 8.1.

TABLE 8.1. Classification of soil particle according to size of different systems in world

System	***Soil particles and sizes (diameter, upper limit, in mm)***									
International Society of	Coarse sand			Fine sand		Silt			Clay	
Soil Sciences (ISSS)	2.0- 0.2			0.2-0.02		0.02-0.002			<0.002	
United States Department of Agriculture	Very coarse sand	Coarse sand	Medium sand	Fine sand	Very fine sand	Silt			Clay	
(USDA)	2.0-1.0	1.0-0.50	0.5-0.25	0.25-0.10	0.10-0.05	0.05-0.002			<0.002	
British Standard	Coarse sand		Medium sand	Fine sand		Coarse silt	Medium silt	Fine silt	Clay	
Institution System (BSI)	2.0-0.6		0.6-0.2	0.2-0.06		0.06-0.02	0.02-0.006	0.006-0.002	<0.002	
Mohr's ten Fraction System	Very coarse sand	Coarse sand	Medium sand	Fine sand	Very fine sand	Coarse silt	Medium silt	Fine silt	Clay	Colloidal clay
	2.0-1.0	1.0-0.5	0.5-0.2	0.2-0.1	0.1-0.05	0.05-0.02	0.02-0.005	0.005-0.002	0.002 0.0005	<0.0005

Characteristics and physical nature of soil separates

Sands are large sized particles and have the large size of pore spaces. Hence, they facilitate percolation and encourage aeration. Their water holding capacity is low. They do not possess plasticity. Clay particles are smaller in size and possess fine pore spaces. With decreasing particle size, there is decrease in aeration and percolation rate. The water holding capacity of clay is very high. Properties such as plasticity, swelling, cohesion etc., are very high. Silt particles are intermediate in size. Silts also show properties somewhat intermediary between sands and clays (Table 8.2).

TABLE 8.2. Comparative characteristics of different soil separates

	Characteristics	***Sand***	***Silt***	***Clay***
1.	Size (mm)	2.0-0.02	0.02-0.002	< 0.002
2.	Visibility	Visible by naked eye	Visible by micro-scope	Visible by ultra microscope
3.	Water holding capacity	Low	Medium	High
4.	Total pore space	Least	Medium	Highest
5.	Size of pore	Large	Medium	Very small
6.	Air and water movement	Very rapid	Moderate	Slow
7.	Plasticity, swelling, cohesion adhesion	Very low	Moderate	Very high

8.	Feel on rubbing between thumb and fingers	Gritty	Feel Like flour or talcum powder	Feel very plastic and sticky when wet and become hard under dry condition
9.	Tillage	Easy	Moderate	Difficult
10.	Fertility	Very low	Moderate	High
11.	Minerals	Quartz, dominates	Feldspar, Mica, HHmatite, Quartz	Kaolinite, Montmorillonite, Illite
12.	Chemical activity	Chemically inactive	Slightly active	Chemical activity

Textural Classes

Textural names are given to soils based on the relative proportion of sand, silt and clay. So that are preponderantly clay are called clay (textural class); those with high silt content are silt (textural class); those with a high sand percentage are sand (textural class). A soil that does not exhibit the dominant physical properties of any of those three groups is called loam. The textural triangle (proposed by USDA) is used to determine the soil textural name after performing mechanical analysis in the laboratory (Fig. 8.1).

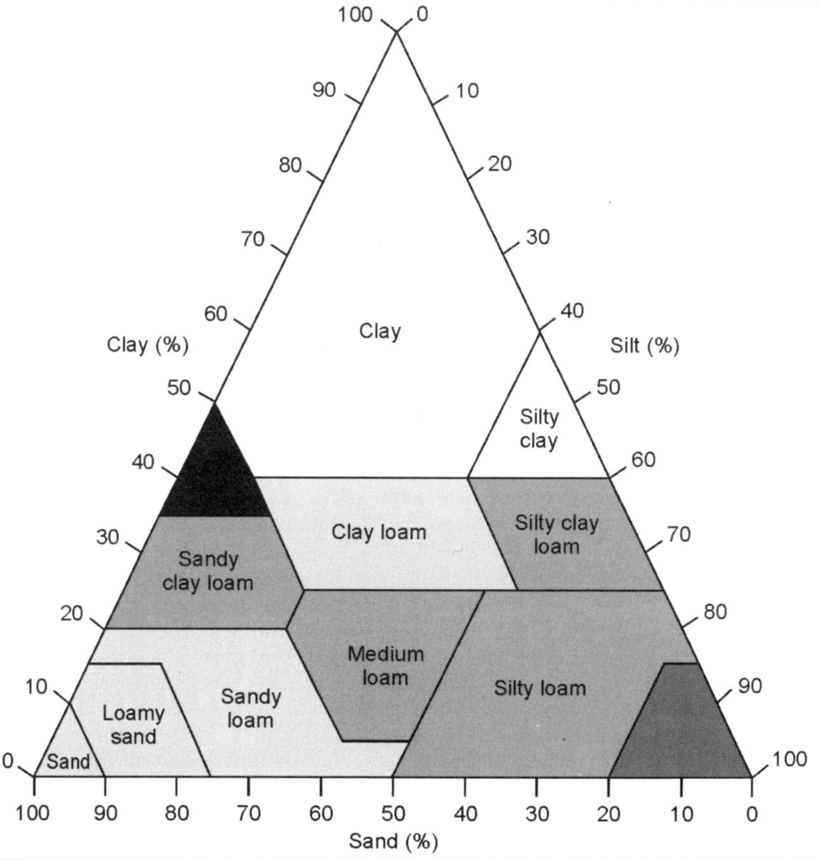

Fig. 8.1. Triangular textural diagram

TABLE 8.3. Fourteen Soil Textural Classes Proposed by USDA, Characteristics and Behavior

Group Name	*Texture*	*Basic soil texture*	*WHC*	*Tillage operation*	*Soil fertility*	*Macro Poro*	*Micro Pore*	*Movement of water and air*	*Chemical activity*	*Infiltration*	*Permeability*	*CEC C mol (r^+) kg^{-1}*	*Specific gravity*	*B.D. (g/cc)*	*Wt. of soil $kg\ m^{-1}$*	*Porosity (%)*	*Buffering capacity*	*Use chemical amendment*
Sandy	**Coarse Texture**	Sand	Low	Very easily	Low	More	Less	Rapid	Less active	Rapid >54 mm hr^{-1}	Very rapid 160 mm	Low 1-5	Less 45 $cm^2\ g^{-1}$	High 1.6	High 1603	Less about 40%	Low about 40%	Less
		Loamy sand																
Loamy Soil	**Mod. Coarse Texture**	Sandy loam																
		Fine sandy loam																
	Medium Texture	Very fine sandy loam																
		Loam																
		Silt loam																
		Silt																
	Mod. Fine Texture	Clay loam																
		Sandy clay loam																
		Silty clay loam																
Clayey	**Fine Texture**	Sandy clay																
		Silty clay																
		Clay	High	Difficult	High	Least	More	Slow	More active	Very slow <1 mm hr^{-1}	Very slow <1.25 mm hr^{-1}	High >30	More 150-200 $m^2\ g^{-1}$	Less 1.1	Low 1100	More >58%	High	High

WHC—Water holding capacity, CEC—Cation exchange capacity, B.D.—Bulk Density.

(2) SOIL STRUCTURE

The arrangement of soil particles and their aggregate into certain defined patterns is called ***soil structure***. The primary soil particles sand, silt and clay usually grouped together in the form of aggregates. Natural aggregates are called ***peds*** whereas ***clod*** is an artificially formed soil mass. Soil structure is studied in the field under natural conditions and it is described under three categories.

Ped. Natural aggregate is called ped (Unit of soil structure).

Clods. It is used for coherent mass of soil broken into any shape by artificial means such as tillage.

Fragments. It is broken by peds.

Aggregate. Many soils particles held in a single mass or cluster, such as a clod, crumb, block, or prism.

Classification of Soil Structure

A. Grade. Degree of distinctness of peds.

B. Class. Size of peds

C. Type. Shape or form and arrangement pattern of peds

(A) Grade

(*i*) ***Structure less*** : no visible peds are aggregates.

(*ii*) ***Weak structure*** : weakly formed aggregates non durable, and unclear.

(*iii*) ***Moderate structure*** : moderately good formed aggregate fairly durable, but clear.

(*iv*) ***Strong structure*** : very good formed aggregates, quite durable and permanent.

(B) Class :

Class	Platy/ Laminar	Crumby	Prismatic/ Columnar	Blocky
(*i*) Very fine or very thin	< 1 mm	< 1 mm	< 10 mm	< 5 mm
(*ii*) Fine or thin	1-2 mm	1-2 mm	10-20 mm	5-10 mm
(*iii*) Medium	2-5 mm	2-5 mm	20-50 mm	10-25 mm
(*iv*) Coarse	2-10 mm	—	50-100 mm	25-50 mm
(*v*) Very coarse	> 10 mm	—	> 100 mm	> 50 mm

(*i*) **Plate like structure.** In this structural type of aggregates are arranged in relatively thin horizontal plates. The horizontal dimensions are much more developed than vertical. When the unit is thick, they are called **platy,** and when thin, **laminar**. Platy soil structure is most noticeable in the surface layers of virgin soils but may be present in the sub soil. Platy type is often inherited from the parent material, especially those laid down by water.

(*ii*) **Prism like.** The vertical axis is more developed than horizontal, giving a pillar like shape. When the top of such a ped is rounded, the soil structure is termed as **columnar**, and when flat, **prismatic**. They commonly occur in sub soil horizons in arid and semi arid regions.

(C) Type : There are four principal forms of soil structure

Type of Structure	Description of Aggregates	Sub-group	Location	Aggregate size mm
Platy structure	(*i*) Aggregate are plate like, plate overlaps slow move-ment of water into the soil. (*ii*) Horizontal axis of aggre-gate are more developed then vertical axis with different thickness.	On the basis of thickness of aggregate are: **(*i*) *Platy*** : when structural unit are thick  (a) Platy (b) Luminar **(*ii*) *Laminar*** : when structural unit are thin	'A' horizon of humid region soil	1-10 mm
Prismatic structure	(*i*) Aggregates are prism like with flat are rounded top (*ii*) Vertical axis of aggregate bigger then horizontal axis	On the basis of top of aggregate are **(*i*) *Prismatic*** : when top of aggregate are flat  (a) Prismatic (b) Columnar **(*ii*) *Columnar*** : when top of aggregate is rounded	(*i*) B' horizon of arid and semi-arid region (*ii*) salt affected areas (*iii*) poor drained soil of humid region (*iv*) compacted clayey soils	10-100 mm
Blocky structure	(*i*) Aggregates are cube like with flat of rounded outer (*ii*) Horizontal axis and vertical axis of aggregates are roughly are equal	On the basis of shape and outer surface of aggregates, it can be divided into three type **(*i*) *Angular blocky*** : outer surface of aggregates are flat  (a) Angular blocky (b) Sub-angular blocky **(*ii*) *Sub-angular blocky*** : when sheet and sites of aggregates are rounded	'B' horizon in humid region	5-50 mm
Spheroid structure	(*i*) Aggregate are rounded curved or irregular outer surface (*ii*) Horizontal axis and verti-cals axis are generally equal	On the basis of pores, it be divided tow type **(*i*) *Granular*** : it is less pores  (*a*) Granular (*b*) Crumby **(*ii*) *Crumby*** : it is more absorbent	'A' horizon of grass land, pasture, fertile cultivated land and rich in organic soils	1-10 mm

(*iii*) **Block like.** All these dimensions are about the same size and the peds are cube like with flat or rounded faces. When faces are flat and the edges sharp angular, the structure is named as **angular blocky**. When the faces and edges are mainly rounded it is called **sub angular blocky**. These types usually are confined to the sub soil and characteristics have much to do with soil drainage, aeration and root penetration.

(*iv*) **Spheroidal (sphere-like).** All rounded aggregates (peds) may be placed in this category, although the term more properly refers to those not over 0.5 inches in diameter. These rounded complexes usually lie loosely and separately. The aggregates of this group usually termed as **granular** which are relatively less porous, when the granules are very porous, the term used is **crumby** (Figs. 8.2, 8.3, and 8.4).

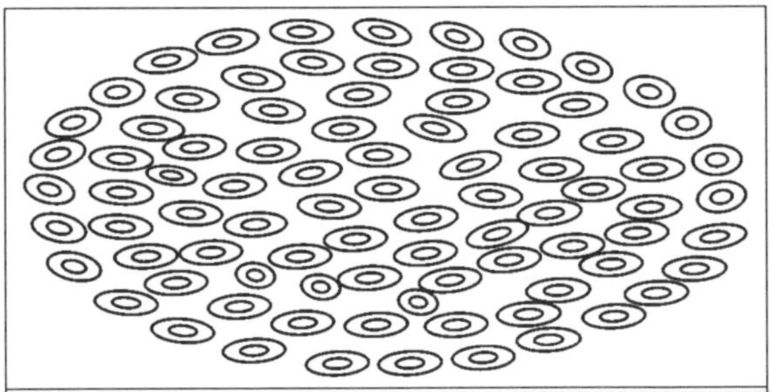

Fig. 8.2. Example of sphere like structure

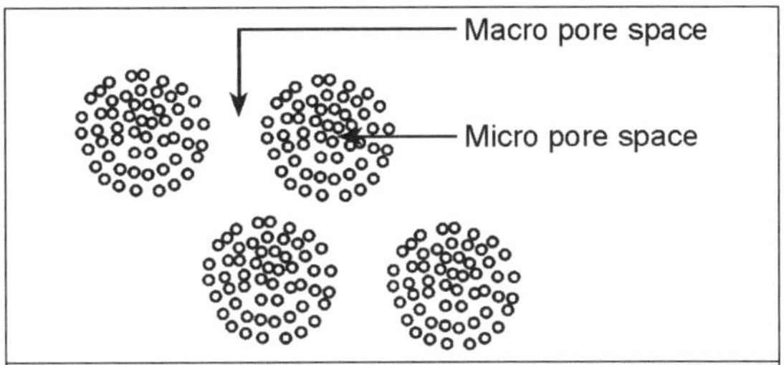

Fig. 8.3. Arrangement of particles in sphere like structure

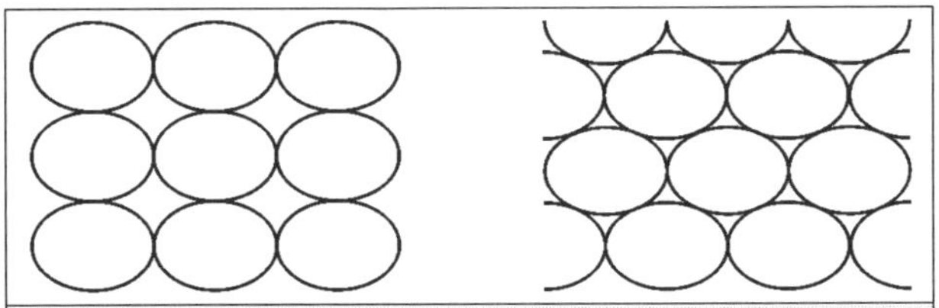

Fig. 8.4. Arrangement of sphere particles in two ways

STRUCTURE FORMATION (GENESIS)

The mineral colloids (colloidal clay) by virtue of their properties of adhesion and cohesion, stick together to form aggregates. Sand and silt particles can not form aggregates as they do not posses the power of adhesion and cohesion. The amount and nature of colloidal clay influence the formation of aggregates. The greater the amount of clay in a soil, the greater is the tendency to form aggregates. Clay particles smaller than 0.001 mm aggregates very readily.

Genesis of Soil Structure

↓

Flocculation

↓

Cementation

↓

Granulation

↓

Stabilization of Aggregates (Soil Structure)

The mechanism of structure (aggregate) formation is quite complex. In aggregate formation a number of primary particles such as sand, silt and clay are brought together by the cementing or binding effect of soil colloids to form a compound or secondary particles. It is mainly the arrangement of these secondary particles that imparts structure to a soil mass. The cementing materials taking part in aggregate formation are colloidal clay, iron and aluminum hydroxides and organic matter.

Iron and aluminum hydroxide act as cementing agent in binding the soil particles together. These are also responsible for the formation of aggregates by cementing sand and silt particles. Organic matter plays an important part in forming soil aggregates. The humic acid and other sticky product produced during the decomposition of organic matter help in aggregate formation.

MECHANISM OF SOIL AGGREGATION

Russel (1934) gave the hypothesis for mechanism of soil aggregates. In a hypothesis put forward by Russel (1934) to explain the mechanism of aggregate formation is assumed that clay particles are held together by bridges of oriented of water molecules between the dissociated cations and the fixed charges on the surface of the clay particles.

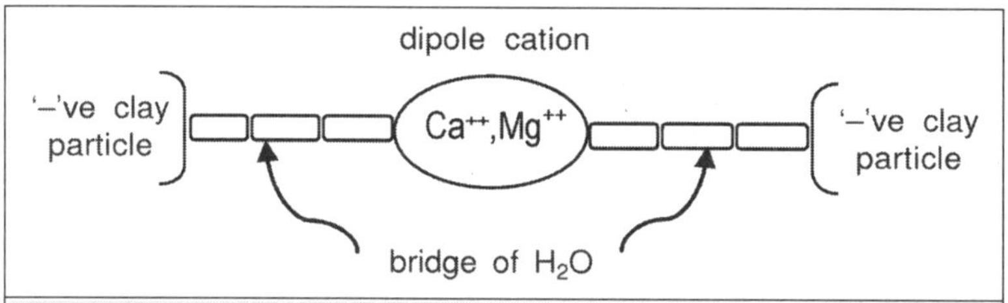

Fig. 8.5. Russel hypothesis

The obtained evidence that strong clay crumbs can only be formed by drying clay dispersed either in water or a few polar liquid like alcohol.

Aggregate formation in soil is largely a function of

(*i*) Silt and clay content.

(*ii*) Organic compounds present in the soil.

(*iii*) The microbial activity.

(*iv*) The concentration of irreversible soil colloids.

(*v*) The long range and vander wal's force acting between the charge clay materials and the polymers presents.

Besides these, many salts, parent material, climate and some of the soil forming processes also affect granulation. Cation effect, effect of colloid and effect of organic matter also affects.

Method of Soil Structure Evaluation

(*i*) Stability against disruption during wet sieving.

(*ii*) Stability against the impact of falling drop to water.

(*iii*) Stability against disintegration during leaching with dilute NaCl solution.

(*iv*) Stability against slaking when pretreated with alcohol or other organic liquids.

Stability of soil aggregates

These are three major influences aggregates stability

1. The temporary mechanical binding action of by micro organisms, especially the thread-like filaments of fungi, fungal mycelia. These effects are pronounced when fresh organic matter is added to soils and are at maximum a few weeks or months after this application.
2. The cementing action of the intermediate products of microbial synthesis and decay such as by microbial product gums and certain polysaccharides compound are sometimes called "pro-humus constituent" and are clearly effective as aggregate stabilizers at least several months.
3. Stable humus components acts as cementing agent and in addition of this certain inorganic compounds such as oxides of Fe also help in cementing aggregates and making them stable.

Soil structural unit prepared by

(*a*) Continuous biochemical breakdown of organic matter to replenish the polysaccharides and other organic gums which gradually oxidize.

(*b*) High levels of polyvalent cations produced by continued weathering of mineral in-situ and decomposition of fresh organic matter.

(*c*) The continued availability of iron oxide cements.

The chemicals used to test their effects on soil structure fall under the following groups :

(*i*) Naturally occurring polyuronic acid salt and other closely related polysaccharides. They have been found to improve soil structure very much but their application is not considered practicable.

(*ii*) Sodium and potassium silicates; these are also reported to give excellent stabilization of soil crumb at relatively high levels of application *i.e.* 0.25 to 0.1 per cent. The application of sodium silicate at these high levels indicated a toxic effect on soil micro flora while at lower doses the aggregating effect was not significant.

(*iii*) The next group of chemicals comprises of sodium acetate dimethyl dichlorosilane and some of rasin derivatives which bring about crumb stability by water proofing action. Their application through improves soils and their soil structure reduces markedly the water holding capacity of soils and their moisture equivalent.

(*iv*) Krillim; in order to overcome these handicaps the Monsanto Scientific company (USA) has synthesized a few polyelecrolytes are **CRD-186 (Carboxylated polymer), DRD-189 CI, CII** and **CIII** etc.

Factors affecting soil structure

The following factors influence the formation of soil structure in the arable condition.

(1) Climate. Climate influence the aggregate formation, in arid region, there is very little aggregation of primary particles while in semi arid region, the degree of aggregation is greater than arid region.

(2) **Organic matter.** Organic matter improves the soil structure in both sand and clay soils. During the decomposition the by product produced help in binding the various particles, while in clay soils it modifies the cohesion properties and thereby improve the soil structure.

(3) **Tillage.** Cultivation or use of implements influence the soil aggregate, if at high moisture content tillage is carried out big clods may come out while too low moisture will break the aggregates. Use of heavy implements will break the soil structure.

(4) **Plant roots.** The root secretions may also act as cementing agents and binds various soil particles. The plant roots, on decay, may also bring about granulation due to the production of sticky substances.

(5) **Fertilizers.** Certain fertilizer like sodium nitrate destroys the soil aggregates while calcium ammonium nitrate helps in the development of soil structure.

(6) **Wetting and drying.** When a dry soil is wetted, the soil colloids swell on absorbing water. On drying, shrinkage produced strains in the soil mass give rise to crack which break it up into clods and granules of various sizes.

Importance of soil structure

Soil structure influences indirectly by the formation of an array of pores of various shapes and sizes. These pores are controlling factors governing water, air and temperature in soil. The roles of soil structure in relation to plant growth are as under :

1. Soil structure influences the amount and nature of porosity.
2. Structure controls the amount of water and air present in soil. Not only the amount of water and air dependent on soil structure, but also their movement and circulation are also controlled by soil structure.
3. It affects tillage practices.
4. Structure controls runoff and erosion.
5. Platy structure normally hinders free drainage whereas sphere like structure helps in drainage.
6. Crumby and granular structure provides optimum infiltration, water holding capacity, aeration and drainage. It also provides good habitat for microorganism and supply nutrients.

(3) SOIL DENSITY

Density represents weight (mass) per unit volume of a substance.

$$\text{Density} = \frac{\text{Mass}}{\text{Volume}}$$

Soil density is expressed in two well accepted concepts (*a*) particle density and (*b*) bulk density.

Particle density: The weight per unit volume of the solid portion of soil is called ***particle density***. Particle density is also known as **true density.** Generally, particle density of normal soils is 2.65 g/cc. This is high when heavy mineral is present in the soil *viz.* magnetite and limonite. Increase in the organic matter of the soil decreases the particle density. Particle density varies with texture of soils (Table 8.4).

TABLE 8.4. Particle density of different soil textural classes

Textural class	Particle density (g/cc)
Coarse sand	2.655
Fine sand	2.659
Silt	2.798
Clay	2.837

Bulk density. The oven dry weight of a unit volume of soil inclusive of pore spaces is called ***bulk density***. The bulk density of a soil is always smaller than its particle density. Bulk density normally decreases as mineral soils become finer in texture. The Bulk density of organic matter is about 0.5 g/cc. The bulk density varies indirectly with the total pore space present in the soil and gives a good estimate of porosity of soil. Bulk density is of greater important than particle density in understanding the physical behavior of soils. Soils with low bulk densities have favorable physical conditions (Table 8.5).

TABLE 8.5. Bulk density of different soil textural classes

Textural class	Bulk density (g/cc)	Pore space (%)
Sandy soil	1.6	40
Loam	1.4	47
Silt loam	1.3	50
Clay	1.1	58

Using the bulk density of any soil the weight of that soil can be calculated unto the desired depth.

Example. If the bulk density of the cultivated field is 1.48 g/cc what will be the weight of hectare filed (soil) to the depth of 15 cm.

Volume of the soil (Field) of hectare field (soil) to the depth of 15 cm.

= Length × Width × Depth

= 100 × 100 × 0.15 = 1,500 cubic meter

1 cubic meter = 1 × 100 × 1 × 100 × 1 × 100

= 10,00,000 cubic centimeter

1500 cubic meter = 1,500 × 10,00,000 = 1,50,00,00,000 cubic centimeter

Weight of 1 cubic centimeter = 1.48 g

So in this case weight 1,50,00,00,000 cubic centimeters will be

= 1,50,00,00,000 × 1.48

(Volume of 15 cm Hectare furrow × Bulk density)

= 2,22,00,00,000 g

i.e. $\frac{2,20,00,000}{1,000}$ = 22, 20,000 kg/ha to the depth of 15 cm

(4) POROSITY OF SOIL

Pore space

The volume of soil mass that is not occupied by soil particles is known as ***pore space***. This space is occupied either by air or water. It directly controls the amount of water and air in the soil and thus indirectly controls plant growth and crop production. There are two types of pore (1) Macro pore and (2) Micro pore and both are important for crop growth.

(1) Macro pore or non capillary pore. Pores more than 0.06 mm in diameter are considered as macro pores. These pores allow readily movement of air and water and do not hold much water under normal condition. Sands and sandy soils have a large number of macro pores.

(2) Micro pore or capillary pore. In contrast, in the micro pores, movement of air and water is restricted to some extent. Clays and clayey soils have a greater number of micro pores. Size of the individual pores, rather than total pore space in a soil is more significant in its plant growth relationship. Equal distributions of micro and macro pores are much desirable for better aeration, permeability, drainage and water retention.

Soil porosity. Soil porosity is the percentage pores space. Porosity refers to that percentage of soil volume which is occupied by pore spaces. It can be calculated by the formula :

$$\text{Porosity} = 100 - \frac{\text{Bulk density}}{\text{Particle density}} \times 100$$

Since, % pore space + % solid space = 100

and % pore space = 100 – % solid space

$$\% \text{ Solid space} = \frac{\text{Bulk density}}{\text{Particle density}}$$

$$\text{Porosity (\% pore space)} = 100 - \frac{\text{Bulk density}}{\text{Particle density}} \times 100$$

Example. A soil having bulk density of 1.3 and particle density of 2.65 have the following percentage of pore space.

$$\text{Porosity} = 100 - \frac{1.3}{2.65} \times 100 = 50.94\%$$

Factors affecting the soil porosity

(1) Soil texture. In sandy soils, pores are quite large, thus total pore space is less. In fine textured soils, there is possibility of more granulation and more total pore space because there are macro pores between individual particles and within granules micro pores (Table 8.6).

TABLE 8.6. Relation between textural class and pore space

Textural class	*Clay content*	*Av. Pore space (%)*
Heavy Clay	> 55	51.09
Clay	40-55	48.45
Sandy Clay Loam	20-30	45.45
Sand	< 10	42.54

(2) Soil structure. Good aggregated soil structure is having greater pore space than the soil having single grain structure or structure less. Soil with same size aggregate but one is single grain structure while other is aggregate structure, more space will be in later on because of additional pore space between the primary particles. Granular or crumbly type of structure has more porosity than plate like.

(3) Arrangement of soil particle. When the spheres like particles are arranged in columnar form it gives the most open system of packing. Thus, the number of pore space will be less. When the particles are arranged in the pyramidal form it gives the closest system of packing. So in this system porosity would be more.

(4) Organic matter. Increasing in the organic matter content in the soil, increase in the percentage of pore space.

(5) Micro-organisms. Micro-organisms like earthworm and insects increase the macro pores in the Soil.

(6) Depth of the soil. Pore space in the sub-soil is generally low compared to surface soil layers.

(7) Cropping. Cropping tends to lower the total pore space in comparison to virgin or uncropped soils. This reduction is associated with a decrease in the organic matter content. Continuous cropping often results in a reduction of large or macro pore spaces (Table 8.7).

TABLE 8.7. Effect of continuous cropping on total pore space

Soil Treatment	*Organic matter*	*Pore space %*		
	%	*Total*	*Macro*	*Micro*
Virgin Soil	5.6	58.3	32.7	25.6
Cultivated Soil	2.9	50.2	16.0	34.2

Soil compaction

Compaction is the dynamic behavior of soil. The degree of compaction depends upon the nature of soil, amount of energy applied, water content and extent of manipulation of the soil. Compaction is also associated with the rearrangement of the soil solid particles so that soil water and soil air are compressed within the pore space. An increase in water content decreases cohesion between the particles and thereby facilitating compaction. In many soils, a compacted layer is commonly found at the bottom of the zone of ploughing. This layer is termed as '***ploughed sole***'. Age-old practices of tillage using heavy farm equipments create the problem of surface and sub-surface compaction in soils. These hard compact layers often restrict root penetration and growth and also reduce the water and nutrient uptake by crops. Soil compaction changes soil moisture and thermal regimes and mechanical resistance in soils. However, in highly coarse textured soils, loamy sand soils, compaction may be a boon to water retention and reduce percolation loss of water.

Significance and manipulation of densities

Changes in bulk density for a given soil can alert soil managers to change the soil quality and ecosystem functions. Increases in bulk density indicate a poor environment for root growth, reduce aeration and water infiltration. Particle and bulk densities are used to calculate porosity of soil. Bulk density is used to calculate total water storage capacity per soil volume and evaluate soil layers to determine root penetration and adequate aeration.

Tillage may temporarily loosen the soil surface, in long term intense tillage increases bulk density. The effect of cultivation on bulk density can be minimize by adding crop residues or farm manures in large amounts and rotating cultivated crops with a grass sod. Repeated use of heavy machinery can form plough pan below ploughed layer. Large chisel-type plough can be used in sub soiling to breakup dense subsoil layer, thereby permitting root penetration by lowering bulk density of soil.

(5) SOIL COLOUR

The colour of soil varies widely. It is an easily observable characteristic and is an important criterion in description and classification of soils.

Colour of a soil is inherited from its parent rock material (termed as lithochromic) for example red soils developed from red sand stone. Often the soil colour is a result of soil forming process and is termed as acquired or pedochromic. The soil colour is best determined by the comparison with the Munsell colour.

The colour of the soil is a result of the light reflected from the soil. Soil colour rotation is divided into three parts :

Hue. It denotes the dominant spectral colour (red, yellow, blue and green)

Value. It denotes the lightness or darkness of a colour (the amount of reflected light)

Chroma. It represents the purity of the colour (strength of the colour)

The **Munsell** colour notations are systematic and letter designations of each of these three variables (Hue, Value and Chroma). For example, the numerical notation 2.5YR5/6 suggests a hue of 2.5 YR, value of 5 and chroma of 6. The equivalent or parallel soil colour name for this Munsell notation is red.

TABLE 8.8. Soil colour developed by deferent sources and processes in soil

Soil Colour	*Developed by*
1. Black/dark grey colour	Due to organic matter
2. Brown colour	Mixture of organic matter and FeO
3. Red colour	Due to present of ferric oxide (Hematite)
4. Yellow colour	Due to poor drainage, degree of hydration 2 Fe_2O_3 (yellow) +$3H_2O$ ≡♦ $2FeO_3.3H_2O$ (red)
5. Green colour	Glauconitic mineral
6. White colour	Due to presence of high amount of Lime, Gypsum, Kaolinite, Feldspar, Quartz, Muscovite
7. Bluish/greenish colour	Due to poor drainage and due to presence of ferrous compound
8. Mottling colour	Due to water fluctuation in soil and due to alternating of oxidizing and reducing reaction
9. White colour on saline soil	Due to excess amount of sulphate, chlorite and sodium salts
10. Brown colour of sodic soil	Due to excess amount of $NaNO_3$
11. Black colour of sodic soil	Due to excess amount of Na_2CO_3
12. Red colour of podzol soil	Due to presence of hematite
13. Ash colour of podzol soil	Due to eluviated humus, sesquive oxide and small clay particles by percolation from 'A' horizons.
14. Brick like red colour of laterite soil	Due to presence of hematite in 'A' horizons
15. Black colour of Black cotton soil	Due to clay humus complex titini-ferrous magnetite compound
16. Blue colour of organic soil	Due to presence of Fe as ferrous form
17. Brown colour	Due to presence of magnetite mineral
18. Black colour	Due to excess amount of magnese oxide (MnO_2)
19. Yellow colour	Due to excess amount of goethite mineral
20. Dark colour soils	Due to excess amount of Fe and Mn

Soil colour and composition

(*a*) **Black and dark gray colour.** The variations from black to dark gray colour of soil are mainly due to organic matter.

(*b*) **Brown colour.** This is the most common soil colour and is due to a mixture of the organic matter and iron oxides.

(*c*) **Red yellow colour.** Red colour is associated with unhydrated ferric oxides, whereas yellow colour indicates some degree of hydration.

(*d*) **White colour.** Silica and lime generally impart white colour.

(*e*) **Bluish and greenish colour.** Some of the bluish and greenish colours are due to the presence of ferrous compounds. This reducing condition occurs in drained soil.

(*f*) **Mottling colour.** Colour variation or mottling in soils indicates alternating oxidizing and reducing conditions due to a fluctuating water table.

CHAPTER 9

Soils Air

A part of the soil volume that is not occupied by soil particles, known as ***pore space***. Pore spaces are filled partly with soil water and partly with soil air. As the pore space is occupied by the both water and air, the volume of air varies inversely with that of water. As the moisture content of the soil increases, the air content decreases and *vice-versa*. The constant movement of air in the soil mass resulting in the renewal of gases is known as ***soil aeration***. Thus, a well-aerated soil is one in which gases are available to growing aerobic organism (including higher plants) in sufficient quantities and in the proper proportions to encourage optimum rates of the essential metabolic processes of these organisms.

COMPOSITION OF SOIL AIR

The soil air contains a number of gases of which nitrogen, oxygen, carbon dioxide and water vapour are the most important. Soil air constantly move from the soil pores into the atmosphere and from the atmosphere into the pore space. Although soil air and atmospheric air differs in the composition. Soil air contains a much greater proportion of carbon dioxide and a lesser amount of oxygen than atmospheric air. At the same time, soil air contains a far greater amount of water vapour than atmospheric air. The amount of nitrogen in soil air is almost the same as in the atmosphere. The soil air contains a number of gases (Table 9.1) of which nitrogen (79.2%), oxygen (20.6%) and carbon dioxide (0.25%). Whereas atmospheric air contains gases *i.e.*, nitrogen (79.0%), oxygen (20.97%) and carbon dioxide (0.03%).

TABLE 9.1. Composition of soil and atmospheric air

Air	*Percentage by Volume*			
	Nitrogen	*Oxygen*	*Carbon dioxide*	*Other*
Soil air	79. 20	20.60	0.25	
Atmospheric air	79.00	20.97	0.03	

Factors affecting composition of soil air

The composition of soil air is influenced by nature and condition of soil, type of crop, microbial activity and seasonal variations.

Exchange of gases between soil and atmosphere

(1) Mass flow. Mass flow of air is due to pressure difference between the atmosphere and the soil air. Rain or irrigation water displaces soil air into atmosphere. As the soil dries up, atmospheric air enters the soil pores.

- With each rain or irrigation, a part of soil air moves out in the atmosphere air, it is displaced incoming of water.
- When soil moisture is lost by evaporation, then atmospheric air enters into soil.
- When soil air gets heated during the hottest part of day, then soil air expended air moves out in the atmosphere.
- Soil air cools during the night, then cooled air contact with atmospheric air resulting atmospheric air down it.

(2) Diffusion. Most of the gaseous interchange in soils occurs by diffusion. When partial pressure of CO_2 is greater in soil air than atmospheric air, CO_2 moves out into the atmosphere (Fig. 9.1).

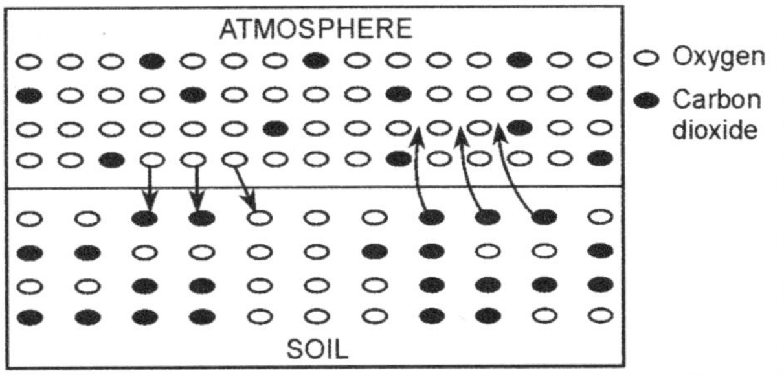

Fig. 9.1. Gaseous exchange between soil and atmosphere (diffusion)

Influence of soil air on plant growth

(1) *Plant and root growth*: When the supply of oxygen is inadequate, the plant growth either retards or ceases completely as the accumulated CO_2 hampers the growth of plant roots.

(2) *Microorganism population and activity*: The deficiency of air (oxygen) in soil slows down the rate of microbial activity, decomposition of organic matter, nitrification, sulphur oxidation etc.

(3) *Formation of toxic material*: Poor aeration results in the development of toxin and other injurious substances such as ferrous oxide, H_2S gas, CO_2 gas etc. in the soil.

(4) *Water and nutrient absorption*: A deficiency of oxygen has been found to check the nutrient and water absorption by plants.

(5) *Development of plant diseases*: Insufficient aeration of the soil also leads to the development of diseases. *e.g.* wilt of arhar and gram, dieback of citrus and peach.

CHARACTERIZATION OF SOIL AERATION STATUS

Several methods have been to characterize the soil aeration status; some of these are described below :

(*a*) Air filled porosity. The air-filled porosity (*fa*) of a soil can be determined by finding total pore space (S) and water content on volume basis (θ) by the equation

$$fa = S - \theta$$

The air-filled porosity can also be evaluated using air space pycnometer and tension-table methods.

(*b*) Composition of soil air (Percentage composition of different components of soil air). The oxygen and carbon dioxide content of the gas samples, taken from soil air, can be determined using of chemical or gas analyzer or gas chromatographic method.

(*c*) Amount of carbon dioxide given off at soil surface. The amount of carbon dioxide is determined for a definite area of the soil surface. It gives an idea about the microbial and root activity in the soil.

(*d*) Air permeability. Air permeability of soil is a parameter which indicates its readiness it's transmit gases when difference in the build up. The percentage, size and community of pore with in the soil and occupied by air determine the permeability of a soil, special instruments like 'air permeability' and 'Gasometer' are used to determine air permeability under field and laboratory conditions. This method gives a better idea of renewal of soil gases than the actual availability of oxygen to plant roots.

(*e*) Apparent diffusion coefficient. Diffusion is the principal mechanism which indicates the exchange of gases between the soil and the aerial atmosphere. Oxygen normally diffuses into the soil and carbon dioxide diffused out into the atmosphere. The apparent diffusivity is used to characterize a soil for its aeration status.

(*f*) Equivalent diffusion coefficient. In length of unit cross section area through which free diffusion will supply oxygen to a given point at the same rate as it is supplied by the soil.

(*g*) Aeration factor. It is a ratio of oxygen consumption by soil microbes under optimum respiratory condition to the consumption in the presence of soil expressed in percentage of the optimal value.

Redox Potential

The oxidized and reduced state of chemical elements in the soil gives an idea about its aeration status. In a well-aerated soil, the oxidized states of element such as those of iron as ferric (Fe^{3+}), manganese as manganic (Mn^{+++}), nitrate (NO_3^-) and sulphate (SO_4^{2-}) dominate. In poorly-aerated soils, the reduced forms of these elements such as ferrous iron (Fe^{2+}), manganous manganese (Mn^{2+}), oxides of nitrogen (NO_x) and sulphate (S^{2-}) are found.

The oxidation reduction (redox) potential (E_h) of soil can be measured by inserting a cylinder electrode in the soil solution. It provides a measure of the soil tendency of a system to reduced or oxidize substances. The value of E_h can be interpreted up to a certain extent in terms of the ratios of certain oxidizing and reducing organic and inorganic materials present in the soil system. The value of E_h is positive and may be as high as +0.5 volt under strong oxidizing conditions. It is low and even negative when elements are present in reduced forms. E_h values have the advantage of providing a measure of intensity of reduction under conditions having no molecular oxygen. It is, therefore, useful in characterizing the soil reaction in the range below which diffusion of oxygen is zero, for example, in rice fields where under water. The oxidize and reduced forms of certain elements in soil and the E_h values at which change in the form occurs are given in Table 9.2.

TABLE 9.2. The oxidized and reduced states of certain elements in soil and the redox potential (E_h) at which change in the form occurs

State of element		*(E_h) at which change in the form occurs*
Oxidized	*Reduced*	
O_2	H_2O	0.38 to 0.32
NO_2	N_2	0.28 to 0.22
Mn^{3+}	Mn^{2+}	0.28 to 0.22
Fe^{3+}	Fe^{2+}	0.18 to 0.15
SO_4^{2-}	S^{2-}	–0.12 to –0.18
CO_2	CH_4	–0.20 to –0.28

Oxidation Diffusion Ratio (ODR)

It is the best measurement of aeration status of oxygen diffusion rate (ODR) in soils. It checks the amount of oxygen available to roots or to get an impression of soil structure. Oxygen diffusion rate (ODR) is the rate at which oxygen diffuses at roots. Method of determining ODR is the platinum electrode technique.

TECHNIQUES FOR THE MEASUREMENT OF ODR

Principles: When a certain electric potential is applied between a platinum electrodes inserted into the soil a reference electrode, oxygen (O_2) is reduced at platinum electrode surface. The general reaction taking place at platinum micro electrode surface in the reduction of O_2 is in two steps involving two electrons in each step. The reactions in two different media are :

In acid soils :

$$O_2 + 2H^+ + 2e^- = H_2O_2$$

$$H_2O_2 + 2H^+ + 2e^- = 2H_2O$$

$$\overline{O_2 + 4H^+ + 4e^- = 2H_2O}$$

In neutral or alkaline soil :

$$O_2 + 2H_2O^+ + 2e^- = H_2O_2 + 2OH^-$$

$$H_2O_2 + 2H^+ + 2e^- = 2H_2O$$

$$\overline{O_2 + 2H_2O^+ + 4e^- = 4OH^-}$$

The platinum electrode, an electric current flows between the two electrodes and is proportional to the rate of oxygen reduction. The rate of oxygen reduction is in turn related to the rate at which it diffuses to the electrode.

Analogs to measuring of oxygen movement to plant root; the rate of oxygen diffusion is measured by inserting by small platinum wire electrode into the soil. The apparatus consist of a platinum microelectrode which is pushed into the soil to desired depth and an electrical cell is formed by increasing into soil nearby a saturated calomel electrode. The calomel electrode through a galvanometer is connected to positive terminal of an external source of direct current. Its negative terminal is connected to the platinum micro-electrode.

TABLE 9.3. Critical of oxygen diffusion rate (ODR) for different crops

Crop	*ODR (10^{-8} g cm^{-2} min^{-2})*
Maize	30.0
Soyabean	28.4
Wheat (Unirrigated)	26.9
Wheat (Irrigated)	26.3
Peas (Unirrigated)	32.9
Peas (Irrigated)	39.5
Toria	22.3

The result of measurement is an electric current which is related to the rate of oxygen flux at the electrode surface and is given by Equation :

$$i \times 10^{-6} = nFAf$$

where, i is electric current in micro-amperes, n is number of electrons required for reduction of one molecule of oxygen which is 4, F is the Faraday's constant, A is the area flux or ODR to the electrode surface in number of molecule of oxygen per second per cm^2. The ODR is calculated by Equation :

$$\text{ODR} = (i \times 60 \times 32 \times 10^{-6})/(4 \times 96500 \times \text{A})$$

$$(0.497 \times 10^{-8} \times \text{i})/\text{A (g cm}^{-2}\text{ min}^{-1})$$

The requirement of ODR of a number of crops ranges from 22.9×10^{-8} to 39.5×10^{-8} g cm^{-2} min^{-1} (Table 9.3) in general, the critical ODR values of soils in which roots many plants will not grow is the order of 20×10^{-8} g cm^{-2} min^{-1}.

Fick's Law. According to Fick's law, diffusion of the concentration gradient, the diffusion co-efficient of the medium, and the cross-sectional area.

$$dQ = DA\left(\frac{dc}{dx}\right)dt$$

where, dQ is mass flow (moles) during the time at across area A (sq cm), dc/dx the concentration gradient [moles/c.c. (cm)], and D the proportionality constant or diffusion coefficient (sq cm/sec.).

D depends upon the property of the medium as well as the gas. It varies directly with the square of the absolute temperature and inversely with the total pressure.

The diffusion coefficient of O_2 is about 1.25 time that of CO_2. The rate of diffusion of CO_2 and O_2 in air is nearly 10,000 times greater than in water. The greater solubility of CO_2 in water increases its concentration gradient and will be transferred in water at a higher rate than O_2.

Effect of poor aeration on higher plant

Higher plants are affected by poor aeration in four ways :

(*a*) The growth of root is curtailed

(*b*) Absorption of nutrient is decreased

(*c*) Absorption of water decrease

(*d*) Formation of inorganic toxic compounds

Management of slowly permeable soil

Slowly permeable soil can be managed as fallows :

(*i*) Vertical mulching
(*ii*) Addition of organic matter
(*iii*) Land grading-prepared ridge
(*iv*) Ridge Planning
(*v*) Raised beds and sunken beds

Aeration Requirements of Plants

Grain crops are more resistance to less aeration than leguminous and oil seeded crops. Oat and wheat requires more than 10 per cent and beat requires more than 15 per cent air. For root development less in soils having <10 per cent O_2 and totally stopped at 5 per cent O_2. Presence of >10 per cent CO_2 in soil air completely effect the plant growth.

❑❑❑

CHAPTER 10

Soils Temperature

Agriculture is the exploitation of solar energy in presence of water and nutrients for plant growth. The solar energy is the main source of heat for soil, which determines the thermal regime of soil and growth of plants.

Net Radiation. It is the difference between the total radiation and the radiation leaving the surface. Another definition is sum of the net short wave radiation and received the net long wave radiation.

Albedo. The percentage incident of global radiation reflected by the surface is known as albedo.

Stefan-Boltzman law. The long-wave radiation is proportional to the fourth power of the absolute temperature and the efficiency of the radiating surface. A black body is a perfect absorber and emitter. The energy RB emitted from a black body as long-wave radiation can be expressed quantitatively by the Stefan-Boltz as a law, $RB = T^4$.

Source of Soil Heat

(1) Solar Radiation. The main source of soil heat is the energy of sun's rays (radiant energy) that reach to the earth after they pass through the atmosphere. The exposure of the earth to the heat of the sun warms the surface of the soil on which the rays fall.

- Radiant energy reach the earth after they pass through the atmosphere, in winter season 50 cal^{-1} cm^{-2} $year^{-1}$, while in summer season 500-700 cal^{-1} cm^{-2} $year^{-1}$.
- The solar radiation received only 0.5 per cent received as agricultural crops, less then 10 per cent *i.e.*, 0.05 per cent recovered as several crops and fruits.

(2) Conduction. The inner atmosphere of the earth is very hot; the conduction of the heat to the soil environment is very slow. Generally, during night, the upper most surface soil becomes cooler then sub-surface soil. Thus heat flow from the regions of sub-soil to the regions of surface soil (cooler soil layer).

(3) Bio-chemical reaction. Some amount of heat is liberated in the chemical and biological process.

(4) Rain. The occurrence of warm rain during the winter months may raise the temperature of the soil.

(5) Vegetation. Vegetation plays a significant role of soil heat because of the insulting properties of soil cover. Bare soil is unprotected from the direct rays of the sun and becomes very warm during the hottest part of the day.

Absorption and Loss of Soil Heat

Solar energy is primary source of energy to heat soil. But clouds and dust particles intercept the sun's rays and absorb, scatter or reflect most of their energy. Only about 35-40 per cent of the solar radiation actually reaches the earth in cloudy humid regions and 75 per cent in cloud-free arid areas. The global average is about 50 per cent.

Fig. 10.1. Relation between soil heat and solar radiation

Out of the total solar energy reaching the earth only about 10 per cent is absorbed by the soil and can be used to warm it.

The major impact of vegetation are associated with (*i*) the albedo effect (absorptivity of soil), (*ii*) decreasing the depth of penetration of global radiation through the canopy, (*iii*) increasing the latent heat in evapo-transpiration, and (*iv*) decreasing the rate of heat loss from the soil through its insulating influence.

Factors affecting absorption of heat

The factors influencing the amount of energy absorbed by soil are :

1. Colour. Dark coloured soils absorb more energy than lighter coloured soils. This does not mean that dark soils are always warmer. In fact, dark soils usually are rich in organic matter and hold large amount of water, which requires comparatively more energy to be warmed.

2. Slope. If the incoming path of the rays is perpendicular to the soil surface energy absorption is greater than to the sloping surface, receiving the rays.

3. Vegetative cover. Bare soils warm up more quickly and cool off more rapidly than those covered with vegetation.

Loss of Soil Heat

(1) Radiation. The quantity of heat so absorbed by the soil does not remain constant. A part is lost to the air by radiation.

(2) Conduction. Some heat transmitted to lower layers of soil by conduction.

(3) Evaporation. In the process of evaporation of soil water a large amount of heat is used. This result in a cooling effect especially at the surface.

(4) Rain. During summer months, generally rain has a cooling action in soil, because rain will usually have a lower temperature than soil.

Thermal Properties of Soils

The thermal properties of the soil are characterized in terms of specific heat, heat capacity, thermal conductivity and thermal diffusivity.

Specific Heat

It may be defined as the amount of heat required to raise the temperature of one gram of a substance by 1°C. The specific heat of dry soil (0.2 cal g^{-1}) is only about $1/5^{th}$ that of water (1 cal g^{-1}). Hence, moist soils are cooler due to their high specific heat and also due to the heat energy spent in evaporation of soil moisture.

1 Joule = 0.239 cal

1 cal = 4.19 joule

Substances	*Specific Heat (cal g^{-1})*	*Heat Capacity*
Water	1	1
Ice	0.5	0.46
Organic matter	0.46	—
Humus	0.44	0.56
Mineral soil	0.18	—
Dry soil	0.20	0.50
Sand	0.10	—
Clay	0.22	0.05
Coarse quartz	0.191	0.5
Fine quartz	0.189	0.5
Apatite	0.183	—
Hematite	0.165	0.75
Granite	0.19	0.50
$CaCO_3$	0.20	0.54
Calk	0.21	0.46
Wood	0.42	0.38
Mica	0.206-0.208	0.59
Air	0.24-0.25	0.003
Feldspar	0.294-0.208	0.205

Heat Capacity

The heat capacity is defined as the ratio of heat supplied to a body to the corresponding rise its temperature, and is given by Equation :

$$C = \frac{\Delta Q_h}{\Delta T}$$

where, C is the heat capacity, ΔQ_h is the quantity of heat supplied to body and ΔT is the increase in its temperature (°C).

The heat capacity of a given materials is equal to its specific heat multiplied by its mass. The specific heat of soil varies with various constituents. It is found that quartz has the lowest specific heat and humus has the greatest. It influenced by humus and water content of the soil.

$$\text{Heat capacity (cal m}^{-3}\text{)} = \text{specific heat} \times \text{mass of density}$$

Thermal Conductivity

The thermal conductivity of a soil is defined as the amount of heat passing in unit time through a unit cross section area of the soil under a unit temperature gradient applied in the direction of this heat flow. *or* The quantity of heat passing in unit time through a unit area of soil under a unit temperature difference between the faces is known as thermal conductivity of soil.

It is the ability of a substance to transfer heat from molecule to molecule. For this reason, it is sometimes called *molecular conductivity*. ***Thermal conductivity*** is defined as the quantity of heat transmitted through unit length of a substance per unit cross section, per unit of temperature gradient per unit of time. The thermal conductivity of soil depends on its water content, texture, structure, mineralogical composition, organic matter content and compaction. In general, the thermal conductivity of soil varies in the order: sand > loam > clay > peat. The thermal conductivity of quartz, water and air are in the ratio 333 : 23 : 1.

Thermal Diffusivity

It is defined as the ratio of thermal conductivity to heat capacity. It is a measure of rate at which changes in temperature occurred in the body. It is increased with increasing bulk density, heat capacity and degree of saturation with moisture content.

$$\alpha = \frac{\lambda}{C_v} = \frac{\text{Thermal conductivity}}{\text{Volumetric heat capacity}}$$

or,

$$\alpha = \text{Thermal conductivity/specific heat} \times \text{density}$$

$$\text{Thermal receptivity} = \text{1/thermal diffusivity}$$

It is proportional to the thermal conductivity and inversely proportional to the heat capacity on a volume basis.

Thermal diffusivity is a measure of the rate at which changes in temperature occur in the body. The higher moisture content is the higher thermal diffusivity of a soil.

Effect of soil temperature on plant growth

There are various influences of soil temperature on soil fertility by changing the soil environment which, in turm affects on plant growth.

(*i*) *Germination of seeds*. If the temperature is too low, the seed fails to germinate. On the other hand, seeds may be injured if the temperature will be very high.

(*ii*) *Physical properties of soil*. Soil structure is greatly influenced by the temperature.

(*iii*) *Microbial activity*. The activity of micro-organisms is lowest when soil temperature is below 5°C and above 54°C. The optimum temperature for the activity of most of the micro-organisms is in the range of 25-35°C.

(*iv*) *Decomposition of organic matter in soil*. At low temperature the rate of organic matter decomposition is low resulting on various toxic organic substances in soil and the high temperature the rate of the same is very fast resulting beneficial products of organic matter decomposition and hence influence the plant growth.

(*v*) *Absorption of water*. Variation in soil temperature affects the absorption of soil-water by the plant roots.

(*vi*) *Availability of nutrients*. Temperature influences the solubility reactions of different nutrients and releases larger amount of nutrient elements in the soil solution at higher temperatures.

(*vii*) *Root growth*. Low temperature encourages wheat succulent roots with little branching, while high temperatures encourage a browner, finer and much more freely branching root system.

(*viii*) *Plant diseases*. At low temperatures, the soil contains many weekly parasitic fungi which will grow actively and very rapidly and so those will kill the seedlings.

Importance of Soil Temperature in Agriculture

(1) Promotes the chemical and biological activities.

(2) All vital processes can be continued between 5 to 25°C temperature beyond this range life process cease to function.

(3) The optimum temperature varies for biological activities and for different plant species.

(4) Soil temperature is an important factor controlling plant growth and chemical and biological activities.

Decomposition of organic, matter mineralization of organic nitrogen, germination of seeds and plant growth increase with an increase in temperature but at very high temperature, this activities start to stop out of which mostly all biological activities.

(5) Temperature also affects crop production *viz*.

(*i*) Germination (*ii*) Plant Growth

(*iii*) Nutrient water absorption (*iv*) Photosynthesis

(*v*) Evaporation

(*vi*) Effect on reproduction stage *i.e*. flowering, production and grain filling stage

Since sub soil reproduction lags surface soil temperature, subsoil reaction rates will also lag surface soil reaction rates. Many other factors also influence reaction rates in the subsoil. For microbial processes, the lack of organic matter and smaller microbial population are important.

ALBEDO

Soils	*Albedo value*
Wet soil	0.16
Moist soil	0.10-0.15
Dry soil	0.23
Water	0.03-0.1
Earth surface	0.4

(*i*) It is also known as absorptivity.

(*ii*) The term albedo means white colour.

(*iii*) Albedo is the ratio of out going radiation to incoming radiation.

$$\text{Albedo} = \frac{\text{Out going radiation}}{\text{Incoming radiation}}$$

(*iv*) Light colour has higher albedo value than the dark colour soil.

(*v*) Lower albedo value means higher absorption of solar radiation.

(*vi*) Moist soils are albedo value 0.10-0.15 and thus increase as soil dries.

(*vii*) It is generally used in controlling of soil temperature.

Method of soil temperature measurement

Contact type

(*i*) By metallic thermometer

(*ii*) Mercury or alcohol thermometer

(*iii*) Constant pressure, *or* Constant volume thermometer

(*iv*) Thermostare

(*v*) Thermocouple thermometer

Non Contact type

(*i*) Optical pyrometer

(*ii*) Total intensity radiometer

(*iii*) Infrared thermometer

MANAGEMENT OF SOIL TEMPERATURE

The primary source of heat energy to soil being the sun, practices encouraging the heat absorption and the flow in soil and those discouraging heat loss to the atmosphere would help in storage and temperature rise. The soil temperature under field conditions can thus be altered by mulching and vegetation, tillage, compaction, irrigation and drainage.

(*a*) Use of mulch and vegetation

Mulches, such as straw, tend to buffer the extremes in soil temperature. Soil temperature is maintained by cover of soil surface by different type of mulch, *i.e.* temperature residues, wheat straw, plastic shoots, etc.

Soil mulch cool of the soil during day and warming during night. During summer in hot weather it keep the soil cooler than soil without soil mulch, while in winter mulches act as buffer, prevent the rapid fall in soil temperature.

Soil temperature is influenced by soil cover and especially by organic residues or other types of mulches placed on the soil surface. Mulches are definitely temperature modifier. During hot weather they keeps soil cooler than the soils without cover, while in winter the mulches buffer, prevent the rapid fall in soil temperature.

Mulching with the polyethylene sheet raises the soil temperature during the day. Mulches also conserve soil moisture. A polyethylene film laid on a soil surface is transparent only to the incoming radiations. The outgoing radiation is inhibited due to the condensation of water vapour and the presence of dust particles on soil side of the polyethylene surface.

The vegetation, like straw mulch also intercepts both the incoming as well the outgoing radiation from the soil and therefore, residues the temperature fluctuations. The overall effect depends on the proportion of shaded soil. Air temperature above a crop is lower than at the surface of soil on a clear night. Soil under vegetation warms up more slowly in winter than a bare soil. A soil under dense vegetative canopy may remain at a uniform temperature in surface layers.

(*b*) Tillage

Tillage of any kind affects the pore size distribution and wetness and consequently the soil temperature. The tillage forming ridges often creates a range of soil temperature regime. Rapid changes in soil temperature are observed on ridges, whereas furrows are generally cooler. In poorly drained soils, ridging improve the soil aeration. A tilled surface soil is generally warmer during the day time because of its higher porosity and low thermal conductivity than a compacted untilled soil.

(*c*) Soil Compaction

Compaction in soil brings its particles closer and regulates temperature in the root zone. The abrupt changes of soil temperature, as observed in the surface layer of the loose soil, do not occur in a compact soil due to its high thermal conductivity. The soil compaction under field condition is often achieved using a tractor or bullock drawn roller.

❑❑❑

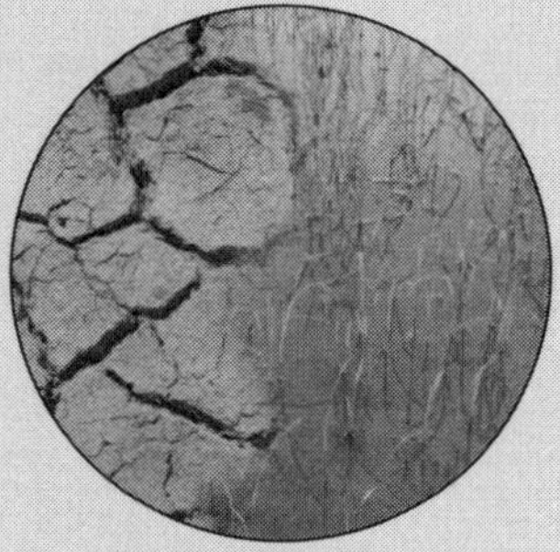

CHAPTER 11

Soil Water

Water is the essential either in small amount or in excess of all living being. In absence of water life of any living being, creature, animal, micro-organisms, vegetations and plants is impossible. Water is present in every living being in biochemical or other form, mainly in protoplasm of vegetations and in creatures is present to some degree.

Importance of water in agriculture

Water is necessary for plants and vegetations as follows :

(*i*) Used as food material.

(*ii*) Water is very essential in decomposition of organic matter and bio-chemical reactions.

(*iii*) It is the part of protoplasm in plants and micro-organisms.

(*iv*) Due to universal solvent it keeps essential plant nutrients in solution form.

(*v*) Transpiration of water always occurs from which plant cell always remain turgid.

(*vi*) An important process photosynthesis is depend on water.

Water work as in soil activities as fallows

(*i*) Weathering and transformation of rocks and minerals.

(*ii*) Improvement of soil structure.

(*iii*) Development of soil and soil profile.

(*iv*) Important role in reclamation of Usar (saline and alkali) and acid soil.

(*v*) Maintaining soil temperature.

Water content in soil is called ***soil moisture***. The water is held within the soil pores. Soil water is the major component of the soil in relation to the plant growth. If the moisture content of a soil is optimum for plant growth, plants can readily absorb the soil water. Much of water remains in the soil as thin film. Soil water dissolves salts and makes up the soil solution, which is important as medium for supplying nutrients to growing plants.

Structure and related properties of soil water

The ability of water to influence so many soil processes is determined by the structure of the water molecule.

Polarity or Dipole character

The arrangement of three atoms in a water molecule is not symmetrical. The hydrogen atoms are attached to oxygen in a V-shaped arrangement at an angle of only 105° as shown in Fig. 11.1, this result in an asymmetrical molecule with the shared electrons being closer to the oxygen than to the hydrogen.

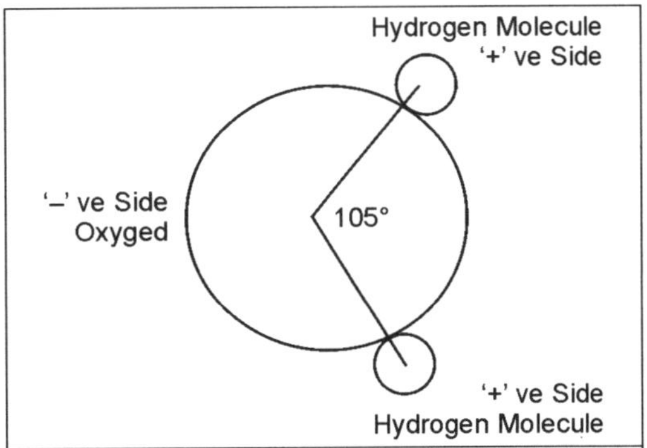

Fig. 11.1. Two dimensional representation of water molecule

Each water molecule carries both negative and positive charges. The hydrogen end of a water molecule is positive while oxygen end is negative. This accounts for the polarity of water. The clay particle is negatively charged.

The retention of water molecules on the surface of clay micelle is based on its dipole character. By virtue of the dipole character and under the influence of electrostatic forces, the molecules of water get oriented (arranged) on the surface of the clay particles in a particular manner. The positive end of water molecule gets attached to the negatively charged surface of clay and leaving its negative end outward. The water molecules attached to the clay surface in this way present a layer of negative charges to which another layer of oriented water molecules is attached (Fig. 11.2).

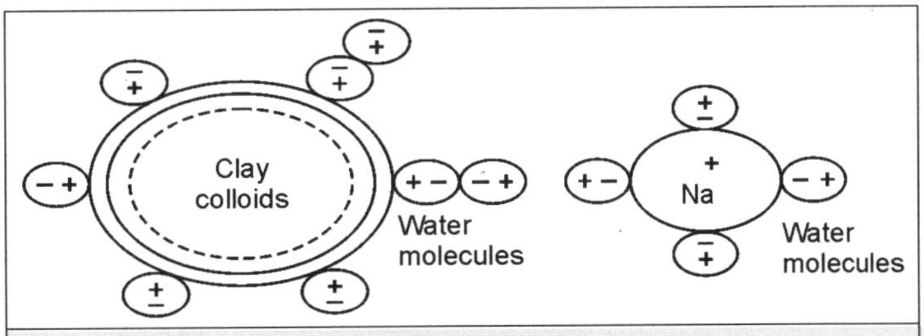

Fig. 11.2. Orientation of water molecules on the surface of clay micelle and cation

HYDROGEN BONDING

The phenomenon by which hydrogen atoms act as links between water molecules is called ***hydrogen bonding***. This type of binding accounts for polymerization and for the relating high boiling point, specific heat and viscosity of water. It is also responsible for the structural rigidity of crystals and some organic compounds like proteins. Hydrogen bonding also accounts for two basic forces *viz*., cohesion and adhesion, responsible for water retention and movement in soils and its utilization.

Cohesion and adhesion forces

These two basic forces are responsible for water retention in the soil. One is the attraction of molecules for each other *i.e.*, cohesion. The other is the attraction of water molecules for the solid surface of soil *i.e.*, adhesion. By adhesion, solids (soil) hold water molecules rigidly at their soil water interfaces. These water molecules in turn hold by cohesion. Together, these forces make it possible for the solids to retain water.

Surface tension

This phenomenon is commonly evidenced at water air interfaces. Water behaves as if its surface is covered with a stretched elastic membrane. At the surface, the attraction of the air for the water molecules is much less than that of water molecules for each other. Consequently, there is a net downward force on the surface molecules, resulting in sort of a compressed film (membrane) at the surface. This phenomenon is called ***surface tension.***

Soil Water Retention and Potentials

The soils hold water (moisture) due to their colloidal properties and aggregation qualities. The water is held on the surface of the colloidal and other particles and in the pores. The force responsible for retention of water in the soil after the drainage has stopped are due to surface tension and surface attraction and are called ***surface moisture tension.*** This refers to the energy concept in moisture retention relationships. The strength with which water is held in the soil is called ***water potential***. The force with which water is held is also termed as ***suction***.

Total Soil Water Potential

The total soil water potential is defined as "the amount of work that must be done per unit quantity of pure water in order to transport reversibly and isothermally an infinitesimal quantity of water from a pool of pure water at a specified elevation at atmospheric pressure to the soil water (at the point under consideration)." The definition stresses that soil water potential is the difference between the energy state of soil water and that of pure free water.

Total soil water potential is in effect the sum of the potentials resulting from various forces acting on soil water. Thus, the *gravitational, matric,* and *osmotic* potentials are the differences in free energy resulting from the gravitational, matric, and osmotic forces, respectively.

The gravitational, matric and osmotic potential are summarized as below :

Gravitational potential	Matric potential	Osmotic potential
1. The force of gravity act on soil water, the water attraction being toward the earth center	It is the result of adsorption and capillarity, the attraction of soil solids to water provide a matric force markedly reduce the free energy	It is attributed to the presence of solute in the soil which reduce the free energy of water
2. It is always positive because gravitational potential is independent of relative elevation *i.e.* height of water column	It is always negative because of matric force it reduce free energy of adsorbed water molecules and those held by cohesion	It is always negative due to the presence of solutes it adsorbed the water by attractive osmotic force reduce free energy
3. —	It effect on retention and movement of water in soil	It effect on water uptake important in saline soil

These relationships can be expressed by

Ψ_w	=	Ψ_g	+	Ψ_m	+	Ψ_s
Soil water potential		Gravitational potential		Matric potential		Osmotic potential

Gravitational potential

The force of gravity acts on soil water the same as it does on any other body, the attraction being toward the earth's center. The gravitational potential (Ψ_g) of soil water may be expressed mathematically as $\Psi_g = gh$, where g is the acceleration of gravity and h is the height of the soil water above a reference elevation. The gravitational potential of soil water above the reference point will always be positive. It is independent of chemical and pressure conditions of soil water and dependent on relative elevation. Gravity plays an important role in removing excess water from the upper rooting zones following heavy precipitation or irrigation.

Matric potential

Matric potential is the result of two phenomena, adsorption and capillarity. The attraction of soil solids and their exchangeable ions for water provide matric force that markedly reduces the free energy of soil water as compared to that of unabsorbed pure water. Consequently, matric potentials are always negative. The matric potential exerts its effect not only on soil moisture retention but on soil water movement as well.

Osmotic potential

The osmotic potential is attributable to the presence of solutes in the soil *i.e.* soil solution. The solutes reduce the free energy of water, primarily because the solute ions or molecules attract the water molecules. Unlike the matric potential, the osmotic potential has little effect on the mass movement of water in soils. Its major effect is on the uptake of water by plant roots. The root membrane, which transmits water more freely than solutes, permits the osmotic effects to be exerted, a matter of considerable importance if the solute content of soils is high. The osmotic potential also affects the movement of water vapor since water vapor pressure is lowered by the presence of solutes. It is negative.

Suctions and tensions

The terms "tension" and "suction" have the advantage over "potential" in that they are expressed in positive rather than negative units.

Method of expressing energy levels

Several units have been used to express the differences in energy level of soil water. A common means expressing tension (negative potential) is in terms of the height in centimeter just equals to the tension under consideration.

The greater the centimeter height, the greater is tension measured, to avoid the use of large number (cms), Schofield (1935) suggested using of pF which is defined as "the logarithm of soil moisture tension (negative potential) expressed in centimeter height of water column". Soil tension expressed relationship of different units as:

1 atmosphere = 1.0133 bar
= 760 mm of Hg or 750 m of Hg cm
1 atm = 1000 cm of water
= 14.7 Ib/sq inch
= 1.013 dyne/sq m
1 bar = 1023 cm of water = 0.987 atm

TABLE 11.1. Approximate equivalents of common means of expressing differences in energy level of soil water

Height of water column (cm)	*Pressure bar/atm*	*pF*	*Soil water tension (bar)*	*Remark-I*	*Remark-II*
0 (0)	0	0	0.0	Saturated point	**Super available water**
10.2 (10)	0.01	1	–0.01		P = < 1/3 bar
102 $(10)^2$	0.1	2	–0.1		P = < 2.54
204	—	2.2	–0.2		
306 (346)	1/3	2.53 or 2.54	–0.3	Field capacity	**Available water**
1,023 (1,000)	1	3	–1.0		P = <1/3-15
10,230 (10,000)	10	4	–10		pF = 2.54-< 2.54
15,345 (15,849)	15	4.18 or 4.20	–1	Wilting point	
31,713 (31,623)	31	4.50	–31	Hygroscopic point	**Unavailable water**
1,02,300 (1,00,000)	100	5	–100		
10,00,000	1,000	6	–1,000	Air dry soil	P = > 15-10,000
1,00,00,000	10,000	7	–10,000	Oven dry soil	PF 4.50-7

*bars-To obtain an expression of soil water tension in the SI unit mega Pascal (MPa), multiply the number of bars by 0.1.

SOIL MOISTURE ENERGY CURVES

Hysteresis

This phenomena is occurring when soils (clayey) are alternately wetted and dried, result of desorption of soil commonly called 'hysteresis' of soil water characteristics or it is defined as alternate wetting and drying of clay soils, result sorption and desorption is called hysteresis.

Desorption is a drying of completely saturated soil, while sorption is wetting of an initially dry soil. The difference between sorption and desorption is due to hysteresis which is mainly caused due to entrapped air clogs some pores and prevent effective contact between other as soil is referred.

The hysteresis effect may be attributed to several causes :

(1) The geometric non-uniformity of individual pores (which are generally irregular shaped voids inter connected by smaller passage), which results in the "inkbottle" effect.

(2) The contact-angle is greater and hence, the radius of curvature is greater, in an advancing meniscus that in the case of a receding once. A given water content will tend therefore to exhibit greater suction in desorption than sorption.

(3) Entrapped air, which further decreases the water content of clay of newly wetted soil. Failure to attain true equilibrium can accentuate the hysteresis effect.

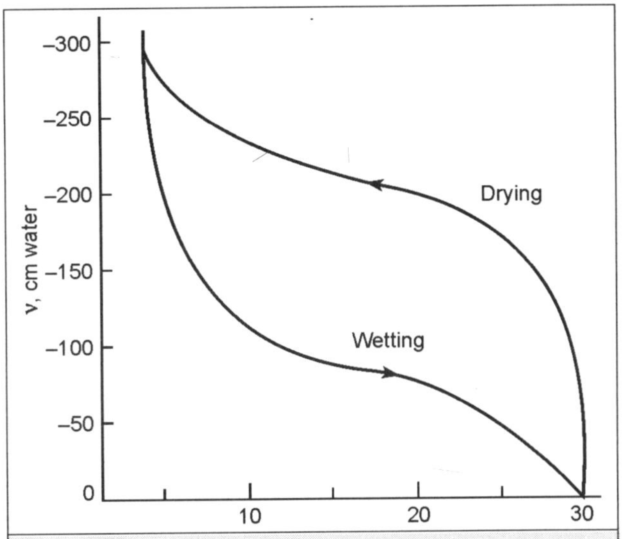

Fig. 11.3. Water content, q_v (per cent)

(4) Swelling, shrinking phenomena, which result in differential changes of soil structure, depending on the wetting and drying history of the sample. The gradual solution of air or the release of dissolved air from soil water can also have a differential effect upon the suction-wetness relationship in wetting and drying systems.

PHYSICAL CLASSIFICATION OF SOIL WATER

Briggs proposed depending upon the physical forces and the mode of retention, soil water may be divided into 3 categories *viz*.

(1) Gravitational water,

(2) Capillary water, and

(3) Hygroscopic water.

1. Gravitational water

Gravitational water occupies the larger soil pores (macro pores) and moves down readily under the force of gravity. Water in excess of the field capacity is termed gravitational water. Gravitational water is not use to plants because it occupies the larger pores. It reduces aeration in the soil. Thus, its removal from soil is a requisite for optimum plant growth.

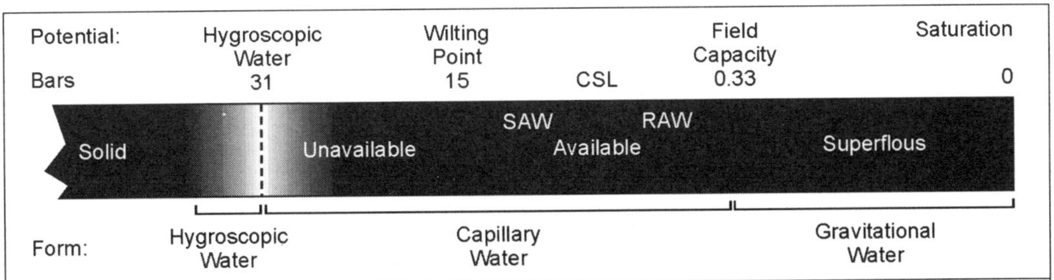

Fig. 11.4. Physical classification of soil water

2. Capillary water

Capillary water is held in the capillary pores (micro pores). Capillary water is retained on the soil particles by surface forces. It is held so strongly that gravity cannot separate it from the soil particles. The molecules of capillary water are free and mobile and are present in a liquid state. Due to this reason it evaporates easily at ordinary temperature. Though, it is held firmly by the soil particle, plant roots are able to absorb it. Capillary water is, therefore, known as ***available water***.

3. Hygroscopic water

The water held tightly on the surface of the colloidal particles is known as ***hygroscopic water***. It is essentially non-liquid and moves primarily in the vapour form. Hygroscopic water held so tenaciously by soil particles that plants cannot absorb it. Some microorganism may utilize hygroscopic water.

As hygroscopic water is held tenaciously by surface forces its removal from the soil requires a certain amount of energy. Unlike capillary water which evaporates easily at atmospheric temperature (Fig. 11.5), hygroscopic water cannot be separated from the soil unless it is heated.

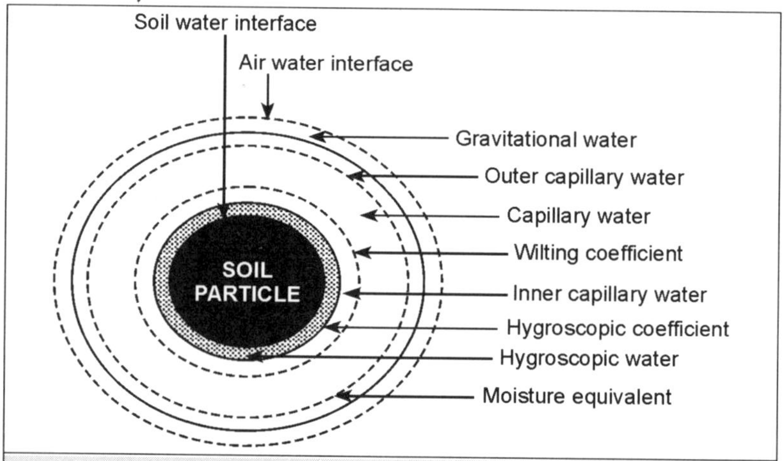

Fig. 11.5. Different forms of soil water

SOIL MOISTURE CONSTANTS

Earlier classification divided soil water into gravitational, capillary and hygroscopic water. The hygroscopic and capillary waters are in equilibrium with the soil under given condition. The amount of water that a soil contains at each of three equilibrium points is known as soil ***moisture constant***. The soil moisture constants represent definite soil moisture relationship and retention of soil moisture in the field. Following are the soil moisture constants.

(1) Field capacity

Field capacity is the capacity of the soil to retain water against the downward pull of the force of gravity. At this stage only micro pores or capillary pores are filled with water and plants absorb water for their use. At field capacity water is held with a force of 1/3 atmosphere. Water at field capacity is readily available to plants and microorganism.

(2) Wilting coefficient

As the moisture content falls, a point reached when the water is so firmly held by the soil particles that plant roots are unable to draw it. The plant begins to wilt. At this stage even if the plant is kept in a saturated atmosphere it does not regain its turgidity and wilts unless water is applied to the soil. The stage at which this occurs is termed the ***wilting point*** and percentage amount of water held by the soil at this stage is known as the ***wilting coefficient***. It represents the point at which the soil is unable to supply water to the plant. Water at wilting coefficient is held with a force of 15 atmospheres.

(3) Hygroscopic coefficient

Hygroscopic coefficient is the maximum amount of hygroscopic water absorbed by dry soil under standard conditions of humidity (50% relative humidity) and temperature (15ºC). This tension is equal to a force of 31 atmospheres. Water at this tension is not available to plant but may be available to certain bacteria.

(4) Available water capacity

The amount of water required to apply to a soil at the wilting point to reach the field capacity is called the '***available water***'. The available water is the difference in the amount of water at field capacity (–0.3 bar) and the amount of water at the permanent wilting point (–15 bars).

(5) Maximum water holding capacity

It is also known as ***maximum retentive capacity***. It is the amount of moisture in a soil when its pore spaces both macro and micro capillary are completely filled with water. It is a rough measure of total pore space of soil.

(6) Sticky point moisture

The sticky point represents the maximum moisture content at which a soil remains friable.

TABLE 11.2. Type of soil water available to plant at different suction force

Soil water	*Tension (bar/atm)*	*pF*
Hygroscopic water	31-10,000	4.5-7
Hygroscopic coefficient	31	4.5
Wilting point	15	4.18 or 4.20
Field capacity	1/3 (0.1-1/3)	2.54 or 2.53
Capillary water	1/3-31	2.54-2.50
Available water	1/3-15	2.54-4.18
Moisture equivalent	1-1/3	3-2.70
Gravitational water	< 1/3	< 2.54
Water holding capacity	0	0

ENTRY OF WATER INTO SOIL

(1) Infiltration

Infiltration refers to the downward entry of water into the soil surface. Infiltration is a surface characteristic so primarily influenced by the condition of the surface of soil. A compact surface permits infiltration. Soil surface with vegetative cover have more infiltration rate than bare soils. Warm soils absorb more water than cold one. Coarse surface texture (Sandy), granular structure and high organic matter content in surface soil, all help to increase infiltration. Infiltration rate is comparatively lower in wet soils than dry soils. It is express as $mm\ hr^{-1}$.

Classification

Infiltration Class	*Infiltration Rate (mm/hr)*	
Very slow	< 1	Clay
Slow	1-5	↓
Moderately slow	5-20	
Moderate	20-63	
Moderately rapid	63-127	
Rapid	127-254	
Very rapid	> 254	Sand

(2) Percolation

The movement of water through a column of soil is called ***percolation***. Percolation is important for two reasons. First, percolating waters are the only source of recharge of ground water can again be used through wells for irrigation. Second, percolating waters carry plant nutrients down and often out of reach of plant roots (leaching). Percolation is dependent on rainfall. In dry region, percolation is negligible but in region of high rainfall, percolation is usually high. Sandy soils permit greater percolation in comparison to clayey soils. Vegetation and high water table reduce the percolation losses. Percolation losses of water are not harmful but the nutrients that are leached along with the percolation water are of serious consideration. Losses of calcium and magnesium are the greatest but phosphorus is lost by leaching in trace (very less). It is expressed by $mm\ min^{-1}$.

(3) Permeability

Permeability indicates the relative ease of movement of water within the soil. The characteristics that determine how fast air and water move through the soil are known as ***permeability***. The term ***hydraulic conductivity*** is also used which refers to the readiness with which a soil transmits fluids through it. The permeability is basically dependent on the pore-size distribution in the soil. The macro pores increases the permeability. The pore size distribution is greatly determined by the extent of aggregation in the soil. The larger the aggregate, the greater is the amount of non-capillary (macro) pores. The permeability of soil usually decreases with depth, as the sub-soil layers are more compact reduces the macro pores. More content of organic matter and vegetation increase permeability. Normally permeability decreases with increasing fine texture, but the extent of aggregation in fine-textured (clay) soils may override the effects of texture. If irrigation water is high in sodium content, it would cause dispersion of soil (soil becomes compact) and thus reduce permeability. It is expressed in *cm* hr^{-1}.

Infiltration Class	*Infiltration Rate (mm/hr)*	
Very slow	< 1	Clay
Slow	1-5	↓
Moderately slow	5-20	
Moderate	20-63	
Moderately rapid	63-127	
Rapid	127-254	
Very rapid	> 254	Sand

Drainage

The purpose of drainage is to remove the excess water from the soil ensure proper soil aeration. When soil gets saturated with water, the entire pore space is occupied by water and soil aeration is cut off. Also, water ponded at soil surface cuts off gaseous exchange between atmospheric and soil air even if there are enough air-filled pores in the soil below. Draining out the excess water to create air porosity creates soil condition favorable for soil aeration.

Drainage is of two types *viz*., (*i*) **surface drainage :** To ensure adequate soil aeration, the ponded water must be removed through gravity flow or pumping out and (*ii*) **sub-surface drainage :** In order to ensure adequate soil aeration and prevent soil salinization, water table must be kept below a certain level.

Soil-Water Movement

Three types of water movement within the soil are recognized : (*i*) saturated flow, (*ii*) unsaturated flow and (*iii*) water vapour movement.

(*i*) Saturated flow of water : Condition of soil, when all large and small pores are filled with water is called saturated. Saturated flow takes place when the soil is saturated. The direction of flow is from a zone of higher moisture potential to a lower moisture potential. Generally, water percolates down (vertically) into the lower layers. But horizontal flow also occurs with very less rapidly in comparison to vertical flow. Horizontal movement is much more evident in the clay soil, whereas vertical movement is much more evident in sandy loam.

Saturated flow occurs in the soil when water is under tension. The rate of saturated flow is stated two equations.

1. Law of Poiseuille's

This law expresses the flow of water in a narrow tube and is given by the formula

$$\delta = \frac{P\pi R^4}{8NL}$$

where, δ = volume of flow

P = pressure difference dyne-sec cm^{-2}

R = radius of tube, cm

N = viscosity of liquid dyne sec^{-1}, dyne.sec cm^{-2} (poise)

L = length of tube, cm

i.e., the rate of flow of liquid through a narrow tube is proportional to the fourth power of radius of the tube (R^4) and to the pressure (P) and inversely proportional to the viscosity of the liquid and the length of the tube.

2. Darcy's law

Darcy law is the stress that velocity of flow (q) of a liquid (water) through a porous medium is proportional to the force (i) causing the flow and hydraulic conductivity (K) of the medium.

This expresses as under

$$q = k.i, \quad K = \frac{(\Delta L)}{H}$$ Flow velocity K depend on size of pores

where, q = flux in cm/sec

$$q = \frac{\theta}{At} = \frac{V}{At} = \frac{\Delta H}{L}$$

where, θ = Volume of water (V) flowing through unit cross sectional area (A) per unit time (t)

$$\left(\frac{cm^3}{cm^2} = \frac{1}{sec} = cm\ sec^{-1}\right)$$

q/i = K = hydraulic conductivity cm/sec

i = hydraulic gradient which is the head drop per unit distance

$$i = \Delta H/L$$

where, H is the head of drop between two points

L is the length

***(ii)* Unsaturated flow of water.** Soil pores contain some air as well as water is called unsaturated soil. Under field conditions most soil-water movement occurs where the soil pores are not completely saturated with water. The soil macro pores are mostly filled with air, and the micro pores with water and some air. Water movement under these conditions is very slow compared to that occurring when the soil is saturated. Movement will be from a zone of low suction (thick moisture film) to one of high suction (thin moisture film). The prominence of finer (capillary) pores in the clay soil encourages more unsaturated flow than in the sand.

Unsaturated flow processes are in general complicated and difficult to describe qualitatively of often changes in states and content of soil water during flow.

The general equation is;

$$q = K(\psi) = \frac{(\Delta L)}{H}$$

where, K(ψ) = function of suction

H = head drops between two point

L = length

The movement of water under saturated and unsaturated condition is summarized below :

Movement of water under saturated condition	*Movement of water under saturated condition*
1. Saturated flow takes place when soil pores are completely filled with water	1 Unsaturated flow occurs when the pores in even the wet test soil zones are partially filled with water *i.e.,* air filled
2. Saturated flow in soil occurs through not under tension $Q = K\,[(\Delta L)/L]$	2. Unsaturated flow in soil occurs through under tension $q = K(\psi)[(\Delta L)/L]$
3. The moving force is the gradient of a positive potential	3. In an unsaturated soil, a water is under tension; it is equivalent to a negative unsaturation.
4. Pores are water filled and conductive water and hence continuity is maintained	4. Pores become air filled and the conductive position of the cross sectional area decreased correspondingly.
5. The rate of saturated flow in soils of different texture is in the order of sand > loam > clay	5. The rate of unsaturated flow in soils of different texture is in the order of sand < loam < clay

***(iii)* Water vapour movement.** There are two types of water vapour movement : (*a*) *internal movement*, the change from the liquid to the vapour state takes place within the soil, that is, in the soil pores, and (*b*) *external movement,* occurs at the land surface and the resulting vapour is lost to the atmosphere by diffusion and convection (surface evaporation).

METHOD OF SOIL MOISTURE DETERMINATION

Measurement of Soil Moisture Methods

Direct Method

(*i*) Gravimetric method
(*ii*) Volumetric method
(*iii*) Sprit burning method
(*iv*) Infra red valence method

Indirect Method

(*i*) Gypsum block method
(*ii*) Neutron scattering method
(*iii*) Tensiometer or Psycrometer
(*iv*) Pressure plate & Pressure membrane apparatus

Direct Methods

***(i)* Gravimetric method.** The gravimetric method is a direct measurement of soil water content and is therefore the standard method by which all indirect methods are calibrated. The gravimetric water content, also called mass water content, is the ratio of the weight loss in drying to the dry weight of the soil sample. The mass water content can be expressed as mass water percentage by multiplying it with 100 ($\theta\ m$). This method involves collecting soil sample from the field using soil probe or auger from representative depths in the root zone and then determining its moist and dry weights. The moist weight is determined by weighing the soil sample as it is at the time of sampling, and the dry weight is obtained after drying the soil sample in an oven at 105°C for 24 hours or more to get a constant dry weight. The weight loss represents the soil water.

$$\theta m = \frac{Wmn - Wds}{Wds} \times 100$$

$$= \frac{\text{Weight of moist soil} - \text{Weight of oven dry soil}}{\text{Weight of oven dry soil}} \times 100$$

***(ii)* Volumetric method.** The volumetric water content (θ *v*) is defined as the volume of water present in a given volume (usually 1 m^3) of dry soil. When (θ *v*) multiplied by 100 it gives volume water percentage. This method involves collecting soil sample from the field using core sampler of known volume from representative depths in the root zone and then determining its moist and dry weights and calculating the volume wetness by the following relationship :

$$\theta v = \frac{Wms - Wds}{Vt \times \rho w} \times 100$$

$$\theta v = \frac{\text{Weight of moist soil} - \text{Weight of oven dry soil}}{\text{Weight of oven dry soil}} \times 100$$

***(iii)* Spirit burning method.** Soil moisture from the sample is evaporated by adding alcohol and igniting. Provided the sample is not too large, the result can be obtained in less than 10 minutes. About 1.0 ml of spirit or alcohol per g of soil sample at field capacity and 0.5 ml at permanent wilting point is adequate for evaporating the soil moisture. This method is not recommended for soils with high organic matter content.

***(iv)* Infrared moisture balance.** It consists of a 250 watt infrared lamp, sensitive torsion balance and autotransformer (Fig. 11.6). All housed in an aluminium cabinet. The radiation emitted by infrared lamp quickly vaporizes the soil moisture. The instrument is directly calibrated in per cent moisture. It gives fairly reliable moisture estimates in about 5 minutes.

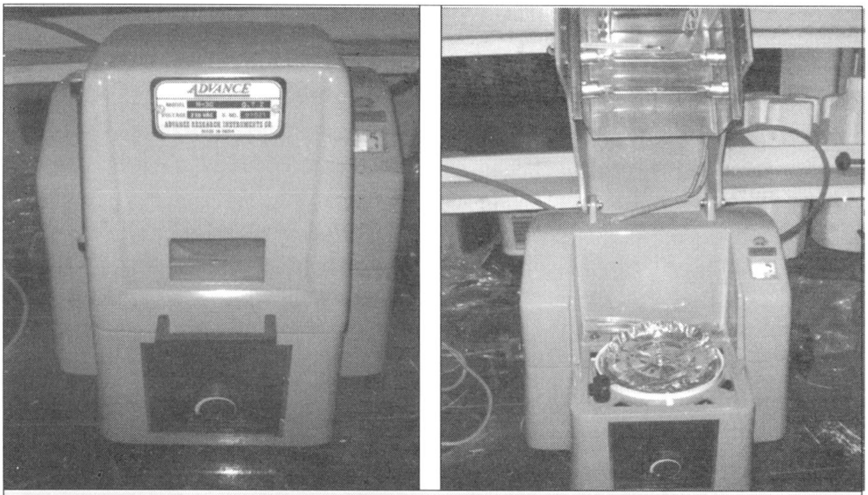

Fig. 11.6. Infrared moisture balance

Indirect Methods

***(i)* Electrical resistance blocks.** Gypsum blocks or electrical resistance blocks, with two electrodes, is placed at a desired soil depth and allowed to equilibrate (Fig. 11.7). Electrical resistance of the block is measured by a meter based on the principal of Whetstone Bridge.

Electrical resistance of the soil decreases with increase in water content. Soil water content is obtained with calibration curve, for the same block, of electrical resistance against known soil water content. Resistance blocks read low resistance (400-600 ohms) at field capacity and high resistance (50,000 to 75,000 ohms) at wilting point.

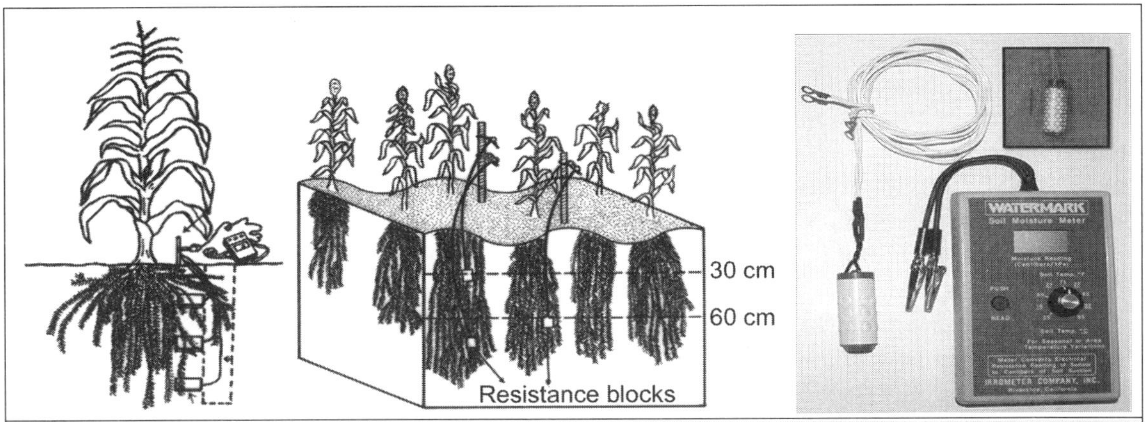

Fig. 11.7. Measurement of soil moisture by Resistance blocks

(*ii*) **Neutron scattering technique.** First developed in the 1950s, the neutron scattering method has gained widespread acceptance as an efficient and reliable technique for monitoring soil moisture in the field. The neutron moisture meter consists of two main components (Figure 11.8) *viz.*, a probe containing a source of fast neutrons (americium and

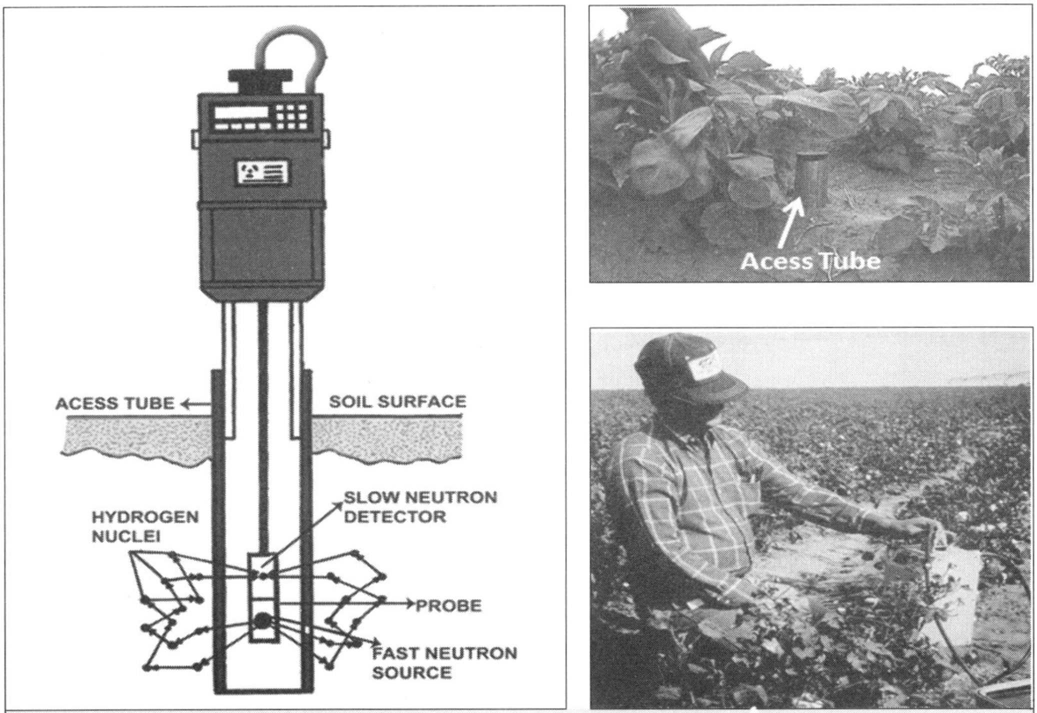

Fig. 11.8. Measurement of soil moisture by neutron probe

beryllium) and boron trifluoride (BF3) gas as a detector of slow neutrons, which is lowered into a hollow access tube pre-inserted into the soil, and a scaler or rate meter usually battery powered and portable to monitor the flux of the slow neutrons that are scattered and attenuated in the soil. The fast neutrons (having an energy range of 2-4 MeV and an average speed of about 1600 km/sec) are emitted radially into the soil, where they encounter and collide elastically with hydrogen nuclei (namely protons). Through repeated collusions, the neutrons are deflected and "scattered", and they gradually loose some of their kinetic energy. As the speed of the initially fast neutrons diminishes, it approaches a speed of 2.7 km/sec, equivalent to a energy of about 0.03 eV. Neutrons slowed down to such a speed are said to be thermalized and are called slow neutrons. The slow neutrons thus produced scatter randomly in the soil, quickly forming a cloud of constant density around the probe. The density of sow neutrons formed around the probe is nearly proportional to the concentration of hydrogen in the medium surrounding the probe, and therefore approximately proportional to the volume fraction of water present in the soil. The slowed or thermalized neutrons are detected by slow neutron detector containing BF3 gas, which is then transmitted through electric pulses to the scaler and is displayed as moisture content.

***(iii)* Tensiometer.** The tensiometer is an instrument designed to provide a continuous indication of the soil's matric suction (also called soil-moisture tension) in situ (Fig. 11.9). The tensiometer consists of a porous ceramic cup, connected through a tube to a vacuum gauge (or manometer), all parts filled with water. When the cup is placed in the soil where the

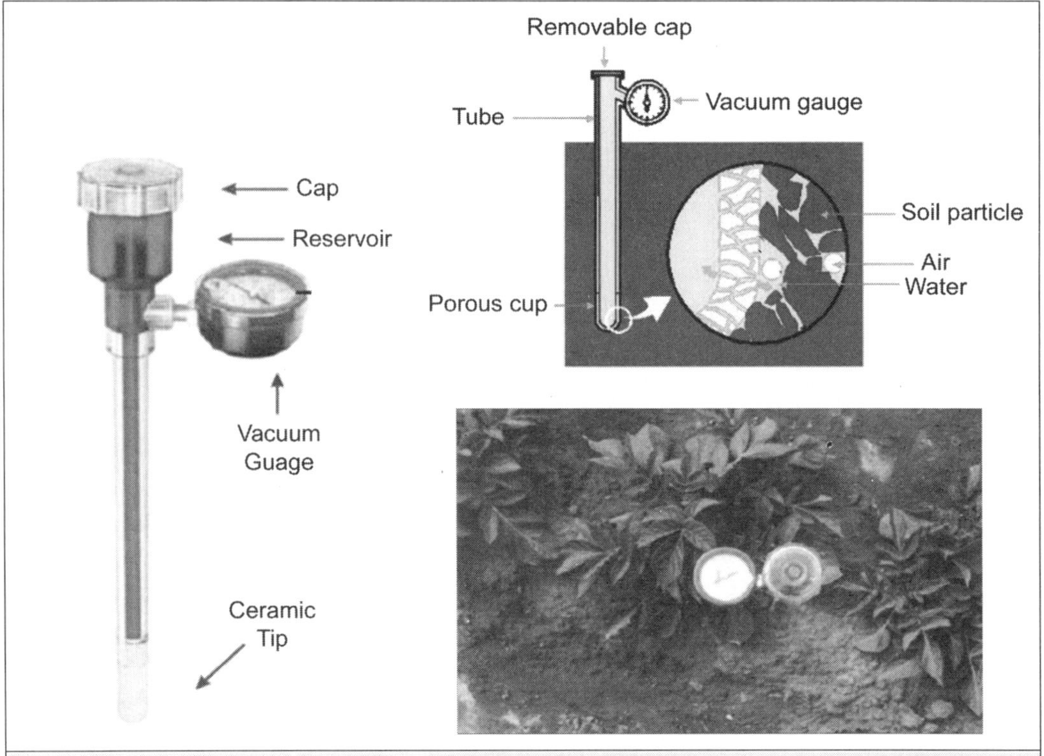

Fig. 11.9. Measurement of soil moisture by Tensiometer.

suction measurement is to be made, the water inside the cup comes into hydraulic contact and tends to equilibrate with soil water through the pores in the ceramic walls. When initially placed in the soil, the water contained in the tensiometer is generally at atmospheric pressure (essentially, 0 bars tension). Soil water, being generally at sub-atmospheric pressure (or higher tension), exercises a suction, which draws out a certain amount of water from the rigid and air tight tensiometer. Consequently, the pressure inside the tensiometer falls below atmospheric pressure. The subpressure is indicated by a vacuum gauge or manometer. A Tensiometer left in the soil for a period of time tends to track the changes in the soil's matric suction. As soil moisture is depleted by drainage or plant uptake, or as it is replenished by rainfall or irrigation, corresponding readings on the Tensiometer gauge occur.

Suction measurements by tensiometry are generally limited to matric suction values below 1 bar or 100 kPa. However in practice, under field conditions the sensitivity of most tensiometers is a maximal tension of about 0.85 bars or 85 kPa.

(iv) **Pressure plate and Pressure membrane apparatus.** Laboratory measurements of soil water potential are usually made with pressure membrane and pressure plate apparatus. It consists of ceramic pressure plates or membranes of high air entry values contained in airtight metallic chambers strong enough to withstand high pressure of 15 bars or more (Fig. 11.10). The apparatus enables development of soil moisture characteristic curves over a wide range of matric potential.

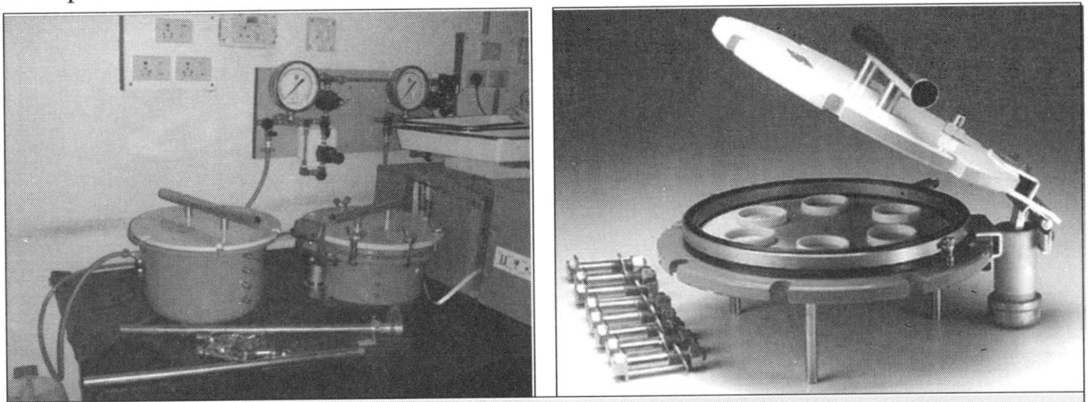

Fig. 11.10. Pressure plate and membrane apparatus

The porous plates are first saturated and then soil samples are placed on these plates. Soil samples are saturated with water and transferred to the metallic chambers. The chamber is closed with special wrenches to tighten the nuts and bolts with required torque for sealing it. Pressure is applied from a compressor and maintained at a desired level. It should be ensured that there is no leakage from the chamber. Water starts to flow out from saturated soil samples through outlet and continues to trickle till equilibrium against the applied pressure is achieved. Soil samples are taken out and oven dried to constant weight for determining moisture content on weight basis. Moisture content is determined against pressure values varying from –0.1 to –15 bars. The values of moisture content so obtained at a given applied pressure are used to construct soil moisture characteristic curves.

❑ ❑ ❑

CHAPTER 12

Dynamic Soil Properties

The behavior of soil to an applied stress is expressed in term of dynamic properties of soils which are mostly governed by two physical properties—*adhesion* and *cohesion;* refers to the attraction of a liquid phase such as water on the surface of a solid particles. *Cohesion* is the attraction between similar phases. In soils, cohesion is bonding force of the particles due to vander waal's forces, electronic attraction of negatively charged clay edges, cationic bridge, cementation effects of organic matter and surface tension force, etc. *Cohesion* also takes place between the water molecules which remain as films between the adjacent soil particles.

Soil dynamic properties are follows :

(*i*) Soil Compaction
(*ii*) Soil Compression
(*iii*) Soil Crusting
(*iv*) Soil Consistency
(*v*) Soil Plasticity
(*vi*) Soil Swelling
(*vii*) Soil Shrinking
(*viii*) Shear Strength of Soil
(*ix*) Soil Tilth and Soil Tillage
(*x*) Soil Puddling
(*xi*) Soil Flocculation
(*xii*) Soil Deflocculation

(*i*) Soil Compaction

Soil compaction, encompasses compression plus increase in density of a soil. It is the dynamic behavior of soil. The degree of compaction depends upon the nature of soil, amount of energy applied, water content and extent of manipulation of the soil. Compaction is also associated with the rearrangement of soil particle so soil water and soil air are compressed within the pore spaces.

Because the incompressible nature of soil particles and high internal friction, dry soil can not be compacted to high densities. An increase water content decrease cohesion between the particle and internal friction, thereby facilitating compaction. During compaction, the density of soil under load with increase in soil water content up to certain limit, beyond which further addition of water does not increase compaction because of incompressible nature of soil solids and water. This critical limit is called *Procter moisture content*.

In many soils, a compacted layer is commonly found at the bottom of the zone of ploughing. This layer is also termed as '*plough-sole*'. Age-old practices of tillage using wooden plough and in the farm practice including use of tractor and other heavy farm equipments create the problem of surface and sub-surface compaction in soil. These hard compact layers often restrict root penetration and growth and also reduce water and nutrient uptake by crops. Soil compaction changes soil moisture retention, soil thermal regimes and mechanical resistance in soil. For enhancing crop growth, the management practices be able to break the hard compacted layer and should avoid or reduce its formation. However, in highly coarse-texture sandy, loamy sand soils, compaction may be a boon to enhance the water retention and reduce percolation water.

(*ii*) Soil Compression

Soil compression is defined as the change in volume of a soil under applied stress, whereas of a soil compaction refers to the increase in density of a soil as result of applied pressure or load.

Volume of soil is consisted of solid phase and the void between it, which are occupied by water and air. So compression donates the decrease in the void ratio per increment of applied pressure or load. The increase in compression with each increment of pressure can be expressed by the equation:

$$Y = ae^{-bx}$$

where 'y' is the amount of compression, 'x' is the pressure, and 'a' and 'b' are constants.

Compression takes place with increment in pressure due primarily to particle orientation and changes in the size of the colloidal micelles. Soils may be compressed under low or high pressure. In the latter case, the soil expends when the pressure is removed because of swelling of micelles. Compressor is affected by the nature of clay mineral, the type of exchangeable cation and the degree of polarity of organic liquids, which increase in soil moisture content, compression increase to a maximum and then decrease with further increase in moisture content. The maximum compression occurs within the plastic range of soil moisture content.

(*iii*) Soil Crusting

Soil crusting is the thin compact layer of higher bulk density formed at the soil surface following dispersion of natural soil aggregate as a result of wetting and impact of raindrops and its subsequent rapid drying due to radiant energy of sun.

Crust formation. When the raindrops strike the exposed dry soil surface, there is disintegration and dispersion of the aggregates. The finer clay particles move down along with infiltrating water and clog the pores immediately beneath the surface. Also, the dispersed soil may remain in suspension, coarse particle start to settle out, but fine clay particles remain in suspension. As the water evaporate, clay settle on top of coarse particles, forming of a crust on drying. The soil particle tends to pull together due to surface tension forces and form a dense strong soil layer with decrease porosity. Soil crusting is the major structural feature of soils of arid and semi-arid regions. The problem of crusting is severe in silty clay loams of older alluvial terraces and levees due to their unsuitable soil structure.

(*iv*) Soil Consistency

Soil consistency represents at varying moisture conditions, the degree and kind of cohesion and adhesion of soil material. ***Cohesion*** refers to the attraction of substances of like characteristics such as that are of one water molecule for another. ***Adhesion*** is attraction of unlike materials, for example, attraction between soil and water molecule. Consistence of soil depends on the texture, colloids, structure and especially the moisture content of soil. The consistency of soil is generally described at three soil moisture levels *viz*., wet, moist and dry.

(*a*) Consistency when soil is wet. When soil is at field capacity the consistency is described in terms of stickiness and plasticity.

Stickiness. The quality of adhesion to other objects is called stickiness. The degree of stickiness is identified by the following terms: non sticky, slightly sticky, sticky and very sticky.

Plasticity. Plasticity is the capacity of the soil to mould. When stress is applied, the shape changed and after removing the stress it keep the changed shape, Terms used to describe the degree of plasticity are: non plastic, slightly plastic, plastic and very plastic.

(*b*) Consistency when soil is moist. For slightly wet condition of the soil (moisture content between air dry and field capacity) consistency is described in the following terms.

Type	***Characteristics***
Loose	Non coherent
Very friable	Coherent but easily crushed
Friable	Easily crushed
Firm	Crushed under moderate pressure
Very firm	Crushed only under strong pressure
Extremely firm	Resist crushing between thumb and forefinger

(*c*) Consistency when soil is dry. Under dry condition of the soil (air dry) consistency is characterized by rigidity and hardness.

Type	***Characteristics***
Loose	Non coherent
Soft	Breaks under slight pressure between thumb and forefinger to a powdery mass
Slightly hard	Breaks under pressure
Hard	Breaks with difficulty under pressure
Very hard	Very resistant to pressure can not be broken between thumb and forefinger
Extremely hard	Extreme resistance to pressure cannot be broken in the hand

Significance of soil consistence. Optimum soil consistence increases water holding capacity and plant food material. Thus, it increases the fertility of the soil.

The phenomena of soil consistency are friability, plasticity, stickness and resistance to compression and shear strength or bearing strength. Soil consistency is defined as the manifestations of the soil physical forces of cohesion and adhesion acting with in the soil at various moisture content. These manifestation include,

1. The behavior toward gravity, pressure, thrust and pull.
2. The tendency of the soil mass to adhere to foreign bodies or substances.
3. Sensation evidenced as feel by fingers of the observer.

Scouring point, another important character of consistency is the scouring point. This point represents that moisture content at which the soil no longer sticks to a foreign object. With highly plastic soils, the scouring point lies slightly below the liquid limit, with slightly plastic soil it occurs above the liquid limit.

(*v*) Soil Plasticity

It is the capacity of the soil to be molded that is to change in shap in response to stress and to keep that shape when the stress is removed without rupturing and cracking. Moist clays exhibit degree of plasticity.

(*a*) Upper plastic limit. It is also called liquid limit. It represents the moisture content of soil at a point where the soil-water mass just flow under an applied force and fails to maintain its shape.

(*b*) Lower plastic limit. Lower plastic limit refers to the moisture content of a soil at point where its consistency changes from plastic to friable and the soil-water mass is unable to change shape continuously under the influence of an applied force, and ultimately the mass breaks into fragments.

(*c*) Plasticity number (Index). If refers to the difference between moisture contents of a soil at upper plastic limit and lower plastic limit. Different soils are characterized by a specific plastic number of indexes of plasticity.

The following general tends have been reported for plastic limit :

(*i*) Sodium saturated soils exhibit the lowest plastic limit, the second lowest liquid limit and the highest plasticity index (in three out of five).

(*ii*) K-saturated soil shows the lowest plasticity index and the lowest liquid limit of the basic cations.

(*iii*) Ca-Mg saturated soils behave a like, the plastic and liquid limits are generally higher than those of K or Na systems.

(*iv*) H-saturated soils fluctuate over a wide range.

(*vi*) Soil Swelling

In addition to absorbing on their surface clay particles absorb large amounts of water in the spaces between their structural units. These cause clays to swell, this concept attempt to distinguish sharply between capillary intake and swelling.

The process of swelling is explained on the basis of two types of hydration of the colloid :

(*i*) Water molecules are oriented at the surface of the clay result of the electrical properties of the liquid and the exchangeable cation and the surface

(*ii*) Water may be absorbed because of osmotic effects. Short range interacting force operating between the unit layers of expending clay minerals or between the planar surfaces of domains of individual crystals. Osmotic type of swelling is caused by the long range interacting forces that produce osmotic swelling which is an expression of the double layer repulsión.

Swelling is governed by :

(*i*) Nature of clay mineral.

(*ii*) Associated cation size and its charge.

(*iii*) Bonding energy of cation.

Montmorillonite with an expending crystal lattice, absorbs the largest amount of water and swell enormously while kaolinite with non-expanding lattice swells very little in water and little is intermediate in this respect.

Swelling decreases in the following order :

Vermiculite > Monmorillonite > Bedillite > Illite > Kaolinite

Mechanism of swelling :

(*i*) Polar liquids bound at the surface of a solid thereby increasing its active volume.

(*ii*) Liquid associated with the solid body as a soil solution (non-polar molecules).

(*iii*) Polar liquids reacting with solids to form a complex compound.

(*iv*) Divalent cation reduced swelling due to columbic attraction that reduce or prevent entry of water between the sheets to cause lattice expansion

Major factors affecting on swelling are :

(*i*) Clay and organic matter content.

(*ii*) Mineralogical composition of clay.

(*iii*) CEC and exchangeable cations.

(*iv*) Use of chemicals and FYM.

(*vii*) Soil Shrinking.

On drying of the absorbed moist the clay shrinks, which is the cause of the cracks in clayey soils during summer. The shrinkage varies with the different clays from 20 to 40 per cent. Montmorillonite shrink and cracks much more than either Illite or Kaolinite.

Shrinkage decreases in the following order :

Vermiculite > Monmorillonite > Bedillite > Illite > Kaolinite

The amount of shrink-swell in a soil depends upon the clay present and the amount of each clay. In addition, the changes in soil water content and in the cation on the clay surfaces and in the solution have significant effects.

Swell-shrink behavior in a soil follows the following trends :

More smectite = more swell-shrink

More Kaolinite = less swell-shrink

Lower valence cation on CEC (*e.g.* Na^+ versus Ca^{++}) = more swell-shrink

Lower soluble salts in soil solution = more swell-shrink

(*viii*) Shear Strength of Soils

The shear strength of a soil is the maximum internal resistance of a soil to the movement of its particle that is resistance to slipping or sliding of soil over soil.

The forces that resist shear are internal or inter granular friction and cohesion. According to Coulamb's law :

$$Q = S + C + \tan \theta P$$

where,
$Q =$ angle of fraction
$S =$ shear strength
$C =$ cohesion
$P =$ effective pressure normal to the shear plane
$\tan \theta =$ coefficient of fraction

There are two widely accepted methods for determining the shear strength of soils

(*i*) The direct shear test

(*ii*) Textural shear tests or triaxial compression

(*ix*) Soil Tilth and Soil Tillage

Soil tilth may be defined as the sum of all physical attributes of a soil, is the summation of those physical properties that determine crop production. The soil attributes that go to make up the tilth of a soil are :

(*i*) Granulation and its stability

(*ii*) Moisture content

(*iii*) Aeration

(*iv*) Infiltration

(*v*) Drainage

(*vi*) Capillary water capacity.

This means that is related to the size of distribution of the soil aggregates. Good soil tilth is manifested in the friable range of soil consistency. It is a dynamic soil condition and tends to deteriorate under the usual cropping and tillage operations.

Tillage can produce good tilth by loosening and granulation the soil. By breaking up the soil mass, infiltration of rainfall and aeration increase, and soil strength is decreased. It is important to point out that range friable consistency in which tilth reaches an optimum is the same range in which the soil can be tilled with the least output of power and with its best effects upon granulation.

(*x*) Soil Puddling

Soil puddling, in general, refers to the destruction of soil aggregates into ultimate soil particle at moisture content near saturation.

Those soils in which the clay fraction disperses when the soil is worked wet, from a random gel-like structure of the soil particles. The micro aggregates are 'destabilized' by puddling. As water dries up, the soft, puddle soil will tend to 'harden'.

Advantage and disadvantage of soil puddling

Advantage

1. Less power required for tillage.
2. Easy to transplanting paddy due to soft mud. Plants are pursed into the mud with thumb and forefinger.
3. Weeds are controlled by puddling. Buried weeds in the mud do not come out easily.

4. Loss of water by percolation is reduced because of soil structure less soil and the formation of tillage pan.
5. Increase the availability of nutrients, specially phosphorus, iron and manganese.
6. Establish a reduced soil condition, which improves soil fertility and fertilizer management.
7. Reduced draft requirements for primary and secondary tillage.
8. Take advantages of monsoon rains by the time puddling has been completed.

Disadvantage

1. Required large volume of water for puddling the soil.
2. Soil structure destroyed.
3. In paddy field, other upland crop may not grow well due to structure less soil and presence of tillage pan.
4. Because absence of air in the paddy field, toxic substances like hydrogen sulphide, ferrous oxide etc., are formed.
5. Loss of nitrogen (denitrification) is also occurred in water-logged paddy field.
6. Root development is poor.

(*xi*) Soil Flocculation

Co-angulations of the dispersed particle are called flocculation. Suspension of colloid are extremely stable and do not settle down. It to such suspensions, a small quantity of inorganic acid or salt added; the colloids are coagulated and settle in the form of flakes of flocculate, this phenomena is called flocculation. Suspended colloidal clay particles almost immediately flocculate and sink to the bottom by adding a few drops of lime water, the same action apparently takes place in the soil much less rapidly.

The flocculating capacity of the common cations may be roughly in the order :

$$Al^{+++} > H^+ > Ca^{++} > Mg^{++} > K^+ = NH_4^+ > Na^+$$

The monovalent ions K, Na, NH_4 particularly Na tends to work in opposite direction *i.e.* deflocculation. This amounts for the dispersed sticky and puddle condition of alkali soil dominated by Na.

(*xii*) Soil Deflocculation

Colloidal suspensions are extremely stable and do not stable down *i.e.* remain in dispersed sticky condition is called deflocculation.

The monovalent ion K^+, Na^+, NH_4^+ particularly Na^+ tends to work in the opposite direction *i.e.* deflocculation.

The deflocculation capacity of common cations may be in order

$$Al^{+++} = H^+ < Ca^{++} < Mg^{++} < K^+ = NH_4^+ < Na^+$$

i.e. monovalent ions K^+, Na^+, NH_4^+ have highly deflocculating capacity than divant cation Ca^{++} Mg^{++}. This accounts for dispersed sticky and puddle cation of alkali soils dominated by Na^+. The deflocculation deteriorated the soil structure.

❑❑❑

SOIL CHEMISTRY

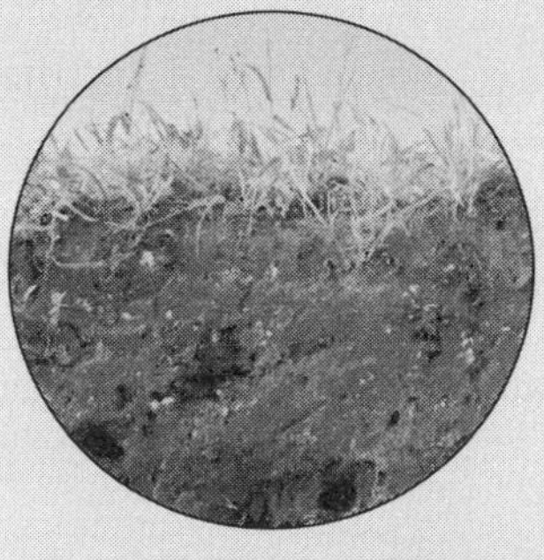

CHAPTER 13

Soil Colloid and Ion Exchange

A colloidal system is a heterogeneous mixture of at least two phases in which phase is dispersed in a state of fine subdivision (particle size 1mm to 1nm) in another continuous medium. When the dispersed phase is solid (*e.g.* soil colloidal particles) and dispersion medium is water (*e.g.* soil water), the colloidal system is referred to as a 'sol'. The properties particular to a colloidal system, which distinguish them from suspensions (particle size >1 μm), and true uni-phase solutions (particle size <1 μm), are primarily those arising from the large interfacial area, which is charged, characterizing the colloidal system in soils may be attributed to the large specific surface (or interface) charge density. The fact of soil colloid and ion exchange are given below :

- Next to photosynthesis and respiration, no process in nature is more vital to plant and animal life than the exchange of ions between soil particles and plant roots.
- The cation and anion exchanges occur mostly on the surfaces of the finer or colloidal fractions of both the inorganic and organic matter (clay and humus).
- Colloids are substances whose particle size is about 1 to 1000 nm when they are mixed with another substance, usually air or water.
- Colloids are action sites for chemical reaction, microscopic, large surface area. The larger the surface area, the better they are for chemical reaction.
- Molecules of some compounds can come within the colloidal range but most colloids consist of aggregate of molecules. Colloids are so ubiquitous in nature and so distinctive that they have common names as fog, smoke, aerosol, foam, emulsion, soil and clay. All are small particles suspended in a fluid.

NATURE OF SOIL COLLOIDS

The clay fraction of soil contains particles having less than 0.002 mm size. Most of these particles and especially these, which are smaller than 0.001 mm, possess colloids properties. Hence these particles are known as soil colloids.

As the coarser fraction of clay is very small, for practical purpose, the whole clay fraction is considered colloidal in nature.

There are four major types of colloids present in soil;

1. Layer silicate clays
2. Iron and Aluminum oxide clays
3. Allophane and associated clays
4. Humus

Generally two types of soil colloids are common, inorganic and organic. The inorganic colloid or colloidal clay is derived from the weathering of rocks and other parent materials and consists mainly secondary minerals.

The organic colloids are derived from the decomposition of plant and animal residues and by synthetic processes by soil micro-organisms (Humus).

These two together form the colloidal complex of the soil. Soils formed in temperate and humid regions usually contain more organic colloids than those formed in arid and semi-arid regions.

The soils formed in semi-arid, tropical and subtropical regions, almost the whole of the colloidal complex consists of inorganic colloids.

In peat soils, it consists entirely of organic colloids. The most of the inorganic colloidal material is in crystalline form, while the organic colloidal material is in amorphous form.

Constituents

Oxygen	—	OH^- or O^{2-} (surrounds cations and determines structure)
Silicon	—	Si^{4+}
Aluminum	—	Al^{3+}
Base Cations	—	Na^+, Ca^{2+}, K^+, Mg^{2+}

The soil particle is be lived to be composed of a mineral grain (like sand or soil) which is completely enveloped in a, layer of colloidal gel, which is partly organic and partly inorganic. The smaller the grain, the thicker is the layer of colloidal material. Though most of the colloidal material in soil is present in this form, it also exists in the soil as independent aggregates.

The crystal unit of colloidal particle, which forms the nucleus and is negatively charged and behaves like a large anion is known as micelle, which attracts and adsorbs the positively charged cations. These together forms the (double electric layer) double ionic layer of which the negative charge of the micelle constitutes the inner ionic layer and the positive charge of the cations, the outer ionic layer.

The negatively charged nucleus or micelle, which is also known as an acidoid, is surrounded by positively charged cations. When it is suspended in water, the water molecules surround the clay micelles as well as the cations; which are also held electro statistically. Each clay or colloidal particle thus carries a large number of cations, each surrounded by a swarm of water molecules, on its external as well as internal surfaces.

PROPERTIES OF SOIL COLLOIDS

1. Brownian Movement

A continuous agitation of particles in colloidal system caused by unbalanced impacts with molecules of surrounding medium is known as Brownian movement.

When a suspension of colloidal particles examined under a microscope, the particles seem to oscillate. The oscillation is due to collision of colloidal particles or molecules with each other and with those of liquid in which they are suspended. The smaller the particles, the more rapid is the movement and more often does it colloide, with an increase in its size, the movement slows down and hence the size of the particles become bigger than 0.001 mm, it almost cases to move *i.e.* settle down.

The Brownian movement is responsible for the flocculation or coagulation of colloidal particles. When the particles in suspension colloid with each other, they adhere together under certain circumstances and form a sort of loose aggregated of flocks which settle down.

2. Non-Permeability

Colloides are unable to pass through a semi-permeable membrane. Even though, the colloidal particles are extremely small, they are bigger than the molecules of crystalloids dissolved in water. The membrane allows passing water and dissolved substances through its pores, retains the colloidal particles. This property is used to separate colloidal material from its mixture with the crystalloids by dialysis or ultra filtration.

3. Electric Charge

Soil colloids posses negative charge. When an electric current is passed through a suspension of soil colloidal particles, they migrate to anode (positive electrode), indicating that they carrying negative charge. Depending on the magnitude of the change (zeta potential), the particles either remain in suspension or coalesces (unite) and settle down. When the charge is high, the particles repeal each other and remain in suspension. When it reduced or brought to zero, they attract and adher to each other and form flocks and settle down as sediment, The higher the zeta potential, the greater is the stability of the suspension and *vice-versa*.

(*a*) Zeta potential. The magnitude of negative charges on colloidal particles is known as 'zeta potential'. The zeta potential varieties with nature of colloidal particles and nature of adsorbed cation, its size and degree of hydration. *e.g.*

- Montmorillnolite > Illite > Kaolinite.
- Monovalent cations than divalent cations.

  $Na^+ > K^+ > NH_4 > Mg^{++} > Ca^{++}$
- Equal ionic size : Lower valences ions-higher valences ions.

  $Li^+ > Mg^{++}, NH_4 > Ba^{++}$
- Equal valency **:** Greater effective size small effective size.

  $Na^+ > K^+, Li^+ > NH_4^+$

When cations are hydrated, they carry a swarm of water molecules, which form shell around each ion. The smaller the size of the cation, the greater is the thickness of water shell. The lithium and Na^+ ions are smaller than K^+ and NH_4^+ when they are non-hydrated but Li and Na^+ ions carry a thicker water-shell and hence have a larger effective size than K^+ and NH_4^+ ions. Li^+ and Na^+ are having more zeta potential than K^+ and NH_4^+ ions.

Hydrated Na^+ ions have a larger effective diameter than K^+ and NH_4^+ ions; Na-clay has a greater zeta potential than K^+ and NH_4-clays. Similarly Mg-clay has a greater potential than Ca-clay. H^+ ions are exception as they behave like polyvalent cations and hence H-clay has the lowest zeta potential.

Type of cation Non-hydrated (Absolute size)	*Size of ion Hydrated A° (Effective size)*	*(Radius in (millivolts) meq*	*Zeta potential*	
			KCl	*FV*
Li-Clay	0.78	7.3	58.8	21.6
Na-Clay	0.93	5.6	57.6	11.2
K-Clay	1.33	3.8	56.4	7.8
NH_4-Clay	1.43	1-43 to 3-80	56.0	5.8
Mg-Clay	0.78	10.8	53.9	3.9
Ca-Clay	1.06	9.6	52.6	3.0
Ba-Clay	1.43	8.8	50.8	3.3
H-Clay	Very small	—	48.4	1.5

***(b)* Development of negative charge on soil colloids.** Colloidal clays develop negative electric charge in two ways.

(*i*) The dissociation of H from OH groups attached to silicon in silica of the clay mineral, leaves residual oxygen carry in a negative charge. On account of the presence of a large number of OH groups in the silicate clay minerals, when the colloidal clay is suspended in water, negative charge is being developed.

(*ii*) Due to the isomorphous replacement of ion are silica and alumina sheets of the clay mineral, negative charge is developed.

Fig. 13.1. Negative charge due to isomorphism substitution

(*a*) In kaolinite, ionization of OH groups is mainly responsible for the negative charge. It is negligible.

(*b*) In montmorillonite and illite minerals, the negative charge is developed in both ways but more by isomorphous substitution.

In replacement of trivalent Al^{+3} by divalent Mg^{+2} in the alumina sheets of montmorillonite loans the clay mineral with greater number of negatively charged ions.

In Illitic minerals, the substitution of tetravalent Si^{+4} by trivalent Al^{+3} in silica sheets is responsible for negative charge.

The negative charge is the result of an unbalance of charges in the atom is structure of crystal lattice. In order to balance these excess negative charges, colloidal particles attract and counter ions or cations.

(*c*) Amphoteric nature of colloids (+ and –)

- **Negative charges.** A net negative charge is found in minerals where there has been an isomorphous substitution of a lower charged ion (*e.g.* Mg^{2+} for a higher-charged ion (*e.g.* Al^{3+}).
- **Positive charges.** Isomorphous substitution can also be a source of positive charges if the substituting cation has a higher charge than the ion for which it substitutes.
- pH-dependent charges

4. Adsorption

Colloidal particles possess the power of adsorbing gases, liquids and even solids from their suspension. The phenomenon of adsorption is confined to the surface of colloidal particles. The molecules or ions of adsorbed accumulate at the colloidal water interference where are retained on the surface of the colloidal particles.

The soil colloids exert a selective adsorption of ions and hence all ions are not adsorbed to the degree. *e.g.* H^+, NH_4^+, K^+, Mg^{2+}, PO_4^{3-}, Al^{3+} ions are adsorbed more readily; Na^+ and SO_4^{2-} ions are adsorbed less readily; while NO^-_3, Cl^- and HCO^- ion are not adsorbed or very little if at all.

In most cases, adsorption takes place by exchange of ions. The colloidal particle removes a specific ion from the solution and substitutes an ion from its surface, which is passed on to the solution.

The adsorption of ions is governed by (1) The type and nature of ion, (2) ion concentration, (3) the type of colloidal particle.

1. The ions having higher valences are adsorbed more strongly and its replacement or exchange from colloidal particle is more difficult. Hence Al^{3+} is adsorbed more strongly than Ca^{2+} and Mg^{2+} and they more than Na^+ and K^+.

2. H^+ ions behave as polyvalent cations. Hence they are adsorbed strongly than even divalent cations.

(*i*) For cations of same valency, the higher the atomic weight, the greater is the adsorption.

(*ii*) Therefore Ca > Mg, and K > Na.

With increase in the concentration of cation solution, its adsorption and replacing power is increases.

(*iii*) With increase in zeta potential of ion, its adsorption decreases.

(*iv*) Type of colloidal particle has also considerable influence on the adsorption and replacement of cations. *e.g.* Cation adsorbing and Cation exchange capacities are in the order of Montmorillonite > Illite > Kaolinite.

Adsorption of anions. The chief anions present in soil are HCO_3^{2-}, NO_3^-, $H_2PO_4^-$, SO_4^{2-}, HPO_4^{2-}, OH^- and anions of humic acids.

(*a*) The adsorption of anions depends upon nature of clay particles, type of ions, concentration of ion and pH of the medium.

(*b*) HCO_3^{2-}, Cl^- and NO_3^{2-} are not adsorbed by clay or very slightly if it all. SO_4^{2-} is adsorbed to a greater extent while the adsorption of phosphate is the greatest.

(*c*) Adsorption of anions increases with decrease in pH.

(*d*) In highly acid soils, small quantities of even chloride ions are adsorbed.

(*e*) The adsorption of phosphate ions is the lowest when the medium is neutral. Therefore, availability more it increases when pH either falls or rises; due to fixation of phosphate by Fe and either falls or rises; due to fixation of phosphate by Fe and Al hydroxides in acid range and by combining ability in alkaline range.

(*f*) The sesquioxide clay *i.e.* hydrous Fe and Al oxides have a higher adsorptive capacity especially for phosphate ions than silicate clay.

(*g*) Among the clay minerals, kaolinitic clay has a greater anion adsorbing capacity than montmorollonitic and illitic clays.

The property of adsorption plays an important role in soil fertility. It is due to this property that a soil is able to hold water and plant nutrients and keep them available for the use of plants. It enables the soil colloids to function as a reservoir of nutrients for plant use. Soluble substances added to the soil in the form of fertilizers are retained in it's because of the power of adsorption that soil colloids possess otherwise they would be lost from soil through leaching. At the same time, this property enables plant nutrients to be retained in the soil. So formation of problematic soils and their reclamation amendments required.

5. Flocculation

(*a*) As long as the colloidal particles remain charged, they repel each other and the suspension remains stable.

(*b*) If they lose their charges or if the magnitude of the charge is reduced; the particles coalesce (unite) and form floccs or loose aggregates and settle out. This phenomenon of coalescence and formation of floccs is known as flocculation.

(*c*) The reverse process of flocculation *i.e.* the breaking up of floccs into individual particles is known as deflocculation or dispersion.

(*d*) The magnitude of the charge depends on the nature of adsorbed cations which in turn depends on the nature of the substance dissolved in the liquid in which the colloidal particles are suspended. When an electrolyte like a neutral or acid-salt is added to a colloidal suspension, it reduces the particles and brings about flocculation. In this respect acids are more powerful than their corresponding acid salts. Among salts, calcium salts are more powerful than sodium or potassium salts.

(*e*) If an alkali or alkaline salt is added to the suspension, it deflocculates or disperses the colloidal particles.

(*f*) In other words, clay having high zeta potential is more difficult to flocculate than those having low zeta potential.

(*g*) Clays saturated with monovalent cations which develops high potential (Li-clay, Na-clay.) also have high flocculation. Values *i.e*. they require large quantities of the electrolytes to flocculate them than those saturated with divalent cations. Flocculation value of KCl in term of symmetry concentration *i.e*. the number of meq of adsorbed ions in the system. H is exception and behaves like a polyvalent cation. Hence its flocculation value is the lowest

(*h*) The stability of the clay suspension increases rapidly with small increase in zeta potential. H-clay is more highly flocculated than Ca-clay,

Hence the beneficial effect of the addition of lime to acid soil is not due to improvement in chemical and biological properties. While in case of saline and alkaline soils, addition of Ca improves physical structure of soil by replacing Na by Ca.

(*i*) Flocculation is also brought about when the cation of the added electrolyte is the same as that adsorbed on clay or colloids of sodium chloride or sulphate is added. As long as sodium salt is present, Na-clay remains flocculated; no sooner is the salt is washed out, than clay particles are dispersed again.

(*j*) The phenomenon of flocculation plays an important role in the cultivation of soils. When clay particles are flocculated, the soil on drying develops a number of fine cracks giving rise to small clods of a crumby nature. Such a soil allows free movement of air and water.

Though flocculation is not itself granulation, it is a prerequisite to the aggregation of colloidal particles. For the development of proper crumb structure and tilth. The clods formed of flocculated clays are water stable; they retain their shape and do not run readily into paste when wetted. A flocculated soil is less sticky and can be molded to any desired shape, which is retained even at high moisture content. These characteristics impart a mellow tilth to the soil, which allows the use of cultivation implements at relatively high moisture content.

(*k*) If the particles are deflocculated, the aggregates are dispersed, the setting of individual particles takes place; hence water logged, the movement of water and air is impended and soil remains wet and cold. On drying such a soil forms large hard clods and develops very few cracks, the clods are unstable and run easily to paste when wetted. The soil becomes sticky and can be molded only at relatively low moisture content. It easily gets puddled when cultivated at high moisture content.

6. Swelling

When a colloidal substance becomes in contact with water, it absorb water and swells there is disappearance of certain amount of water. This phenomenon is known as imbibitions. Though the colloidal material is increases in volume of swelling, there is an actual contraction of the total volume of the system.

The amount of water imbibed and the increase in volume of colloids depends on the type of (1) colloidal clay (2) the nature of adsorbed ions. (3) liquid.

1. Montmorillonitic clay having an expanding lattice structure imbibes a greater

amount of water and swells to a greater extent than kaolinitic clay. Ilitic clay is intermediate, while the sesquioxide clay does not swell at all.

2. In general Na^+ ions cause more swelling than Ca^{++} and H^+ ions.
3. Swelling also depends upon the nature of the liquid used. Polar liquids like benzene, xylene etc. does not cause any swelling.
4. Swelling of clay is less in salt solution than in pure water.

Under field conditions, the swelling of the soil is accompanied with the development of a considerable pressure. The absorption of water in the capillaries entraps a certain amount of air in the soil pores. At first, the entrapped air is compressed, but ultimately the pressure of air increases as more water is absorbed.

7. Heat of Wetting

During the imbibitions of water by soil colloidal material, a certain amount of heat is evolved. The heat so evolved is known as heat of wetting. Heat is also evolved when soil clay is wetted with liquids other than water such as alcohol, benzene etc. but the evolution of heat is usually more with water than other liquids.

The heat evolved is due to a change in state of water molecules attached to the surface of clay particles, which get oriented under the influence of electrostatic forces when water is adsorbed. It is also due to the heat of hydration of the adsorbed ions. The heat so evolved represents the loss of energy with which hygroscopic water is adsorbed by clay and colloidal particles.

The amount of heat evolved with the (1) amount and (2) nature of colloidal material and the type of adsorbed cations. (3) initial moisture status.

1. The greater the amount of clay present in a soil is greater is the heat is evolved. Hence fine textured soils evolved more heat in wetting than coarse textured soils.
2. Montmorillonitic clay involves more heat than illitic clay and illitic clay more than kaolinitic clay.
3. Divalent cations are responsible for greater heat of wetting than monovalent cations.
4. Under the field conditions, the amount of heat evolved are also varies with the initial moisture content of the soil. The greater the original moisture content, the less is heat evolved. Hence a dry soil evolves the greatest amount of heat of wetting while the soil whose moisture content is the same, as hygroscopic coefficient evolves no heat.

8. Cohesion and Adhesion

- Clay particles possess the properties of cohesion and adhesion. Cohesion is the phenomenon of sticking of colloidal particles with each other. *i.e.* sticking together of particles of the same or similar nature (clay + clay). Adhesion is the phenomenon of sticking colloidal particles to the other substances, which comes in contact with them (clay + sand).
- While forming aggregates, the colloidal clay particles unite with each other by virtue of the property of cohesion.

- When clay particles envelope sand particles or when they stick to the moludboard or a plough is due to the force of adhesion or with water.
- When colloidal substances are wetted, water first adheres to the particles and then brings about cohesion between two or more adjacent colloidal particles.
- Cohesion and Adhesion are properties of the surface activity of colloidal particles. They vary with the (1) nature and (2) shape of colloidal particles, and (3) the amount of water present in the colloid-water system.
- Montmorillonite clays have very large surface area exhibit greater cohesion and adhesion than kaolinitic clays.
- Platy particles possess greater cohesive forces than round or spherical particles.
- As most of the colloidal clay particles are plate shaped, they possess greater cohesive and adhesive force properties.
- For a given type of clay, cohesion varies inversely with the amount of water. The greater the amount of water, the lesser is the cohesion and vice-versa.
- Maximum cohesion takes place when the moisture contents are just sufficient to form a very thin film between adjacent particles to hold them together. If the moisture content increases, cohesion decreases, as the thick moisture film cannot hold the particles together. When dried the particles remain united because of the forces of molecular cohesion or coherence of the colloidal particles. It is due to this property of cohesion that clay particles are able to form aggregates.

9. Plasticity

In a field at normal moisture level, colloidal particles of soil are present in gel condition. Like other gels, soil colloids possess the property of plasticity *i.e.* they can be molded into any form or shape. When clay is needed small quantity of water, the water molecules enter the space between adjacent crystal units of particles. The water so adsorbed acts as a binding agent. Being platy in shape, the clay particles orient themselves with the result that they slide over each other, forming a thin film of adsorbed water between them. At this stage, the clay acquires a plastic consistency *i.e.* they do not stick to the fingers and yet contains sufficient moisture hold the particles together so as to be worked and formed into any desired shape. The shape can be changed without producing any cracks, and it remains unchanged when dried.

Though sand and silt particles can also be molded when wet, they full to powder again when dried. They have no power of cohesion and adhesion, and possess no plasticity.

Sol. Sol is a homogenous colloidal system containing colloidal particles and liquid in which liquid is more than colloidal particles and the system can be poured easily. If liquid is water then it is termed as hydrosol.

Gel. In gel, the liquid is less hence the colloidal particles come nearer and form a network of chain like structure. The pores are filled with water and held by cohesive and adhesive forces. When water is used as liquid, it is termed as hydro gel.

Under normal field conditions, *i.e.* at normal moisture status, the colloidal particles are in gel condition; while they are in sol state when soil is saturated with water.

DEFINITION OF CLAYS

Clays are the active mineral portion of soils dominantly colloidal and crystalline. The crystalline nature of clays is such that they have definite repeating arrangement of atoms which are composed of O_2 atoms with Si and Al atoms holding the O_2 together by ionic bonding.

Formation of Soil Colloids

Layer Silicate Clays. These may develop from chemical alterations of primary minerals such as micas or feldspars. Alternatively, these may precipitate from soil solution containing dissolved Al and SiO_2. The particular layer silicate that precipitates depends on relative stability in the prevailing soil chemical environment. In general, the 2 : 1 minerals are less stable under hot and wet conditions than are the 1 : 1 minerals.

Al and Fe oxides. In a general sequence, these minerals are the end products of a sequence leading from primary minerals to 2 : 1 clays to 1 : 1 clays. Therefore, the Al and Fe oxides are stable mineral colloids.

Examples : $Al(OH)_3$ (gibbsite), FeOOH (goethite) and Fe_2O_3 (hematite).

Amorphous colloids. Weathering of volcanic ash releases substantial quantities of dissolved Al and SiO_2 which precipitate as amorphous allophane.

Organic colloids. Complex organic molecules formed by microbial transformation of biomolecules.

Classification of Clays

Clays are usually given group names based on their structure or on purely chemical composition. There are three groups.

(*i*) **Silicate clays.** These are crystalline clays *e.g.* Montmorillonite, Illite, Vermiculite, kaolinite and chlorite. Each crystalline clay is like a particular deck of cards. Each card represents a layer each of which is an exact replication of each other layer.

(*ii*) **Amorphous clays.** These are non-crystalline, which have silica, they are mixtures of Si and Al that have not formed well oriented crystals but sometimes have high cation or anion exchangeable capacity.

(*iii*) **Sesquioxides.** These consists of groups of Fe, Al and Si oxides clays. They are present in condition where there is excessive leaching caused by rainfall and sometimes intensive weathering of minerals in humid warm climate. They can be crystalline or amorphous.

Structures of Layer Silicate Clay

This implies the basic building blocks of clays. All soil clays are formed from the same 2 basic structural units. It is the way these 2 basic building units are put together that gives the soil clay distinctly different properties. They are :

1. Silica tetrahedron. This is a silica dominated sheet is a unit composed of one silicon atom surrounded by four oxygen atoms.

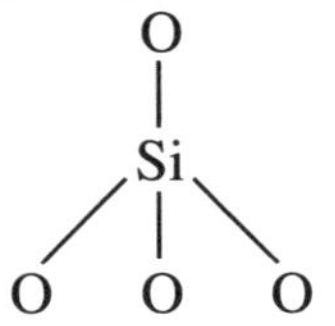

SiO_4

2. Aluminum and/or Mg octahedron. In this unit, an Al or Mg is surrounded by 6 oxygen atoms or hydroxyl groups, the centers of which define the apices of an 8-sided solid.

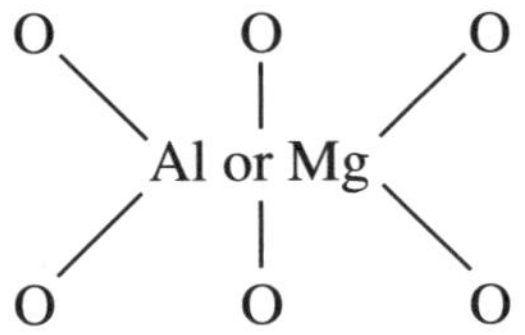

Al_2O_6 or Mg_3O_6

DISTRIBUTION OF CLAY MINERALS

Varies within the profile as well as geographically depending upon climate (internal and external) and parent material. The different soil orders, therefore, tend to differ in clay mineralogy.

Order		*Dominant Clay Minerals*	*Order*		*Dominant Clay Minerals*
Aridisols	—	2 : 1	Ultisols	—	1 : 1 > Al + Fe oxides > 2 : 1
Vertisols	—	2 : 1 smectites	Spodosols	—	Al + Fe oxides = 1 : 1
Mollisols	—	2 : 1 > 1 : 1	Oxisols	—	Al + Fe oxides > 1 : 1
Alfisols	—	2 : 1 = 1 : 1			

Note that the mineralogy of the sequence of increasingly weathered soil orders Alfisols, Ultisols and Oxisols, is reflected in the dominant clay mineralogy of these orders.

STRUCTURE OF LAYER SILICATE CLAY (SILICATE MINERAL CHEMISTRY)

Most of the silicate clays are made up of planes of oxygen atoms with silicon and aluminums atoms holding the oxygen together by ionic bonding, which is the attraction of positively and negatively charged atoms. Three or four planes of oxygen atoms with intervening silicon and aluminums ions make up a layer. One clay particle is composed of many layers stacked like a deck of cards.

On the basis of the number and arrangement of silica and alumina sheets, silicates clays may be classified into four different groups.

(*i*) 1 : 1 type minerals

(*ii*) 2 : 1 type minerals (expand between crystal units);

(*iii*) 2 : 1 type non-expanding minerals; and

(*iv*) 2 : 2 type minerals.

(*i*) 1 : 1 type minerals. The most important mineral in this type, commonly found in soils, is *kaolinte* whose structure is shown in figure below. The chemical composition of kaolinite is $Si_4Al_4O_{10}(OH)_8$. Two sheets of each crystal unit of kaolinite are held together by oxygen atoms which are mutually shared by the silicon and aluminium atoms in their respective sheets. These units are held together very rigidly by hydrogen bonding (-H-) to the oxygen plane of the adjacent layer. So the lattice is fixed and kaolinite mineral does not allow water to penetrate between the layers and has no plasticity, cohesion, shrinkage and swelling properties. Besides kaolinite, there are other minerals in this type namely halloysite, anauxite, and dickite.

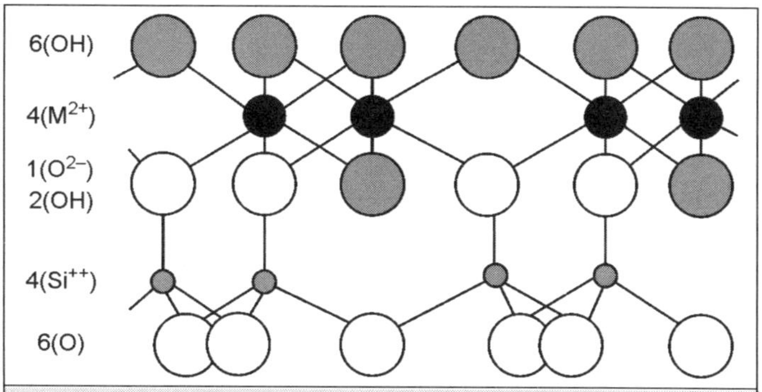

Fig. 13.2. Structure of kaolinite (1 : 1 layer silicate) mineral

- 1 : 1 structure : (1 tetrahedral + 1 octahedral)
- No ion substitution-low charge, low CEC, few adsorbed cations
- Low Si/Al ratio-forms in hot/wet climates (Ultisols, Oxisols)
- Formed by crystallization in SiO_2 poor, acid solutions (Ultisols)
- Platelets bind to each other through H-bonding
- Large particles from platelet bonding

***(ii)* 2 : 1 type minerals (Expanding lattice type).** There are some important minerals in this type which includes montmorillinite (smetitic group), vermiculite and other smecitic group of group of minerals like beidellite, montmorillonite, and saponite etc.

Montmorillonite is the best known example of this type of minerals and its structure is shown below.

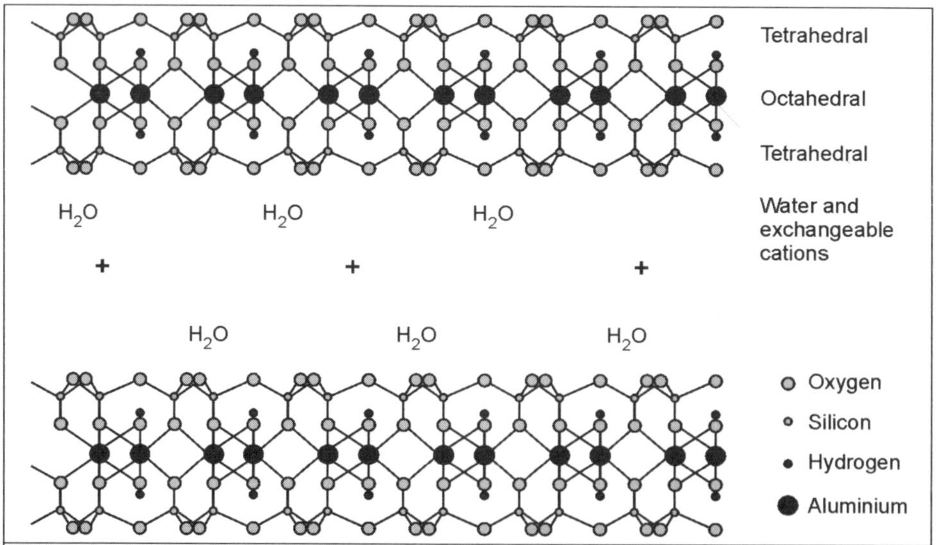

Fig. 13.3. Structure of montmorillonite (2 : 1 layer silicate) mineral

The flake like crystals of this mineral are composed of 2 : 1 type crystal units. These crystal units are loosely held together by very weak oxygen-to-oxygen linkage. Water molecules as well as cations are attracted between crystal units, causing expansion of the crystal lattice. The spacing (C-Axis) of the layers ranges from 12 to 18 Å (1.2-1.8 nanometers) and is variable with the exchangeable cation species and the degree of inters layer salvation. Montmorillinites are the swelling and sticky clays. Internal surface, cohesion, and plasticity of this mineral are also very high. The size of this mineral is very small (0.01-1.0 microns). On drying it shows shrinkage and as a result of wide cracks usual form as soils dominated this type of mineral. The dry aggregates or clod is very hard, making such soils difficult to till.

- 2 : 1 structure 2 silica tetrahedral sandwiching 1 Al octahedral
- Little substitution in tetrahedral sheet
- Mg^{2+} substitutes for Al^{3+} in octahedral sheet - negative charge only clay with substitution in octahedral sheet
- Forms from solution high in Mg^{2+} and silica (semi-arid)
- Cations adsorbed in interlayer with water
- Expanding clays of Vertisols
- High negative charge (high CEC-80 Cmol(P^+) kg^{-1}

Vermiculite clays are common in most soils. The structure of vermiculite is similar to that of hydrous mica structure but also has the layers held more weakly together by hydrated magnesium (six water molecules in octahedral coordination with Mg^{2+}) rather than tightly half by potassium ions (K^+). Thus vermiculite has swelling but not as much as montmorillonite. It has a high cation exchange capacity.

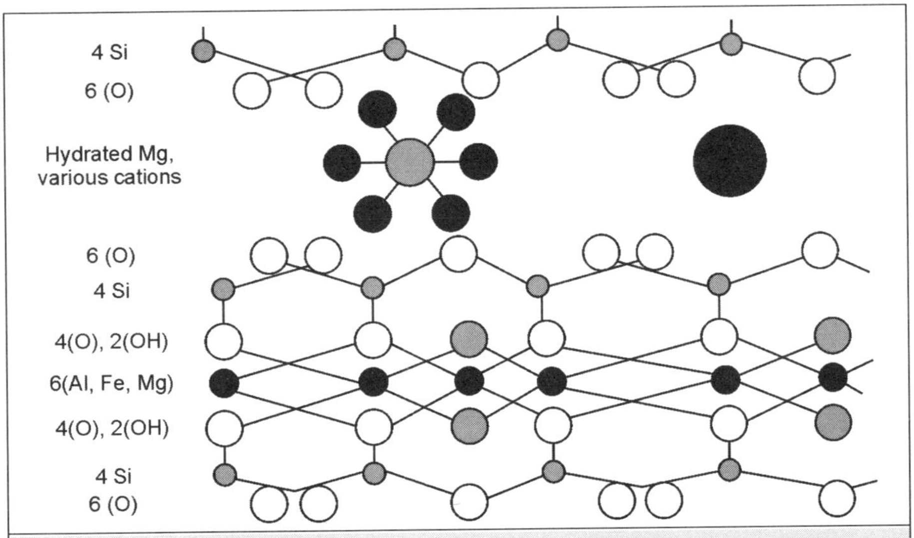

Fig. 13.4. Structure of Vermiculite (2 : 1 layer silicate) mineral

- 2 : 1 Structure two types dioctahedral and trioctahedral
- Al^{3+} substitutes for Si^{4+} in tetrahedral sheet very high negative charge (large CEC-100 $Cmol^+/Kg$)

- Hydrated cations in inter layers (expands slightly)
- Some Mg^{2+} substitutes for Al^{3+} in dioctahedral sheet (more negative)
- Some Fe^{3+} substitutes for Mg^{2+} in trioctahedral sheet (positive charge)
- Charge near surface holds cations and plates tighter than Montmorillinite
- Forms by alteration (not crystallization) from micas platelets pop apart and K^+ replaced by hydrated cations

***(iii)* 2 : 1 non-expanding type minerals.** In this group, hydrous mica or illite is the most important in soils. Like montmorillonite, illite has a 2 : 1 type lattice. The structure of illite is presented diagrammatically in figure 13.5. However, about 15 per cent of silicon in silica sheets is substituted by aluminium. The excess of negative charge is satisfied largely by potassium in the inter lattice layers, thus making the lattice structure of non-expanding type. Hence Illite is relatively non expansive. Thus hydrous mica has slight to moderate swelling. The properties of water absorption, cation exchange and other physical properties lie in between those of kaolinite and montmorillonite type of minerals.

- 2 : 1 Structure with K^+
- Derived from mica-K hydrous mica
- Sufficient K^+ to hold plates together
- Formed by alteration of mica-edges fray
- Forms on bottom of seafloor by K^+ addition to montmorillonite or vermiculite (heat and pressure)

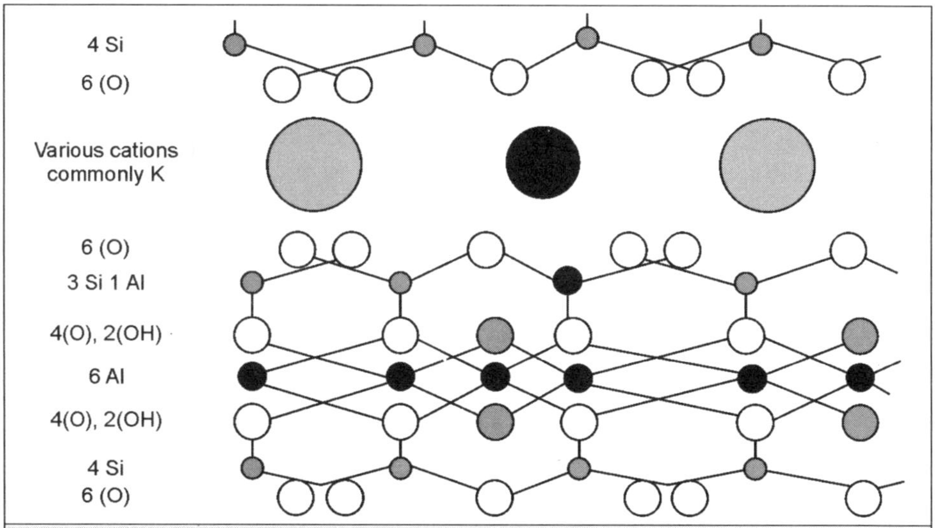

Fig. 13.5. Structure of illite (2 : 1 non expanding type) mineral

***(iv)* 2 : 2 type minerals. Chlorite (2 : 2 or 2 : 1 : 1 layer silicates).** Occurs extensively in soils, chlorites are basically silicates of magnesium with same iron and aluminium percent and it is composed of alternate talc (similar to a montmorillonite crystal unit) and brucite [$Mg(OH)_{10}$] layers. Chlorite mineral is similar to the unit of lattice of vermiculite, except the hydrated Mg in vermiculite is a firmly bonded magnesium hydroxide octahedral sheet. Thus a layer of chlorite has 2 silica tetrahedral, an aluminium octahedral and a magnesium octahedral sheet (2 : 2 or 2 : 1 : 1). Chlorite does not swell on wetting and has low CEC. It is almost non-expanding type of mineral because of its very little water absorption.

Chlorite (2Si : 1Al : 1Mg)

- 2 : 1 : 1 Structure or 2 : 2 structure
- Trioctahedral $Mg(OH)_2$ sheet serves as interlayer (Brucite)
- Al^{3+} substitutes for Mg^{2+} in interlayer-positive charge sheet
- Al for Si in tetrahedral sheet-negative charge + Interlayer bind sheets together, replaces adsorbed cations
- Forms by precipitation of oxides in inter layers of montmorillonite or vermiculite
- Intermediate CEC due to interlayer

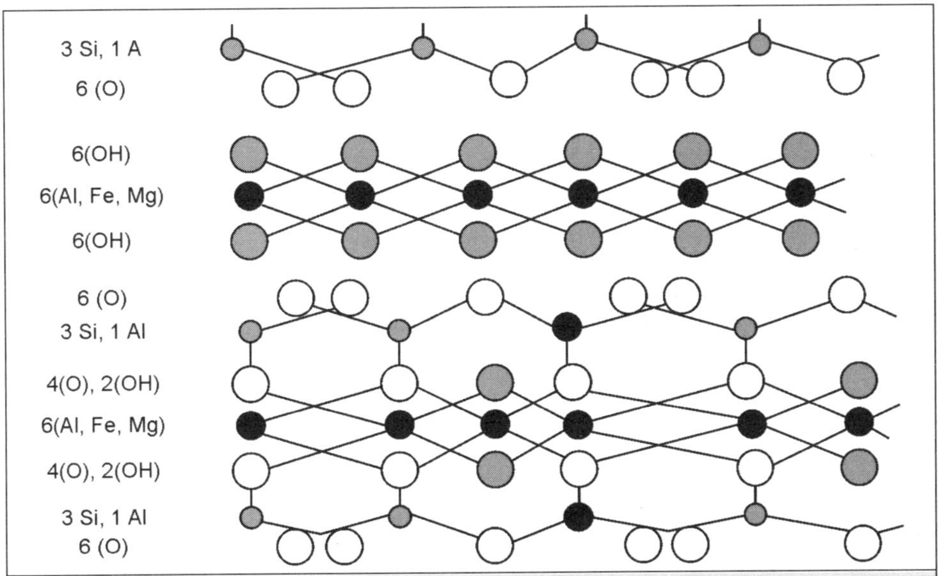

Fig. 13.6. Structure of Chlorite (2 : 2 layer silicate) mineral

The comparative properties of most important types of silicate clay minerals found in soils are given in table 13.1.

ION EXCHANGE PHENOMENA

Ion-exchange is defined as a reversible process by which cations and anions are exchanged between solid and liquid phases, and between solid phases it in close contact with each other. For the exchange of cations and anions the term is used as cation and anion exchange respectively.

Adsorption is defined as a phenomenon by which an increased in concentration or an accumulation of an ion species on a solid occurs due to ion exchange or other reactions. Desorption is a phenomenon by which the replacement or release of an adsorbed ion species occurs.

TABLE 13.1. Comparative properties of silicate clay minerals

Properties	*Montmorillonite*	*Illite*	*Kaolinite*
Structure	2 : 1 lattice	2 : 1 lattice	1 : 1 lattice
Substitution	Substitution in octahedral sheet by Mg or Fe	Substitution in tetrahedral sheet by Al	No substitution
Size (microns)	0.01-1.0	0.1-2.0	0.1-5.0
Shape	Irregular flakes	Irregular flakes	Hexagonal crystals
Surface area(m^2/g)	700-800	100-120	5-20
Cohesion, Plasticity and swelling capacity	High	Medium	Low
External surface and Internal surface	Very high	Medium	Not at all
CEC (Cmol(P^+)kg^{-1})	80-100	15-40	3-15
Anion exchange capacity (AEC)	Low	Medium	High

Chemical and physical processes are intimately related with ion exchange phenomenon which includes weathering of minerals, nutrient adsorption by plants, swelling and shrinkage of clay and leaching of electrolytes. Ion exchange particularly cation exchange, therefore, is considered as the most important process in soils.

Kind of exchangeable ions

The electric charge on the soil particles is neutralized by an equivalent amount of oppositely charged ions known as exchangeable, counter ions, which are held to the surface mainly by coulomb forces and Van-de-Waals forces.

In most of the soil exchangeable cations are Ca^{2+}, Mg^{2+}, H^+, K^+, Na^+ NH_4^+ of which Ca^{2+} is the dominant exchangeable ion. In strong acid soils $Al(OH)_2^+$ may act as a dominant exchangeable ion. Whereas in alkali soils sodium ion (Na^+) becomes dominant and the most common anions are $SO^2{}_4{}^-$, Cl^-, HCO_3^-, etc.

Electroneutrality, positive and negative charges must be equal or else electric charge,

Soluble Cations, electrically neutralized by soluble anions of equal total charge.

Exchangeable Cations, electrically neutralized by surfaces of solids with negativecharge.

Ion exchange process

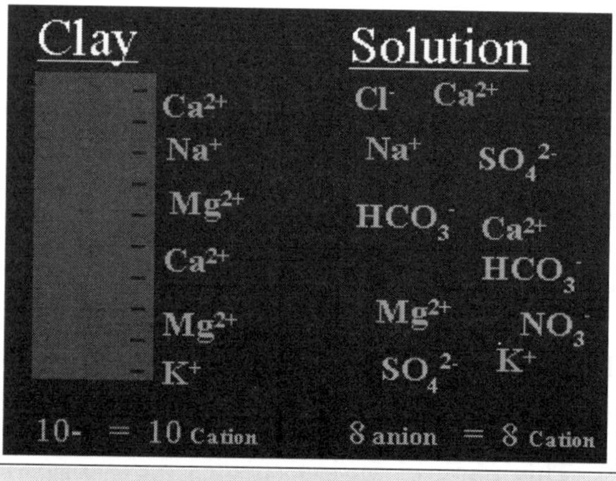

Fig. 13.7. Cation dissociation in clay and soil solution

Dissociation and adjustment

1. adsorbed cation breaks away from surface (nanosecond)
2. unstable state with no electroneutrality
3. negative site adsorbs any cation from solution (strength, probability)

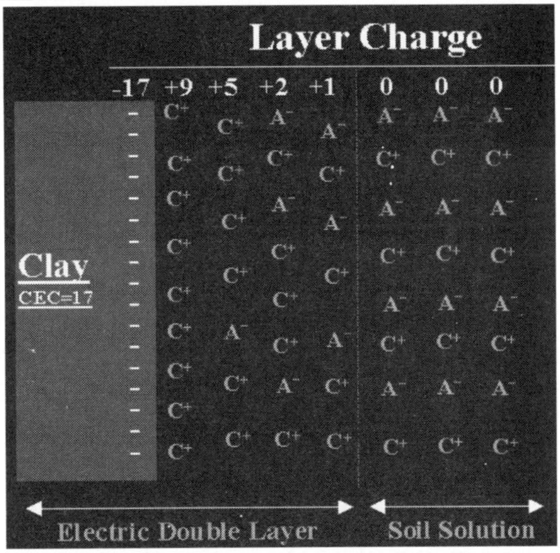

Fig. 13.8. Layer charges of cation and anion in soil clay

The exchange of cations in the soil takes place between :

(*i*) Cations in the soil solution and those on the exchange complexes of soil (clay crystal and humus).

(*ii*) Cations released by plant roots and those on the exchange complexes of soil.

(*iii*) Cation on the surface of either two clay crystals, two organic colloids (humus) or a clay crystal and a humus particle.

The Electric Double Layer. Distribution of cations and anions next to clay surface is continuous

- 1st layer-negative charge of clay surface
- 2nd layer-cation excess over anions away from surface
- Some cations are held tightly right next to the surface
- Others held more loosely further away
- Anion exclusion zone next to surface
- Soluble cations are reached only when [cations] = [anions]

This phenomenon the exchange of cations between soil and salt solution is known as cation exchange or base exchange and the cations that take part in this reaction are called as exchangeable or replaceable cation or bases.

Cation exchange reaction is reversible and considered as anion redistribution. From the above three points it is clear that cation exchange takes place on the surfaces of clay and humus colloids as well as on the surface of plant roots.

The most important cations in soils are calcium (Ca^{2+}), magnesium (Mg^{2+}), hydrogen (H^+), sodium (Na^+), potassium (K^+) and aluminium (Al^{3+}).

Cation Exchange Capacity

This phenomenon the exchange of cations between soil and salt solution is known as cation exchange or Base Exchange and the cations that take part in this reaction are called as exchangeable or replaceable cation or bases.

The cation exchange capacity is defined as the amount of cations adsorbed by the soil colloids which are exchangeable by electrolyte solution at pH 7 or at suitable pH and it is expressed in meq per 100 gm.

The CEC of soil represent capacity of the colloidal complex to exchange all its cation with the cation of the electrolyte. It also represents the total cation adsorbing capacity of soil.

The CEC of soil varies with its (1) clay (2) organic matter content (3) type of predominant clay mineral present. The soils which in content very little organic matter, the clay may be taken to vary with clay content and type of clay mineral in soil.

The soil rich in montmorillonite and vermiculite are high in CEC, while those rich in kaolinite, Illite and hydrous oxides are low in CEC.

The CEC of mineral soil may range from 5 to 50 or 60 meq/100 gram, whereas, the CEC of organic soils may exceed 200 meq percentage 100 gm.

CEC of different minerals and soil {C mol(p^+)/kg}

Humus	— 100-300	Mica	— 50
Vermiculite	— 100-200	Black cotton soil	— 30-60
Montmorillonite	— 80-100	Red soil	— < 20
Saponite	— 69-81	Laterite soil	— < 16
Nantronite	— 57-64	Muscovite	— 11
Chlorite	— 20-40	Sand	— 1-5
Illite	— 15-40	Fine sandy loam	— 5-10
Kaolinite	— 3-15	Clay loam	— 15-30
Sisquioxide	— > 3 about 4	Clay	— > 30
Acide sulphate soil	— 10-25	Dicotyledons roots	— 50-100
Organic soil	— 50-100	Monocotyledons	— 10-15

C-axis of different clay minerals

Kaolinite	— 7.2 Å	Montmorillonite	— 9.6-18 Å or more
Illite	— 10Å	Mica	— 9.6 Å
Chlorite	— 14 Å	Hallosite	— 10.2 Å
Vermiculite	— 10-15 Å or more		

Replacing power of cations :

The replacing power of cations varies with the (1) type of ion, (2) its size, (3) degree of hydration, (4) its valency, (5) its concentration, (6) kind of clay mineral etc.

In general, the replacing power of monovalant cation is in the following order.

$$H^+ > Rb^+ > K^+ > Na^+ > Li^+$$

Divalent cations : $Al^{2+} > Ba^{2+} > Sr^{2+} > Ca^{2+} > Mg^{2+}$

In field condition, the replacing power of cations is as under

$$H^+ > Ca^{2+} > Mg^{2+} > NH_4 > K^+ > Na^+$$

strongly held loosely held

Strongly replaces other ions low replaced by other ions.

FACTORS AFFECTING THE CATION EXCHANGE

(1) Valency of cations

Cations having higher valency are strongly held or adsorbed on the colloids than the cations having lower valency *e.g.* Al^{2+} is strongly bound than Ca^{2+} and Na^+. Hydrogen (H^+) is exception, because it acts like a polyvalent ion even though it is monovalent, H is more strongly bound even than Al^{3+} because it has higher affinity for oxygen which is present on the edges of silicate clay minerals.

(2) Zeta potential

Zeta potential is the magnitude of negative charge on the colloidal particles. Cations which have lower valiancy are more hydrated and have higher zeta potential. So the Na^+ has higher zeta potential as compared to Ca^{++}. Those cations, which have higher zeta potential, are loosely held and easily replace and hence Na^+ is easily replaced than Ca^{++}.

(3) Water hull

Every cation carries some water with it. This water remains around the cation as a very thin film, which is called water hull. As the valency of the cation decreased, it has higher water hull and therefore, it remains away from the clay particles. Hence, it is loosely held and easily replaced. This is because of decrease in the force of attraction between the two particles.

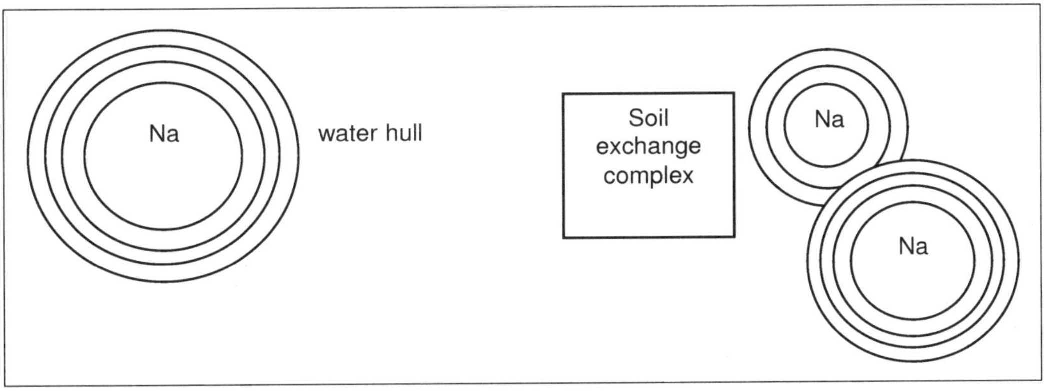

(4) Presence of complementary ions

In case of particles A, the complementary ion of Ca^{++} is hydrogen. H^+ is more strongly bound than Ca^{++}. Therefore, in this case Ca^{++} will be replacing first. In case of B particles, the complementary ion of Ca^{++} and K^+. Ca^{++} is more strongly bound than K^+. Therefore the K^+ will be replaced first.

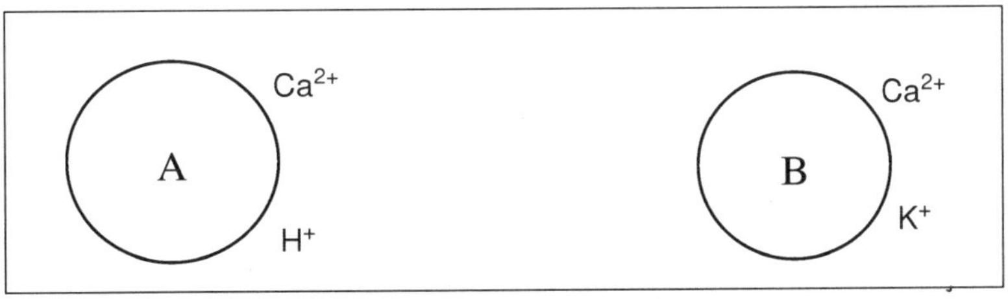

(5) Types of silicate clay mineral

In case of kaolinite monovalent cations are more strongly held than divalent cations. While in case of montmorillonite, divalent cations are strongly held than monovalent cations. The normal order of adsorbed cations on clay particles is :

$$H^+ = Al^{3+} > Ca^{2+} = Mg^{2+} > K^+ = NH^+{}_4 > Na^+$$

The amount of exchangeable cation

The amount of exchangeable cations present in soils varies with type of soil

Soil type	*Clay*	*CEC meq %*	*Exchangeable bases*
Black soils			
Deep black	62.0	71.4	71.0
Medium black	40.6	51.4	50.9
Alluvial soils			
Sandy loam	22.2	28.3	27.2
Sandy	8.9	19.0	17.9
Calcareous	9.2	6.8	5.9
Lateritic soils			
High level (Sesquioxide clay)	54.6	20.9	15.2
Low level	35.7	13.4	12.3

Black soils contain a greater amount of exchangeable cation than alluvial or leteritic soils. They are also rich in exchangeable calcium.

The amount of total exchangeable varies with the amount of colloidal clay present in soil. Hence, clayey soils contain greater amount of total exchangeable cation than sandy soil.

It also depends upon the nature of the predominant clay mineral present in the soil colloids, *e.g.* leteritic soils have a high clay content than alluvial soils, while, they are poor in exchangeable cations.

Kaolinite clay minerals have a lower cation adsorbing capacity than other clay minerals. Hence, the amount of exchangeable cations clay present in the soil.

Since, the colloidal fraction of an agricultural soil is a homogeneous mixture of clay minerals together with humic substances of variable composition, the relationship does not strictly hold true.

Base Saturation

Base saturation presents the total exchangeable bases (Ca^{2+}, Mg^{2+}, K^+, Na^+) expressed as a percentage of the total cation adsorbing or cation exchange capacity of a soil. It can be calculated as;

$$PBS = \frac{100 \times B}{CEC}$$

where, PBS = Percentage base saturation

B = Total base

CEC = Cation Exchange capacity

Example CEC = 25 meq/100 gram soil
Ca = 10 meq/100 gram soil
Mg = 5 meq/100 gram soil
Na = 4 meq/100 gram soil
K = 3 meq/100 gram soil

Total = 22

H = 25 – 22 = 3 meq/100 gram soil

$$\text{Percent base saturation} = \frac{22 \times 100}{25} = 88\%$$

$$\text{Percentage base unsaturation} = \text{Exchangeable H} = \frac{3 \times 100}{25} = 12\%$$

$$\text{Ca} = \frac{10 \times 100}{25} = 40\%$$

$$\text{Mg} = \frac{5 \times 100}{25} = 20\%$$

$$\text{Na} = 4 \times 4 = 16\%$$

$$\text{K} = 3 \times 4 = 12\%$$

Exchangeable Ca is 10 meq/100 gm soil

Exchangeable Ca is 10 × 20 = 200 mg/100 gm soil

Exchangeable Ca is200 mg × 10 = 2000 ppm

Meq × Eq. Wt. = mg, mg% × 10 = ppm

(1) ppm × 2 = lb/acre = 2000 × 2 = 4000 lb/acre

(2) ppm × 2.24 = kg/ha, 2000 × 2.24 = 4480 kg/ha

(3) lb/acre × 1.12 = kg/ha, 4000 × 1.12 = 4480 kg/ha

(4) ppm × 0.9072 = kg/acre, 2000 × 0.9072 = 1814.4

1.12 = 2.471 Acre = hectare, 2.204 lb = kg

1.12 = 0.4536/0.4047 kg/acre ha = acre

(5) $\text{lb/acre} \times \frac{0.4536}{4000} \times 0.4536 = \text{kg/acre} = 1814.4$

(6) $\text{kg/acre} \times \frac{2.471}{1814} \times 2.471 = \text{kg/acre} = 4483 \text{ kg/ha.}$

Similarly for Mg : 5 meq/5 × 12 = 60 mg% = 600 ppm
Na : 4 meq/4 × 23 = 92 mg% = 920 ppm
K : 3 meq/3 × 39 = 117 mg% = 1170 ppm
H : 3 meq 3 × 1 = 3 mg% = 30 ppm

For replacement one of meq of each other, the quality

Required will be	H	=	Ca	=	Mg	=	Na	=	K	
	1		1		1		1		1	meq/100 g soil
	1		20		12		23		39	mg/100 g soil

The percentage base saturation is very high in case of black and alluvial soils, while it is low in lateritic soils. With increase in pH, percentage base saturation and percentage of exchangeable Na increases.

In general, soils formed under arid and semiarid regions are base saturated, giving a percentage base saturation of 90-100%. Soils formed in cool temperature and moist regions are usually base unsaturated; the extent of base unsaturation depends on the amount of exchangeable hydrogen present.

The extent of base saturation or the proportion of exchangeable hydrogen is an important property on which the fertility of a soil depends considerably. It also influences soil reaction or pH value of soil.

ANION EXCHANGE

The anion exchange phenomena take place when there are positive charges on the clay particles. The +ve charges associated with hydrous oxide of iron and aluminum 1 : 1 type clay and amorphous minerals, give rise to the adsorption of anions. This anion is subject to replacement by other anions just as cations replace each other. Anion exchange is the exchange of anions between solid and liquid phases and is due to the lowering of pH. When the pH is reduced, there is activation of the basic groups ($R\text{-}OH^-$) by increased acceptance of protons (H^+) from surrounding. Therefore it is pH dependent.

Accepting the proton as shown below develops the positive charge :

$$R.OH + HCl \longrightarrow R.OH_2 + Cl$$

$$R.OH_2 + HCl \longrightarrow R.OH_3 + Cl$$

This adsorbed negatively charged anion is replaceable as under :

$$\underset{\text{Soil solution on exchangeable complex}}{R.OH_2 + Cl + H_2PO_4^-} \longrightarrow \underset{\text{Soil solution}}{R.OH_2 + H_2PO_4 + Cl}$$

This phosphate ion adsorbed in this way is known as solid bound phosphate.

$$\underset{\text{OH}^- \quad \text{Soluble}}{\boxed{\text{Colloids}} + H_2PO_4} \rightleftharpoons \underset{\text{Insoluble/Fixed}}{\boxed{\text{Colloids}} - H_2PO_4^- + OH^-}$$

In this way there is fixation of phosphate ion, in which OH ion of silicate clay mineral is substituted by H_2PO_4 ion by isomorphous substitution. The H_2PO_4 ion becomes a part of the silicate clay mineral and the phosphate fixed by this way is known as colloid bound phosphate. This phosphate is not exchangeable and available to the plant. It has been observed that anion exchange increases with the acidity. The anions like NO_3^- and OH^- are not bound at pH above 7. The bounding strength (adsorbing power) of anions is in the order of:

$$Cl^* = NO_3^* < SO_4 < PO_4$$

* are not held by the soil colloids and are lost due to the leaching

or, $OH > H_2PO_4 > SO_4 > NO_3$ (relative order of anion exch.)

Importance of Anion Exchange

The adsorption of phosphate ions by clay particles from soil solution reduces its availability to plants. This is known as phosphate fixation.

$$\underset{\text{Available}}{OH - Clay + H_2PO_4} \rightleftharpoons \underset{\text{Unavailable}}{H_2PO_4 - Clay + OH}$$

The phosphate ions react with the hydrous oxides and get fixed forming insoluble hydroxy phosphate of iron and aluminium.

$$\underset{\text{Available}}{Al(OH)_3 + H_2PO_4} \rightleftharpoons \underset{\text{Unavailable}}{Al(OH)_2 \, . \, H_2PO_4 + OH}$$

Ion Exchange Formulae

To describe ion-exchange process and predict on ion distributions, several formulae have been proposed. Among all formulae Freunlich's well known adsorption isotherm may be mentioned. The Freundlich's formula is parabolic type, empirical and can not therefore, given a maximal adsorption value.

Ion exchange equation may be classified into three groups :

(*i*) Empirical *e.g.* Freundlich's adsorption isotherm

(*ii*) Kinetic and statistical *e.g.* lengmuir's isotherm

(*iii*) Mass action *e.g.* Gapon ; Kerr, Hoffman and Griess

Application of milliequivalent concepts to the practical field

This concept can be used for the calculation of the lime required in the field. For instance, 1 me of hydrogen can be replaced on the colloids by 1 me of $CaCO_3$ (lime stone). Then calculate the amount of lime ($CaCO_3$) required in kg/hectare furrow slice to replace that 1 me of hydrogen.

We know, 1 me of H^+/100g = 1 me of $CaCO_3$/100g.

= 1 mg of H^+/100g can replace 100/2

= 50 mg of $CaCO_3$/100 g

In other words,

50 mg of $CaCO_3$/100 g will be required to replace 1 mg of hydrogen/100 g

Since 1 me of hydrogen/100 g can be expressed as 22 kilograms of hydrogen per hectare furrow slice.

So 1 me of $CaCO_3$/100 g can also be expressed as 22 × 50 or 1100 kilograms of $CaCO_3$ per hectare furrow slice.

Exchangeable Cation as Plant Nutrients

It is the established that exchangeable (cation and anions) ions serve as plant nutrients. Growing plants absorb the nutrients not only from soil solution but also from the exchange complex.

When plant roots come in contact with colloidal particles, they absorb exchangeable cations directly by inter-exchange of contact exchange between the root hair and colloidal complex.

Plant roots are known to give off CO_2 and certain other acidic substances. The excretion of these compounds creators H^+ at the root-colloid interface, which bring about transfer of the adsorbed cations from the surface of colloidal particles to surface of roots.

The intense activity of O.M. in the immediate vicinity of root hairs further helps by producing large volumes of CO_2 in increasing the transfer of cations from soil to plant roots.

Exchangeable cations also serve as plant nutrients when they are transferred from the colloidal surface to soil solution by exchange reaction; from which the plant roots absorb them. The liberation of H^+ ions in the soil water system helps to facilitate the transformer.

EXCHANGEABLE CATIONS IN RELATION TO FERTILITY

The proportion of exchangeable bases to exchangeable hydrogen *e.g.* percentage base saturation in soil has a profound effect on its physical properties and fertility.

In normal fertility soils, the total exchangeable bases (Ca^{2+} Mg^{2+} K^+ Na^+) constitute about 80 to 90 per cent of the CEC in these soils exchangeable H ion is usually under 20% and calcium forms the predominant exchangeable base, constituting 60 to 80% of the total exchangeable cations.

Ca-clay

The predominance of exchangeable calcium gives rise to Ca-clay, which imparts a neutral reaction to the soil. pH value varies from 6.5 to 7.5.

When a soil contains Ca-clay it posses an excellent physical condition. It develops good crumb structure by virtue condition and aggregation of the primary particles, which allows free movement of water without causing stagnation and contains sufficient air for the proper aeration of plant roots & micro-organism such a soil, is highly productive especially if it is supplied with necessary plant nutrients.

Na-clay

When exchangeable Na forms more than 15% of the CEC gives, rise to alkaline soils. The pH value of such soils is usually greater than 8.0. When the proportion of exchangeable Na exceeds these limits or saturates the colloidal complex, the clay is turned in to a Na-clay. Such soil is highly alkaline and the pH value ranges from 9 to 12. Alkaline soils are less fertile, and extreme cases, they are unproductive and barren.

The preponderance of Na-clay in an alkaline soil almost completely destroys its physical condition. Such a soil is devoid of crumb structure, gets easily dispersed, and becomes sticky when wet. It is unable to sustain plant growth under conditions.

H-clay

When the proportion of exchangeable H is high, it gives rise to acid soil. In such soils, exchangeable Ca is correspondingly low and in highly acid soil it is almost absent.

In the cases of soils having H-clay, the acid condition of soil makes it less fertile and less productive. Such soils allow only acid tolerant crops to grow. When the pH falls below the critical value; Al, Fe & Mn are liberated in soluble forms; which may prove toxic to the growing plants. H-clay is unstable, hence in concate with neutral salts, it supplies H^+ ions and liberates Al, Fe, Mn, etc. in soluble form. In such conditions, even acid tolerant crops fail to grow and in extreme cases the soils are almost barren.

The deficiency of available Ca brought about by the preponderance of H-clay also restricts the growth of plants. Especially this soil, which have high Ca requirement.

The microbial activity of the soil is also considerably disturbed. The nitrifying organisms are unable to function under acid conditions. The activity of earthworms is also affected.

CEC of Plant Roots

The plant roots posses the exchangeable capacity of cations. The cations are adsorbed on the rootlets and are in replaceable condition. The negative charges are developed on the roots due to presence of pactic substances. During respiration, CO_2 with water forms carbonic acid ($CO_2 + H_2O \rightarrow H_2CO_3$). H^+ of carbonic acid remains as exchangeable cation on the root surface when this plant roots comes in contact with clay particles, the exchange of cation from particles to the root surface takes place and in this way plant take nutrients from the soil.

(1) Monocot plant roots have low CEC, while dicot plant roots have high CEC.

(2) Plant roots with low CEC (monocot) take more monovalent cations, while plant roots with high CEC (dicot) take more divalent cations.

By this processes, if monocot and dicot plants are side by side or some rows of monocot and some rows of dicot or a rotation of monocot and dicot crops helps in maintaining levels of mono and divalent cations in the soil.

Genesis and Alteration of Soil Colloids

The silicate clays are developed from the wethering of a wide variety of minerals by at least the distinct process.

(*i*) A slight physical and chemical alteration of certain primary minerals.

(*ii*) A decomposition of primary minerals with the subsequent recrystallization of certain of their products in to the silicate clays

Genesis and geographic distribution of soil colloids on the basis of alteration, recrystallization, relative stages of weathering, and genesis of individual silicate clays are formation of the various layer of silicate clays and oxides of iron and aluminum. Fine grained micas, chlorite and vermiculite are formed through rather mild weathering of primary aluminosilicate minerals, whereas kaolinite and oxides of iron aluminum are products of much more intense weathering. Conditions of intermediate weathering intensity encourage the formation of smectite. In each case silicate clay genesis is accompanied by the removal solution of such elements as K, Na, Ca and Mg.

Fine grained micas and magnesium rich chlorites represents earlier weathering stages of the silicate, and kaolinite and iron and aluminum oxide the most advances stages. The smectite represents intermediate stage. Fine grained micas and chlorite are commonly formed from the alteration of muscovite and biotite micas, respectively.. Vermiculites and smectites can be products of weathering of the fine grained micas and chlorites.

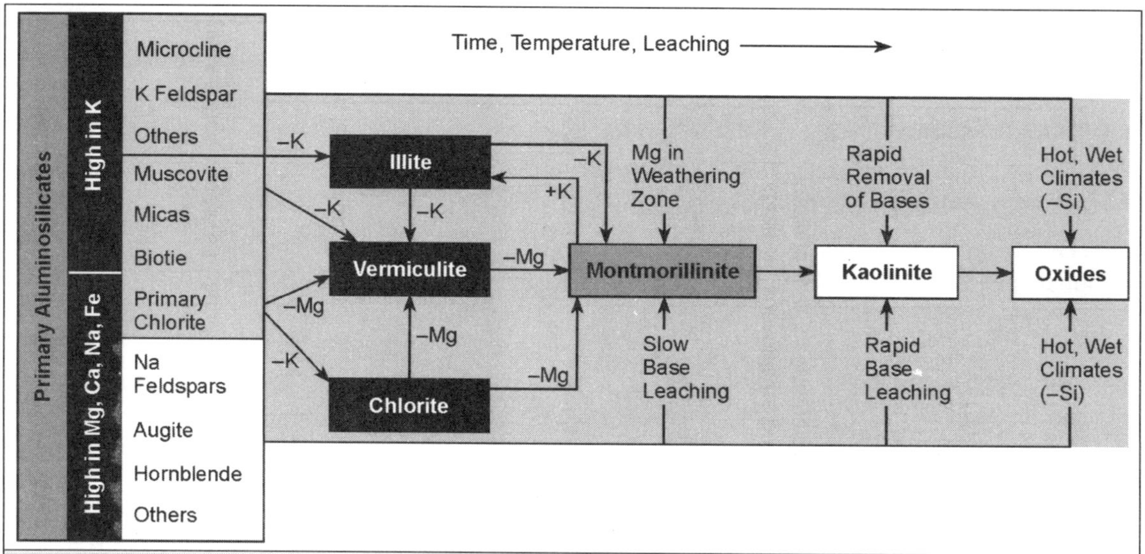

Fig. 13.9. Clay sequences occur through time as conditions change these sequences may be altered by climate and parent material

❑❑❑

CHAPTER 14

Soil Reaction and Buffering

"pH is the negative logarithm of hydrogen ion activity in soil"

The relationship between the concentration of H^+ and OH^- ions in the soil suspension which will determine whether the soil is acidic or alkaline or neutral reaction. Soil reaction can be measured by determining the pH. So pH may defined as the logarithm of the reciprocal of the H^+ ion activity and it can be expressed in moles per litre.

$$pH = \log \frac{1}{A_{H^+}} \text{ or } -\log A_H{}^+$$

where; $A_H{}^+$ is the hydrogen ion activity in moles per litre.

A solution with an H^+ ion activity of 0.001 M will have a pH of 3.0, one with an H^+ ion activity of 0.0001 M, 4.0 and so on.

In any solution in which water is the solvent, the product of the concentration of these H^+ and OH^- ions is approximately 10^{-14} at 25°C

$$H_2O = H^+ + OH^-$$

$[H^+] \times [OH^-] = 10^{-14}$. If pH is 6.0, the H^+ ion concentration of OH^- ions will be $10^{-14}/10^{-6}$ M per litre. At neutrally, the H^+ ion concentration is 0.0000001 M or 10^{-7} per litre of solution.

$$pH = \log \frac{1}{10^{-7}}$$

$$= \frac{1}{0.0000001}$$

$$= \log 10,000,000$$

From pH 7 to 0 the soil is increasingly more acidic more, from pH 7 to 14 the soil increasingly more alkaline (basic). The H^+ ion concentration has a ten fold change between each whole pH number. Thus a soil of pH 5 has 100 times (10^2) more H^+ ions in solution than a soil solution with a pH of 7.0.

Soil solution has acidic ions (H^+, Al^{3+}, $SO_4{}^{2-}$, $NO_3{}^-$) and alkali ions (OH^-, Ca^{2+}, Mg^{2+}, K^+, Na^+) soil solution H^+ ion concentration is greater solution in the OH^- ion concentration is called acidic solution. Solution in which H^+ ions concentration is less then OH^- ion concentration is called alkali or basic solution. Solution in which H ion and OH ion concentration are equal is called neutral solution.

H^+ ion concentration is measured by pH scale. OH^- ion concentration is measured by pOH scale. pH and pOH value are always total 14, if pH value increases then pOH value decreases accordingly (Table 14.1) :

TABLE 14.1. Relationship between pH and pOH

pH	*Acidity (H^+)*		*Alkalinity (OH^-)*	*pOH*
0	1	$= 10^{-0}$	0.00000000000001	14
1	0.1	$= 10^{-1}$	0.0000000000001	13
2	0.01	$= 10^{-2}$	0.000000000001	12
3	0.001	$= 10^{-3}$	0.00000000001	11
4	0.0001	$= 10^{-4}$	0.0000000001	10
5	0.00001	$= 10^{-5}$	0.000000001	9
6	0.000001	$= 10^{-6}$	0.00000001	8
7	0.0000001	$= 10^{-7}$	0.0000001	7
8	0.00000001	$= 10^{-8}$	0.000001	6
9	0.000000001	$= 10^{-9}$	0.00001	5
10	0.0000000001	$= 10^{-10}$	0.0001	4
11	0.00000000001	$= 10^{-11}$	0.001	3
12	0.000000000001	$= 10^{-12}$	0.01	2
13	0.0000000000001	$= 10^{-13}$	0.1	1
14	0.00000000000001	$= 10^{-14}$	1	0

Buffering Capacity

Buffering capacity of a soil indicates resist to abrupt (sudden) change in soil pH by addition of small amount of acid or base forming material for a soil.

Note : buffering action contains reserve acidity and alkalinity

Mechanisms of Buffering

For soil with intermediate pH levels (5 to 7), buffering can be explained in term of the equilibrium that exists among the three principle pool of soil acidity : active, salt replaceable (passive) and residual. If just enough base (lime for example) is applied to neutralize the H^+ ions in the soil solution, they are large replenished the reaction move to right, they minimizing the charge of soil solution pH.

(*i*) Aluminum hydrolysis

In very acid soils (pH 4 to 5.5), hydrolysis, dissolution, or precipitation of gibbsite [Al $(OH)_3$] and other aluminum and iron hydroxide clay minerals provide a major mechanism for pH buffering. They include the associated hydrolysis reactions by high the released Al and Fe ion react with water. For example:

$$Al\,(OH)_2^+ + H_2O \rightleftharpoons Al\,(OH)_3 + H^+$$

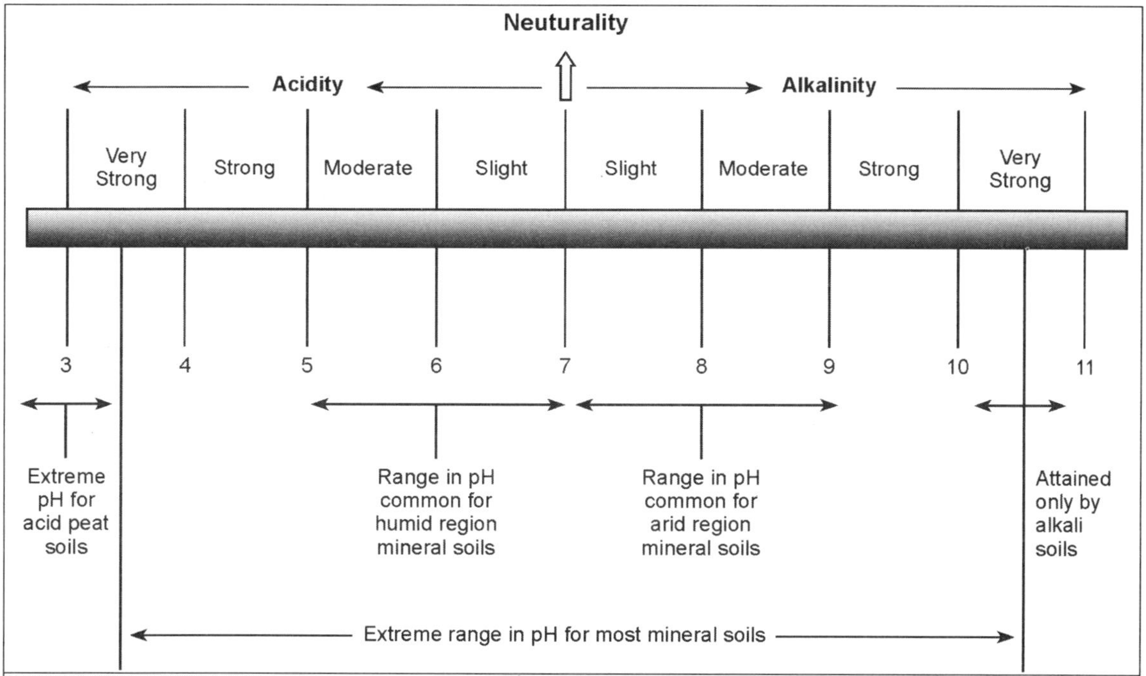

Fig. 14.1. Extreme range in pH for most mineral soils and the ranges commonly found in humid and arid region soils

The addition of H^+ ion would drive these reactions to the left, so relatively few of the H^+ ions would accumulate in the soil solution and the pH would be reduced only moderately. Likewise, if OH^- ions were added, they would remove H^+ from the solution by forming water and therefore force the reaction to the right. In cases, changes in soil solution pH would be buffered.

(*ii*) Organic matter reaction

The protonation and deprotonation of organic matter functional (R-OH) groups provides much of the pH buffering in soils. The tenacity with which H^+ ions are held by organic matter is different for different functional groups and is also influenced by the nature of nearby C to C bonds. Therefore, the soil organic matter, with the complex structure, has many types of sites to which H^+ ions can bond with its complex structure, has many types of sites to which H^+ ions can bond with various degree of strength.

Organic matter also buffers soil pH by the release of aluminum ions from organic complexes in which they are held with varying degrees of strength. If a base is added to raise pH of the solution, more aluminum escapes from these complexes and subsequently replaces the neutralized H^+ ions by hydrolysis reactions.

(*iii*) pH dependent charge site on clay

Aluminum and silicon atoms at surface of clay minerals are bonded to hydroxyl groups and oxygen atoms that can associate with or dissociate with H^+ ions. Adding a base to raise the solution OH^- concentration would induce the dissociation of H^+ ions from these sites, especially on the weathered edges of clays. This release of H^+ ions would buffer the pH by neutralizing most of the added OH^- ions. At the same time, the site from which the H^+ ions dissociated would become negatively charged and would increase the soil's CEC.

(*iv*) Cation exchange

Exchangeable ion on clay and humus are in equilibrium with the ions solution. Therefore, if additional H^+ is added to the soil, most of these ions will de attracted to the cation exchange complex where they will exchange with other ions such as Ca^{++}. The H^+ concentration in the solution will therefore not change very much. If H^+ ions in solution are neutralized by addition of a base, they will be immediately replaced by H^+ ions and various aluminum ions released from exchange sites on clay and humus. Because the relatively small amount of exchangeable in percent in soils, these reactions contribute most significantly to pH buffering when the amount of H^+ ions in solution relatively low (that is, when the pH is above 6).

(*v*) Carbonate dissolution and precipitation

Buffer reaction involving carbonates, bicarbonates, carbonic acid and water are most important in alkaline soils (pH 7 and above).

$$CaCO_3 + H^+ + HCO_3 \longleftrightarrow Ca\,(HCO_3)_2$$

$$Ca\,(HCO_3)_2 + H_2O \longleftrightarrow Ca^{++}\ 2OH^- + 2H_2CO_3$$

If acid were added, the H^+ ions would be consumed as the reactions shifted to the right. If a base were added, the OH^- ions would be consumed and H^+ ions produced as the reaction shifted to the left. In both cases, the pH change would be buffered.

Factor Affecting of Buffering Capacity :

(*i*) A soil containing BSP at 50 equal to highest buffering capacity.

(*ii*) A soil containing large amount of 2 : 1 expending type of mineral (smectite group) produced high buffering capacity in comparison to 1 : 1 type of clay mineral.

(*iii*) A soil containing large amount of clay practices and organic matter contain produced higher buffering capacity.

TABLE 14.2. pH class and pH range of alkaline and acid soils

pH Class	:	*pH Range*
Extremely Acidic Soil	:	< 4.5
Very Strongly Acidic Soil	:	4.6-5.0
Strongly Acidic Soil	:	5.1-5.5
Moderately Acidic Soil	:	5.6-6.0
Slightly Acidic Soil	:	6.1-6.5
Neutral Soil	:	6.6-7.3
Minutely Alkaline Soil	:	7.4-7.8
Moderately Alkaline Soil	:	7.9-8.4
Strongly Alkaline Soil	:	8.5-9.0
Very Strongly Alkaline Soil	:	9.1 or above

Type of Soil Acidity

These are three types of soil acidity on the basis of situation of ions

(*i*) Active acidity

(*ii*) Passive acidity *or* Potential acidity *or* Reserve acidity *or* Accumulated acidity *or* Exchange acidity (*iii*) Residual acidity

Total Acidity = Active Acidity + Passive Acidity

TABLE 14.3. Differentiate between active, passive and residual acidity in soil

Active acidity	*Passive acidity*	*Residual acidity*
(*i*) Soil acidity developed due to H^+ or Al^{3+} ion in soil solution in liquid	(*i*) Soil acidity developed due to H^+ or Al^{3+} ions on soil colloidal complex or exchange side or in solid state is called passive acidity	(*i*) Residual acidity is that which remains in the soils after active and passive acidity have been neutralize
(*ii*) The magnitude of active acidity less	(*ii*) High	(*ii*) Very less
(*iii*) More dangerous then other due to soil solution	(*iii*) Less dangerous then active soil acidity	(*iii*) less dangerous then both

Optimum soil pH range in different soils and crops are given follows :

- Calcareous Soil : 8-8.5
- Salt Affected Soils : > 7.3
- Saline Soil : < 8.5
- Sodic Soil : 8.5-10
- Saline Sodic Soil : > 8.5
- Degraded Alkali Soil : About 6.0 (surface soil), above 8.0 (sub-surface soil)
- Acid Sulphate Soil : < 3.5 or < 4.0
- Alluvial Soil : 7-8
- Black Cotton Soil : 7.8-8.7 (calcareous up to 9.5)
- Red Soil : 6.0-7.3
- Podzol Soil : 5.0-6.0
- Laterite Soil : 5.0-6.0
- Desert Soil : 7.5-9.0
- Tarai Soil : 4.7-5.8
- Organic Soil : 4.0 or < 4
- Forest Soil : 3.5-6.2
- Acid Rain : 2.0-4.5
- Battery Acid : 5.5
- Lemon Jush : 2.0
- Pure Water or Distilled Water : 7.0
- Sea Water : 8.3
- Highest Buffering Capacity in Soil pH : 4.5-6.0

Crops

- Maize, Sorghum, Barley Wheat, Sugarcane : 6.5-7.5
- Lentil, Gram, Pea, Soyabean : 6.0-7.0
- Groundnut : 5.3-6.5
- Oat : 5.0-7.5
- Cotton : 5.0-6.5
- Potato : 5.0-5.5
- Paddy : 4.0-6.0

Factor Affecting of Soil pH

(*i*) A soil containing large amount of clay particles and high content of humus produced acidic nature in soil

(*ii*) Sodium saturated soils have increase the pH value

(*iii*) Ca and Mg saturated soils have lower pH value

(*iv*) A soil having base saturation % low produces pH value is low

(*v*) Tillage operation show to acidic in nature soil or decrease soil pH value

(*vi*) A soil formed in region of high rainfall shows soil in acidic nature

(*vii*) Application of large amount of ammonium sulphte, ammonium chloride fertilizer (acidic nature) up to large period produced soil acidity

(*viii*) A soil containing large amount of $CaCO_3$ soil produce alkaline in nature

Determination of soil pH

Electric method

(*i*) Hydrogen electrode method

(*ii*) Quoin electrode method

(*iii*) Glass electrode method

(*iv*) By pH meter method

(*a*) Electrode pH meter method digital pH meter method

(*b*) Digital pH meter method

(*c*) Handy pH meter method

Colourimetric method

(*i*) By stander colour solution method

(*ii*) By pH leaflets

(*iii*) By universal indicator method–methyl red (4.2-6.3 pH)

- Basic phenolphthalein indicator 8.3-10 pH
- Nitroamine 11-13 pH

Nutrient Availability to Plant

Figure 14.1, shows in general term the relationship between soil pH and the availability of plant nutrients, as well as the activity of soil microorganisms. Note that in strongly acid soils the availability of macronutrients (Ca, Mg, K, P, N and S) as well as molybdenum and boron is curtailed. In contrast, availability of most micronutrient cations (Fe, Mn, Zn, Cu and Co) is increased by low pH, even to extent of toxicity to higher plants and microorganism.

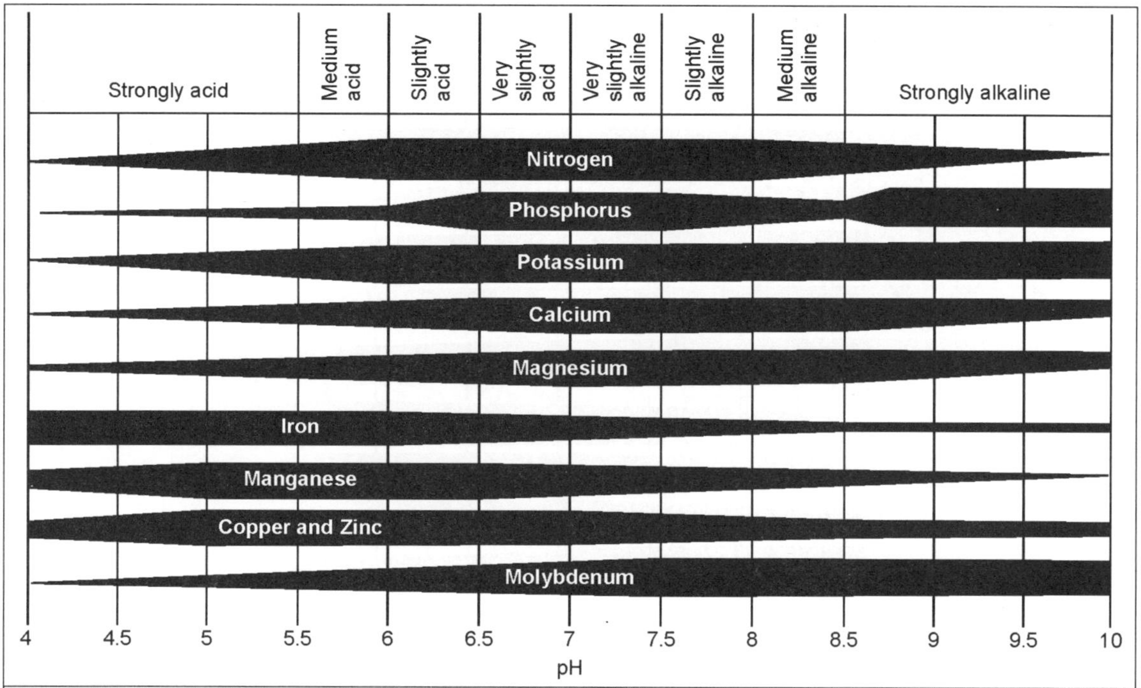

Fig. 14.2. The availability of nutrient in the soil as dependent on soil pH

In slightly to moderately alkaline soils, molybdenum and all of the macronutrient (except) phosphorus are available, but level of Fe, Mn, Zn, Cu, and Co are so low that plant growth is constrained. Phosphorus and boron availability like wise reduced in alkaline soil commonly to a deficient level.

It is difficult to generalize about nutrient pH relationship. However, it appears from Fig. 14.2 that the pH range of 5.5-6.5 may provide the most satisfactory plant nutrient levels overall. However, this generalization may not be valid for all soil and plant combinations. For example, certain micronutrient deficiencies are common on some sandy soils when the soils are limed to pH values of only 6.0 to 6.5.

❑❑❑

CHAPTER 15

Salt Affected Soils

ORIGIN OF SALT AFFECTED SOILS

The soils under consideration owe their distinctive character to the fact that they contain excessive concentration of either soluble salts or exchangeable sodium or both. For agricultural purposes, such soils are regarded as class of problem soils that require special remedial measures and management practices. Soluble salts produce harmful effects to plants by increasing the salt content of the soil solution and by increasing the degree of saturation of the exchange materials in the soil with exchangeable sodium. The latter effects occur when the soluble constituents consist largely of sodium salts, and are of a more permanent nature then the salt content of the soil solution, since exchangeable sodium usually persists after the soluble salts are removed.

Sources of Soluble Salts

The ultimate source of salt constituents found in soils is the primary minerals in the exposed rocks of the earth's crust. The processes of chemical weathering, which include (*i*) Hydrolysis, (*ii*) Hydration, (*iii*) Solution, (*iv*) Oxidation and (*v*) Carbonation, gradually release these salt constituents to the surrounding water.

Solution

Solution, the dissolving of a solid in a liquid, separates solid materials into independent soluble ions, each surrounded by the liquid molecules. Solution permits greater chemical changes than that of un-ionized (usually solid) state. Water is a universal solvent. Most of the minerals are affected by the solvent action of water. Solution helps in a continual loss of weathered material but total removal by simple solution is negligible. Solution is represented by the following typical equation of a salt dissolving in water :

$$\underset{\text{(A soluble salt)}}{NaCl} + \underset{\text{(Water)}}{H_2O} \longrightarrow \underset{\text{(Dissolved ions, surrounded by water molecules)}}{Na^+, Cl^-, H_2O}$$

Hydrolysis

Hydrolysis, which involves the splitting of water into H^- ions and OH^- ions, is the reaction of substances with water to form hydroxides and other new substances that are usually more soluble than the original material. Hydrolysis is conveniently brought about as follows :

Feldspar + Water = Clay mineral + Soluble cations and anions

$$KAlSi_3O_8 + HOH \longrightarrow HAlSi_3O_8 + KOH$$

(Orthoclase: very slowly soluble) (Water) (Acid silicate clay: more soluble) (More soluble)

$$2HAlSi_3O_8 + 8HOH \longrightarrow Al_2O_3.3H_2O + 6H_2SiO_3$$

(Recombination) (Bauxite) (Silicic acid)

Oxidation–Reduction

Oxidation, as referred to in mineral weathering is both the chemical combining of oxygen with a compound and the loss of electrons (change in oxidation number) of some chemical element. Oxidized minerals have a volume increase with added oxygen and are usually softer than the unoxidized material. If the oxidation number of an element is changed, this can also imbalance the electrical neutrality of the mineral, making it more easily attacked by water and carbonic acid (H_2CO_3).

Reduction is the chemical process in which electrons are gained, the negative charge is increased, and the positive charge is decreased.

Hydration

Hydration is the chemical combination of a solid substance *viz.*, a mineral or a salt with water. Hydration water combining within the mineral changes the mineral structure, increasing its volume due to swelling and thereby making it softer, more easily decomposed.

$$Fe_2O_3 + 3H_2O \longrightarrow Fe_2O_3.3H_2O$$

(Hematite) Red (Limonite) Yellow

Carbonation

Carbonation is the combination of carbon dioxide with any base. This process is very much effective of the other chemical weathering processes. The presence of H^+ ions in percolating waters and other inorganic acids like HNO_3, H_2SO_4 and some organic acids accelerate the decomposition of minerals through chemical weathering.

The carbon dioxide gas readily combines with bases to produce carbonates and bicarbonates as :

$$CO_2 + 2KOH \longrightarrow K_2CO_3 + H_2O$$

$$K_2CO_3 + H_2O + CO_2 \longrightarrow 2KHCO_3$$

The soluble salts that occur in soils consist mostly of various proportions of the cations-sodium, calcium and magnesium and the anions-chloride and sulphate. Constituents that ordinarily occur only in minor amounts are the cations-potassium and the anions-bicarbonate, carbonate, borate and to the some extent nitrate. After the process of weathering, the released anions may be transported to ocean through rivers, which may salinize the soil.

1. Carbonates

These salts of calcium, magnesium and sodium occur widely in soils, sub-soils and ground waters of the arid and semi-arid zones.

(*a*) Calcium carbonate. Calcium carbonate by itself has a very low solubility (13.1 mg/l) but in the presence of CO_2 it forms calcium bicarbonate, the solubility of which varies (60-140 mg/l) depending on the amount of CO_2. The solubility of calcium carbonate also depends greatly on the pH value of the system, decreasing significantly with an increase in the pH as shown in Table 15.1 (FAO, 1973). The role of calcium present as native calcium carbonate, which can be utilized in the reclamation of the alkali soil, will, therefore, be conditioned largely by the soil reaction.

TABLE 15.1. Solubility of $CaCO_3$ in mg/l of water as affected by pH and CO_2 content

CO_2 in air (% by volume)	*pH*	*Solubility of $CaCO_3$ (mg/l)*	
		According to Schlesing	*According to Weiner*
0.00	10.23	13.0	13.0
0.03	8.48	63.4	62.7
0.30	7.81	133.4	138.0
1.00	7.47	202.9	210.6
10.00	6.80	470.0	488.9
100.00	6.13	1098.0	1057.7

In view its extremely low solubility; the presence of calcium carbonate in soils is not directly harmful to plants. However, many ground waters contain large quantities of the dissolved calcium carbonate. The insoluble calcium carbonate can occur in surface soils or sub-soils, either free as such or in the form of nodules, known as *kankar*.

(*b*) Magnesium carbonate. Magnesium carbonate has greater solubility than calcium carbonate; and in the presence of carbonic acid (CO_2) its solubility further increases. The solution of magnesium carbonate is strongly alkaline (pH up to 10). The accumulation in soils of magnesium carbonate in the free form is rare. It can, however, occur in soils as insoluble compound with calcium, as dolomite or dolomitic concretions.

(*c*) Sodium carbonate. Sodium carbonate under climate can accumulate in soils in considerable quantities. The various theories postulated for the formation of sodium carbonate in soils include : biogenetic formation, microbial reduction of sodium sulphate, reaction of neutral sodium salts with $CaCO_3$, hydrolysis of exchangeable sodium and subsequent reaction with CO_2, weathering of sodium feldspars, and underground water.

It is highly soluble (170 g/l) and gives strong alkaline reaction corresponding to a pH value of 12. Owing to its great solubility and high alkalinity, it is very toxic to plant life. Besides, sodium carbonate has also the property to peptize soil clays; resulting in poor physical condition of the soil. As in the case of the calcium and magnesium carbonates, sodium carbonate also forms bicarbonate in the presence of CO_2. Many natural waters and ground waters with substantial quantities of soluble salts contain a mixture of sodium carbonate and bicarbonate. Singly or together these two salts also constitute the important components of a large number of salt affected soils in India.

2. Sulphates

The sulphates (salt of calcium. magnesium and sodium with sulphuric acid) are found in varying quantities in the soils and the ground water. In desert and steppe soils these can accumulate up to considerable quantities.

***(a)* Calcium sulphate.** Calcium sulphate, which is known as gypsum, has low solubility (1.9 g/l). It occurs free in many types of desert and semi-desert soils. Under certain conditions it can form massive indurated underground layers, which can obstruct water movement or penetration of roots in the sub-soils. Large deposits of gypsum occur in Rajasthan desert.

***(b)* Magnesium sulphate.** Magnesium sulphate has high solubility (262 g/l) and has been found to occur widely in saline ground waters and soil solutions. It is a common component of most saline soils and is toxic to plants.

***(c)* Sodium sulphate.** Sodium sulphate is one of the main salt constituents in saline ground waters and saline soils. Its toxicity to plant life is very much less than that of magnesium sulphate. The solubility of sodium sulphate (170 g/l) is highly dependent on the temperature. Whereas in the cold seasons, much sodium sulphate may not occur in soil solution, the amounts can double itself in hot seasons. This property is utilized in practice in leaching operations in the reclamation of saline soils.

3. Chlorides

Chlorides of calcium, magnesium and sodium along with their carbonates and sulphates are the other group of salts responsible for developing salinity in the soils. Chlorides predominate more in typical saline soils but when the soil develops alkali conditions, the quantity of chlorides diminishes.

***(a)* Calcium chloride.** Calcium chloride is seldom present in soil solutions or in ground waters unless the total saline contents are very high, *e.g.* of the order of 400-500 g/l. It is a highly soluble salt and has deliquescent properties *viz.*, absorbing vaporized water from the atmosphere.

***(b)* Magnesium chloride.** Magnesium chloride, in enough quantities, also occurs only under highly saline regimes. Because of its ready solubility (353 g/l), magnesium chloride is one of the most harmful salts for plants. Magnesium chloride is also very hygroscopic.

TABLE 15.2. Maximum solubility in water of the more soluble salts found in soils (FAO/UNESCO, 1973)

Salt	*Quantity in g/100 g solution at temperature (°C)*			
	10	*30*	*50*	
Na_2CO_3	10.9	28.4	32.1	Increase 3 times
$NaHCO_3$	7.5	10.0	12.7	
Na_2SO_4	8.3	29.0	31.8	Increase 4 times
NaCl	26.3	26.5	26.9	No effect
$MgSO_4$	22.0	28.0	33.4	
$MgCl_2$	39.8	48.6	54.5	
$CaCl_2$	39.4	50.7	56.0	

(c) **Sodium chloride.** Sodium chloride, also known as common salt, is the most common component of saline soils. It has exceptionally high all-round solubility (264 g/l), which does not change much with the change in temperatures. In the presence of excess of sodium chloride plants do not develop normally. It is however, a component of saline soil the presence of which greatly affects the solubility of other salts in mixed solutions.

4. Complex Solutions

In nature, single salt seldom exist in soils or ground waters. Usually, mixtures of two or more salts occur and these form complex solutions, in which the pattern of solubility of salts, as in single salt solution, is not retained. As a rule, the presence of salts, with a common ion, causes their solubility to decrease. Thus, sodium chloride precipitates it out of the solution. A similar reaction takes place if the common ion is sodium instead if chloride. Thus the solubility of sodium carbonate, sodium sulphate and sodium bicarbonate are sharply depressed by the presence of excess of sodium chloride (Table 15.3).

TABLE 15.3. Solubility of salt as affected by NaCl concentrations

NaCl (g/l)	Solubility (g/l)				
	$MgCl_2$	$CaCl_2$	Na_2CO_3	Na_2SO_4	$NaHCO_3$
0	350	400	170	150	80
100	270	180	130	90	40
200	170	175	90	92	20

Similar effects are also shown by sodium sulphate where the common ion can be either sodium or sulphate; and this salt can depress the solubility of magnesium sulphate and calcium sulphate and also of sodium carbonate and sodium bicarbonate.

In the case of mixture of salts, with dissimilar ions, other chemical laws governing solubility operate. Thus, the solubility of a salt, having lower solubility, increases in the presence of another salt with higher solubility. Here the law of ionic activity coefficient comes into play. Examples are the increased solubility of gypsum ($CaSO_4$) in the presence of sodium chloride; or of calcium carbonate in presence of CO_2. The solubility of gypsum can increase four times (from 0.204 to 0.820 g/l) in the presence of sodium chloride in concentrations of 25 g/l; and that of calcium carbonate ten times (0.0131 to 0.1334 g/l) with a 0.3% of CO_2.

ORIGIN AND NATURE OF SALTS IN SOILS

We can diagrammatically :

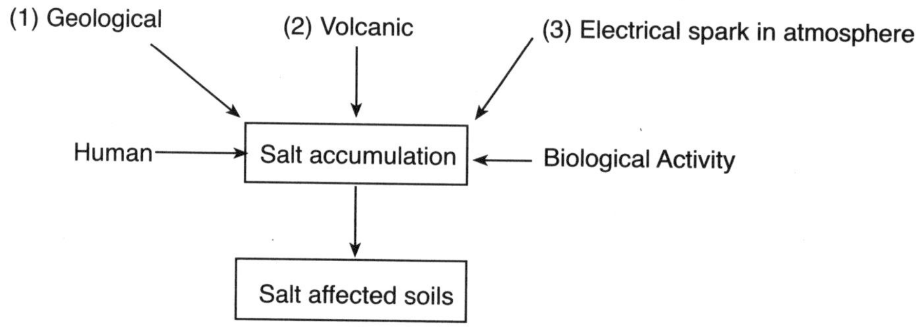

(1) Geological

Due to weathering of primary minerals found in the soils and in the exposed rocks of the earth's crust. These are the original and direct source of all the salts constituents.

The soluble salts that occur in soils consist mostly of various properties of cations Na, Ca, Mg and anions Cl, SO_4. The constituents that ordinarily occur only in minor amounts are the cation K and anions CO_3, HCO_3 and NO_3.

During the process of chemical weathering which involves hydrolysis, hydration, solution, oxidation and carbonation. These constituents are gradually released and made soluble. Boron is the principal source from tourmaline minerals.

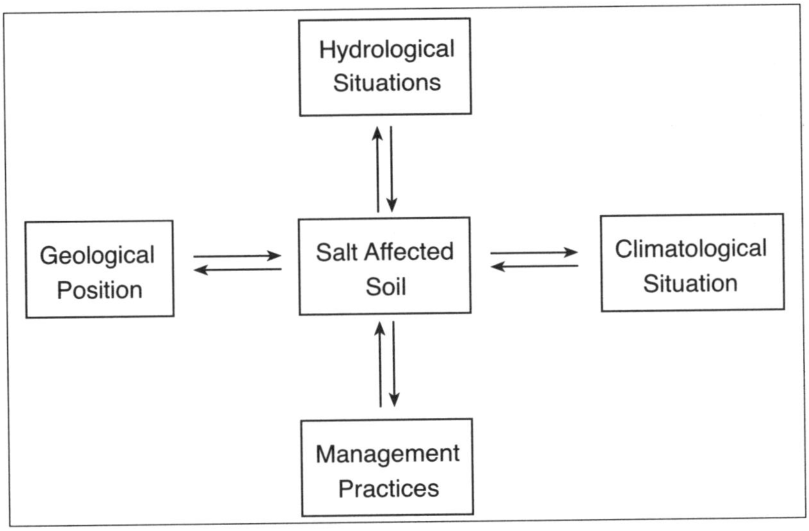

(2) Volcanic

Cl^- and SO_4^{2-}

(3) Electrical spark in atmosphere

SO_4^{2-}, NO_3^- and CO_3^{2-}

(4) Biological activity

CO_3^{2-}, HCO_3^-, NO_3^- in biological activity through different types of micro-organisms and produced different types of acids and these acids release anions.

(5) Human

- Use of saline water
- Use of industrial waste water
- Deforestation-this is indirect effect
- Use of fertilizer and chemical
- Faulty methods for irrigation

(1) Parent Materials. Weathering, hydrolysis, hydration, solution, oxidation, and carbonation

(2) Irrigation water. Source-well, rivers, dams

(3) Ocean water. Coastal area, cyclic salt—sometimes salts are moves inland through the transportation of spray by winds and are called cyclic salt.

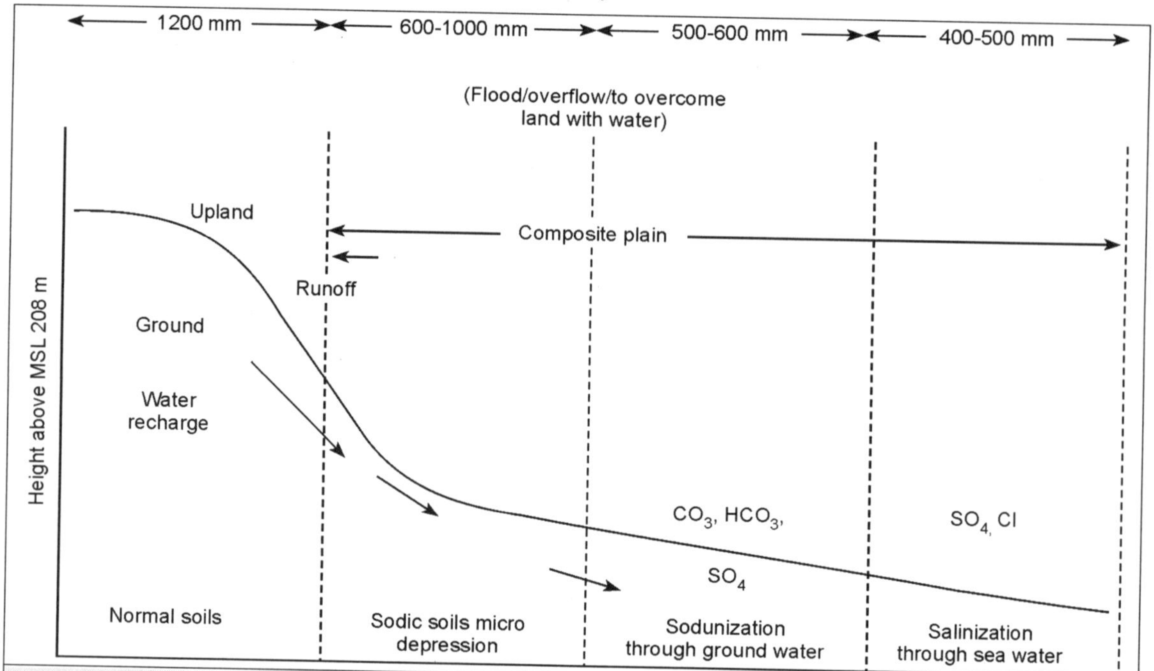

Fig. 15.1. Schematic distribution of salt affected soils as influenced by precipitation, topography, hydrological and hydrochemical factors

CAUSES OF SALINIZATION

Salinization is the accumulation of soluble salts on surface soils, occurs in the following ways :

1. Primary minerals

It is the original and important source of all the salt constituents. During the process of weathering, which involves hydrolysis, hydration, solution, oxidation and carbonation various constituents like Ca, Mg and Na are gradually released and made soluble.

2. Arid and semi-arid climate

Salt affected soils are mostly formed in arid and semi-arid climate where low rainfall and high evaporation prevails. The low rainfall in these regions is not sufficient to leach out the soluble weathered products and hence the salt accumulates in the soils. During rain, the salt dissolves in rainwater and migrates downward. However, due to limited rainfall, the downward movement is restricted to a short distance only. In dry weather, the salts move up with the water and are brought up to the surface where they are deposited as the water evaporates.

3. Sea as a source of salts

The ocean may be the source of salts as in soils where the parent materials consists of marine deposits that were laid down during earlier geological periods and have since been uplifted. The ocean is also the source of the salts in low-lying area along the margin of seacoasts. Sometimes salts is moved inland through the transportation of spray by winds be called "cyclic salts". In Gujarat salts affected soils observed in *Bhal* region is due to marine deposit of receding of the sea while seawater **inundation** is the cause in several coastal regions in south Gujarat.

4. Restricted leaching and transportation

In arid regions, the leaching and transportation of soluble salts to ocean is not as complete as in humid regions. In arid regions the leaching is usually localized in nature and soluble salts may not be transported far. This occur not only because there is less rainfall available to leach and transport the salt but also because of the high evaporation rates which tend to concentrate the salt in the soils and in surface water.

5. Low permeability of the soil

This causes poor drainage by impeding the downward movement of water. Low permeability may be results of an unfavorable soil texture or structure or hard pan/clay pan, because of the low permeability the ground water table may raise or because of continuous deposition of soluble salts in the soils.

6. Ground water

Ground water contains large amounts of water soluble salts which depend upon the nature and properties of the geological material with which water remains in contact where water table and evapotranspiration rate is high, salts along with water move upward through capillary activity and salts accumulation on the soil surface.

7. Irrigation water

The application of irrigation water without proper management (i.e. lack of drainage and leaching facilities) increases the water table and surface salt content in the soils.

8. Poor drainage of soil

During the periods of high rainfall, the salts are leached from the upper layer and if the drainage is impeded, they accumulate in the lower layer. When the water evaporates the salts are left in the soils. Such soils are generally developed in low-lying areas.

9. High water table

The ground waters of arid regions usually contain considerable quantities of soluble salts. If the water table is high, large amount of water moves to the surface by capillary action and evaporated, leaving soluble salts on the surface.

10. Overflow of seawater over lands

Low-lying area near the sea, which gets sea water during tides, salts water accumulates and enriches the soils with salts.

11. Salts blown by wind

In arid regions near the sea, lots of salt are blown by wind year after year and get deposited on the lands. Due to low rainfall they are not washed back to sea thus add salinity to the land. The salinity in Rajasthan has developed to a great extent, due to this reason.

12. Canal as a source of salinization

Although, canal water practically contain very little amount of soluble salts, but during earlier stages, the excess use of canal water hastens the rise of ground water table. When the water table rises to within 5 or 6 feet of the soils surface, ground water move upward into the root zone and to the soil surface. Under such condition, ground water as well as irrigation water contributes to salinization of soils.

CAUSES OF ALKALINITY

Process where exchangeable Na content in soil due to precipitation of Ca and Mg as carbonate—Na_2CO_3 or $NaHCO_3$ by law of mass action, Ca and Mg replaced by Na on exchange complex.

1. Hydrolysis of sodium silicate or weathering of minerals.

$$Na\mathbf{X} + H_2O \text{—hydrolysis} \longrightarrow NaOH + H\,\mathbf{X}$$
$$NaOH + CO_2 \text{—hydrolysis} \longrightarrow NaHCO_3$$
$$2NaHCO_3 \text{—decomposition} \longrightarrow Na_2CO_3 + CO_2 + H_2O$$
$$Na_2SiO_3 \longrightarrow \text{Sodium silicate} \longrightarrow \text{highly sodic}$$
$$NaOH \longrightarrow \text{also highly sodic}$$
$$\text{Clay} \longrightarrow Al_2SiO_4 \longrightarrow \text{Aluminum silicate}$$
$$\text{Sand} \longrightarrow SiO_2 \longrightarrow \text{Silicate oxide}$$
$$\text{Glass} \longrightarrow K_2 \text{ or } NaSiO_3 \longrightarrow \text{Potassium or sodium silicate}$$
$$\text{Talk} \longrightarrow MgSiO_3 \longrightarrow \text{Magnesium silicate}$$
$$\text{Cement} \longrightarrow CaSiO_3 \longrightarrow \text{Calcium silicate}$$

2. Replace Na_2SO_4 or NaCl by $CaCO_3$

$$Na_2SO_4 + CaCO_3 \longrightarrow Na_2CO_3 + CaSO_4$$
$$2NaCl + CaCO_3 \longrightarrow Na_2CO_3 + CaCl_2$$

3. Hydrolysis of exchangeable Na

$$Na\,\mathbf{X}\,Na + H_2O + CO_2 \longrightarrow H\,\mathbf{X}\,H + Na_2CO_3$$
$$Na\,\mathbf{X}\,Na + CaCO_3 \longrightarrow Ca\,\mathbf{X}\,Ca + Na_2CO_3$$
$$Na\,\mathbf{X}\,Na + Ca\,(HCO_3) \longrightarrow Ca\,\mathbf{X}\,Ca + NaHCO_3$$

4. Reduction of Na_2SO_4 through microorganisms

$$Na_2SO_4 + 2C + CO_2 \longrightarrow Na_2S + 2CO_2$$
$$Na_2S + CO_2 + H_2O \longrightarrow H_2S + Na_2CO_3$$

5. Decomposition of organic matter

$$Na_2SO_4 \longrightarrow Na_2S + 2O_2$$
$$Na_2S + 2H_2O \longrightarrow H_2S + 2NaOH$$
$$NaOH + CO_2 \longrightarrow NaHCO_3$$

6. Use of alkali or sodic water for irrigation

7. Excessive use of basic fertilizers

Use of basic fertilizers like Na_2NO_3, basic slag, etc. may develop alkalinity in the soils.

8. Humid and semi-humid regions

Alkaline soils develop in other area also *e.g.* in semi-humid and temperate regions especially in depressions where drainage is defective and where the underground water table is high or close to the surface.

DISTRIBUTION OF SALT AFFECTED SOILS

World	—	952 million hectares	Szabocs (1974)
India	—	7.42 million hectares	Abrol and Bhumbla (1972-73)
U.P.	—	0.958 million hectares	Kanzaria and Patel (1954)

In India the state wise estimated area having salt affected soils is as follows :

TABLE 15.4. State wise estimated salinized area (CSSRI, Karnal)

States	*Area (thousand ha)*	*States*	*Area (thousand ha)*
Gujarat	**1649**	Orissa	135
Rajasthan	1138	Maharashtra	127
Uttar Pradesh	958	Karnataka	179
Punjab	480	Madhya Pradesh	242
Haryana	555	Andhra Pradesh	394
Kerala	45	Tamil Nadu	470
Goa	17	Andaman & Nicobar	1
Bihar	85	Delhi	0.6
Jummu & Kasmir	80	**Total**	**7421**

It is seen from the above data that **Gujarat** and **Rajasthan** has largest salinized area fallowed by U.P., in Uttar Pradesh salt affected area reclaimed by Uttar Pradesh Sodic Land Reclamation Project I & II under financed by World Bank.

Factors for the formation of saline and alkali soils

According to Dubey *et al.* (1984) and Patel *et al.* (1989)

(1) Aridity of climate
(2) Nearness of saline ground water
(3) Salt bearing subsoil strata
(4) Topography
(5) Ingress of sea water
(6) Injudicious use of saline water
(7) Poor quality of underground water
(8) High Water table

Characterization of Salt Affected Soils

The characteristics of different salt affected soils are as under :

1. Saline Non-Alkali Soils

These soils contain primarily the soluble salts of chlorides and sulphates of sodium, calcium and magnesium. The electrical conductivity of the saturation extract (ECe) is greater than 4 dSm^{-1} and the exchangeable sodium percentage (ESP) is less than 15. These soils may contain small quantity of bicarbonates, but soluble carbonates are generally absent. Ordinarily, the pH is less than 8.5. The saline soils are often recognized by the presence of white crusts of salts on the surface. These soils correspond to Hilgard's "**White alkali soils**" and to the "**Solonchaks**" of the Russian soil scientists. The solonchaks have been further classified on the basis of kind of soluble anions present in the soil. Accordingly, these may be

(*i*) Nitrate solonchaks
(*ii*) Chloride solonchaks
(*iii*) Sulphate solonchaks
(*iv*) Borate solonchaks
(*v*) Soda solonchaks
(*vi*) Sulphate chloride solonchaks, etc.

Sometimes the solonchaks may be active or residual. The active solonchaks are connected to ground water through capillary fringe and the residual solonchaks or dry solonchaks are not at all connected to ground water and are observed in extreme arid locations.

- Accumulation of neutral salts.
- Predominantly NaCl and Na_2SO_4. Na_2CO_3 is always absent in saline soils.
- In arid and semi-arid region
- High temperature and low rainfall
- Effect on plant : osmotic pressure increased, hence water come out from the plant into soil (reverse water uptake) and toxic effect of chlorides, borates and magnesium on plant.
- Known as white alkali soils, salts accumulates on soil surface and look whitish.
- White salts on bunds and ridges of beds and irrigation channels.

2. Saline Sodic Soils

These soils are formed as a result of salinization and alkalinization and have high amount of soluble salts and appreciable quantity of sodium on the exchange complex. The ESP of these soils is greater than 15 and the ECe is more than 4 dSm^{-1}. As long as excess salts are present, the appearance and properties of these soils are generally similar to those of saline soils. The pH readings are seldom higher than 8.5 and particles remain in flocculate conditions. If the excess salts are leached down, the properties of these soils may change markedly and became similar to those of non-saline alkali soils. As the concentration of the salts in the soil solution is lowered, some of the exchangeable sodium hydrolyzes and forms NaOH. This may change in Na_2CO_3 upon carbonation reaction. Soil became strongly alkali ($pH > 8.5$), the particles disperse and the soil becomes unfavorable for the entry and movement of water and for tillage. The management of saline sodic soils continues to be a problem until the excess salts and exchangeable sodium are removed from the root zone and a favorable physical condition of the soil is reestablished.

3. Sodic or Alkali Soils

The non-saline alkali soil is applied to soils for which the ESP is >15 and ECe is < 4 dS

m^{-1}. The pH usually ranges between 8.5 and 10. These soils correspond to Hillgard's "Black alkali" soils and in some cases to solonchaks as the latter term is used by the Russian scientists. They frequently occur in semi-arid and arid regions. The drainage and leaching of saline-alkali soils, in absence of gypsum, leads to the formation of such soils. Dispersed and dissolved organic matter present in the such soils may be deposited on the soil surface by evaporation, thus causing darkening and giving rise to the term "Black alkali" the characteristic morphological features of these soils are clay is highly dispersed and is may be transported downward through the soil and accumulated at lower depths. A few cm of the surface soil may be relatively coarse in texture and friable but below, where the clay accumulates, the soil may develop a dense layer of low permeability that may have the presence of carbonate ions, Ca and Mg are precipitated hence, the soil solutions of non-saline alkali soils usually contain only small amounts of these cations, sodium being the predominant one. ESP becomes high. Non-saline alkali soils in some areas of western United States have ESP considerably above 15, and yet the pH readings, especially in the surface soil, may be as low as 6. These soils have been referred to by De Sigmond as "Degraded alkali soils". The physical properties, however, are dominated by the exchangeable Na and are typically those of non-saline alkali soils.

- Known as black alkali due to dissolved organic matter
- Dominant salts are Na_2CO_3 and Na_2HCO_3
- Destroy physical properties of soil

4. Degraded Alkali Soil

If the extensive leaching of a saline-sodic soil occurs in the absence of any source of calcium or magnesium, part of the exchangeable sodium is gradually replaced by hydrogen. The resulting soil may be slightly acid with unstable structure. Such a soil is called degraded alkali or sodic soil.

$$[Clay]\,Na + H_2O \leftrightarrow H\,[clay + NaOH]$$

(Acid soil on the leaching surface horizon)

$$2NaOH + CO_2 = Na_2CO_3 + H_2O$$

(from soil) (Alkali soil in the sub-surface horizon)

Sodium carbonate (Na_2CO_3) dissolves humus and is deposited in the lower layer. The lower layer thus acquires a black colour. At the same time H-clay formed in this way does not remain stable. The process of break down of H-clay under alkaline condition is known as solodisation.

Chemical characteristics

1. The soil pH of surface soil is acidic (pH 6.0). This layer is usually very thin, hardly a few inches in depth.
2. The lower layer which constitutes the main body has a high pH (more than 8.5).
3. ESP is greater than 15 and ECe less than 4 dS/m.
4. The lower layer has black colour and develops prism like structure.
5. Soils became compact and have low infiltration and permeability.

PROBLEMS OF SALT AFFECTED SOILS

1. Saline Soils

There are various problems of saline soils that interfere with the plant growth.

(*i*) Soils are usually barren but potentially productive.

(*ii*) Wilting coefficient of saline soil is very high.

(*iii*) Amount of available soil moisture is low.

(*iv*) Absorption of water and nutrients.

Excessive salts in the soil solution increase the osmotic pressure of soil solution in comparison to cell sap. This osmotic effect increases the potential forces that hold water in the soil and makes it more difficult for plant roots to extract moisture. During a drying period, salt in soil solutions may be so concentrated as to kill plants by pulling water from them (exo-osmosis). Due to high salt concentration plants have to spent more energy to absorb water and to exclude salt from metabolically active sites. At the same time various nutrient elements become unavailable to plants.

(*v*) Salt toxicity : When the concentration of soluble salts increases to a high level then it produces toxic effect directly to plants such as root injury, inhibition of seed germination, etc.

2. Alkali or Sodic Soils

Excess exchangeable sodium in alkali soils affects both the physical and chemical properties of soils.

(*i*) Dispersion of soil colloids. Under alkali conditions, the damage is not due to salt concentration. The influence of exchangeable sodium on the over-all physical properties of soils is associated mainly with the behaviour of the clay and organic matter, in which most of the cation exchange capacity (CEC) is concentrated. The sodium (Na^+) ion adsorbed by clay colloids causes deflocculation or dispersion of clay, which result in a loss of desirable soil structure, and helps for the development of compact soil.

(*ii*) Other physical properties. Due to dispersion and compactness of soil, aeration, hydraulic conductivity, drainage and microbial activity are reduced.

(*iii*) Caustic influence. It results high sodicity caused by the sodium carbonate (Na_2CO_3) and bicarbonate ($NaHCO_3$).

(*iv*) Concentration of hydroxyl (OH^-) ion. High hydroxyl (OH^-) ion concentration no doubt has direct detrimental effect on plants. Damage from hydroxyl ions occurs at pH 10.5 or higher.

(*v*) Specific ion effect. The presence of excess sodium in sodic soils may induce deficiencies of other cation like calcium (Ca^{2+}) and magnesium (Mg^{2+}). The action of sodium in inducing deficiencies of Ca^{2+} and Mg^{2+} appears to be three fold :

(*a*) because sodium is comparatively loosely held in exchangeable form, the ions released to the soil solution in a fractional exchange are mostly sodium ions if the soil has a high exchangeable sodium percentage, (*b*) at the high pH values (sodic soil) usually associated with excess exchangeable sodium in the absence of excess salts, the soil solution contains bicarbonate and carbonate ions that tend to form insoluble precipitates of calcium and magnesium carbonates as follows :

$$Ca^{2+} + CO_3^{2+} = CaCO_3$$

(Soil solution) (Soil solution) (Insoluble precipitation)

(*c*) Exclusion of calcium and magnesium from absorption on competitive basis.

***(vi)* Availability of plant nutrients.** The high pH in alkali or sodic soils decreases the availability of many plant nutrients like P, N, Mg, Fe, Cu, and Zn.

RELATIONSHIP BETWEEN DIFFERENT SALT AFFECTED SOILS AND GROWTH OF DIFFERENT PLANTS

A graphic representation showing the relationship among SAR, ESP, and different salt affected soils is given in Fig. 15.2.

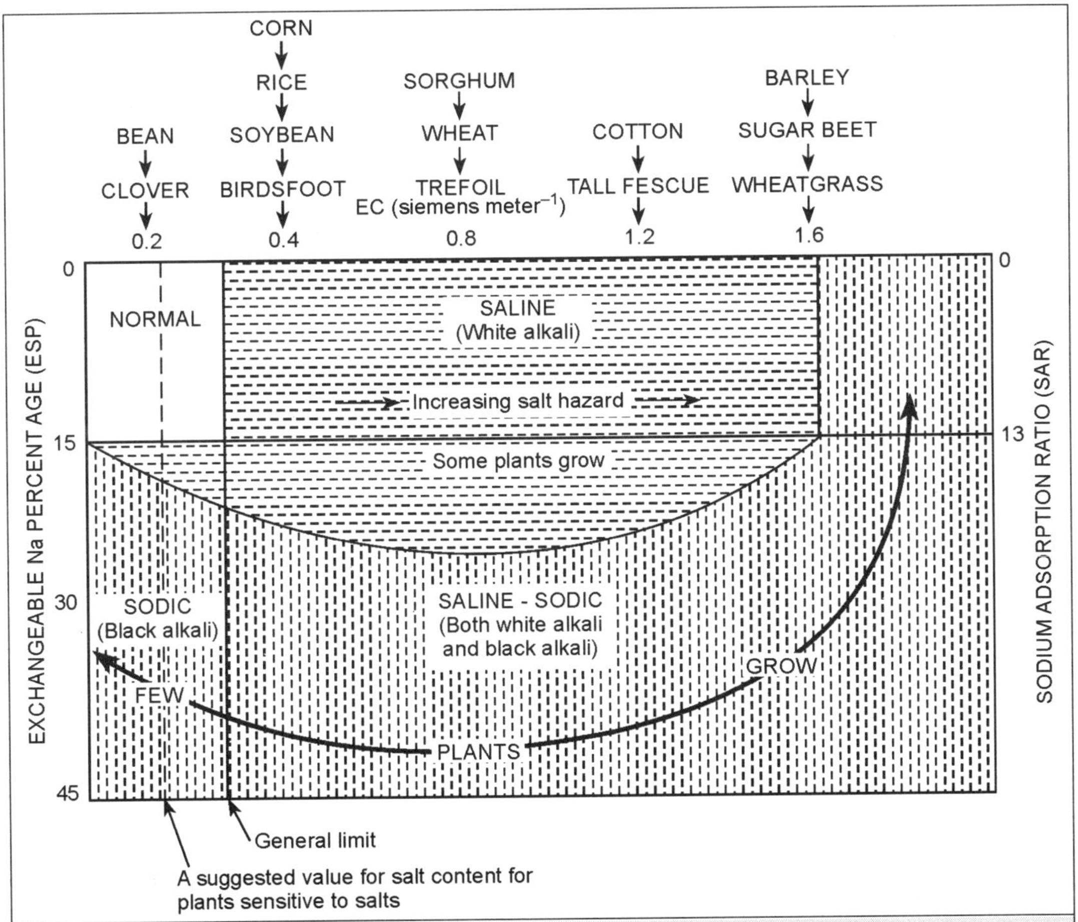

Fig. 15.2. Relationship among SAR, ESP and different salt affected soils

TABLE 15.5. Important Characterisitcs of Salt affected soils

Characteristics	*Saline soil*	*Alkali soil*	*Saline-alkali soil*	*Degraded alkali soil*
1. Content in soil	Excess soluble salts of sodium.	Absence of soluble salt and presence of excess exchangeable sodium on the soil complex.	These soils are both saline and non-saline alkali soil. It is a stage of transition. Soil contains Na-clay as well as soluble salts.	Hydrogen (H^+) ions in the upper layer and sodium (Na^+) in the lower layer.
2. Exchangeable calcium/sodium	Exchangeable calcium	Exchangeable sodium	—	—
3. Colour	White	Black	—	Black in lower layer
4. Soil pH	Less than 8.5	8.5-10	More than 8.5	pH about 6 in the surface soil and pH 8.5 in the lower layer
5. ECe (dSm^{-1})	More than 4	Less than 4	More than 4	Less than 4
6. Exchangeable sodium percentage (ESP)	Less than 15 of total CEC	More than 15 of total CEC	More than 15 of total CEC	Usually more than 15 of total CEC
7. Sodium adsorption ratio (SAR)	Less than 13	More than 13	More than 13	Less than 13 in the surface and greater than 13 in the lower horizon
8. Total soluble salt content	More than 0.1%.	Less than 0.1%	More than 0.1%	Less than 0.1%
9. Dominant salts	Sulphate (SO_4^{2-}) chloride (Cl^-) and nitrates (NO_3^-)	Sodium carbonate (Na_2CO_3)	—	Sodium carbonate (Na_2CO_3) in lower layer
10. Other name	White alkali (Solonchak)	Black alkali (Solonetz)	—	—
11. Organic matter content	Slightly less than normal soils	Very low due to the presence of sodium carbonate (Na_2CO_3) because it absorbs organic matter and so there is great depletion of organic matter. Therefore, these soils are almost barren (Usar)	Variable	Low
12. Physical condition of the soil	Flocculated condition, permeable to water and air. Soil structure optimum.	Deflocculated condition, permeability to water and air is poor. Very poor soil structure.	Flocculated or deflocculated depending upon the presence of sodium salts and Na-clay	Compact low infiltration and permeability. It develops columnar structure
13. Geographic distribution	Arid and semi-arid climate	Semi-arid or semi-humid climate	—	—

CLASSIFICATION OF SALINE SOILS

(1) USSSL

The classification given by USSSL for saline soil is as follows :

ECe millimhos/cm or dSm^{-1}	% salt in saturation extract	Class	Effect on crops
< 2	0 < 0.1	Non saline	Salinity effects mostly negligible.
2-4	0.1-0.3	Very slightly saline	Yield of very sensitive crops may be restricted.
4-8	0.3-0.5	Moderately saline	Yield of many crops restricted.
8-16	0.5-1.0	Strongly saline	Only tolerant crops yield satisfactorily, bare spots appear.
> 16	> 1.0	Very strongly saline	Only a few very tolerant crops yield satisfactorily.

(2) Seth (1967)

Because of the very high relationship of ESP with pH, attempts have also been made to classify the soil into different alkalinity group. The classification proposed by Seth (1967) is as follows :

Group	Alkalinity		Salinity	
	pH ranges (1 : 2 soil water ratio)	Classification	Conductivity (mmhos/cm)(1 : 2 soil water ratio)	Clasification
A	< 8.0	Normal	< 1.0	Normal
B	8.0-8.5	Alkaline	1.0-2.0	Tending to become saline
C	8.5-9.0	Very alkaline	2.0-3.0	Highly saline
D	> 9.0	Highly alkaline	> 3.0	

(3) Soil Survey Manual

Class	Salt %	ECe (dSm^{-1})
Free	< 0.15	< 4
Slightly affected	0.15-0.35	4-8
Moderately affected	0.35-0.65	8-15
Strongly affected	> 0.65	> 15

(4) CSSRI, Karnal (Anon., 1974)

Nature of hazard	Limit of ECe (dSm^{-1})	ESP	pH
Safe	0-2	0-10	< 8.4
Slight	2-4	10-20	8.4-8.8
Moderate	4-8	20-40	8.8-9.4
High	8-16	40-60	9.4-9.8
Very high	> 16	> 60	> 9.8

Classification of Sodic/Alkali Soils

According to USDA based on ESP

Class	alkalinity Class	ESP
I	No alkalinity	< 15
II	Slightly alkalinity	15-25
III	Moderately alkalinity	25-30
IV	Strongly alkalinity	30-50
V	Very strongly alkalinity	> 50

CROP GROWTH ON SALT AFFECTED SOILS

The crop growth on salt affected soils is poor due to one or another reason. The various reasons given for poor crop growth under such conditions are discussed below :

1. Causes of poor crop growth on saline soils

Due to the presence of excess salts and the absence of significant amount of exchangeable sodium, the saline soils are generally flocculated. The permeability is equal to or higher than those of similar non-saline soils. Sodium seldom comprises more than half of the soluble salts, and hence, it is not adsorbed. The higher salt content of these soils is primarily responsible for the low crop yields. Following three theories have been put forward for explaining the phenomena of poor crop growth on saline soil.

(*a*) Water availability theory. Hayward and Spurr (1944) grow corn plants in a nutrient solution and then transferred them to other solutions in which the kind and concentration of solutes were varied. The solutes tested were Na_2SO_4, NaCl, $CaCl_2$, mannitel and sucrose. Measurements of the rate of water absorption by the roots were made over a short period of time just after.

The explanation for the lower yields of the plants with excess $MgCl_2$ and $MgSO_4$ than other salts is that Mg^{+2} had some specific detrimental effect that was not shared by Na and Ca transference of the plants to the new solutions. The rate of water intake was found to decrease with increasing concentration of each solute to be essentially independent of the nature of the solute, when the additions were expressed on an osmotic basis, *i.e.* in terms of the specific free energy of the water.

Wadleigh and Ayers (1945) grew bean plants in cultures of soils that were treated with different quantities of NaCl and were allowed to dry to different degrees before watering. They found that the growth of the plants decreased with an increase in both matrix suction and salt content of the soil, but that it could be expressed to a good approximation as a function of the total suction of the water in the soil, as estimated by the sum of the matrix and solute suction components. The results indicated not only that the salt effect was a water availability effect but also that the soil water, independent of the relative proportion of the matrix suction and solute suction components.

(*b*) Osmotic inhibition theory. According to osmotic inhibition theory, plant growth is inhibited by the excess of solute taken up from saline media. The osmotic inhibition theory thus postulates that the salts act inside the plants, but it does not specify how the inhibition of growth is effected. The inhibition could even result in even part from water deficiency in a sense different from that envisioned by the water availability theory. The presence of excess solutes in the plant decreases the free energy of unit mass of water even though the absolute mass of water in the excess of salts present externally.

(*c*) Specific toxicity theory. According to the specific toxicity theory, soil salinity exerts a detrimental effect on plants through the toxicity of one or more specific ions (cations as well as anions) in the salts present in excess. Accordingly, there may be toxicity of chlorides and bicarbonates (boron) and to a lesser concentration of magnesium or its salts may also induce calcium deficiency.

It is very difficult to isolate any specific postulates as mentioned above for explaining the causes of poor crop growth on saline soil as all are acting simultaneously.

2. Causes of poor crop growth on alkali soils

The primary problem of these soils is high exchangeable sodium, which interferes with the growth of most of crop plants. The soil is generally dispersed, resulting in low permeability. The anions present consist mostly chlorides, sulphates and bicarbonates. A small amount of carbonates often occur. The presence of carbonate increases the pH of the soil and also precipitates the calcium and magnesium. The reasons of low crop production on such soils are as follows :

(*a*) Adverse physical conditions. The alkali soils have poor physical conditions. The permeability of air and water and the hydraulic conductivity are at a lower most state due to breakdown of aggregates and dispersion of individual clay colloids. The breakdown of aggregates is due to dissolution of organic matter, which acts as a cementing agent for binding individual clay particles, due to formation of alkali solution. The dispersed clay plugs all the macro and micro capillaries thereby hampering the movement of air and water. Such dispersed clay swells considerably due to high hydration capacity of Na ions and remain unflocculated in presence of water. The downward movement of water is practically zero and hence they remain waterlogged when irrigation is given or water is added through rain. On drying, such soils form very large clods, which are very hard in nature. The hard crust formation on the surface of the soil is most common characteristics. The tillage operations are very difficult to carry due to increase in bulk density, which is due to deflocculating of clay. Because of very adverse physical conditions, the germination as well as the root growth is considerably reduced. Because of this reduction, the overall crop growth is not at all satisfactory.

(*b*) High sodium on exchange complex. Excess amount of sodium reduces the crop growth considerably *i.e.* there arises a sodium toxicity because of excess concentration of Na. The plants exhibit the deficiency of Ca and to some extent Mg due to well-known principle complementary ion effect *i.e.* higher concentration of Na would reduce the uptake of Ca^{++} and Mg^{++}. The relative concentrations of Ca and Mg in such soils are low due to precipitation of these ions during process of alkalization. The relationship such as Ca/Na, Mg/Na, (Ca + Mg)/Na or K/Na are well-known and antagonistic relationships.

(*c*) Effect of high pH. The solution soils have high pH and the values range from 8.5 to as high as 10 or 11. The high pH reduces the availability of Zn, Cu, Mn and Fe. The microbial activity is also at standstill due to unfavorable pH and the processes of mineralization, ammonification or nitrification are practically negligible. Apart from nutritional deficiency due to high pH, the higher concentration of OH^- ion itself is not favorable to crop growth.

In case of saline-alkali soils excess sodium may reduce the crop growth. However, the physical conditions of such soils are not disturbed due to excess amount of salts.

PRINCIPLES AND DIFFERENT METHODS OF RECLAMATION

Principles for any reclamation technique to be permanent, three essential requirements have to be met with (Kelley, 1951).

(*i*) The land must be prevented from reverting to original conditions.

(*ii*) Salts of alkali must be removed from red zones.

(*iii*) The repair of the damage, already done to the soil, should be substantial.

Methods of Reclamation

I. Mechanical

1. Construction of embankment to prevent tidal see water.
2. Land leveling and contour bunding.
3. Establishment of drainage network.
4. Breaking of hardpan in the subsurface layer through boring auger hole.

II. Hydrological

1. Flushing 2. Leaching 3. Drainage

III. Chemical

1. Use of amendments

IV. Physical

1. Scrapping of salt crust.
2. Deep tillage, sub soiling, profile inversion.
3. Use of soil conditioners *e.g.* sand, *tanch*, ash, manures and synthetic polymers like PVAC, PAM, and PVPC.

V. Biological

1 Use of manures

2. Green manure

3. Selection of salt tolerant crops after afforestation

Hydrological method

1. Flushing. The salts can be removed by flushing which is the surface washing out of salts with the runoff water, which is collected at the slopy end of the field. One serious drawback with flushing, as a means of removing soluble salts is its inability to flush through the soil and the salts have to come up to the surface for being removed through flushes. The flushing method is employed where moisture transmission characteristics into the profile are extremely poor. The USSSL does not advocate flushing as an effective means for washing out the salts.

2. Leaching

(A) *Time of leaching.* Most desirable time is when soil is dry. Excessive drying and shrinking of very fine textured soils, however, may oppose leaching since water will move through the cracks of the soil so fast that leaching of salts is poorly accomplished. Leaching is necessary when the salt level of the soil solution begins to approach that of the specific salt tolerance of the crop to be grown and not after each growing season. The salt present in the irrigation water used must not be allowed to accumulate in excessive amounts during the crop season. Therefore, it may be necessary to leach the salt during crop season.

(B) *Frequency of leaching.* Frequency of leaching depends on several factors as follows :

(*i*) Poorer the quality of water, the more frequently the soil must be leached.

(*ii*) A fine textured soil requires more water than coarser textured soil to wet the same depth. More impermeable soil, the more water is required per single irrigation at less frequent intervals.

(*iii*) A soil having low underground water table depth will need more frequent leachings with less amount of water per irrigation.

(*iv*) The frequency will be more in summer as compared to winter.

The use of canal water or water having good quality is most desirable. Simultaneously, the provision for drainage by suitable method and an outlet for drained water should also be provided. This requires considerable knowledge of hydrology as well as drainage engineering.

Effect of leaching on soil nutrients. In general, due to heavy leaching, the losses of N, P, Mn and Zn have been observed under various experiments. The degree of deficiency has to be worked out independently in each case and adequate fertilization with macro as well as micronutrients should be made for successful crop production.

Leaching Requirement (LR). The leaching requirement may be defined as the fraction of the irrigation water that must be leached through the root zone to control soil salinity at any specific level.

The leaching requirement (LR) is simply the ration of the equivalent depth of the drainage water to the depth of irrigation water and may be expressed as a fraction or as per cent. Under the assumed conditions (uniform aerial application of irrigation water, no rainfall, no removal of salt in the harvested crop and no precipitation of soluble constituents in the soil), this ration is equal to the inverse ratio of the corresponding electrical conductivities as follows :

$$LR = \frac{D_{dw} \times 100}{D_{iw}} = \frac{EC_{iw} \times 100}{EC_{dw}}$$

where, LR = Leaching requirement expressed in percentage

D_{dw} = Depth of drainage water in inches

D_{iw} = Depth of irrigation water in inches

EC_{iw} = Electrical conductivity of the irrigation water in dSm^{-1}

EC_{dw} = Electrical conductivity of the drainage water in dSm^{-1}

In applying this equation, a value is usually assumed for EC_{dw} (8 dSm^{-1} for most of the field crops) to represent the maximum soil salinity that can be tolerated. For irrigation waters with conductivities of 1, 2 and 3 dSm^{-1}, respectively, the leaching requirement will be 13, 25 and 38 per cent (taking the value of EC_{dw} as 8 dSm^{-1}).

3. Drainage. Drainage in agriculture is the process of removal of excess water from soil. Excess water discharged by flow over the soil surface is referred to as surface drainage, and flow through the soil is termed internal or subsurface drainage. The term "artificial drainage" and "natural drainage" indicate whether or not man has changed or influenced the drainage process. The design of drainage systems is influenced by many factors which taken into consideration *e.g.* drainage requirement, water transmission properties of soil and boundary conditions, water application efficiency, physiography of land, etc. The types of relief drains are pumped wells; tile or open drains may serve of these purposes. The drain should be placed below 2 m depth with a distance of 25 to 75 m according to soil texture orienting perpendicular to the direction of ground water flow.

CHEMICAL PROCEDURE–USE OF AMENDMENTS

In case of saline-sodic and sodic soils, the exchange complex is saturated to varying degree with Na. The reclamation procedure in such cases also involves the use of amendments for replacing exchangeable Na.

A. Different types of amendments

The chemical amendments are used as under :

1. Soluble calcium salts *e.g.*

(*i*) Calcium chloride ($CaCl_2.2H_2O$)
(*ii*) Gypsum ($CaSO_4.2H_2O$)
(*iii*) Calcium sulphate ($CaSO_4$)

2. Acid or acid formers e.g.

(*i*) Sulphur (S)
(*ii*) Sulphuric acid (H_2SO_4)
(*iii*) Iron sulphate ($FeSO_4.7H_2O$)
(*iv*) Aluminium sulphate ($Al_2(SO_4)_3.18H_2O$)
(*v*) Lime sulphur (calcium poly sulphide) (CaS_5)
(*vi*) Pyrites (FeS_2)

3. Calcium salt of low solubility

(*i*) Ground lime stone ($CaCO_3$)
(*ii*) By-product lime from sugar factories *e.g.* pressmud

The kind and amount of chemical amendment to be used for the replacement of exchangeable Na in soils depend upon the soil characteristics, the desired rate of replacement and economic considerations. Soluble calcium salts are preferred when soil does not contain alkaline earth carbonates or calcium carbonate. Acid or acid formers are preferred when soil contains alkaline earth carbonates or $CaCO_3$. Acid or acid formers are also used along with calcium salt of low solubility but the rate of reaction is very low.

B. Advantages and disadvantages of amendments

The $CaCl_2$ is highly soluble and Ca is readily available but its cost is a prohibitive factor. Iron and aluminium sulphates also hydrolyse readily in the soil to form H_2SO_4 but here also the cost is acting. Amendment, which can be used in calcareous soils but it requires special equipments and is hazardous in handling. Sulphur is a slow acting amendment and large applications are needed. It requires more time for complete oxidation. In cool winter season, the oxidation rate is too slow to give satisfactory results. Since the oxidation process is fully microbial, an optimum amount of moisture has to be maintained continuously in the soil. The soil should not be leached until sufficient time has been allowed for most of the sulphur to oxidise. Limestone is a low cost amendment but the solubility is affected by pH of the soil and particle size of the amendment. Pressmud, a byproduct from sugar factories, contains about 70 to 80% $CaCO_3$ and about 80% organic matter. Since Ca is present as $CaCO_3$, it is slow acting amendment requiring acid or acid formers. As against carbonation process, pressmud from sugar factories employing sulphitation process has superior reclamation value, as it contains sulphate of lime instead of its carbonate. Like S, pyrite has to be oxidized first which is a slow process and the rate of reaction depends on particle size. Again the application of pyrites at higher rate markedly decreases its oxidation rate. It is a cheap amendment.

Gypsum is the most common amendment used for reclaiming saline-sodic as well as non-saline sodic soils. It is a low cost amendment and the rate of reaction in replacing Na is limited on its solubility in water, which is about 0.25% at ordinary temperature. Khosla and Abrol have recommended a size of 0.59 mm (30 mesh) for maximum reactivity of gypsum. However, for practical purposes 2 mm size (10 mesh screen) is sufficient. While applying gypsum, mixing it in shallow depth (upper 10 cm depth) is more effective. It is applied by broadcast method or incorporated by disc plough. Gypsum is applied at the time of ponding or leaching. Gypsum directly prevents crust formation, swelling, dispersion and acts as mulch in case of surface application and indirectly increases porosity, structural stability, infiltration and hydraulic properties, soil tilth, drainage and leaching and reduces dry soil strength.

C. Chemical reactions of amendments in soil

The following chemical reactions illustrate the manner in which various amendments react in the different classes of alkali soils. In these equations the letter **X** represents the soil exchange complex.

Class 1. Soils Containing Alkaline-Earth Carbonates

Gypsum :

$$2Na\mathbf{X} + CaSO_4 \leftrightarrow Ca\mathbf{X}_2 + Na_2SO_4$$

Sulphur :

(1) $2S + 3O_2 \leftrightarrow 2SO_3$ (microbiological oxidation)

(2) $SO_3 + H_2O \leftrightarrow H_2SO_4$

(3) $H_2SO_4 + CaCO_3 \leftrightarrow CaSO_4 + CO_2 + H_2O^*$

(4) $2Na\mathbf{X} + CaSO_4 \leftrightarrow Ca\mathbf{X}_2 + Na_2SO_4$

Lime-Sulphur (Calcium Polyphosphate) :

(1) $CaS_5 + 8O_2 + 4H_2O \leftrightarrow CaSO_4 + 4H_2SO_4$

(2) $H_2SO_4 + CaCO_3 \leftrightarrow CaSO_4 + CO_2 + H_2O^*$

(3) $2Na\mathbf{X} + CaSO_4 \leftrightarrow Ca\mathbf{X}_2 + Na_2SO_4$

Iron Sulphate :

(1) $FeSO_4 + H_2O \leftrightarrow H_2SO_4 + FeO$

(2) $H_2SO_4 + CaCO_3 \leftrightarrow CaSO_4 + CO_2 + H_2O$*

(3) $2Na\mathbf{X} + CaSO_4 \leftrightarrow Ca\mathbf{X}_2 + Na_2SO_4$

*The reaction of H_2SO_4 and $CaCO_3$ may also be written as follows : $H_2SO_4 + 2CaCO_3 \leftrightarrow CaSO_4 + Ca(HCO_3)_2$. Under these conditions the $Ca(HCO_3)_2$ as well as the $CaSO_4$ would be available for reaction with exchangeable sodium and 1 atom of sulphur when oxidized to H_2SO_4, could theoretically result in the replacement of 4 sodium ions by calcium.

Class 2. Soils Containing No Alkaline-Earth Carbonates; pH 7.5 or Higher

Gypsum : Same as in class 1.

Sulphur : Steps (1) and (2) as in class 1.

(3) $2Na\mathbf{X} + H_2SO_4 \leftrightarrow 2H\mathbf{X} + Na_2SO_4$

Lime-Sulphur : Step (1) as in class 1.

(2) $10Na\mathbf{X} + 4H_2SO_4 + CaSO_4 \leftrightarrow 8H\mathbf{X} + Ca\mathbf{X_2} + 5Na_2SO_4$

Iron Sulphate : Step (1) as in class 1.

(2) $2Na\mathbf{X} + H_2SO_4 \leftrightarrow 2H\mathbf{X} + Na_2SO_4$

Limestone :

(1) $2Na\mathbf{X} + CaCO_3 \leftrightarrow Ca\mathbf{X}_2 + Na_2CO_3$

(2) $Na\mathbf{X} + HOH \leftrightarrow NaOH + H\mathbf{X}$

(3) $2H\mathbf{X} + CaCO_3 \leftrightarrow Ca\mathbf{X}_2 + CO_2 + H_2O$

Class 3. Soils Containing No Alkaline-Earth Carbonates; pH Less Than 7.5

Gypsum : Same as in class 1 and 2.

Sulphur : Same as in class 1 and 2.

Lime-Sulphur : Same as in class 2.

Iron Sulphate : Same as in class 2.

Limestone: Same as in class 2, and if exchangeable hydrogen is present :

(1) $2H\mathbf{X} + CaCO_3 \leftrightarrow Ca\mathbf{X}_2 + CO_2 + H_2O$

Control. The retardation of evaporation is an important feature of the control of salty Soils. This will not only save moisture but will also retard the upward translocation of soluble salts into the root zone. Salt free irrigation water should be used. The use of salt resistant crops is an important feature of the successful management of saline and alkali soils.

Highly salt resistant crops	—	Barley, Sugarbeat, cotton etc.
Moderately salt resistant crops	—	Wheat, rice, maize etc.
Low salt resistant crops	—	Beans, raddish etc.

Other Methods (Salt Precipitation Theory)

Besides these, recently salt precipitation theory is employed satisfactorily for the reclamation of sodic soils. The elimination of salts and exchangeable sodium from soils by leaching is presently practising, but the leached salts have been washed into groundwaters or streams, making those waters more salty and again that too much salty water is used for irrigation purpose. Due to such use the soils are further subjected to salt problems. With this view, a new concept in managing salty soils has been developed and that is known as **precipitation of salts**.

This idea suggests that instead of leaching salts completely away, they can be leached to only 0.9-1.8 m deep (3-6 ft) where much of the salt would form slightly soluble gypsum ($CaSO_4.2H_2O$) or carbonates ($CaCO_3$, $MgCO_3$) during dry periods and not react any longer as soluble salts.

The amount of salt precipitating out will vary with the cation and anion composition of those salts. The ions precipitating will be mostly those of calcium, magnesium, carbonate, bicarbonate and sulphate. Estimates are that 30 per cent of the total salts may eventually precipitate. The rest two-third of salts cause very little effect on the yields of corn and tomatoes.

The management technique is simply to apply less water, but to do it more carefully to ensure uniform depth of wetting.

Gypsum requirement (GR)

The main principle for the reclamation of sodic or alkali soils is to replace exchangeable Na by another cation calcium (Ca^{2+}), of all calcium compounds, gypsum ($CaSO_4.2H_2O$) is considered the best and cheapest for the reclamation purpose. Calcium (Ca^{2+}) solubilized from gypsum replaces sodium (Na^+), leaving soluble sodium sulphate (Na_2SO_4) in the water, which is then leached out. Gypsum requirement (GR) is expressed as me of Ca^{2+} per 100 gm soil.

The gypsum requirement (GR) is the calculated amount of gypsum necessary to add to reclaim the soil. For calculating the dosage of gypsum needed to reclaim a particular alkali soil, advantage is taken of the assumption that through the use of calcareous amendment, the desired level of quantitative replacement of exchangeable sodium from the soil by calcium is possible. Since an exchangeable sodium percentage (ESP) of 10 and below is considered safe for tolerable physical condition of the soil, replacement by calcium to this level (ESP, 10) is all that is attempted in practice, through for certain tolerant crops like paddy, wheat and barley the replacement may be attained to higher ESP level than 10. Gypsum requirement is determined from the formula

Gypsum requirement (GR) *i.e.* me of Ca^{2+}/100 g soil

$$= \frac{[\text{ESP (initial)} - \text{ESP (final)} \times \text{CEC}]}{100}$$

ESP (initial) is obtained from the analysis of soil before reclamation or application of gypsum; ESP (final) is usually kept at 10 and CEC is the cation exchange capacity in me/ 100 g or Cmol(P^+) kg^{-1} of the soil.

For example, the gypsum requirement of a soil having initial ESP 60, final ESP 10 and CEC 30 Cmol(P^+) kg^{-1} will be :

$$\text{me of } Ca^{2+}/100\text{g soil} = \frac{[60 - 10] \times 30}{100} = \frac{50 \times 30}{100} = 15$$

Since one hectare of soil to a depth of 15 cm (6 inches) weighs approximately 2×10^6 kg and 1 me of replaceable gypsum as $CaSO_4.2H_2O$ equals 860 ppm of amendment, the theoretical amount of gypsum required per hectare will be :

$$\text{Theoretical amount of gypsum (kg) ha}^{-1} = \frac{860}{106} \times 2 \times 10^6 \times 15$$
$$= 1720 \times 15$$
$$= 25800 \text{ kg}$$
$$= 25.80 \text{ tons}$$

This has to be multiplied by the purity factor of gypsum to arrive at the field requirement of the amendment. Once, the gypsum requirement in tons per hectare is known the equivalent quantities of other chemical ameliorants can be calculated from the following conversion table 15.6.

TABLE 15.6. Estimated efficiencies for various materials used to reclaim sodic soils compared to gypsum

Amendment	*Amount (tons) equivalent to 1 ton of gypsum*
Gypsum ($CaSO_4.2H_2O$)	1.00
Sulphuric acid (H_2SO_4)	0.57
Sulphur (S)	0.18
Iron sulphate ($FeSO_4.7H_2O$)	1.62
Lime sulphur (Calcium polysulphide) containing 24 per cent sulphur)	0.75

It is evident that quantitative replacement of sodium by calcium from the soil exchangeable complex is never possible. Two factors which govern the level of equilibrium in soils and soil solutions between sodium and calcium ions are : (*i*) initial exchangeable sodium percentage of soil and (*ii*) the total cation concentration of the soil solution. Usually to compensate for these factors, the U.S. Salinity laboratory staffs recommend that the gypsum requirement obtained by calculation may be multiplied by 1.25 to obtain the desired level of sodium replacement.

The efficiency of gypsum and other amendments will depend on the fineness as well as purity of the material. Usually, fineness with particle size of 2 mm or 0.59 mm (10 or 30 mesh sieve) has been found optimum for the amelioration purpose. Through incorporation and mixing of the amendment in the soil is another important factor in determining its beneficial effect. However, the calculation for the actual amount of gypsum for field application is not possible because various other side factors interferes with the determination of exchangeable sodium percentage (ESP) *viz*. texture, surface area and type of clay minerals, organic matter and exchangeable magnesium. In India, it is evident that even 50 per cent of the theoretical gypsum requirement for replacement of exchangeable sodium in sodic soils has improved their physical conditions and assisted response to management practices.

The amount of gypsum ($CaSO_4. 2H_2O$) and sulphur (S) required to ameliorate the sodic soil on the basis of exchangeable sodium is given in table 15.7.

TABLE 15.7. Amount of amendments required to reclaim sodic soils on the basis of exchangeable sodium

Exchangeable sodium (mg/100 g soil)	*Gypsum (t/ha)*	*Sulphur (t/ha)*
1	2.12	0.40
2	4.25	0.80
3	6.50	1.20
4	8.62	1.60
5	10.75	2.00
6	12.87	2.40
7	15.00	2.80
8	17.12	3.20
9	19.37	3.60
10	21.50	4.00

D. Quantity of amendments to be added

The weight of the gypsum worked out on the basis of Schoonover's method is not entirely applied in the soil or 100 per cent of GR is never applied in the soil. These are evidences to show that even 50 per cent of the theoretical gypsum requirement for replacement of exchangeable Na in alkali soils has improved their physical properties and assisted response to management practices. Generally, 50 to 75 per cent of GR (as determined by Schoonover's method) has been found most satisfactory in many types of soils.

The equivalent proportion of different amendments in relation to 1 ton of gypsum is as Table 15.6.

Gypsum is the most common amendment that is used for the purpose of reclamation. The rate of addition of gypsum can be determined by estimating the gypsum requirement (GR) of a soil by Schoonover's method. Alternatively, the GR can also be determined by knowing the exchangeable Na in soil and working out the extent of reduction of Na on equivalent basis. The gypsum requirement for replacing 1 me of Na upto a soil depth of 15 cm comes to about 1.92 tonnes/ha. Since an ESP of 10 and below is considering safe for tolerable physical condition of the soil, replacement by calcium to this level is all that is attempted in practice.

E. The organic amendments

The organic amendments as such do not help in replacing the exchangeable Na as against the gypsum or other amendments. Primarily, they improve the physical condition of the soil by improving the aggregation in the soil. The most common organic amendment is the FYM which is added in the first year of reclamation @ 50 tonnes/ha and is reduced to half in succeeding years. The efficiency of gypsum has been found to increase when it is applied along with FYM. Molasses and pressmud, which are sugar factory waste, have also been used. Molasses contain 60-70% carbohydrates, 4-5% potash, 2% lime and 0.5% each of N, P_2O_5, H_2SO_4 and iron and aluminium oxide.

Green manuring with Dhaincha (*Sesbania aculeata*) has been found most successful. The juice of green plants can neutralize high alkalinity, its initial pH being 4.01, with only slight rise even within a month. In black cotton soil, it thrives well under moderately saline conditions and can with stand high alkalinity, water logging or drought so that it is remarkably suited in that region to alkali soils, characterized by such adverse conditions. Sulphurated hydrogen is generated by the decomposition of Dhaincha.

Paddy straw or rice husk have also been used at a rate varying between 15 to 30 tonnes/ha. Weeds like *Argemone mexicana* has been found very suitable for alkali soils. It contains (on dry weight basis) 1.8% KNO_3, 0.3% $CaHPO_4$, 0.4% $CaSO_4$, 4.2% organic acid and 0.8% sugar. When powder of argemone was added to the soil @ 2.5 tonnes/ha, it lowered the soil pH from 10.0 to 7.8 which slowly leveled to 8.5 in 30 days. The other weeds found suitable for the purpose of green manuring are ***Ipomea grandiflora*** and ***Pongamia glabra.*** The Russian workers have suggested the addition of cellulose with sufficient addition of nitrogen for easy decomposition.

Management Practices

During the process of reclamation of salt affected soils the field is not kept fallow. Growing of crop is always practiced as the roots of the growing crop exert a marked beneficial effect on the process of leaching by improving the state of aggregation of soil. A crop can be grown by adopting following practices :

A. Selection of crop

The selection of crop is based on tolerance of a crop to either salinity or sodicity. The list of salt tolerant as well as sodium tolerant crops is given below :

TABLE 15.8. Yield decrease of certain crops due to variable salt levels in soil solutions

Crop	*EC x 10^3 of saturation extract causing yield decreases*		
	10%	*25%*	*50%*
Field crops			
Barley for grain	12	16	18
Sugarbeet	10	13	16
Cotton	10	12	16
Safflower	8	11	12
Wheat	7	10	14
Sorghum	6	9	12
Soybean	5.5	7	9
Sugarcane	3	7	5.5
Rice	5	6	8
Corn	5	6	7
Bean	1.5	2	2.5

Vegetable crops			
Beet (garden)	8	10	12
Tomato	4	6.5	8
Cabbage	2.6	4	7
Potato	2.5	4	6
Sweet potato	2.5	3.5	6
Onion	2	2.5	4
Carrot	1.5	2.5	4

The salt tolerance limits given in Table 15.9 are general. The salt tolerance of a crop would vary according to age of the crop or the growth stage. It will also vary according to variety of a given crop. Hence considerable work is needed for establishing these limits for local crops and their varieties.

TABLE 15.9. Tolerance of various crops to ESP

ESP	*Class*	*Crop*
2-10	Very sensitive	Deciduous fruits, Nuts, Citrus, Avocado
10-20	Sensitive	Beans
20-40	Moderately tolerant	Clover, Oats, Tall fescue, Rice, Dallis grass
40-60	Tolerant	Wheat, Cotton, Alfalfa, Barley, Tomatoes, Beet
More than 60	Highly tolerant	Crested wheat grass Tall wheat grass Rhodes grass

B. Tillage

Deep tillage should be practiced as it increases the permeability of the soil thereby facilitating leaching of salts. It also makes the root zone more friable. If the subsoil layer has accumulation of salts or sodium, the deep tillage is not advisable.

TABLE 15.10. Relative tolerance of crop plants to salt

High salt tolerance	*Medium salt tolerance*	*Low salt tolerance*
FRUIT CROPS		
Date palm	Pomegranate, Fig, Olive, Grape, Cantaloup	Pear, Apple, Orange, Grapefruit. Prune, Plum, Almond, Apricot, Peach, Strawberry, Lemon, Avocado
VEGETABLE CROPS		
ECe × 10^3 = 12	ECe × 10^3 = 10	ECe × 10^3 = 10
Garden beets, Kale, Asperagus, Spinach	Tomato, Broccoli, Cabbage, Black pepper, Cauliflower Lettuce, Sweet corn, Potatoes (White Rose), Carrot, Onion, Peas, Squash, Cucumber	Radish. Celery Green beans
ECe × 10^3 = 4	ECe × 10^3 = 4	ECe × 10^3 = 3

FORAGE CROPS		
ECe × 10^3 = 18	ECe × 10^3 = 12	ECe × 10^3 = 12
Alkali sacaton Salt grass Nuttall alkaligrass Bermuda grass Rhodes grass Rescue grass Canada wildrye Western wheatgrass Barley (hay) Brids foot trefoil	White sweet clover, Yellow sweet clover, Perennial ryegrass Mountain brome, Strawberry, Clover, Dallis grass. Sudan grass, Hubam clover, Alfalfa (California common), Tall fescue, Rye (hay) Wheat (hay), Oats (hay) Orchardgrass, Black gram Meadow fescue, Reed canary Smooth brome, Tall meadow, oatgrass, Cicer milkvetch, Sourclover Sickle milkvetch,	White Dutch clover Meadow foxtail Alsike clover Red clover Ladino clover
ECe × 10^3 = 4	ECe × 10^3 = 4	ECe × 10^3 = 2

TABLE 15.11. Screening of varieties of different crops for saline condition

Crop	*Varieties*
Wheat	Kharachia, J-24, Popatia, Arnej-206, Sonalika, Kalyan Sona
Bajra	B.K.-560, GHB-235, MH-169, MH-179, GHB-227 for fodder
Cotton	G.Cot.D.H.-7, Dhumal, Kalyan
Sugarcane	Co.8338, Co.791
Groundnut	JL-24, J-11, Robert, Punjab-1
Castor	GCH-4, SKF-73, GAUCH-1, VP-1
Jowar	Gundari, C-10-2, CSH-5, S.R.F.-204 for fodder
Paddy	T.N.-1, Jaya
Mustard	Varuna, A.S.-10
Sunflower	EC-68414, EC-68415
Pigeon pea	GT-100, GT-1
Chick pea	ICCC-4, JCP-29

C. Layout

Crop sown in furrow show better performance than those in flat layout. Salt accumulate on ridges leaving the furrow relatively free of salts. However in alternate furrow irrigation system, sowing at ridges can be advocated.

D. Seed rate and spacing

Higher seed rate and closer spacing have been found satisfactory as high plant populations insures against the failure of germination due to salt stress.

E. Irrigation and drainage

Maintenance of low moisture stress by frequent irrigation and applying water in excess enables the plant to grow better. Among the methods of irrigation, the minimum salt accumulation takes place in the order of drip > sprinkler > flood basin > ridge furrow.

F. Fertilizers

A higher dose of N, P_2O_5 and K_2O than recommended dose has given higher yields of many crops such as rice, barley, wheat, etc. Addition of micronutrients, particularly Zn, Fe and Mn has helped in increasing the yield. In saline conditions urea, single super phosphate and calcium ammonium nitrate, while in sodic conditions ammonium sulphate and diammonium phosphate found more effective. In highly sodic condition, foliar application of urea is the only effective and economical method of fertilization. In highly saline condition phosphatic fertilizer did not found economical.

The complete package of practices for a crop to be grown in a given type of problematic soil has to be established experimentally. This requires laboratory experiments.

❑❑❑

CHAPTER 16

Acid and Acid Sulphate Soils

DISTRIBUTION

Out of 157 million hectares of cultivable land in India, approximately 49 mha of land are acidic, in which 26 mha of land having soil pH value less than 5.6 and the rest 23 mha of land having soil pH range 5.6 to 6.5.

Soil Groups	*pH Range*	*Area (mha)*	*States*
1. Laterites soils	4.8-7.0	12.65	Mysore, MP, Eastern *ghat* region of Orissa, WB, South Maharashtra, Kerala, Malabar Coast, Assam, parts of Santhal Parganas and Singhbhum in Bihar
2. Laterite and lateritic red soils	5.0-7.0	11.80	Kerala, Orissa, WB and Assam, parts of Santhal Parganas and Singhbhum in Bihar, Mysore, Bihar, MP, UP
3. Mixed red and black/yellow soils	5.5-6.5	23.66	Mysore, Bihar, MP, UP

The soils having low pH values have been observed in Assam, Kerala and parts of U.P., H.P., W.B., Bihar, Orissa and T.N. states.

A. CAUSES OF SOIL ACIDITY

1. Excessive Rainfall

In soils of dry region, a large supply of bases is usually present because little water passes through the soil. With an increase in rainfall, the content of soluble salts is reduced to a low level and gypsum and $CaCO_3$ are removed in the order named. With further increase in rainfall, a point is reached at which the rate of removal of bases exceeds the rate of liberation from non-exchangeable forms. The considerable loss of bases due to intensive rainfall and leaching reduces the pH of the soil as well as increase the concentration of H^+ on exchange complex.

2. Ionization of Water

The water may ionize and contribute H^+ on exchange complex as follows :

$$H_2O \longrightarrow HOH \longrightarrow H^+ \, OH^- \longrightarrow H^+[\mathbf{X}] + \text{Bases} + OH^-$$

3. Contact Exchange

The contact exchange between exchangeable H on root surface and the bases in exchangeable form on soil particle may take as follows :

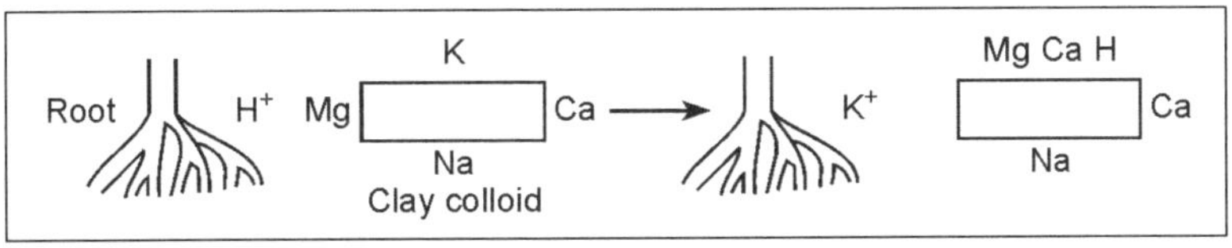

4. Soluble Acid Production

The decomposition of organic matter in the soil produces many organic as well as inorganic acids. These acids may contribute H^+ on exchange complex.

5. Use of Nitrogenous Fertilizers

Continuous use of nitrogenous fertilizers containing NH_4-N or giving NH_4-N on hydrolysis (*i.e.* urea) produce various acids in soils *e.g.* 1 mole of NH_4 in NH_4NO_3 gives 2 moles of HNO_3; 1 mole of $(NH_4)_2SO_4$ gives 2 moles of HNO_3 + 1 mole of H_2SO_4; 1 mole of NH_4OH gives 1 mole of HNO_3.

Thus, continuous use of such fertilizers will produce acidity in soil.

6. Oxidation of FeS

FeS or iron poly sulphide accumulates under anaerobic conditions as a result of reduction of Fe^{3+} and SO_4. Under aerobic conditions, they will be oxidized and will produce H_2SO_4 as follows :

$$4FeS_2 + 15O_2 + 2H_2O \longrightarrow 2Fe_2(SO_4)_3 + 2H_2SO_4$$

Under such conditions, soil pH values of 2 to 4 are frequently observed.

7. Hydrolysis of Fe^{3+} and Al^{3+}

The Fe^{3+} and Al^{3+} ions may combine with water and release H^+ as follows :

$$Al + H_2O \longrightarrow Al(OH) + H$$

$$Al(OH) + H_2O \longrightarrow Al(OH)_2 + H$$

$$Al(OH)_2 + H_2O \longrightarrow Al(OH)_3 + H$$

The hydrogen produced may enter on exchange complex.

8. Acidic Parent Material

Some soils have developed from parent materials which are acid, such as granite and that may contribute to some extent soil acidity.

9. Acidification from the Air

Industrial exhausts, if contain appreciable amount of SO_2 may cause acidity in soil in course of time due to dissolution of SO_2 in water (rain) as follows :

$$SO_2 + H_2O \longrightarrow H_2SO_3$$

(Rain water) (Sulphonic acid)

The phenomenon gives acid rain. In soil, the reaction may be as follows :

$$2H_2SO_3 + O_2 \longrightarrow 2H_2SO_4$$

B. FORMS OF ACIDITY

Because of the increase in H ion concentration in soil solution some of them occupy the position on exchange complex because of its very high replacing ability. The situation gives high H ion concentration in soil solution and on exchange complex, or the acidity in solution and on exchange complex. The acidity in soil solution is known as active acidity and is measured by pH. The acidity on exchange complex is known as passive acidity or reserve acidity and is measured by determining the exchangeable H by $BaCl_2$ + Triethanol amine reagents. The total acidity or the titratable acidity is summation of H ion concentration present in solution as well as on exchange complex which can be measured by titration. All the forms of acidity are in equilibrium.

C. PROBLEMS IN ACIDIC SOILS

Problems of soil acidity may be divided into three groups which are as follows :

1. Toxic Effects

(*a*) Acid toxicity

(*b*) Toxicity of different nutrient elements

2. Nutrient Availability

(*a*) Non-specific effects

(*b*) Specific effects (*i*) Exchangeable bases

(*ii*) Nutrient imbalances

3. Microbial Activity

1. Toxic effects

(*a*) Acid Toxicity. The higher hydrogen ion concentration is toxic to plants under strong acid conditions of soil. The acid toxicity includes possible toxicities of acid anions as well as H^+ ions.

(*b*) Toxicity of Different Nutrient Elements

(*i*) *Iron and Manganese*. The concentration of these two ions (Fe^{2+} and Mn^{2+}) in soil solution depends upon the soil reaction or pH, organic matter and intensity of soil reduction. Due to increase in organic matter content in the soil the population of soil microbes increases and very rapidly used up the soil oxygen and results reduction of soil. As a result of soil reduction, the nutrient elements like Mn^{3+} and Fe^{3+} reduce to Mn^{2+} and Fe^{2+}, respectively and increase their concentration to a very high and toxicity of these elements develops. Due to such toxic effects, a physiological disease of rice is found in submerged soils, which is popularly known as *browning disease*.

(ii) Toxicity of Aluminium (Al). The toxicity of aluminium may be greatly influenced by the accompanying cations. The toxicity of aluminium tends to decrease with an increase in the concentration of other cations such as calcium. Aluminium toxicity is a problem in both upland and lowland soils. Aluminium toxicity in soils affects plant growth in various ways:

(*i*) It restricts the root growth.

(*ii*) It affects various plant physiological processes like division of cells, formation of DNA and respiration, etc.

(*iii*) It restricts the absorption and translocation of some important nutrient elements from soil to the plant like phosphorus, calcium, iron, manganese, etc.

(*iv*) It causes wilting of plants.

(*v*) It also inhibits the microbial activity in the soil.

2. Nutrient Availability

(*a*) Non-specific Effects. It is associated with the inhibition effect of root growth and thereby affects the nutrient availability.

(*b*) Specific Effects

(i) Exchangeable Bases. There are two aspects of availability of exchangeable bases *i.e.* ion uptake process and the release of bases from the exchangeable form may be adversely affected due to soil acidity. Due to complementary ion effect exchangeable bases are released preferentially in fractional exchange. Deficiency of bases like Ca^{2+} and Mg^{2+} are found in acid soils.

(ii) Nutrient Imbalances. It is evident that soluble iron, aluminium and manganese are usually present in their higher concentrations under moderate to strong acid soils. Phosphorus reacts with these ions and produces insoluble phosphatic compounds rendering phosphorus unavailable to plants. Besides these, fixation of phosphorus by hydrous oxides of iron and aluminium or by adsorption, the availability of phosphorus is decreased. In acid soils, iron, manganese, copper and zinc are abundant, but molybdenum is very limited and unavailable to plants. In acid soils having very low pH, the availability of boron may also be decreased due to adsorption on sesquioxides, iron and aluminium hydroxy compounds. Nitrogen, potassium and sulphur become less available in an acid soil having pH less than 5.5.

3. Microbial Activity

It is well-known that soil organisms are influenced by fluctuations in the soil reaction. Bacteria and actinomycetes function better in soils having moderate to high pH values. They can not show their activity when the soil pH drops below 5.5. Nitrogen fixation in acid soils is greatly affected by lowering the activity of *Azotobacter* sp. Besides these, soil acidity also inhibits the symbiotic nitrogen fixation by affecting the activity of *Rhizobium* sp. Fungi can grow well under very acid soils and caused various diseases like root rot of tobacco, blights of potato, etc.

D. RECLAMATION OF ACIDIC SOILS

Principles of Liming Reactions

The reclamation of acidic soils is done by addition of liming material which may be calcitic limestone ($CaCO_3$) or dolomitic limestone [$CaMg(CO_3)_2$]. The rate of lime requirement is determined in the laboratory by method of Shoemaker (1961). The particle size of liming material affects the rate of neutralization reaction. Both these limestones are sparingly soluble in pure water but do become soluble in water containing CO_2. The greater the partial pressure of CO_2 in the system, the more soluble the limestone becomes. Dolomite is some what less soluble than calcite. The reaction of limestone ($CaCO_3$) can be written as :

$$CaCO_3 + H_2O + CO_2 \longrightarrow Ca\,(HCO_3)_2$$

$$Ca\,(HCO_3)_2 \longrightarrow Ca^{2+} + 2HCO_3^-$$

$$\underset{\text{(From soil solution)}}{H^+ + CO_3^-} \longrightarrow \underset{\text{(from lime)}}{H_2CO_3 \cap H_2O + CO_2}$$

In this way hydrogen ions (H^+) in the soil solution react to form weakly dissociated water, and the calcium (Ca^{2+}) ion from limestones is left to undergo cation exchange reactions. The acidity of the soil is, therefore, neutralized and the per cent base saturation of the colloidal material is increased.

The process of changing pH by the addition of lime [$Ca(OH)_2$] is illustrated in the following figure.

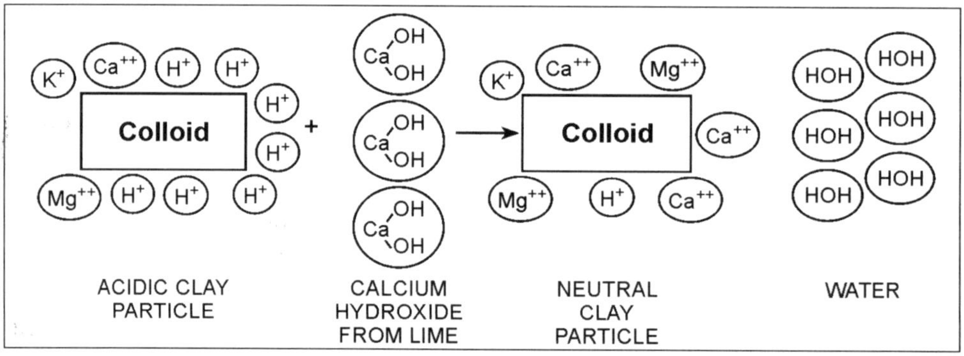

Why Gypsum is not considered as a Liming Material ?

Gypsum is not considered as liming materials because on its application to an acid it dissociates into (Ca^{2+}) and sulphate (SO_4^{2-}) ions :

$$CaSO_4 \leftrightarrow Ca^{2+} + SO_4^{2-}$$

The accompanying anion is sulphate and it reacts with soil moisture produces mineral acid (H_2SO_4) which also increases soil acidity instead of reducing soil acidity.

Kinds of Liming Materials

There are various kinds of liming materials that are used for the correction of soil acidity.

***(i)* Oxides of lime.** It is normally called burned lime or quick lime. Oxide of lime is more caustic than limestones. Burned lime is produced by heating limestone and dolomite as follows :

$$\underset{\text{(Limestone)}}{CaCO_3 + \text{Heat}} \longrightarrow CaO + CO_2$$

$$CaMg(CO_3)_2 + \text{Heat} \longrightarrow CaO + MgO + 2CO_2$$

***(ii)* Hydroxides of lime.** It can be produced by adding water to burned lime and is called slaked lime.

$$\underset{\text{(Burned lime)}}{CaO + H_2O} \longrightarrow \underset{\text{(Slaked lime)}}{Ca(OH)_2}$$

It is more caustic than burned lime. It is kept open in the moist air, then combination of calcium hydroxide occurs as follows :

$$Ca(OH)_2 + CO_2 \longrightarrow CaCO_3 + H_2O$$

In case of $Mg(OH)_2$,

$$Mg(OH)_2 + CO_2 \longrightarrow MgCO_3 + H_2O$$

***(iii)* Carbonates of lime.** These are by-products of certain industries and so the content of calcium and magnesium varies. The two important minerals are found in this group-calcite ($CaCO_3$) and dolomite [$CaMg(CO_3)_2$].

***(iv)* Other liming materials.** Slags (blast furnace slag, basic slag and electric slag), coral shell, chalk, wood ash, press mud, by-product materials of paper mills, sugar factories, fly ash and sludge, etc. are considered as liming materials and also used for the amelioration of soil acidity.

Efficiency of Liming Materials

The efficiency of liming materials can be judged on the basis of following important factor because of varying neutralizing capacity of different liming materials :

(*i*) Neutralizing value (N.V.) or calcium carbonate Equivalent of liming materials
(*ii*) Purity of liming materials and
(*iii*) Degree of fineness of liming materials.

***(i)* Neutralizing value (N.V.) or Calcium Carbonate Equivalent (CCE).**

Calcium carbonate equivalent (CCE) is defined as the acid-neutralizing capacity of an agricultural liming material expressed as a weight percentage of calcium carbonate.

$$\text{CCE of a liming material} = \frac{\text{Molecular weight of } CaCO_3}{\begin{array}{c}\text{Molecular weight of liming material}\\ \text{whose CCE is to be determined}\end{array}} \times 100$$

Example : Calculate the CCE of dolomite, $CaMg(CO_3)_2$

Solution : In dolomite, there is mixture of $CaCO_3$ and $MgCO_3$. Both are almost equally effective in neutralizing soil acidity. Considering the materials as two separate liming materials present in the dolomite. So the molecular weight of dolomite may be considerable

184/2 = 92 since 84 gms of $MgCO_3$ will neutralize the same amount of acid as 100 gms of $CaCO_3$.

$$\text{CCE of a liming material} = \frac{\text{Molecular weight of } CaCO_3}{\text{Molecualr weight of dolomite}} \times 100$$

$$= 100/92 \times 100$$

$$= 108.7$$

Neutralizing value or CCE of same liming materials is given in table 16.1.

TABLE 16.1. Neutralizing value of some liming materials

Liming materials	*Neutralizing value of CCE (%)*
Calcium oxide (CaO)	179
Calcium hydroxide [Ca $(OH)_2$]	136
Dolomite [CaMg $(CO_3)_2$]	108.7
Calcite ($CaCO_3$)	100
Basic slag ($CaSiO_3$)	86

***(i)* Purity of liming materials.** The more purer the liming material, the higher will be its effectiveness for the amelioration of soil acidity.

***(ii)* Degree of fineness of liming materials.** The rate reaction of liming materials with an acid soil depends upon its fineness because finer materials are coarse, the reaction will be slight. The magnitude of reaction of such reaction as affected by the fineness of liming materials can be evaluated by measuring the charge of soil pH. The amount of finer fraction of liming materials will be enquired much less as compared to pH. The amount of finer fraction of liming materials will be required much less as compared to coarse fractions of the material to achieve a certain pH.

The fineness is measured in terms in terms of the ability of a material to pass through a sieve having 60 holes of equal size in one linear inch. Such a sieve is called a 60 mesh sieve and a material passing through such a sieve is allotted 100% efficiency rating. One such scale used in Ohio (USA) is given below :

Liming materials	*Efficiency of rating (%)*
1. Material passing through a 60 mesh sieve	100
2. Material passing through a 20 mesh sieve but not a 60 mesh sieve	60
3. Material passing through a 60 mesh sieve but not a 20 mesh sieve	20

Per cent Effective Calcium Carbonate (CCE) or (Neutralizing Index)

The effective calcium carbonate (CCE) rating of a limestone or liming materais is one product of its calcium carbonate equivalent (CCE) and the fineness factor. The fineness factor is the sum of the product of the percentage of material in each of the three size fractions multiplied by the appropriate effectiveness factor.

$$\text{Per cent ECC or N.I.} = \text{CCE} \times \text{fineness factor}$$

Chemical Reactions between Liming Materials and Acid Soils during the Process of Amelioration

(i) **Oxides of lime (CaO).** When oxides of lime like CaO are applied to an acid soil, it reacts almost immediately as follows :

$$\text{Soil}\left]\begin{matrix}H\\H\\H\end{matrix}\right. + H_2O + 2CaO \longrightarrow \begin{matrix}H\\Ca\\Ca\end{matrix}\left[\text{Soil} + Al(OH)_3\right.$$

(ii) **Hydroxides of lime [$Ca(OH)_2$].** When hydroxides of lime like $Ca(OH)_2$ is applied for the reclamation of an acid soil, the following chemical reaction takes place :

$$\text{Soil}\left]\begin{matrix}H\\H\\H\end{matrix}\right. + 2Ca\,(OH)_2 \longrightarrow \begin{matrix}H\\Ca\\Ca\end{matrix}\left[\text{Soil} + Al(OH)_3 + H_2O\right.$$

(iii) **Carbonates of lime ($CaCO_3$).** When carbonates of lime like calcite is applied to an acid soil, a part of $CaCO_3$ undergo solution and combines with H_2CO_3 to form soluble $Ca(HCO_3)_2$. This calcium bicarbonate in solution from reacts with the soil colloids with the evolution of CO_2 as follows :

$$CaCO_3 + H_2CO_3 \longrightarrow Ca(HCO_3)_2$$

$$Ca(HCO_3)_2 + \begin{matrix}H\\H\end{matrix}\left[\text{Soil} \longrightarrow [\text{Soil} + 2H_2O + 2CO_2\right.$$

and the rest portion of the limestone goes in close contact with the soil colloids in solid condition as follows

$$H\,[\text{Soil} + CaCO_3 \longrightarrow Ca\,[\text{Soil} + H_2O + CO_2$$

E. SELECTION OF CROP

The crop should be selected on the basis of their tolerance to acidity. The relative yield of different crops at different pH values is given in following table.

Crops	Relative yield at pH value				
	4.7	5.0	5.7	6.8	7.5
Corn	34	73	83	100	85
Wheat	68	76	89	100	99
Oats	77	93	99	98	100
Barley	0	23	80	95	100
Alfalfa	2	9	42	100	100
Soybeans	65	79	80	100	93

The acid tolerant crops may be selected from above data. The crops may be also chosen on the basis of toxicity of Al and Mn. Cauliflower and other plants belonging to *Brassica* species are tolerant to high Al concentration while sugarbeet and oats are tolerant to high Mn concentration. The intermediate tolerant crops for Al are oats and for Mn, potato and barley. Sugarbeet and barley are sensitive to high Mn concentration. The type of crop to be grown depends not only on pH of the soil but also on concentration of Al and Mn.

Characteristics of Acid Soils

1. Acid soils have low pH and high proportion of exchangeable H^+ and Al^{3+}.
2. Kaolinite and illite types of clay minerals are dominant in these soils.
3. These soils have low CEC and low base saturation.
4. These soils have high toxic concentration of Al, Fe and Mn and deficiency of Ca and Mg.
5. These soils have nutrients and microbial imbalances.
6. These soils are generally low in available phosphorus and high P_2O_5 fixation capacity.
7. Soil acidity inhibits biological N-fixation.

Management of Acid Soils

(1) **Growing acid tolerant crops :** In acid soils tolerant crops should be grown. Choice of crops may be done according to soil pH.

(*a*) High acid tolerant crops : Rice, potato, sweet potato, oat, castor, etc.

(*b*) Moderate acid tolerant crops : Barley, wheat, maize, turnip, brinjal, etc.

(*c*) Slightly acid tolerant crops : Tomato, carrot, red clover.

(2) **Ameliorating the soils through the application of amendments :**

(*a*) Lime stone ($CaCO_3$)

(*b*) Quick lime (CaO)

(*c*) Hydrated (slag) lime [$Ca(OH)_2$]

(*d*) Dolomitic limestone [$CaMg(CO_3)_2$]

(3) **Use of basic fertilizers :** $NaNO_3$ and basic slag, etc.

(4) **Soil and water management :** Proper soil and water management checks leaching of bases and enhances decomposition of organic matter.

Lime Requirement of Acid Soils

For reasonable crop production on acid soils, pH range from 6.0 to 7.0 is considered good. The amount of lime required to be added to acidic soil to raise the pH to a desired value is known as lime requirement.

The lime requirement of the soil is not only related to the soil pH but also to its buffer or CEC. Some soils are highly buffered than others and therefore, the lime requirement of soils having the same pH may differ considerably. The buffering capacity or CEC depends upon the amount and type of clay and organic matter present in the soil. The larger these amounts, the greater will be the buffering capacity. Therefore, soils containing clay, peat, muck will be highly buffered and need less lime requirement than that required by coarse textured soils which have low clay and organic matter content.

Acid Rain

When airborne sulfur oxides (mostly SO_2) and nitrogen oxides (NO) are converted to

H_2SO_4 and HNO_3 through oxidation and dissolved in rain drops. Rain water made acidic by these strong acids may have a pH as low as 2.

Beneficial Effect of Lime

(1) Lime makes P_2O_5 more available.

(2) Lime increase availability of N, increase nitrification and nitrogen fixation.

(3) Organic matter decomposition is increased.

(4) Lime makes K more available.

(5) Bacterial growth more beneficial.

(6) Harmful Al, Fe and Mn are rendered insoluble.

(7) Ca and Mg make available.

(8) Improve physical condition of soils.

(9) Checks soil erosion.

(10) Fertilizers effectiveness increase.

(11) Plant diseases.

ACID SULPHATE SOILS

Soil with sufficient sulphides (FeS_2 and others) to become strongly acidic when drained and aerated enough for cultivation are termed acid sulphate soils or as the Dutch refer to those soils *cat clays*. When allowed to develop acidity, these soils are usually more acidic than pH 4.0. Before drainage, such soils may have normal soil pH and are only *potential acid sulphate soils*. Generally acid sulphate soils are found in coastal areas, where the land is inundated by salt water. In India, acid sulphate soil is mostly found in Kerala, Orissa, Andhra Pradesh, Tamil Nadu and West Bengal. The area covered under acid sulphate soils in Thailand and India combined is about 2 million acres.

Formation of Acid Sulphate Soils

Lands inundated with waters that contain sulphates, particularly salt waters, accumulate sulphur compounds, which in poorly aerated soils are bacterially reduced to sulphides. Such soils are not usually very acidic when first drained in water.

When the soil is drained and then aerated, the sulphide (S^{2-}) is oxidized to sulphate (SO_4^{2-}) by a combination of chemical and bacterial actions, forming sulphuric acid (H_2SO_4). The magnitude of acid development depends on the amount of sulphide present in the soil and the conditions and time of oxidation. If iron pyrite (FeS_2) is present, the oxidized iron accentuates the acidity but not as much as aluminium in normal acid soils because the iron oxides are less soluble than aluminium oxides and so hydrolyze less.

Reactions Involving the Formation of Acid Sulphate Soils

Acid sulphate soils form due to oxidation of sulphides in soils. The slow oxidation of mineral sulphides in soils is non-biological until soil pH reaches an acidity of pH 4.0, but the process is not well understood. Below pH 4.0, the bacteria *Thiobacillus ferroxidans* are the most active oxidizers and the activity builds up rapidly.

$$\underset{\text{(Elemental sulphur)}}{2S + 3O_2 + 2H_2O} \xrightarrow{\text{Microbial oxidation}} \underset{\text{(Sulphuric acid)}}{H_2SO_4}$$

$$\underset{\text{(Hydrogen sulphide)}}{H_2S + 2O_2} \xrightarrow{\text{Microbial oxidation}} \underset{\text{(Sulphuric acid)}}{H_2SO_4}$$

Non-biological

$$\underset{\text{(Iron pyrite)}}{2FeS_2 + 2H_2O + 7O_2} \longrightarrow \underset{\text{(Ferrous sulphate)}}{2FeSO_4} + \underset{\text{(Sulphuric acid)}}{2H_2SO_4}$$

Accelerated by bacteria *(Thiobacillus ferroxidans)*

$$\underset{\text{(Ferrous sulphate)}}{4FeSO_4 + O_2 + 2H_2SO_4} \longrightarrow \underset{\text{(Ferric sulphate)}}{2Fe_2(SO_4)_3} + 2H_2O$$

Rapid in acid pH (non-biological)

$$FeS_2 + 7Fe_2(SO_4)_3 + 8H_2O \longrightarrow \underset{\text{(Ferrous sulphate)}}{15FeSO_4} + 8H_2SO_4$$

Management of Acid Sulphate Soils

Management techniques are extremely variable and depend on many specific factors *viz.*, the extent of acid formation, the thickness of the sulphide layer, possibilities of leaching or draining the land, etc. The general approaches for reclamation are suggested below:

***(i)* Keeping the area flooded.** Maintaining the reduced condition of flooded (anaerobic) soil inhibits acid development, which requires oxidation. This solution almost limits the use of the urea to rice growing. Unfortunately, droughts occur and can in short time periods cause acidification of these soils. The water used to flood the potential acid sulphate soils often develop acidity and injure crops.

***(ii)* Controlling water table.** If a non-acidifying layer covers the sulphuric horizon, drainage to keep only the sulphuric layer under water (anaerobic) is possible.

***(iii)* Liming and leaching.** Liming is the primary way to reclaim any type of acid soil. Acid soil may require 11-45 metric ton per hectare of lime in a 20-year period whereas, acid sulphate soils may require from several metric tons per hectare per year, up to 224 metric ton per hectare (100 t/acre) within a 10 year period or less.

If these soils are leached during early years of acidification, lime requirements are lowered. Leaching, however, is difficult because of the high water table commonly found in this type of soil and low permeability of the clay. Sea water is sometimes available for preliminary leaching.

Problem

If a sandy soil having cation exchange capacity (CEC) 20 cmol(p^+) kg^{-1} and 30 per cent base saturation at pH 4.5. Calculate the theoretical amount of lime ($CaCO_3$) required per hectare of land (0-15 cm depth) for raising base saturation to 60 per cent [weight of soil per hectare furrow slice (0-15 cm depth) = 2.2×10^6 kg].

$$\text{Percent base saturation (PBS)} = \frac{\text{me of basic cation (S)}}{\text{Total exchangeable cations (T)}} \times 100$$

Base saturation of the soil before lime application (initial) = 30%

Base saturation to be raised through liming (final) = 60%

me of base cations initially percent in the soil (S)

$$= \frac{\text{T} \times \text{BS (percentage)}}{100}$$

$$= 20 \times 30/100 = 6$$

Again, me of basic cations at 60% base saturation (S)

$$= \frac{\text{T} \times \text{BS}}{100}$$

$$= 20 \times 60/100 = 12$$

So, me of basic cations will be required to raise the base saturation at 60%

$$= (12 - 6) = 6$$

$$\begin{aligned} \text{1 me H/100 g} &= \text{50 mg/100 g lime} \\ &= \text{500 mg/1000 g lime} \\ &= \text{500 ppm} \\ &= 500 \times 2.24 \text{ kg/ha} \\ &= 1120 \text{ kg/ha} \\ \text{6 me H} &= 1120 \times 6 \text{ kg/ha} \\ &= 6720 \text{ kg/ha} = 67 \text{ quintals of lime will be required.} \end{aligned}$$

❑❑❑

CHAPTER 17

Quality of Irrigation Water

All natural waters used for irrigation contains inorganic salts in solutions which are derived originally from the rocks or solid phase material through which water percolates. The most common dissolved constituents are chlorides, sulphates and bicarbonates of Ca, Mg and Na. The concentration and proportion of these salts determine the suitability of water for irrigation. Other constituent such as B, Li, F or other ions, which have a toxic effect on plants, may occur in lesser amounts in irrigation water. If water used for irrigation contains excessive quantities of the constituents noted above, it might affect the growth of plants in three ways *viz.*,

(*a*) as a result of adverse changes in the physical characteristics of the soil,

(*b*) the increased osmotic pressure of the soil solution may decrease the physiological availability of moisture to plants,

(*c*) accumulation of certain ions in the soil solution that may have a specific toxic effect upon the physiological processes of the plant.

Therefore, the question arises "What should be the ideal quality of water to be used for irrigation ?" Different workers for judging the quality of waters have proposed various standards. The ten generally recognized criteria for judging the quality of irrigation water are as under :

A. QUALITY OF IRRIGATION WATER

1. Salinity Hazard

Continuous use of water having high salt content will convert a normal soil into a saline soil. On the basis of electrical conductivity (EC) measurements, the waters were divided into four classes by USSSL as follows :

TABLE 17.1. Permissible limit of salinity hazard in irrigation water

EC (dSm^{-1} at 25 °C)	Salt Conc.	Salinity Class	Symbol	Inference
0-0.25	< 0.16	Low	C_1	(*i*) Can be used for most soil for most crops (*ii*) Little likelihood of salinity
0.25-0.75	0.16-0.50	Medium	C_2	(*i*) Can be used with moderate leaching (*ii*) Moderate salt tolerant crops should be grown
0.75-2.25	0.50-1.50	High	C_3	(*i*) Cannot be used where drainage is restricted (*ii*) Salt tolerant plant and additional management practices should be followed
2.25-5.00	1.5-3.0	Very High	C_4	(*i*) Not suitable for irrigation (*ii*) Can be used occasionally with leaching (*iii* Salt tolerant crop should be grown with additional management practices

2. Alkali Hazard

The continuous use of water having high concentration of Na will convert a normal soil into an alkali soil. The sodium adsorption ratio (SAR) developed by USSSL expresses the relative activity of Na ions in cation exchange reactions with the soil. The exchangeable Na percentage (ESP), which the soil will attain when the soil and water are in equilibrium, can be predicted approximately from the value of SAR of water. Accordingly, the waters are divided into four classes with respect to the Na hazards as follow :

SAR concept for quality of irrigation water was given by L.A. Richards

$$SAR = \frac{Na}{\sqrt{(Ca + Mg)/2}}$$

TABLE 17.2. Classification on the basis of SAR of water

SAR value	Class	Symbol	Inference
0-10	Low Na	S_1	(*i*) Can be used for all soils with little danger of harmful Na level development (*ii*) The Na sensitive crops are affected
10-18	Medium Na	S_2	(*i*) Sodium hazard likely in fine textured soil (*ii*) Can be used on soils having high permeability
18-26	High Na	S_3	(*i*) May produce harmful level of exchangeable Na in most soils except gypsiferous soils (*ii*) Requires special management practice like good drainage, high leaching and addition of organic matter and gypsum
More than 26	Very high	S_4	(*i*) Unsatisfactory for irrigation except at low and perhaps medium salinity of irrigation water, special management as above should should be made

Adjusted SAR

In the earlier definition of SAR was, SAR = Na/√(Ca+Mg)/2, me/l.

It is the ratio of concentration of Na to concentration of Ca + Mg and all these concentrations are expressed in meq/l.

The SAR indicates the tendency for the soil to become higher in exchangeable Na. Higher SAR value means higher exchangeable Na percentage and lower soil permeability. If irrigation water contains CO_3^{2-} and HCO_3^- ions, these will precipitate Ca and Mg, which increases the SAR. The formula, taking into account these changes, is called the Adjusted SAR. It is defined as :

$$\text{Adj SAR} = \text{Na}/\sqrt{(\text{Ca} + \text{Mg})/2}\ [1 + (8.4 - \text{pHc})]$$

$$\text{pHc} = (pk_2' - pk_c') + p(HCO_3^-) + p(Ca^{2+}+Mg^{2+})$$

where, $(pk_2' - pk_c')$ = concentration of total cation (Ca^{2+}+Mg^{2+} and Na^+ ions me/l)

$p(HCO_3^-)$ = concentration of HCO_3^- and CO_3^{2-} ions me/l

$p(Ca^{2+}+Mg^{2+})$ = concentration of Ca^{2+} and Mg^{2+} ions me/l

Some parameters for the calculation of Adj. SAR values

Ion conc. (meq/l)	*$(pk_2' - pk_c')$**	*p(Ca + Mg)*	*$p(HCO_3)$***
0.5	2.11	3.60	3.30
1.0	2.13	3.30	3.00
4.0	2.20	2.70	2.40
8.0	2.25	2.40	2.10
10.0	2.27	2.30	2.00
20.0	2.35	2.00	1.70
30.0	2.40	1.82	1.52
40.0	2.44	1.70	1.40
50.0	2.47	1.60	1.30

*Total cation content in water (Ca + Mg + Na ions) (me/l)

** Sum of CO_3 + HCO_3 ion

Calculate Adj. SAR for irrigation water which contains 7.0 me/l of Ca^{2+}, 2 me/l of Mg^{2+}, 5.0 me/l of Na^+ and 4.0 me/l of HCO_3^- and a total ionic concentration of 14.0 me/l.

$(pk_2' - pk_c')$ at 14 me/l total ions = 2.30

p(Ca+Mg) = (7 + 2) me/l = 2.35

$p(HCO_3)$ = 4 me/l = 2.40

pHc = (2.30) + (2.40) + (2.35) = 7.05

$$\text{Adj. SAR} = 5/\sqrt{(7 + 2)/2}\ [1 + (8.4 - 7.05)]$$

$$= 5/\sqrt{4.5}\ [1 + 1.35]$$

$$= 2.36 \times 2.35$$

$$= 5.55$$

So adj SAR of the irrigation water is 5.55 rather than the uncorrected SAR of 2.36.

3. Salt Index (SI)

Salt index concept was given by Puri

$$SI = (\text{Total Na} - 2.45) - [(\text{Total Ca} - \text{Ca in } CaCO_3 \text{ in } CaCO_3) \times 4.85]$$

All cations express as ppm

(*i*) If salt index value is negative (–ve) that is good water for irrigation.

(*ii*) If salt index value positive (+ve) that is harmful water for irrigation.

4. Bicarbonate Hazard (RSC)

The bicarbonate ions are primarily important because their tendency to precipitate Ca and to some extent Mg, in the soil solution as their normal carbonates *e.g.*

$$Ca + 2HCO_3 \longrightarrow CaCO_3 + CO_2 + H_2O$$

The CO_3^{2-} ions are seldom present in water but HCO_3^- ions may be present in appreciable proportion of the total anions present in irrigation water. Based on the theory of precipitation of Ca and Mg, F.M. Eaton (1950) suggested the concept of "Residual Sodium Carbonate" commonly known as RSC. The RSC can be found out by following equation :

$$RSC = (CO_3^{2-} + HCO_3^-) - (Ca^{2+} + Mg^{2+})$$

where; concentrations of all ions are expressed in meq/lit.

It is obvious from above equation that as the Ca and Mg are lost from the soil solution by precipitation, the relative proportion of Na remaining in water is increased. Thus, the alkali hazard as defined by the SAR is increased. The standard for RSC as given by USSSL as follows :

RSC (meq/lit)	*Quality of irrigation water*
Less than 1.25	Probably safe for most purpose
1.25-2.50	Marginal can be used on light textured soil with adequate leaching and application of gypsum
More than 2.50	Not suitable for irrigation purposes

5. Boron Hazard

Boron is very toxic to plants at low concentration in the soil solution. Because boron tends to accumulate in the soil from even low concentration in the irrigation waters, it is necessary to consider this constituent in assessing the quality of irrigation waters. The USDA has suggested the type of crops to be grown with respect to boron content in irrigation water. The limits are as under :

Boron content of irrigation water (ppm)	*Boron tolerance of crops*	*Crops to be grown*
0.3 – 1.0	Sensitive	Citrus, Apricot, Peach, Apple, Pear, Plum, walnut
1.0 – 2.0	Semi-tolerant	Sweet potato, Oats, Sorghum, Maize, Wheat, Barley, Radish, Peas, Tomato, Cotton, Potato, Sunflower
2.0 – 4.0	Tolerant	Carrot, Cabbage, Onion, Beans, Sugarbeet, Alfalfa, Date

6. Soluble Sodium Percentage (SSP)

$$\text{Soluble Sodium Percentage (SSP)} \frac{\text{Na}}{\text{Ca + Mg + Na}} = \times 100$$

where, all soluble cations are expressed in meq l^{-1}

Irrigation water having SSP value of 60 and above are considered as harmful.

7. Magnesium Hazard

It is believed that one of the important qualitative criteria in judging the irrigation water is its magnesium content in relation to total divalent cations, since high magnesium adsorption by soils affects their physical properties. A harmful effect on soils appears when Ca : Mg ratio declines below 50.

$$\text{Mg-adsorption ratio} = \frac{Ma^{2+}}{Ca^{2+} + Mg^{2+}}$$

Magnesium hazard in irrigation water is expected having Mg : Ca ratio more than 1, and Ca : Mg ratio declines blow 50.

8. Nitrate Concentration

Very frequently ground waters contain high amount of nitrate. When such type of irrigation water is applied on soils continuously various physical properties will be affected very badly which causes poor growth of the plants.

Nitrate Concentration (me/l)	*Remark*
< 5	Good
5-30	Moderate
> 30	Hazardous

9. Lithium

Lithium is an important trace element which may be found in most of saline ground water and irrigated soils. It has been found that small concentrations (0.05-0.1 ppm) of lithium in irrigation water produced toxic effects on the growth of citrus crops. It has also been reported that saline soils of varying degrees found in India contain lithium upto 2.5 ppm. Fortunately the germination of majority of crops including rice, wheat, barley, etc. is not affected with this level of lithium content in soils.

10. Other Hazards

(*i*) Chlorides. The grading of irrigation waters based on chloride content as proposed by Schofield is as under :

Chloride (meq/lit)	*Remark*
0-4	Excellent
4-7	Good
7-12	Permissible
12-20	Doubtful
More than 20	Unsafe

(*ii*) Fluorides

Fluoride (ppm)		
(*i*) < 1	Low	Safe
(*ii*) 1-2	Medium	Marginal
(*iii*) > 2	High	Unsafe

(i) Other elements

The safe limit for other elements present in irrigation water is as follows :

Element	For waters used continuously on all soil (ppm)	For used up to 20 years on fine textured soil at pH 6.0 to 8.5 (ppm)
Alluminium (Al)	5.00	20.00
Arsenic (As)	0.10	2.00
Copper (Cu)	0.20	5.00
Fluorine (F)	1.00	15.00
Lead (Pb)	5.00	10.00
Lithium (Li)	2.50	2.60
Manganese (Mn)	0.20	10.00
Molybdenum (Mo)	0.01	0.05
Selenium (Se)	0.02	0.02
Zinc (Zn)	2.00	10.00
Iron (Fe)	5.00	20.00

TABLE 17.3. Guidelines for irrigation water quality established by the World Food and Agriculture Organization (FAO)

Water constituent	Intensity of problem*		
	No problem	Moderate	Severe
— Salinity (dSm^{-1})	< 0.75	0.75-3.0	> 3.0
Permeability (rate of infiltration affected)			
— Salinity (dSm^{-1})	> 0.5	0.5-0.2	< 0.2
Adjusted SAR; soils are			
— Dominantly montmorillonite	< 6	6-9	> 9
— Dominantly illite-vermiculite	< 8	8-16	> 16
— Dominantly kaolinite-sesquioxides	< 16	16-24	> 24
Specific ion toxicidy			
— Sodium (as adjusted SAR)	< 3	3-9	> 9
— Chloride ($meq1^{-1}$)	< 4	4-10	> 10
—Boron ($meq1^{-1}$)	< 0.75	0.75-2.0	> 2.0
Miscellaneous			
— NO_3^--N or NH_4^+-N ($meq1^{-1}$)	< 5	5-30	>3.0
— HCO_3^- ($meq1^{-1}$) as damaged by overhead sprinkler	< 1.5	1.5-8.5	8.5
— pH	6.5-8.4	—	0-5, 9.5 +

*Based on the assumptions that the soils are sandy loam to clay loams, have good drainage, are in arid to semi-arid climates, irrigation is sprinkler or surface, root depths are normal for deep soil, and the guidelines are only approximate.

(*ii*) Pollutants

Many substances that are discharged as industrial wastes into surface streams may have phytotoxic properties. Great caution should be exercised in the use of irrigation water that is suspected of containing phytotoxic pollutants.

B. SUITABILITY OF IRRIGATION WATER [SI = *f* (QSPCM)]

It is said that "probably too much emphasis has been placed on an attempt to answer the question. How good is the water ?" rather than "What can be done with this water ?" The suitability of irrigation water (SI) will be determined by following five factors (f) :

$$SI = f(QSPCM).$$

(*a*) **Quality of irrigation water.** Amount, nature and proportion of various cations and anions present in the water.

(*b*) **Nature of the soil to be irrigated.** Texture, structure, drainage, permeability, and depth of water table, chemical composition of the soil, pH, and $CaCO_3$ content will determine the effect of irrigation water on the soil.

(*c*) **Nature of the crop plants to be grown.** Water, which may not be suitable for very sensitive crop, may be excellent for tolerant crops.

(*d*) **Climatic conditions.** High temperature and less humidity will require more number of irrigation.

(*e*) Management level of the irrigation.

USE OF SALINE WATER

Even the water containing high amount of dissolved salts has been used successfully in highly permeable sandy soils. Similarly, the water showing considerable alkali hazards have also been used successfully on permeable soils or by addition of gypsum and FYM on semi-permeable soils. The high RSC content can be corrected by addition of gypsum and the water can be used for the purpose of irrigation. Attempts have also been made for using saline

TABLE 17.4. Tentative water quality ratings for Indian conditions

Soil groups	*Soil texture*	*Clay content (%) to salinity*	*Crop tolerance*	*Upper permissible limits for water (EC × 10^3)*	
				No drainage limitation	*Ground water level less than 1.51 m*
Deep black and alluvial	Clayey	30	Fairly	1.5	0.75
			High	2.0	1.0
	Clay loam	20-30	Fairly	2.0	1.0
			High	4.0	2.0
Alluvial	Loam	10-20	Fairly	4.0	2.0
			High	6.0	3.0
	Sandy loam to sandy	10	Fairly	6.0	3.0
			High	8.0	4.0

waters by diluting it with good quality water or by giving alternate irrigation with good and bad quality water.

The waters having high salinity can be used successfully in lighter textured soils by growing salt tolerant crops.

Leaching requirement (LR)

The LR has been defined as "The fraction of the irrigation water that must be leached through the root zone to control salinity at any specified level". Thus, by applying large quantity of water, saline water can be used for irrigation. The formula for LR is :

$$LR = \frac{D_{dw} \times 100}{D_{iw}} \quad \text{or} \quad \frac{EC_{iw} \times 100}{EC_{dw}}$$

where, LR = Leaching requirement expressed in percentage

D_{dw} = Depth of drainage water in inches

D_{iw} = Depth of irrigation water in inches

EC_{iw} = Electrical conductivity of the irrigation water in dSm^{-1}

EC_{dw} = Electrical conductivity of the drainage water in dSm^{-1}

It is expressed as percentage.

In applying the equation, a value is usually assumed for EC_{dw} to represent the maximum soil salinity that can be to rated by a crop.

NUMERICAL PROBLEMS

Example 1

An irrigation water having EC value of 45 mSm^{-1} (millisiemens per meter) contains calcium (Ca^{2+}) and magnesium (Mg^{2+}) 2.0 and 1.0 meq/l, respectively. Calculate (i) the concentration of sodium (Na^+) in meq/l and soluble sodium percentage (SSP) of the irrigation water (ii) SAR of the irrigation water. Give comments on the irrigation water.

(*i*) Na in meq/l $= \frac{EC}{100} - (Ca^{2+} + Mg^{2+})$

$= \frac{450}{100} - (2 + 1)$

$= 4.5 - 3$

$= 1.5$ mg/l

Soluble Sodium Percentage

(SSP) $= \frac{Na \times 100}{Ca + Mg + Na}$

$= \frac{1.5 \times 100}{(2 + 1 + 1.5)}$

$= 150/4.5$

$= 33.33$

(*ii*) SAR $= \frac{Na^+}{\sqrt{\frac{Ca^{2+} + Mg^{2+}}{2}}}$

$= 1.5/\sqrt{[(2+1)/2]}$

$= 1.5/\sqrt{(3/2)}$

$= 1.5/1.224$

$= 1.225$

The irrigation water has no sodium hazard and it can be safely used for the irrigation purposes.

Example 2

Work out the LR for water having 2000 mmhos/cm EC value. The crop has capacity to with stand salinity to the extent of 8 mmhos/cm. Five cm of water is applied for irrigation.

$$LR = \frac{EC_{iw} \times 100}{EC_{dw}} = 2 \times 100/8 = 25\%$$

(2000 mmhos/cm = 2 mmhos/cm)

25% water should be given extra for irrigation or 6.25 cm of water (5 cm + 1.25 cm which is 25% of 5 cm) must be given to leach down the excess of salts. Generally the LR value should be kept below 25% as excess value will induce wasteful use of water and reduce the irrigation efficiency. It will also raise the underground water table depth or will increase the drainage requirement. Thus, for reducing the value of LR, salt tolerant crops should be chosen.

Example 3

An irrigation water sample on analysis gives the following results :

$$EC \times 10^6 = 1200 \text{ mmhos/cm or } 1.2 \text{ mmhos/cm or } dSm^{-1}$$
$$Ca + Mg = 8 \text{ meq/l}$$

Calculate the followings :

(1) Total salts in ppm and % (2) Na me/l and SAR (3) Salt added in kg/ha per irrigation (Depth of irrigation = 5 cm)

(*i*) ppm $= 640 \times EC \times 10^3$

$= 640 \times 1.2 = 7680 = 768$ ppm

(*ii*) % salt $= 768/10{,}000 = 0.0768\%$ or

$= EC \times 10^3 \times 0.064 = 1.2 \times 0.064 = 0.0768\%$

(*iii*) SAR first Na meq/l $= ECe \times 10 - Ca + Mg$

$= 1.2 \times 10 - 8 = 12 - 8 = 4$ meq/l

$$SAR = \frac{Na^+}{\sqrt{\frac{Ca^{2+} + Mg^{2+}}{2}}} = 4/\sqrt{8}/2 = 4\sqrt{4} = 4/2 = 2 \text{ SAR}$$

(*iv*) Salt kg/ha

(*a*) ppm = mg/l = 768 mg/l

(*b*) gram/l = 0.768

(*c*) kg/l = 0.768/1000

$100 \times 100 \times 0.05 =$ 500 cu.m. water/ha

$$\frac{500 \times 1000}{1} \times \frac{0.768}{1000} = 500 \times \frac{768}{1000} = \frac{3840}{10} = 384 \text{ kg/ha salt added}$$

Example 4

An analysis of irrigation water as under :

(1) *EC = 2.6 dSm*$^{-1}$

(2) *Ca + Mg = 18 meq/l*

(3) CO_3 *= 3.5 meq/l*

(4) HCO_3 *= 21.5 meq/l*

Calculate : (1) % salt, (2) Total cation concentration, (3) ppm salt, (4) Na concentration me/l, (5) SAR, (6) RSC, (7) Amount of salt added in soil kg/ha and GR of kg/ha per irrigation. (Note: Depth of irrigation water = 6 cm.)

(1) ppm salt $= 640 \times EC \times 10^3$

$= 640 \times 2.6$

$=$ 1664 ppm salt = 1.424 g/l salt

(2) % salt = ppm/10,000 OR $0.0640 \times EC \times 10^3$

$= 0.1664$

(3) Cation concentration $= EC\ (dSm^{-1}) \times 10 = Ca + Mg + Na$

$= 2.6 \times 10 = 18 + Na$

$= 26 - 18 = Na$

$= 8 = Na$ meq/l

(4) SAR $= Na/\sqrt{}Ca + Mg/2 = 8/\sqrt{3} = 8/3 = 2.67$

(5) RSC $= (CO_3 + HCO_3) - (Ca + Mg)$

$= (3.5 + 21.5) - (18)$

$= 25 - 18$

$=$ 7 meq/l

(6) Amount of salt added per irrigation per hectare

$$6 \text{ cm/ha} = \frac{6 \times 100 \times 100}{100} = 600 \text{ cu.m. water/ha}$$

1 cu.m. = 1000 litres

600 cu.m = 6,00,000

1664 mg/l = 1.664/1000 g/l

$6{,}00{,}000 \times 1.664/1000 =$ 998.4 kg/ha/irrigation

<1.25, 1.25-2.5, >2.5 7 RSC – 2.5 = 4.5 RSC to be reduced by gypsum

RSC Z me/l = $Z \times 86$ mg/l GR

$= Z \times 0.086$ g/l GR

$= Z \times 8.6$ g/100 l GR

$= 4.5 \times 8.6 = Y$ g/100 l GR

$$= \frac{Y \times 6{,}00{,}000}{100 \times 1000} = 6Y = 4.5 \times 8.6 \times 6$$

$=$ 232.2 kg ha GR

Example 5

Calculate Adj. SAR for irrigation water which contains 7.0 meq/l of Ca^{2+}, 2 meq/l of Mg^{2+}, 5.0 meq/l of Na^+ and 4.0 meq/l of HCO_3^- and a total ionic concentration of 14.0 meq/l.

Some parameters for the calculation of Adj. SAR values

Ion conc. (meq/l)	$(pk_2' - pk_c')$*	p(Ca + Mg)	$p(HCO_3)$**
0.5	2.11	3.60	3.30
1.0	2.13	3.30	3.00
4.0	2.20	2.70	2.40
8.0	2.25	2.40	2.10
10.0	2.27	2.30	2.00
20.0	2.35	2.00	1.70
30.0	2.40	1.82	1.52
40.0	2.44	1.70	1.40
50.0	2.47	1.60	1.30

*Total cation content in water (Ca + Mg + Na ions) (meq/l)

**Sum of CO_3 + HCO_3 ion

$(pk_2' - pk_c')$ at 14 meq/l total ions = 2.30

p(Ca + Mg) = (7 + 2) meq/l = 2.35

$p(HCO_3)$ = 4 meq/l = 2.40

pHc = (2.30) + (2.40) + (2.35) = 7.05

$$\text{Adj. SAR} = 5/\sqrt{(7+2)/2}\,[1 + (8.4 - 7.05)]$$

$$= 5/\sqrt{4.5}\,[1 + 1.35]$$

$$= 2.36 \times 2.35 = 5.55$$

So adj SAR of the irrigation water is 5.55 rather than the uncorrected SAR of 2.36.

Example 6

If a sandy soil having cation exchange capacity (CEC) 20 Cmol(p^+) kg^{-1} and 30 per cent base saturation at pH 4.5. Calculate the theoretical amount of lime ($CaCO_3$) required per hectare of land (0-15 cm depth) for raising base saturation to 60 per cent [weight of soil per hectare furrow slice (0-15 cm depth) = 2.2×10^6 kg).

$$\text{Per cent base saturation (BS)} = \frac{\text{meq of basic cation (S)}}{\text{Total exchangeable cations (T)}} \times 100$$

Base saturation of the soil before lime application (initial) = 30%

Base saturation to be raised through liming (final) = 60%

$$\text{me of base cations initially present in the soil (S)} = \frac{T \times BS\ (\text{percentage})}{100}$$

$$= 20 \times 30/100 = 6$$

Again, me of basic cations at 60% base saturation (S)

$$= \frac{T \times BS}{100} = 20 \times 60/100 = 12$$

So me of basic cations will be required to raise the base saturation at 60%

= (12 – 6) = 6

1 me H/100 g = 50 mg/100 g lime

= 500 mg/1000 g lime

= 500 ppm = 500 × 2.24 kg/ha

= 1120 kg/ha

6 me H = 1120 × 6 kg/ha

= 6720 kg/ha = 67 quintals of lime will be required.

Example 7

Irrigation water containing 414, 120 and 24 mg/l of Na, Ca and Mg, respectively. Calculate (1) Total cation concentration meq/l) (2) SAR (3) EC value (mSm^{-1}) (4) OP (5) Total dissolve salt (mg/l).

Na = 414 mg/l = 414/23 = 18 meq/l

Ca = 120 mg/l = 120/20 = 6 meq/l

Mg = 24 mg/l = 24/12 = 2 meq/l

Total cation concentration = Ca + Mg + Na = 6 + 2 + 18 = 26 meq/l

SAR = Na/√Ca + Mg/2 = 18/√6 + 2/2 = 18/√4 = 18/2 = 9

EC × 10^3 = Total cation(meq/l)/10 = 26/10

= 2.6 mmhos/cm or dS/m

OP = EC × 10^3 × 0.36 = 2.6 × 0.36 = 0.936 bars

Total dissolved salts = Ca + Mg + Na = 414 + 120 + 24 = 558 mg/l

Example 8

An analysis of irrigation water is as under :

(i) EC 250 mS/m, (ii) Ca + Mg = 9 meq/l (iii) CO_3 + HCO_3 15.0 meq/l (iv) Depth of irrigation water 5 cm/ha (10 irrigations were given)

Calculate : (i) Na meq/l, (ii) SAR, (iii) ppm and % salt, (iv) Amount of salt added through irrigation water (kg/ha), (v) RSC and necessary to workout GR of irrigation water and give your comment.

EC = 250 mS/m = 2.5 dS/m

Total cation meq/l = EC × 10^3 × 10 = 2.5 × 10 = 25 meq/l

Na meq/l = Total cation – (Ca + Mg) = 25 – 9 = 16 meq/l

SAR = Na/√Ca + Mg/2 = 16/√9/2 = 16/√4.5 = 16/2.12 = 7.55

% salt = EC × 10^3 × 0.064 = 2.5 × 0.064 = 0.16%

ppm salt = % salt × 10,000 = 0.16 × 10,000 = 1600 ppm

5 cm/ha irrigation = 100 × 100 × 0.5 = 500 cu.m/irrigation

10 irrigations = 500 × 10 = 5000 cu.m

1 cu.m = 1000 l water hence 5000 cu.m

= 5000 × 1000 = 50,00,000 l

0.16% salt means 0.16 kg/100 l water so 50,00,000 × 0.16/100 = 8000 kg/ha

or 1600 ppm = 1600 mg/l = 1.6 g/l = 50,00,000 × 1.6/1000

= 8000 kg/ha

RSC = $(CO_3 + HCO_3) - (Ca + Mg)$ = 15 – 9 = 6 meq/l

Initial RSC – Final RSC = 6 – 2.5 = 3.5 meq/l to be reduced

1 meq RSC = 86 mg gypsum/l

= 0.086 g/l

3.5 meq RSC = 3.5 × 0.086 = 0.301 g/l

So for 1 litre = 0.301 g gypsum

Hence 50,00,000 l = 0.301 × 50,00,000/1000 = 1505 kg gypsum/ha

Comment : EC = 2.5 mmhos/cm = 2500 micromhos/cm = C_4 = Salinity hazard

SAR = 7.55 = S_1 = Low Na water = can be used

RSC = 6 = not suitable for irrigation

Example 9

A soil having CEC 25 me/100 g soil and various cations are present in following proportion :

Ca : 10 meq/100 g K : 1 meq/100 g

Mg : 5 meq/100 g Na : 3 meq/100 g

by using these data calculate the following values :

(i) % base saturation, (ii) % base unsaturation, (iii) Ca, Mg, Na and K kg/ha, (iv) Workout lime requirement to neutralize the soil acidity.

%base saturation = me of basic cations/CEC × 100

= 10 + 1 + 5 + 3/25 × 100 = 19/25 × 100 = 76%

% base unsaturation = 100% base saturation = 100 – 76 = 24%

Ca = 10 meq/100 g = 10 × 20 mg/100 g = 200 mg/100 g

= 2000 mg/1000 g = 2000 ppm = 2000 × 2.24 = 4480 kg/ha

Mg = 5 meq/100 g = 5 × 12 = 60 mg/100 g

= 600 mg/1000 g = 600 ppm = 600 × 2.24 = 1344 kg/ha

Na = 3 meq/100 g = 3 × 23 = 69 mg/100 g

= 690 mg/1000 g = 690 ppm = 690 × 2.24 = 1545.6 kg/ha

K = 1 meq/100 g = 1 × 39 = 39 mg/100 g

= 390 mg/1000 g = 390 ppm = 390 × 2.24 = 873.6 kg/ha

H = CEC – total cations = 25 – 19 = 6 meq H/100 g

1 meq H/100 g = 50 mg lime/100 g

= 500 mg/1000 g = 500 ppm = 500 × 2.24 = 1120 kg/ha

6 meq H/100 g = 6 × 1120 = 6720 kg/ha lime

❑ ❑ ❑

CHAPTER 18

Soil Pollution

Pollution—What is it ?

The term pollution is derived from a *Latin* word Polluere, which means "to soil" or "to defile".

Pollution may be defined as "an undesirable change in the physical, chemical and biological characteristics of air, water and soil which affects human life, lives of his related other useful living plants and animals, industrial progress, living conditions and cultural assets."

Soil pollution is defined as the build-up in soils of persistent toxic compounds, chemicals, salts, radioactive materials, or disease causing agents, which have adverse effects on plant growth and animal health.

"Pollution occurs when a product added to our natural environment adversely affects nature's ability to dispose it of. This product could be a naturally occurring material contamination such as pesticides, detergents, fertilizers."

Pollution. Pollution contaminates things and makes them unclean or impure.

Pollutant. A pollutant is defined as a constituent in the wrong amount, at a wrong place or at the wrong time.

There are many different ways that soil can become polluted, such as :

- Seepage from a landfill
- Discharge of industrial waste into the soil
- Percolation of contaminated water into the soil
- Rupture of underground storage tanks
- Excess application of pesticides, herbicides or fertilizer
- Solid waste seepage

The most common chemicals involved in causing soil pollution are :

- Petroleum hydrocarbons
- Heavy metals
- Pesticides
- Solvents

Types of Soil Pollution

1. Agricultural Soil Pollution
   (*i*) pollution of surface soil (*ii*) pollution of underground soil
2. Soil pollution by industrial effluents and solid wastes
   (*i*) pollution of surface soil (*ii*) disturbances in soil profile
3. Pollution due to urban activities
   (*i*) pollution of surface soil (*ii*) pollution of underground soil

Sources of Soil Pollution

(*a*) **Agrochemicals.** (1) Pesticides (2) Insecticides (3) Herbicides (4) Fungicides (5) Fertilizers

(*b*) **Industrial wastes.** (1) Effluents (2) Dust and other wastes (3) Radioactive wastes (4) Heavy metals (5) Acid precipitation

(*c*) **Urban wastes.** (1) Municipal solid waste (2) Municipal sewage (3) Vehicular exhaust

(*d*) **Rural wastes.** (1) Home wastes (2) Litter (3) Livestock wastes (4) Plant residues (5) Sediments

Causes of Soil Pollution

A soil pollutant is any factor which deteriorates the quality, texture and mineral content of the soil or which disturb the biological balance of the organisms in the soil. Pollution in soil has adverse effect on plant growth.

Pollution in soil is associated with :

- Indiscriminate use of fertilizers
- Indiscriminate use of pesticides, insecticides and herbicides
- Dumping of large quantities of solid waste
- Deforestation and soil erosion
- Polluted water discharged from factories
- Runoff from pollutants (paint, chemicals, rotting organic material) leaching out of landfill
- Oil and petroleum leaks from vehicles washed off the road by the rain into the surrounding habitat
- Chemical fertilizer runoff from farms and crops
- Acid rain (fumes from factories mixing with rain)
- Sewage discharged into rivers instead of being treated properly
- Over application of pesticides and fertilizers
- Purposeful injection into groundwater as a disposal method
- Interconnections between aquifers during drilling (poor technique)

- Septic tank seepage
- Lagoon seepage
- Sanitary/hazardous landfill seepage
- Cemeteries
- Scrap yards (waste oil and chemical drainage)
- Leaks from sanitary sewers

Effects of Soil Pollution

Agricultural

- Reduced soil fertility
- Reduced nitrogen fixation
- Increased erodibility
- Larger loss of soil and nutrients
- Deposition of silt in tanks and reservoirs
- Reduced crop yield
- Imbalance in soil fauna and flora

Industrial

- Dangerous chemicals entering underground water
- Ecological imbalance
- Release of pollutant gases
- Release of radioactive rays causing health problems
- Increased salinity
- Reduced vegetation

Urban

- Clogging of drains
- Inundation of areas
- Public health problems
- Pollution of drinking water sources
- Foul smell and release of gases
- Waste management problems

Environmental Long Term Effects of Soil Pollution

When it comes to the environment itself, the toll of contaminated soil is even dier. Soil that has been contaminated should no longer be used to grow food, because the chemicals can leach into the food and harm people who eat it.

If contaminated soil is used to grow food, the land will usually produce lower yields than it would if it were not contaminated. This, in turn, can cause even more harm because a lack of plants on the soil will cause more erosion, spreading the contaminants onto land that might not have been tainted before.

In addition, the pollutants will change the makeup of the soil and the types of microorganisms that will live in it.

If certain organisms die off in the area, the larger predator animals will also have to move away or die because they have lost their food supply. Thus it's possible for soil pollution to change whole ecosystems.

Effects of soil pollution in brief :

- pollution runs off into rivers and kills the fish, plants and other aquatic life
- crops and fodder grown on polluted soil may pass the pollutants on to the consumers
- polluted soil may no longer grow crops and fodder
- Soil structure is damaged (clay ionic structure impaired)

- corrosion of foundations and pipelines
- impairs soil stability
- may release vapors and hydrocarbon into buildings and cellars
- may create toxic dusts
- may poison children playing in the area

Control of Soil Pollution

The following steps have been suggested to control soil pollution. To help prevent soil erosion, we can limit construction in sensitive area. In general we would need less fertilizer and fewer pesticides if we could all adopt the three R's: Reduce, Reuse, and Recycle. This would give us less solid waste.

Reducing chemical fertilizer and pesticide use. Applying bio-fertilizers and manures can reduce chemical fertilizer and pesticide use. Biological methods of pest control can also reduce the use of pesticides and thereby minimize soil pollution.

Reusing of materials. Materials such as glass containers, plastic bags, paper, cloth etc. can be reused at domestic levels rather than being disposed, reducing solid waste pollution.

Recycling and recovery of materials. This is a reasonable solution for reducing soil pollution. Materials such as paper, some kinds of plastics and glass can and are being recycled. This decreases the volume of refuse and helps in the conservation of natural resources. For example, recovery of one tonne of paper can save 17 trees.

Reforesting. Control of land loss and soil erosion can be attempted through restoring forest and grass cover to check wastelands, soil erosion and floods. Crop rotation or mixed cropping can improve the fertility of the land.

Solid waste treatment. Proper methods should be adopted for management of solid waste disposal. Industrial wastes can be treated physically, chemically and biologically until they are less hazardous. Acidic and alkaline wastes should be first neutralized, the insoluble material if biodegradable should be allowed to degrade under controlled conditions before being disposed.

Incineration of other wastes is expensive and leaves a huge residue and adds to air pollution. Pyrolysis is a process of combustion in absence of oxygen or the material burnt under controlled atmosphere of oxygen. It is an alternative to incineration. The gas and liquid thus obtained can be used as fuels. Pyrolysis of carbonaceous wastes like firewood, coconut, palm waste, corn combs, cashew shell, rice husk paddy straw and saw dust, yields charcoal along with products like tar, methyl alcohol, acetic acid, acetone and a fuel gas.

SOIL POLLUTION DUE TO FERTILIZERS–EUTROPHICATION AND NITRATE TOXICITY

Although micronutrient heavy metals are often added to fertilizers as needed, the major nutrient fertilizers often contain appreciable concentrations as incidental impurities derived from the raw materials, which are sometimes sufficient to benefit crop growth. Commercial fertilizers may contain a great range of heavy metals, but the highest values for heavy metals are found in phosphatic fertilizers.

Agricultural Chemicals

Metal containing sprays have been regularly used to control pests in horticultural and vegetable crops and in turf. Zinc salts, copper and lead arsenates, and metallo-organic compounds have all been used, and high levels of metal contamination have been documented. In several countries, copper levels of about 1,000 mg kg^{-1} have resulted from extensive use of Bordeaux sprays, that is, copper basic salts (Tiller and Merry, 1982) while use of lead arsenaic sprays has led to soil levels of at least 500 mg Pb kg^{-1} and 100 mg As kg^{-1}. By comparison, uncontaminated soils contained about 20, 10, and 5 mg kg^{-1} for Cu, Pb, and As, respectively. Annual accumulations of Cu, Pb, and As in Australian orchard soils were estimated at about 4, 5, and 1 mg kg^{-1} respectively, that is, about three orders of magnitude higher than the accumulation rates of Cd from phosphatic fertilizers under European and Australian conditions (2-4 g ha^{-1} yr^{-1}). The main hazard from the contamination of horticultural soils is not usually from existing crops but rather in relation to new uses of the soil after orchard or vineyard clearance.

Fertilizer Pollution

The main concern about fertilizers problem is N and P because of the eutrophication problem caused by them in lakes and inland water. The bulk of the evidence shows that the source of pollution of accumulation of NO_3 and PO_4 in lakes is not the fertilizer but numerous other sources. Phosphates have lowest mobility in soils and their principal loss is through erosion. Nitrogen is highly mobile and an all out effort is needed to improve the efficiency of all sources of nitrogenous fertilizers, manures, green manures, etc. In the soil, nitrogen goes into a cycle through various biological and chemical reactions.

***(a)* Nitrogen.** Nitrogen losses are mainly through soil erosion and denitrification. But losses through leaching can be considerably more, particularly under conditions such as rice cultivation. There is considerable evidence that the major cause of nitrate accumulation in the lakes and other water bodies is through soil erosion, leaching from animal manure source such as in large feedlots and dairy farms or dumped manure heaps. This nitrogen in lakes and tanks can cause eutrophication.

Thus chemical changes resulting from fertilization can have considerable impact on the microbial population. Some effects show within a few days, as when added nitrogen speeds up the decomposition of organic materials in the soil. Long-term effects may develop over period of years, as when the acidification effects of ammonium fertilizer cause changes in the microbial population. Fortunately such changes are normal and reversible. The salt effect may dehydrate and kill microbes in a fertilizer band. In this way excess fertilizer nutrients, which are not used by plants, can contribute to pollution. The unused animal waste cause much more pollution than properly handled manure used to fertilizer fields.

***(b)* Phosphorus.** The losses of phosphates from the fertilizer through leaching are very small because of phosphatic fixation phenomenon in the soil, unless a soil is pure sand or is subject to flooding. Fertilizers do not seem to be significantly involved in raising the P level of surface water in ground water. On the other hand, by promoting vegetative cover they help in reducing erosion and thus reduce losses of nutrients to water. The major sources of phosphate loss in soil are from soil erosion, which results in mechanical movement of potentially available P to streams and lakes. The contribution by human and animal wastes, industrial wastes and detergents to P content of streams, lakes and marine and also inland waters are very substantial. Thus, it is not the phosphatic fertilizers but the organic sources of phosphorus, which could be the source of pollution.

(*c*) Potassium. So far as potassium is concerned, its losses from fertilizer sources are low because of rapid movement from soluble to exchangeable and fixed forms and luxury consumption of the nutrients by the crops. However, in sandy soils with low cation exchange capacity and under heavy rain or leaching, there is some chance of loss potassium. On clay and loam soils, it is unlikely that any appreciable amount will move more than 50-70 cm in soil. The content of drainage water is usually less than 0.1 meq/litre. Even with application of 240 kg K/ha the movement of K into the subsoil was less by 30% than in the same soil if there is an adequate supply of N and other nutrients. It shows that from a poor and unfertilized soil, there is a greater chance of K, loss than from a rich and well-fertilized soil.

(*d*) Secondary nutrients. The loss of secondary nutrients from soil is quite high, particularly under high rainfall conditions but there is no evidence that they cause pollution. Magnesium loss in certain areas has been responsible for tetany in cattle. The loss of sulphate in sandy soils is very high.

(*e*) Micronutrients. The micronutrients are so strongly absorbed in the soil that there is little likelihood of their going into the drainage water. However, changes in soil redox potential results in movement of Fe and Mn. which have been traced in the drainage tile lines. The eutrophication of lakes which is caused by the accumulation of nitrates, phosphates and molybdates in lakes is causing quite a concern in the developed countries, but how much of the fertilizer are to blame for it is questionable.

(*f*) Organic fertilizers. Application of organic fertilizers such as FYM provides food sources for soil animals. Moderate application of organic manure improved their populations in grassland. Conversely animal slurry and other nutrient rich organic residues when applied at higher dosage adversely affected the population of soil invertebrates.

EUTROPHICATION

The addition of nutrients to an ecosystem, such as a lake, is an example of something that is good in the right amounts but detrimental when in excess. This addition can be seen as an enrichment of the lake that leads to other slow processes, collectively referred to as the natural aging of a lake. The enrichment process is generally an irreversible one that all lakes experience and is known as eutrophication. The word is derived from the Greeks whereas "eu" means "well" and "trophe" means "nourishment". A simple definition of eutrophication is therefore the naturally occurring biological process of the enrichment of water with nutrients.

Strictly speaking, eutrophication and the aging process are not pollution until the process is accelerated by man. The appropriate terminology is then cultural eutrophication, and this is the focus of the associated pollution problems. Lakes are generally categorized by limnologists according to the degree of nutrient enrichment. A young lake formed during the retreat of the glaciers is a cold, sandy-bottomed, transparent lake with little plant life. It has a low nutrient input or loading and is referred to as an "oligotrophic" lake, from the Greek word "oligo" for poor or few. As a lake becomes older, it gradually receives nutrients and sediments from the surrounding drainage basin. It then experiences an increase in productivity with increased plant growth and some production of gamefish. The lake will eventually become nutrient rich or eutrophic, and plant growth, in the form of microscopic phytoplankton and rooted aquatic plants, can occur to a level in which the water becomes undesirable for various uses. Following are the general steps in the lake aging process :

1. Streams from the drainage basin bring in soil and nutrients to a collective low point that becomes a fertile lake.
2. The increased fertility gives rise to an accumulating growth of both plants and animals.
3. As the lake's biomass increases, organic deposits build up on the bottom and it becomes shallower, richer, and warmer.

Given sunlight and nutrients, plant life abounds and is fed on by primary consumers. The food chain/food web becomes established. If cultural eutrophication comes into play, abundant nutrients become available. The imbalance can result in algae blooms; the explosive growth of one or more types or species to the detriment or exclusion of others. Blooms can occur for long periods of time and extend over large areas having significant impact on the ecology of the ecosystem and even human activities.

Some blooms can be comprised of undesirable blue-green algae not generally good as a food source in the food web. The lake, bay, or canal can become turbid, and thick mats of algae form. Oxygen levels decrease due to elevated BOD as decay accelerates. Shallow waters become choked with rooted plants. The less tolerant species, such as game fish, either die or move out as water quality and conditions deteriorate. As the populations of the original sensitive inhabitants decrease, niches are opened up and the less desirable, more tolerant species increase in population. For example, trout are replaced by perch and bass, which are eventually replaced by carp and catfish. If conditions become extremely eutrophic, varying degrees of anoxia can develop and most species can be eliminated.

During the process, many nutrients are locked into the benthic sediments, so that even if the major inputs of nutrients are cut off, a lake can remain in the eutrophic state for excessive periods of time, drawing on these reserves. It is easy to see how many ways eutrophic lakes are a significant pollution problem. Not only is there a loss of food fish, but also the loss of a water supply and recreation facility, and if conditions are severe enough, unpleasant odors and views detract from any aesthetic values the lake may have had. A particular genera or even a specific species alone is not considered to be a good indicator of pollution or as a warning sign. Within any genera, there may be some species that are good indicators and others that are not. In general, this approach is not reliable because most species are tolerant of a wide range of conditions specific to each species. However, when algae are studied as a community, certain groups of interrelated types may be a reliable index. The most frequent groups are the blue green algae and the dinoflagellates.

Control of Algae and Eutrophication

It should seem apparent at this point that to control eutrophication is both ecologically and economically important. It is almost impossible to resolve natural eutrophication, but it is quite possible to address the problem of cultural eutrophication. Specific controls in certain special circumstances may be helpful if the problem source is limited in scope. They may only help to alleviate the nuisance and may have only a temporary effect. The nuisance algae can be physically removed. Increased flushing or dilution techniques can be used if available. Sometimes increasing the circulation during stagnant periods also can help. This may add dissolved oxygen and lower the temperature of the epilimnion (surface water) to shift conditions away from those optimal for blue-green algae.

The most effective but probably the least desirable from an ecologic standpoint is the use of chemicals. Herbicides can be used but can have undesirable long-term effects. The most common chemical is the algicide copper sulfate, which has been used in controlling algae in water supply reservoirs. It does, however, kill more then just algae. Fish are susceptible to it, and a buildup in benthic sediments is also possible.

Other chemical strategies have included the addition of aluminum, iron and calcium based coagulants/precipitants to directly remove phosphate. This is both temporary and costly and locks the nutrient into the sediments. Chemicals also have been used to shift the pH to a range more favourable to less offensive algae or herbivores. In a very few cases, species have been used to eat excess algae or other plant life.

Toxicity

The toxicity of nitrogen compounds occurs mostly through the ammonia compounds and nitrates. Information on specific toxicity to aquatic species can be obtained from the EPA Quality Criteria for Water (EPA-440/9-76-023), commonly referred to as the "EPA Redbook", which presents information and the rationale for selection of recommended standards for chemical contaminants.

The presence of ammonia is very dependent on the pH. Below a pH of 7, the ammonium ion is predominant; above pH 7, un-ionized ammonia dominates. Toxicity can be increased by a number of factors, including higher temperature and bicarbonate alkalinity or increasing the dissolved oxygen or carbon dioxide concentrations. The criterion for ammonia is 0.02 mg/l for freshwater aquatic life. We should note that untreated domestic waste water may contain up to 50 mg/1 of ammonia, so a direct discharge can pose significant environmental risks.

Because levels of nitrate or nitrite that would be toxic to warm or cold-water fish would rarely occur, no restrictive standards are recommended. However, there is an established standard of 10 mg/1 of nitrate in potable water. Toxic human doses have been reported at 0.56 grams of nitrate per day and 1.04 grams per kilogram of body weight. Other health problems can occur, which will be discussed later. It also has been reported that nitrates in water have caused poor growth in hogs and chickens.

Nitrogen Oxide (NOx)

Even in unpolluted atmosphere, there are present measurable amount of nitrous oxide, nitric oxide and nitrogen dioxide of these nitric oxide (NO) is the pivot compound. It is produced by combustion of O_2 and N_2 during lightning discharges and by bacterial oxidation of NH_3 in soil. NO contacts with air and combines with O_2 or even more readily with O_3 to form the more poisonous nitrogen dioxide (NO_2). NO_2 may react with water vapour in air to form HNO_3. This acid combines with NH_3 to form ammonium nitrate. Fossil fuel combustion also contributes to oxides of nitrogen. About 95% of the nitrogen oxide is emitted as NO and remaining 5% as NO_2. In urban areas about 46% of oxides of nitrogen in air come from vehicles and 25% fro electric generation and the rest from other sources. In metropolitan cities, vehicular exhaust is the most important sources of nitrogen oxides.

(1) Nitrous oxide (N_2O). In atmosphere maximum N_2O levels are about 0.5 ppm, whereas average global level is estimated to be nearly 0.25 ppm. This gas has so far not been implicated in air pollution problem.

(2) Nitric oxide (NO). The chief sources of this gas are the industries manufacturing HNO_3 and other chemicals, and the automobile exhausts. At high temperature, combustion of gasoline produces this gas. A large amount of this is readily converted to more toxic NO_2 in the atmosphere by a series of chemical reactions.

NO is responsible for several photochemical reactions in the atmosphere, particularly in the formation of several secondary pollutants like PAN, carbonyl compounds, etc. in the presence of other organic substances. There is little evidence of the direct role of this gas is causing a health hazard, at the levels found in urban air.

(3) Nitrogen dioxide (NO_2). A deep reddish brown gas, which is the only widely prevalent coloured pollutant gas. This gas is the chief constituent of photochemical smog in metropolitan areas. NO_2 causes irritation of alveoli, leading to symptoms resembling emphysema (inflammation) upon prolonged exposure to 1 ppm level. Lung inflammation may be followed by edema and final death. The MAC for occupational exposure are set at 5 ppm for an 8 hour period. Smokers may readily develop lung diseases as the cigaretts and cigars contain 330-1,500 ppm nitrogen oxides. NO_2 is highly injurious to plants. Their growth is suppressed when exposed to 0.3-0.5 ppm for 10-20 days. Sensitive plants show visible leaf injury when exposed to 4 to 8 ppm for 1-4 hours.

Acid Rains: An Invisible Threat

We have seen that the oxides of sulphur and nitrogen are important gaseous pollutants of air. These oxides are produced mainly by combustion of fossil fuels, smelters, power plants, automobile exhausts, domestic fires etc. These oxides are swept up into the atmosphere and can travel thousands of kilometers. The longer they stay in the atmosphere, the more likely they are to be oxidised into acids. Sulphuric acids and nitric acid are the two main acids, which then dissolve in the water in the atmosphere and fall to the ground as acid rain or may remain in atmosphere in clouds and fogs.

Acidification of environment is a manmade phenomenon. The acid rain is infact a cocktail of H_2SO_4 and HNO_3 and the ratio of the two may vary depending on the relative quantities of oxides of sulphur and nitrogen emitted. On an average 60-70% of the acidity is ascribed to H_2SO_4 and 30-40% to HNO_3. The acid rain problem has dramatically increased due to industrialisation. Burning of fosil fuels for power generation contributes to almost 60-70% of total SO_2 emitted globally. Emission of NOx from anthropogenic sources ranges between 20-90 million tons annually over the globe. Acid rains have assumed global ecological problem, because oxides travel a long distance and during their journey in atmosphere they may undergo physical and chemical transformations to produce more hazardous products.

Acid rains create complex problems and their impacts are far reaching. They increase soil acidity, thus affecting land flora and fauna, cause acidification of lakes and streams thus affecting aquatic life, affects crop productivity and human health. Besides these they also corrode buildings, monuments, statues, bridges, fences, railings etc. British Parliament building also suffered damage due to H_2SO_4 rains. Due to acidity, levels of heavy metals as aluminium, manganese, zinc, cadmium, lead and copper in water increases beyond the safe limits. Over 10,000 lakes in Sweden have become acidified. Thousands of lakes in U.S.A., Canada, Norway have become unproductive due to acidity. Fish population has decreased tremendously, and there are deaths of salman trout etc. The fishless areas (lakes) are now fish graveyards.

Many bacteria and blue green algae are killed due to acidification, thus disrupting the ecological balance. In West Germany nearly 8% of the forests died and nearly 18 million acres of forests are critically affected by acid rains. Forests in Switzerland, Netherlands and Czechoslovakia have also been damaged by acid rains. Nutrients as calcium magnesium, potassium have been leached away from soil by acids.

Acid rains are a great threat to British environment as to Central Europe and Southern Scandivanvia. In 1974 acid rains over Scotland were found to be more sour than vinegar (pH 2.4). This H_2SO_4 shower, 500 times more acidic than rain should naturally be stood as a world record for four years. Much of the falling snow in Britain in now highly acidic. If it does not melt it may turn into a pollution time bomb.

SOIL POLLUTION DUE TO SEWAGE AND INDUSTRIAL WASTES

Sewage is the waterborne waste derived from home (domestic waste) and animal or food processing plants. It includes human excreta, paper, cloth, soap, detergents, etc. These are a major proportion of the pollutants entering our water. There is uncontrolled dumping of wastes of rural areas, towns and cities into ponds, lakes, stream or rivers. Due to accumulation of sewage and other wastes in these bodies, they are not able to recycle them and their self regulatory capability is lost. The decomposition of these wastes by aerobic microbes decreases due to higher levels of pollution. The self-purifying ability of the water is lost and water becomes unfit for drinking and other domestic uses. Since decomposition of sewage and other wastes is largely an aerobic process, accumulation of these in water increases its oxygen requirements (BOD).

Phosphates are the major ingredient of most detergents. They favour the luxuriant growth of algae which from water blooms. The extensive algal growth also consumes most of the available oxygen from water. This decrease in O_2 level becomes detrimental to growth of other organism which produces a foul smell upon decay. Some decomposing plants are known to produce toxins as strychnine which kills animals including cattle.

Sewage

Domestic sewage consists of discharges of dirty water from bathrooms, lavatories and kitchens. It is a complex mixture of mineral and organic matter in many forms, including large and small particles of solid matter, substances in solution, in suspension and in colloidal and pseudo-colloidal dispersion. The sewage also contains living matter, especially bacteria, viruses and protozoa, and is thus an excellent medium for the development of micro-organisms (Mahida). Most of the bacteria are relatively harmless but a few are positively dangerous, being pathogenic or diseases producing. Industrial wastes or trade wastes vary widely with different processes of manufacture and can be as, or even more, objectionable than domestic sewage, as in the case of wastes from slaughter houses, or they may be no more than discoloured water.

The solids in the sewage are both organic and inorganic. The organic matter in sewage consists of nitrogenous materials, carbohydrates, fats and soaps. It is unstable and decomposes, producing unpleasant odours. It is this characteristic of sewage that renders sewage treatment necessary and causes the greatest difficulties in sewage disposal. The inorganic solids are usually innocuous.

Fresh sewage is only slightly turbid but it becomes darker as it gets state or septic. The odour of fresh sewage is faint and not necessarily unpleasant through slightly pungent. Fresh sewage contains a little dissolved oxygen and sometimes small amounts of nitrite and nitrate, especially after rain. Fresh sewage is slightly alkaline but during the oxidation of sewage there is a decrease in alkalinity. State sewage gives off nauseating odours of hydrogen sulphide and other gases. It usually has no dissolved oxygen. When sewage becomes septic, bubbles of gas can be seen breaking on the surface. Prompt and complete removal of domestic sewage from inhabited areas is thus essential to protect health of the community. Similarly, the removal of industrial wastes is also necessary. It is more convinient and almost always less costly to treat a mixture of sewage and industrial waste than to treat the latter separately. This is because it is generally easy to transform the mixture of sewage and trade wastes into a final effluent satisfying the prescribed standards, whereas if trade wastes are treated separately, the process becomes difficult and costly.

Sewage and Sludge

Sewage sludge, which contains valuable amounts of plant nutrients, may also contain potentially toxic heavy metals. The practice of adding sewage sludge to agricultural land is well established now-a-days. No doubt, sludge is a useful and cheap source of N, P, K and it may also improve the physical conditions of the soil. The rates of applications vary considerably but sludge are sometimes regularly applied at 25 tones dry matter per hectare. Some heavy metals are also present in all sludges and will accumulate in soil over the years especially when sludges from industrial areas are applied.

The heavy metal contents of sludges depend to a large extent on the nature of the local industry and on the proportions of industrial and domestic wastes. Table 18.1 gives values for the range and median contents of heavy metals in 42 sludge from England and Wales.

It is obvious from above Table that Zinc is almost always present in the highest amounts and Cu, is often second though Pb, Cr, or Ni may exceed Cu depending on the local industry in sludges derived from domestic sources, only Zn and Cu are present in high amounts though these are well below the content found in most industrial sludges. However, applications of domestic sludges over several years have led to the accumulation of heavy metals, especially Zn in the soils.

Effect of sewage on soil and plant

(*a*) **Irrigation with sewage**. Irrigation with sewage causes, as is the case of irrigation with other water, profound changes in the irrigated soils. Amongst the various changes that are brought about in the soil as a result of sewage irrigation include :

1. Leaching, removal or accumulation of salts
2. Changes in the base exchange status and humus contents
3. Alteration in the soil reaction (pH)
4. Suppression of pore spaces and a consequent reduction of permeability
5. Changes in the state of aggregation and alteration of C : N ratio.

TABLE 18.1. Heavy Metal Contents in Sludges (ppm)

Metal	*Median (ppm)*	*Range (ppm)*
Cd	—	< 60-1500
Co	12	2-260
Cr	250	40-8800
Cu	800	200-8000
Fe	21000	6000-62000
Mn	400	150-2500
Mo	5	2-30
Ni	80	20-5300
Pb	700	120-3000
Ar	120	40-700
Zn	3000	700-49000

(*b*) **Sewage sickness.** The deleterious effects of sewage application to soils and the prevalence of unhygienic conditions on the sewage farms are generally referred to as *"Sewage sickness"*.

In fact, Sewage sickness of soils is a condition of gross water logging. Under waterlogged conditions, with very low or a total absence of air, conditions which suppress microbial activities are created in anaerobic conditions, the microbial population in the soil sets up strong reducing conditions, maintaining a high carbon dioxide concentration and produces reduced compounds such as sulphides which are very toxic to roots.

Methods of control water pollution :

(1) Methods used in wastewater treatment.

(2) Sedimentation is carried out from domestic wastewater.

(3) Usually, the use of such chemical operations as coagulation or neutralization is carried out in industrial wastewater.

(4) Biological methods consist of using living microorganisms in treatment.

(5) The improvement of the wastewater quality and generally, settleable or suspended solids are removed from the sewage by the physical processes of sedimentation in settling tanks (septic thanks).

(6) The biochemical decomposition of the sewage substrate.

(7) Activated sludge, continuously mixed, and actively growing microbial populations.

(8) The best control of water pollution is : "Solution of pollution is dilution."

Methods used in waste water treatment

(1) Physical processes. (*a*) Sedimentation, (*b*) Absorption, (*c*) Cooling

(2) Chemical processes. (*a*) Congulation, (*b*) Neutralization (*c*) Chemical oxidation, (*d*) Chemical reduction

(3) Biological processes.

(***a***) ***Aerobic*** (*i*) Activated sludge process (*ii*) Trickling filters

(***b***) ***Anaerobic*** (*i*) Anerobic digestion (*ii*) Septics/cess pools

(***c***) ***Oxidation ponds or lagoons***

Heavy metals

Pollution of the environment by heavy metals is normally associated with human activity of one kind or another.

Heavy metals are elements having a density greater than 5 in their elemental form and comprise some 38 elements. However, the term usually, and here as well refers to 12 metals that are used and discharged by industry *i.e.*, Cd, Cr, Co, Cu, Fe, Hg, Mn, Mo, Ni, Sn and Zn. Heavy metals mostly find specific adsorption sites in the soil where they are retained very strongly either on the inorganic or organic colloids.

The heavy metals are widely distributed in the environment, in soils, in plants and animals in most of their tissues. The concentrations of individual metals in living tissue are ordinarily very low and must be maintained within narrow limits to permit the optimum biological performance of most organisms. Some heavy metals are essential in trace amounts, namely Co, Cu, Fe, Mn, Mo, Zn for plants and in addition, Cr, Ni, Sn, for animals; Cd, Hg and Pb, have not been shown to be essential for either plants or animals.

CHEMISTRY OF PESTICIDES IN SOIL

Reactions of pesticides with soils

Pesticides are generally applied to soil for controlling soil-borne disease, pests and diseases of plants. In addition to the above, a fraction of all pesticides applied to plants either as spray or dust reach the soil through either runoff from leaves or through wind, rain etc. As soil is a complex physical, chemical and biological system, a number of reactions take place and these modify the efficiency of the pesticides considerably. The activity of pesticides in the soil is controlled largely by the absorption and desorption of the same by soil components.

Clay is considered to be the most reactive part of the soil. The quantity, nature of clay, surface area, soil structure, organic matter, water content, quality of pesticides, temperature and pH of the pesticides and soil largely influence the efficiency of the pesticides applied to the soil. Some pesticides are cationic in nature and are adsorbed on the clay by exchange reactions. Complication of the pesticides with clay affects the bioactivity of pesticides to a greater or lesser extent depending upon the energy of adsorption and desorption. The total change and surface area of the solid components decrease in the order. Organic matter > Vermiculite > Montmorillonite > Illite > Chlorite > Kaolinite on a comparable weight basis, montmorillonite adsorbed about 20 times more of the pesticide than kaolinite. Calcium saturated kaolinite and calcium saturated montmorillonite adsorbed 2.70 and 10.3 mg/g respectively of BHC. Considering the surface area, kaolinite adsorbed (0.18 mg) far more than the montmorillonite (0.0127 mg/g) which shows that BHC competes much more effectively with water on the kaolinite hydroxy surfaces than on the oxygen surfaces of montmorillonite. The finer the particles the greater will be absorption of the pesticide, possibly due to the increased surface area and reactive sites. The adsorption, desorption and degradation also depend on the nature of the cation present originally. Adsorption of paraquat was more complete on Na^+ saturated vermiculite than on Ca^{2+} or Mg^{2+} saturated clay. Dieldrin was degraded much more rapidly on a H^+ or Al^{3+} kaolinite than on Na^+ or Ca^{2+} clay. Certain of the chemical reactions of pesticides are catalyzed by clay in the soils. For this the two silicate surfaces must be in simultaneous contact with the molecule. The catalytic effect of kaolinite, montmorillinite, some talcs, ferric chloride, aluminum chloride and chromium chloride on the conversion of DDT to DDE at 115-120°C has been demonstrated. Iron oxices in the soil appear to catalyze the reaction of DDT. Thermal degradation of DDT was also promoted by the allophenic soils or clays presumably by their amorphous alumina. High iron and aluminum content in the soils favoured adsorption of DDT, dieldrin and BHC.

In addition to the mineral fraction of soils, soil organic matter also influences considerably the adsorption of the pesticides in soils. A humic acid adsorbed 70 times more of linuron and malathion than the K^+ montmorillonite in comparatively similar conditions. Varying quantities of pesticides were adsorbed depending on the stage of decormposion of the organic matter. Organic matter in this way can be said to retard the degradation of the pesticide. Lambert feels that the active fraction of soil organic matter is a better predictor of the adsorption of neutral pesticides. In certain cases, fats, cellulose, waxes, nucleic acids etc. contributed very little to the pesticide adsorption while humic acid, lignin and quinalizarin were highly adsorptive. The microbial degradation of pesticides is however increased by the presence of organic matter as it increases microbial activity.

The amount of pesticide adsorbed depends upon the nature of the pesticides and also soil pH. Phenyl mercuric acetate adsorption on montmorillonite, allophane and kaolinite was remarkably pH dependent. At normal pH values, dilute salts slightly increased adsorption while in concentrated solution, adsorption was sharply increased. Acid clays such as attapulgite ($pK_a < 1$) rapidly degraded heptachlor while incorporation of oxygen containing chemicals such as diethylene glycol increased insecticidal stability. Significant decomposition of chlordane, toxaphene, heptachlor, DDT, aldrin and endrin were noted on acidic diluents like kaolinite and attapulgite. The adsorption of pesticide depends upon the number, type and relative positions of the functional groups. Adsorption characteristically increased with the functional groups such as R_3N^+, $-CONH_2$, $-OH$, $-NHCOR$, $-NH_2$, $-OCOR$ and NHR. Presence of double bonds in the structure of the pesticide increased adsorption affinities.

Water solubility can be considered an approximate indicator of adsorption as, lower the solubility of the pesticides, the greater is the adsorption. Molecular size of the pesticide also modifies the adsorption of the pesticides. Chemically, organophosphates are less stable in water and soils. Some of them like malathion are base hydrolyzed while others like diazionn are acid hydrolyzed. The non-enzymatic hydrolysis are catalyzed by some metabolic ions like Cu^{2+}, the ease of catalytic hydrolysis being dursban > diazinon > ronnel > zytron.

The above reactions of pesticides in soils are modified by the movement of pesticides through leaching, runoff and volatilization, by photodecomposion and microbial activity. Pesticides could be moved in the water phase either through molecular diffusion or through mass transfer. Diffusion occurs only for a few centimeters depth and is modified by factors such as diffusion, coefficient of the soil structure characteristics, soil water content and adsorption of the pesticides on soil. The apparent diffusion coefficient of nonvolatile components increases rapidly with increased moisture since the water path becomes less tortuous. The greater the compaction, the significance of the diffusion process will be less.

Another aspect of molecular diffusion is the volatilization of the pesticide. Volatilization is increased by higher temperature, lower clay content and organic matter content of soils. Volatilization is greater from moist soil than in dry soils and gets greatly reduced when the moisture in soil clays dries to less than monolayer thickness.

Pesticides are degraded by microbes to a considerable extent. Warm soil temperatures, adequate moisture, presence of organic matter, neutral pH etc. promote microbial activity and thus increase the degradation of pesticides. Moisture levels play a significant role in the microbial breakdown of pesticides as they control the rate and nature of microbial population in the soil. Thus the accumulation and degradation of pesticides in soils depends on a large number of other soil factors and these control the efficiency of pesticidal action in soils.

The breakdown products found in soil treated with parathion consist principally of aminoparathion and p-nitrophenol produced by the reducing capacity of yeast, chemical hydrolysis and hydrolytic capability of soil bacteria. *Corynebacterium simplex* is able to convert parathion completely to nitrite in one week. *Rhizobium* coverts parathion to aminoparathion and hydrolystic product diethylphosphorothioic acid.

In soil malathion is also degraded to desmethyl malathion by *Aspergillus*. The degradation of malathion by *Rhizobium* gives dimethyl dithiophosphoric acid. This is desulphurated to dimethyl thiophopsphoric and then to dimethyl phosphoric acid. Carbaryl is hydrolyzed to 1 naphthol in soil mostly by chemical hydrolysis but it is also degraded by a variety of soil organism. It is degraded by the fungus *Gliocladium roseum* to N-hydroxymethyl derivative, 4 and 5 hydroxy derivatives. *Aspergillus terreus*, hydrolyses carbaryl to N-hydroxy derivative which is further hydrolyzed to 1-naphthol.

(i) Sulfonylureas. The major pathways of degradation of this group of herbicides are through chemical hydrolysis and microbial breakdown. The chemical hydrolysis occurs via cleavage of the sulfonylureas bridge. The process is enhanced by lower soil pH, higher soil temperature and moist soil conditions.

(ii) Butachlor. It is subjected to both chemical and microbial degradation in soils breaking even its aniline ring structure.

(iii) Trifluralin. α-α-α-triflurotoleuene-3, 4, 5-triamine serves as the chief intermediate non-phytotoxic compound in chemical degradation of trifluralin in soils, which in aerobic conditions is produced by dealkylation of the herbicide and in anaerobic conditions by its reduction. Further chemical decomposition of triflurotoluene-triamine produces N, CO_2, H_2O and constituent halogens.

(iv) Simazine. Most important step in decomposition of simazine in soils is hydroxylation of the ring at position 2-carbon, displacing chlorine atom from there. The resulting hydroxylation of simazine is favoured by its adsorption on soil colloids, which is rapid at soil pH of less than 7.0. Hydroxylation as a mechanism of chemical degradation of triazines is also extendable to compounds other than simazine, including methylthio and methoxy-s-triazines. In addition to hydroxylation, polysulphide ions can be made to displace chlorine atom from simazine to inactivate the unwanted herbicide residues in soils.

Fat of Pesticides in Soils can be classified as Follows

(1) Transfer

(*i*) Adsorption

(*ii*) Movement: leaching, seepage, capillarity, volatilization, chromatographic movement along colloidal surfaces, soil cracks and runoff and wash off

(*iii*) Plant removal

(2) Decomposition

(*i*) Microbial decomposition. (*a*) Intercellular and (*b*) Extracellular

(*ii*) Chemical decomposition, and Photodecomposition (photolysis)

Decomposition or Degradation Processes

Decomposition or degradation processes means breakdown of herbicides and change their chemical composition are : (1) Biological decomposition and (2) Abiotic decomposition, which includes chemical decomposition and photodecomposition. Transfer processes do not lead to inactivation of herbicides from soils. They may only remove herbicides from the site of their active uptake by plants, temporarily or permanently, but the herbicide structures remain biologically active at some site in soil or atmosphere. For actual inactivation of herbicide, it must undergo molecular change leading to its degradation. In soils, this change may be (*i*) microbial, (*ii*) chemical, or (*iii*) photochemical in nature. Biological decomposition of herbicides includes detoxification by microorganism (Bacteria, fungi, algae, nematodes, protozoa, worms and hundreds of other organisms) and higher plants. A warm, moist, well-aerated, fertile soil with optimal pH is most favourable for higher populations and activity of microorganisms. Under these ideal conditions, microbes can quickly decompose most organic herbicides. Microbial decomposition of many herbicides follows typical growth curves for bacterial populations. In curve, first phase is lag phase(slow rate of decomposition), second is rapid decomposition phase and third is slow decomposition phase.

Microbes degrade herbicides predominantly through hydrolysis, alkylation, dealkylation, oxidation, reduction, hydroxylation, ring cleavage and conjugation.

(A) Microbial Decomposition. Microbial action is a major mode of decomposition of herbicides in soils. Certain polar groups on the pesticide molecules, like $-OH$, $-COO$, $-NH_2$ and $-NO_2$ provide points of attack for the microorganisms. The widely used herbicide groups, *viz*., phenoxies, phenylureas, aliphatic acids, acetanilides, and carbamates are readily attacked by a host of soil microbes. Triazines are also now known to be subjected to simultaneous biodegradation.

The microbiological decomposition is characterized by an initial slow release of CO_2 from soil for some time after addition of the herbicide, called the lag phase, followed by increasing rates of CO_2 evolution, which marks the period of rapid microbial activity. During the lag phase, the relevant microbial population proliferation and intercellular (or extracellular) enzyme potential built-up take place. It is possible, at least in some cases, that such enzymes may be active on alternative substrates to continue their activity over a long period after completing the degradation of the added pesticide.

Scientists verify biodegradation of herbicides in soils indirectly by preventing microbial activity in the perfused soil by the use of a metabolic inhibitor like sodium azide. Directly they elucidate the process by isolation of specific microbes, followed by enrichment of herbicides perfused-soil with the isolates. If enrichment of the soil expedited the evolution of CO_2, biodegradation of the herbicide is usually accepted.

Microorganisms often show cross adaptation, *i.e.*, one species of microorganism initiating decomposition of two or more herbicide structures.

(B) Chemical Decomposition. It involves such processes as oxidation, reduction, decarboxylation, hydroxylation, hydrolysis, dealkylation, conjugation and ring cleavage. Oxidation-reduction reactions involve transfer of electrons from one reactant to another resulting in the formation of electrically charged (ionized) compounds.

In variance with biodegradation, chemical degradation begins as soon as a herbicide is placed in soil, and it continues at a steady or declining rate, depending upon the availability of the reactant. The chemical degradation of herbicides is characterized by first order reaction such as oxidation, reduction and hydrolysis. It is a less common mode of dissipation of herbicides from soils than biodegradation, save a few herbicides like simazine, toluidines, sulfonylureas, etc.

(C) Photo Decomposition. The breakdown of a substance by light. The process begins when the herbicide molecule absorbs light energy, which causes excitation of its electrons and may result in breakage or formation of chemical bonds. Most herbicides are white, or nearly so, and have peak light absorption in the ultra violet range (220-324 nm), whereas yellow compounds such as the dinitroanilines and dinoseb have absorption peaks at about 376 nm. Solar energy below 295 nm reaching the surface of the earth is considered to be negligible.

Photolysis is decomposition of herbicide under the direct effect of solar radiation. The importance of photolysis of herbicides at the soil surface is very difficult to demonstrate because the practical difficulty in differentiating it from volatilization due to heat. Therefore, most of the studies on photolysis of herbicides have been carried out in laboratory conditions where temperatures could be kept sufficiently low to minimize volatilization of the test compound from solid bases like aluminium planchets, filter paper, glass plates and soil surfaces. So far, photolysis is as a process of significant degradation of herbicides in field conditions has been demonstrated for trifluralin, nitralin, PCP, monuron and chloramben. The first two compounds are particularly susceptible to photodecomposition. Incorporation of herbicides into soil could greatly reduce their photodecomposition losses from field applications.

Of the full solar spectrum, ultraviolet component, of 220 to 400 nm wavelength is most active in inducing photolysis reaction in herbicide molecules. It is because in this endeavour light energy of 50 to 120 K Cal/mole of herbicide decomposed is needed, whereas UV rays yield energy of 60 to 143 K Cal/mole. The UV rays are more intense on cloudy days than in open sun and in the morning and evening hours than at noon.

Degradation in Tropical Soils

The microbial degradation of pesticides in soil and aquatic environments has been thoroughly studied. These studies are restricted mostly to aerobic and temperate environments and true half lives can not be determined but their stability follows the order: chlorinated hydrocarbons > organophosphates > carbamates. However in tropical and subtropical environments as exist in India, the mineralization of organic pesticides primarily by microbial action, is expected to be more rapid, It is, therefore, important that a realistic assessment of the persistence of pesticides and their impact on the ecosystem should be made under actual Indian conditions before restricting the use of specific pesticides based on foreign literature of no relevance to Indian conditions because the Indian sub-content, with its elevations and rainfall patterns, enjoys a variety of climatic conditions. In India the climatic conditions are broadly classifieds the tropical monsoon region, having 3 seasons : (*a*) the season from March to June with an increase in temperature from 26 up to 46°C (*b*) the rainy season lasting from June to middle of October where the rainfall may be anywhere between 25-30 cm some times even exceeding 500 cm within a period of 3-4 months and (*c*) the cold season which extends from November to February, when the winds are dry, with a temperature range of 25-10°C.

TABLE 18.2. Stability of phorate in different soil-types

Soil type	*Half life in days*
Forest	49
Alluvial	30
Red	17
Laterite	16
Sandy	19

Since the behavior of the pesticides depends much on the agro climatic conditions and may vary from region to region, some pesticides behave differently under Indian climatic condition (Table). For instance, it has been reported that no aldrin and heptachlor was lost from frozen soils, whereas, 16-27% of the dose applied was lost at 6°C and 86-90% at 46°C. Similarly, temperature has been found to increase the degree of volatilization and adsorption of aldrin from soils. Because sorption is exothermic; increased temperatures release pesticides. Further more, the solubilities of pesticides also vary with temperature differences. Therefore, the were disappearance of an applied pesticide judged by the residue analysis may not necessarily mean that it has been degraded. Volatilization of pesticides, particularly the chlorinated hydrocarbons and their subsequent return through rains in areas where they are not expected is a question that has to be properly evaluated.

TABLE 18.3. Stability of certain insecticides in flooded soil

Insecticides	*Period of persistence* (days)*
Chlorinated hydrocarbons	
alpha-HCH	30-90
beta-HCH	30-90
delta-HCH	30-90
gama-HCH	30-90
DDT	30-90
Methoxychlor	30-90
Heptachlor	30-90
Endrin	55
Organophosphates	
Diazinon	70
Parathion	20-60

*In non-flooded soil, chlorinated hydrocarbon insecticides included in this group persist for several years and organophosphates for six months.

The importance of moisture in the deterioration of pesticides need hardly be stressed because degradation of chlorinated hydrocarbons in flooded soils has been reported. Such a degradation has been traced to the activity of anaerobic bacteria under flooded conditions. Also, persistence of pesticides is largely influenced by the conditions and cultural practices used for specific crops. Thus, lindane (gammahexachlorcyclohexane), known to persist for several years in aerobic upland soils, undergoes fairly rapid decomposition in tropical soils under flooding, the most widely used cultural practice for the major food crop, rice. Likewise, several other pesticides undergo rapid decomposition in soils upon flooding (Table 18.3).

IMPACT OF POLLUTION ON ENVIRONMENT

Ecological Consequences of Heavy Metal Pollution of Soils

The ecological consequences of heavy metal pollution of soils relate largely to heavy metal mobility and solubility. These chemically related factors determine transmission through the soil to the water table, availability to soil microbes, soil animals, agricultural crops and animals, and ultimately to the human population. Leaching of heavy metals through soils to groundwater, even soils treated with sewage sludge, does not however occur to any appreciable extent.

(A) Effects on Biological Activity in Soil. Pollution of soils by heavy metals may inhibit microbial enzyme activity and reduce the diversity of populations of microorganisms and soil fauna. The toxicity of heavy metals to earthworms depends on the chemical form of the pollutant, the earthworm species, and soil factors of Cd, Cu, Ni, Zn, and Pb, Cd appears the most toxic and Zn and Pb the least, with Cu and Ni intermediate in effect. Reductions in populations of soil animals by high concentrations of heavy metals have been documented, for example, in orchard soils suggested that this may only apply at very high concentrations. Smaller populations of soil fauna may affect soil fertility through their role in bioturbation, turnover, and breakdown of organic matter, and soil structure and infiltration. Contaminated soil animals also introduce heavy metals into the food chain of higher animals.

(B) Effect on Soil-Crop-Animal System. At moderate levels of heavy metal concentrations above the deficiency range, most natural soils act as a repository or sink for metals without any obvious effects on soil biological behavior. The important question is the response of plants and animals to increasing concentrations of metals that result from natural variability or from pollution. The extent of transfer of metals from soil to plant depends on the kind of plant, the particular metal involved, and the soil chemical environment.

Uptake of metals by plants reflects increasing levels of metals in soils, especially those metals that are more mobile. Above certain critical concentrations of heavy metals in plants, yield and/or crop quality and animal or human health may be affected. Concentrations of toxic metals require careful monitoring because potentially dangerous levels may be reached in the plant food diet of animals or humans without any evidence of deleterious effects on the plants. This is especially so for Cd and Pb, for which plant toxicity occurs above the concentrations considered desirable for human intake. The reverse is true for other heavy metals, for example, Zn, Cu, and Ni, for which the concentrations causing yield depression of plants are below those of risk to humans and animals if the plants are ingested as food. This provides a built-in safety mechanism for such elements.

Heavy metal pollutants rarely occur alone. The associated elements, frequently other heavy metals, and possibly major nutrients also, can affect the biological effectiveness of the metal in question by additive, synergistic, or antagonistic effects. It is clear that at least as far as Cd is concerned the interactive effects of different metals cannot easily be generalized. Interactions of Cd with Zn, for example, can be positive, negative or nonexistent, depending on the relative concentration levels, the soil and the crop.

The impact of heavy metal pollution on health also depends on the nature of the association of heavy metals with plants. The heavy metals associated with plants are not necessarily absorbed by the root system and translocated within the plant. In some regions, appreciable amounts (and a high proportion) of some heavy metals can adhere directly to leaf surfaces after deposition from the atmosphere. Contamination of pasture plants b the spreading of agricultural waste slurries, and b adhering soil splash and soil dust, also contributes to the metal intake b farm animals. Surficial contamination of food plants and the direct ingestion soil together with forage plants can complicate predictions of health hazard to both animals and humans. Under situations of overgrazing or some soil conditions, animals can incidentally ingest considerable quantities of soil.

TABLE 18.4. Effect of pollutants on human being

Cd	—	Inhibits enzyme containing thiol group. Respiratory position contributes high B.P. and heart disease. *Itai-Itai* disease.
Pb	—	Miscarriages in women, affects lings and central nervous system.
Hg	—	Impairment of vision, madness, paralysis, coma, kidney functioning, mini mata disease.
As	—	Cancer in skin, lungs and liver.
SO_2	—	Attack lungs and respiratory system.
NO_3	—	Methemoglobinemia and Blue Baby Syndrom disease in babies.
Co	—	Blood circulation and affects hemoglobin and headaches.

REMEDIAL MEASURES FOR POLLUTION

Control of pollutants from moving sources

Though many of the above said control methods can also apply to moving sources as well, one very special moving source the automobile-deserves special mention. Engine operation has direct effect on the emissions. Amount of CO, HC and NOx differs during idling, accelerating, cruising and decelerating.

Emission control techniques for the internal combustion automobile engine include tune-ups, catalytic reactors, and engine modifications. A tune-up may have a significant effect on emission components. For example, a high air/fuel ratio (a lean mixture) will reduce both CO and HC, but with increased NOx. The second control strategy, now extensively used, is the catalytic realtor which oxidises the CO and HC to CO_2 and H_2O. The second reactor reduces NOx to N_2. The most popular catalyst seems to be platinum which must be periodically regenerated. However, catalyst reactors have two serious drawbacks. First, they are easily fouled by lead. Infact the move to nonlead gasoline has been prompted by this reason and not by the concern for lead levels in the atmosphere. The second problem with the reactors is that the sulphur compounds in gasoline are oxidised to particulate SO_3, and thus increases the sulphur levels in environment.

In third control technique-engine modification, the stratified charge engine, is used without catalytic reactors. In these engines the cylinders have two compartments, with one compartment receiving a rich mixture, igniting, and then providing a broad flame for an efficient burn in the main cylinder compartment. Other modifications have also been developed. It is difficult lo manufacture a totally dean' internal combustion engine. Electric cars are clean but they can store only limited power and thus their range is limited.

General methods to control air pollution by automobiles and industries have been considered briefly above. Some specific measures to control vehicular and industrial pollutants in air are given below.

Vehicular Pollution

1. To check pollutant emission from vehicular exhaust. This can be achieved by (*i*) using new proportion of gasoline and air, (*ii*) more exact timing of fuel feeding, (*iii*) using gas additives to improve combustion, (*iv*) by injecting air into the exhaust to convert exhaust compounds to less toxic materials, and by (*v*) updating of engine design and/or install abatement equipment (device) to improve combustion with the existing engine design. Carbon monoxide results from low air content of the fuel mixture, whereas NOx production is promoted by high combustion temperatures. Hydrocarbons follow more or less the pattern of CO. The complete elimination of these three pollutants may be achieved by either updating the present design of engines or by making appropriate changes in devices for improving combustion. Very recently, I.K. Bharati of Bombay has claimed to have devised a simple attachment the patented name Thermoreactor, to curb air pollution by motor vehicle. The reactor is fitted to the exhaust tailpipe and it converts carbon monoxide into pure oxygen.

2. To control evaporation from fuel tank and carburetor. This can be done by (*i*) collection of vapours with activated charcol when the engine is turned off and its ignition when the engine is started, (*ii*) subjecting the gasoline in the tank to slight pressure to prevent the gas from evaporation and (*iii*) developing low-volatile gasoline that does not evaporate easily.

3. Use of filters. Some gas vapours escape between walls and the piston which enters the crankcase and then discharge into atmosphere. Hydrocarbons (about 25%) are released in this way. Thus use of filters that capture and recycle these escaped gases in the engine should control the emission of these hydrocarbons.

4. Control through Law. There are to be enforced some standards through Motor Vehicles Act and other acts for design of engines etc. We shall refer to these later.

Industrial Pollution

To check air pollution by industrial plant chimney wastes, we must devise measures for removal of the particulate matter and gaseous pollutants from the wastes. Removal of particulate matter involves their collection under the influence of different forces, thereby moving them continuously out of the gas stream. The equipment used for their removal is (*i*) cyclone collectors, and (*ii*) electrostatic precipitators (ESPs). Thus we have to generate the control technology. At present there are few power plants and industries that have installed the requisite ESPs.

1. Cyclone collectors. Here the waste gas containing particles is subjected to centrifugation. The suspended particles move towards the wall of cylcone body, and then to its bottom and finally discharged out. The cyclone collectors remove about 70% of the particles.

2. Electrostatic precipitators (ESPs). To remove the particles from gas stream, the electrical forces are applied within the chamber in the precipitator. Suspended particles become charged or ionised, and they are attracted to charged electrodes and removed. ESPs can remove 99% of the particulate pollutants from chimney exhaust. ESPs work very well in power plants, paper mills, cement mills, carbon block plants etc. High resistivity dust may make separation in a ESP difficult. To overcome this, fabric filters or begs filters are employed. But fabric filters are unsuitable for wet or sticky particles, extreme corrosive conditions, and high gas temperatures.

Methods to Control Soil Pollution

(1) Greater care in the use of pesticides.

(2) Better land practices to reduce soil erosion and sedimentation.

(3) Improvement of wastes from feedlots.

(4) Disposal of waste accumulation of plant and animal waste without affecting the quality of the air or water.

(5) Percolation is reducing by vigorously growing crop.

(6) Erosion can be greatly reduced by a dense vegetative cover.

(7) The rotation of crops to include meadows in the cropping sequence may reduce soil losses by as much 75 per cent.

(8) Soil losses are reduce by mulching, strip cropping and contour cultivation.

(9) To replace persistent pesticides with readily degradable ones as they are developed and become available.

(10) Reduced nuisance conditions and improved sanitation.

(11) The persistent pesticides are replaced by alternative methods of pest control.

(12) Less persistent pesticides are used or more specific chemicals are used.

(13) The rates of pesticides could be reduced sufficiently.

(14) The greatest hazards chemicals are not used.

(15) To eliminate or drastically reduce the soil application of the toxic metals.

(16) Animal excreta are used in biogas production.

(17) Salts are removed by improved drainage systems.

(18) Soil amendments are used.

(19) Acid rain pollution reduced by S and N oxides eliminate drastically.

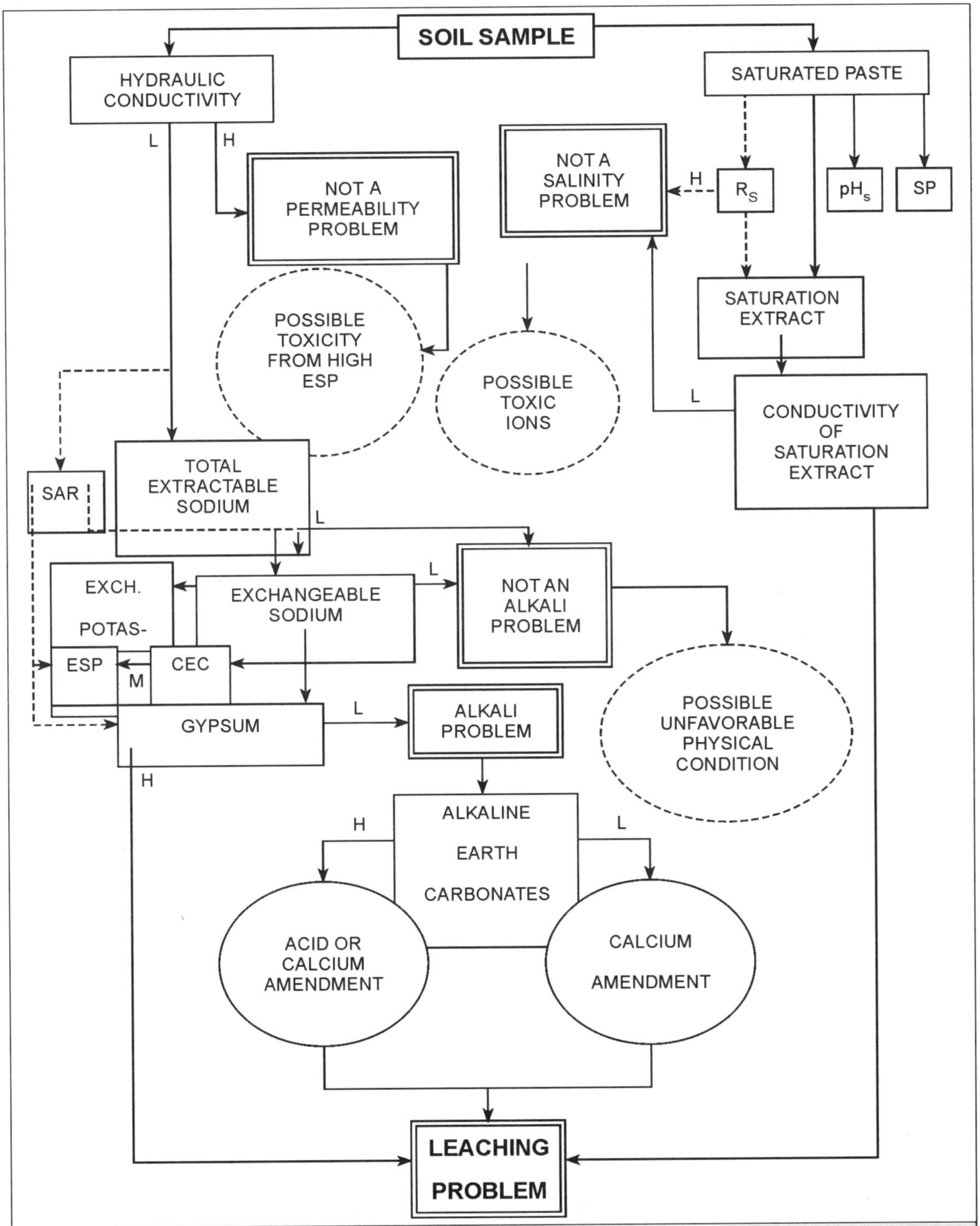

Fig. 18.1. Sequence of determination for the diagnosis and treatment of saline and alkali soils: H, high; L, low; R_S, electrical resistance of soil paste; SAR, sodium adsorption ratio; ESP, exchangeable sodium percentage; CEC, cation exchange capacity.

WATER POLLUTION

Water pollution means the addition of any foreign material (inorganic, radiological or biological) or any physical change in the natural water which may harmful affect the living life (human, agricultural or biological) directly or indirectly, immediately after sometime or after a very long time.

Water is regarded as polluted when it is changed in its quality or composition, directly or indirectly as a result of mankind's activities, so that it becomes less suitable for drinking, domestic, agricultural, recreational, fisheries or other purposes.

Sources of water pollution

Domestic sewage	*Surface runoff*	*Industrial discharge*	*Radioactive wastes*	*Oil pollution*	*Chlorinated hydrocarbon*
• Human excreta • Urine • Kitchen washings • Cloth washings	• Minerals • Organic wastes • Fertilizers • Pesticides	• Heavy metals • Acids • Alkalis • Cyanides	• Nuclear installation • Nuclear test • Nuclear weapons	• Crude • By vehicles • Byproduct of industries	• Organochlorine pesticides • DDT • Dieldrin • Organic phosphorus compounds • Inorganic pesticides

Characteristics of water quality

(1) **Physical.** Temperature, colour, odour, transparency, turbidity, conductivity and solids.

(2) **Chemical.** pH, alkalinity, acidity, hardness, calcium, magnesium, chloride, residual chlorine, hydrogen sulphate, sulphates, sulphite, phosphate, ammonical nitrogen, total nitrogen, nitrate nitrogen, nitrite nitrogen, dissolved oxygen, biochemical demand, chemical oxygen demand and free carbon dioxide.

Dissolved oxygen

Oxygen is a most important element in water quality control. Its presence is essential to maintain the higher forms of biological life and the effect of a waste discharge on a river is largely determined by the oxygen balance of system. Unfortunately oxygen is only slightly soluble in water.

Temperature °C	0	10	20	30
Dissolved oxygen mg/lit.	14.6	11.3	9.1	7.6

Clean surface waters are normally saturated with dissolved oxygen, but such DO can be rapidly removed by the oxygen demand of organic waters. Game fish require at least 5 mg/l DO and coarse fish will not exist below about 2 mg/l DO. Oxygen saturated waters have a pleasant taste and waters lacking in DO have an insipid taste, drinking waters are thus aerated if necessary to ensure maximum DO. For boiler feed waters, DO is undesirable because is presence increase the risk of corrosion.

Oxygen Demand

Organic compounds are generally unstable and may be oxidized biologically of chemically to stable, relatively and inert end products such as CO_2, NO_3 and H_2O. An indication of the organic content of a waste can be obtained by measuring the amount of oxygen required for its stabilization.

Biological Oxygen Demand (BOD)

BOD is the amount of oxygen utilized by microorganisms in stabilizing the organic matter. On an average basis, the demand for oxygen is proportional to the amount of organic waste to be degraded aerobically. Hence, BOD approximates the amount of oxidizable organic matter present in the solution and the BOD value can be used as a measure of waste strength.

The BOD values are thus very useful in process design and loading calculations as well as the measure of treatment plant efficiency and operation. The BOD test is useful in stream pollution control managements and in evaluating the self-purification capacities of streams, which serves as a measure to assess the quantity of wastes, which can be safely assimilated by the stream.

The complete degradation of the organic matter may take as long as 20 to 30 days. Simple organic compounds like glucose are almost completely oxidized in 5 days, while domestic sewage by only about 65% and complex organic compounds might be oxidized only upto 40% in this period. The 20-30 days period is of less significance in practice, therefore, the BOD test has been developed for 5 days at 20°C.

Types of micro-organisms, pH, and presence of toxins some reduced mineral matter and nitrification process are the important factors influencing the BOD test.

Chemical Oxygen Demand (COD)

Chemical oxygen demand is the oxygen required by the organic substances in water to oxidize them by a strong chemical oxidant. The COD usually refers to the laboratory dichromate oxidation procedure.

The determination of COD values is of great importance where BOD values cannot be determined accurately due to presence of toxins and other such unfavourable conditions for growth of microorganisms. The main disadvantage of the test is that oxygen is also consumed by the oxidation of organic matter such as nitrites, sulphides, reduced metal ions, thiosulphate etc. and some organic materials are not oxidized by dichromate method such as benzene, pyridine and few other cyclic organic compounds.

The COD test gives no indication of whether or not the waste is degradable biologically and nor does it indicate the rate at which biological oxidation would proceed and hence the rate at which the oxygen would be required in a biological system.

NATURE OF THE PROBLEM

Although water pollution is an age old problem but in this modern age, the problems like population increase, sewage disposal, industrial waste, radioactive waste, etc. have polluted our water resources so much as about 70% rivers and streams not only of India but of all the countries contain polluted waters. Some important sources of water pollution along with the constituents which pollute the rivers, stream and fields are as under :

(A) Domestic Sewage

It is very serious pollutant of wells and rivers which are important sources of our drinking water and irrigation water. Water from these sources contains high amount of (1) Nitrite (2) Nitrate (3) B.O.D. (4) C.O.D. (5) Chloride (6) Sulphate (7) Total dissolved salts. These are in high concentrations toxic and destroy fish and plant life.

(B) Industrial Waste

The trade wastes and effluents (flowing out from sewage tanks) of industries play a significant role in pollution of water. The industries are as under:

(1) Pulp and paper factory. The chemicals used in the industry are (*i*) Alum (*ii*) Talc (*iii*) Rosin (*iv*) Chlorine (*v*) Caustic soda (*vi*) Soda ash (*vii*) Dry ice (*viii*) Magnesium bisulphide and sulphuric acid, besides clay.

Inference. The lignite should not be allowed to discharge as it completely destroys that fauna and flora and impairs the productivity.

(2) Distillery. In India, annual distillery discharge wastes approximate between 100-110 million litres, directly into the river.

Inference. The distillery wastes are highly organic in nature and because of its high biochemical oxygen demand (B.O.D.) quickly removes the oxygen from the water and unless waste is diluted can produce pollution hazards in the aquatic ecosystem. Both BOD and COD were indicating high values as a result of which oxygen was mostly absent.

The diluted distillery effluent (1 : 200) dilution gives birth to number of green and blue green algae.

(3) Potassic fertilizer. The potassic fertilizer contains 37% K_2O rest being silica, calcium, iron and some sodium is the end product of the process.

(4) Electroplating plants. They contain harmful heavy metals and cyanides which cause excessive acidity or alkalinity in water of rivers and stream, which is very harmful for aquatic life.

(5) Asbestos. It occurs in four forms (*i*) Chrysotile (*ii*) Crocidolite (*iii*) Tremolite (*iv*) Amosite. It can create cancer of intestine, lungs and stomach.

(6) Silt. It is a component of the soil which has a diameter of 0.02 mm. sandy loam and loam soils contain silt. The silt and other particles are carried from land to water and caused by secondary pollution of water resources. The silt particles generally choke irrigation channels and rivers and also disturb the aquatic life.

(7) Alcohol industry. In the fermentation of molasses besides alcohol we get glycerine, succinic acid, acetaldehyde, ethyl alcohol, acetic acid and fuse oil as by-products.

(8) Detergents. The detergents cause serious pollution in water resources as they contain phosphate. The phosphates are responsible for the growth of algae which deplete the dissolved oxygen. When algae die, they release their component inorganic and organic substances back into water and so become pollutants themselves.

(9) Steel industry. The major pollutant effects in the waste waters from steel plants are (*i*) pH value 8.5 to 9.5 (*ii*) Phenol (*iii*) Ammonia (*iv*) Thiosulphate.

Inference. The effluent is toxic to aquatic life as it contains high value of BOD, phenol, cyanides and other constituents and a very low value of dissolved oxygen. The high pH value also causes toxicity in the water. At low value of dissolved oxygen fishes also die out.

(10) Tanning industry. The chrome tanning industry effluent gives the (*i*) Hexavalent chromium (*ii*) BOD (*iii*) Chloride (*iv*) pH value 5.5 to 9.0. These constituents are responsible for water pollutions.

(11) Cane sugar industry. The effluents are discharged during manufactures of sugar and they contain high polluted contents.

Inference. As the effluent contains a high degree of organic pollution hence if effluent stagnate in an area for a few hours, biological action starts and septic condition gives H_2S gas. Moreover, the oxygen is also exhausted giving death of fishes and other aquatic life. The water is extremely harmful to the plants.

(12) Oils. Oils are very toxic substances which affect the living organisms in water.

(13) Pesticides and herbicides. The use of pesticides and herbicides has increased all over the world due to man's desire to increase the production of grains and other agricultural products. These components when sprayed on plant to kill harmful pests and weeds percolate through soil and get dissolved in soil water thus polluting it. The compounds accumulated in the bodies of aquatic plants and animals. Some amount is also found in the milk of cow, etc., in the vegetables and in eggs and other eatable things.

(14) Radioactive waste. The wastes from atomic reactors, hospitals, etc. are most dangerous because their radioactivity cannot be destroyed at man's will. These wastes destroy the aquatic plants and animals to a great extent. They generally cause gene mutations, ionization of body fluids and chromosomal mutations.

❑❑❑

CHAPTER 19

Plant Nutrition

Plant like human beings and animals require food for their growth and development. The food of the plant is composed of certain chemical elements often referred to as plant nutrients or plant food elements. Green plants are autotrophic or self-nourishing, and they are too able to manufacture carbohydrates from raw are inorganic materials and thus nourish themselves. The conception of elements as plant nutrients was oriented by Liebig in 1840 when he put forward his revolutionary theory of 'Mineral Nutrition'.

Plant Nutrient

All through thirty five elements, such as Carbon (C), Hydrogen (H), Oxygen (O), Nitrogen (N), Phosphorus (P), Potassium (K), Calcium (Ca), Magnesium (Mg), Sulphur (S), Iron (Fe), Manganese (Mn), Zinc (Zn), Copper (Cu), Boron (B), Molybdenum (Mo), Chlorine (Cl), Nickel (Ni), Vanadium (V), Sodium (Na), Cobalt (Co), Silicon (Si), Aluminium (Al), Lead (Pb), Iodine (I), Chromium (Cr), Arsenic (As), Bromine (Br), Rubidium (Rb), Strontium (Sr), Gallium (Ga), Lanthanum (La), Lithium (Li), Yttrium (Y), Zirconium (Zr) and Selenium (Se) are considered for nutrient of plants. Out of these seventeen elements (table 19.1) considered as essential plant nutrient for growth and development of plants.

Criteria for Essential Plant Nutrients

Arnon (1954) has laid down the following criteria for essentiality of elements in plant nutrients :

(*i*) The plant must be unable to grow normally or complete its life cycle in the absence of element.

(*ii*) The element is specific and can not be replaced by other element.

(*iii*) The element plays a direct role in metabolism.

(*iv*) The deficiency symptoms of the element can be corrected or prevented by the application of that element only.

Essential Plant Nutrients

Carbon (C), Hydrogen (H), Oxygen (O), Nitrogen (N), Phosphorus (P), Potassium (K), Calcium (Ca), Magnesium (Mg), Sulphur (S), Iron (Fe), Manganese (Mn), Zinc (Zn), Copper (Cu), Boron (B), Molybdenum (Mo), Chlorine (Cl), Nickel (Ni) are recognized as universally essential element for plants. There is convincing evidence that these mineral elements are essential requirements for plants, algae, bacteria, fungi and green plants.

Beneficial Elements

The Vanadium, Silicon, Aluminum, Iodine, Selenium and Sodium, which have been shown to be essential for particular species of plants, there are several other elements, rubidium, strontium, chromium and arsenic, which at very low concentrations and often under specific conditions have been shown to stimulate growth of certain plants or to have other beneficial effects. These elements, the essentiality for growth and metabolism has not been established but exert beneficial effects at very low concentrations are often referred to as 'beneficial elements'.

Classification of Essential Plant Nutrients

TABLE 19.1. Critical information on nutrient in relation to plants

Nutrient	Essentiality Discovered authors (Discoverer)	Year of discovery	Plant Usable form	Average concentration in plant tissue	Relative numbers of atoms compared to Mo as one
H	Since time	—	H_2O	6%	60,000,000
O	Since time	—	H_2O, O_2	45%	30,000,000
C	Priestley *et al.*	1800	CO_2	45%	30,000,000
N	Theodore de Saussure	1804	NO_3^-, NH_4^+	1.5%	1,000,000
P	C. Sprengel	1839	$H_2PO_4^-$, HPO_4^{2-}	0.2%	30,000
K	C. Sprengel	1839	K^+	1.0%	400,000
Ca	C. Sprengel	1839	Ca^{2+}	0.5%	200,000
Mg	C. Sprengel	1839	Mg^{2+}	0.2%	100,000
S	Sachs and Knop	1860	SO_4^{2-}	0.1%	30,000
Fe	E. Gris	1843	Fe^{2+}	100 mg/kg	2,000
Cu	A.L. Sommer & Lipman	1931	Cu^{2+}	6 mg/kg	100
Mn	J.S. McHargue	1922	Mn^{2+}	20 mg/kg	2000
Zn	Sommer & Lipman	1926	Zn^+	20 mg/kg	300
B	K. Warington	1923	H_3BO_3, $H_2BO_3^-$, HBO_3^{2-}, BO_3^{3-}	20 mg/kg	2000
Mo	D.I. Arnon and P.R. Stout	1939	MoO_4^{2-}	0.1mg/kg	1
Cl	T.C. Broyer, A.B. Carlton	1954	Cl^-	100 mg/kg	3,000
Ni	P.H. Brown *et al.*	1987	Ni^{2+}	0.1 mg/kg	1-2

Plant takes H, O and C from air and water its Average concentration in plant tissue and relative numbers of atoms compared to Mo are 6 per cent and 60,000,000, 45 per cent and 30,000,000 and C 45 per cent and 30,000,000, respectively.

TABLE 19.2. Source of plant nutrient in soils

Element	*Source*	*Source of Plant Nutrient in Soils*
C	Air	—
H	Water	—
O	Air/water	—
N	Soil/fertilizer	The main source of N in soil is organic matter.
P	Soil/fertilizer	Apatite, Alluminium Phosphate, Organic Matter.
K	Soil/fertilizer	Orthoclase, Muscovite, Biotite.
Ca	Soil/lime	Gypsum, Hornblende, Augite, Lime, Apatite, Lime.
Mg	Soil/lime	Dolomite, Augite, Biotite, Olivine, Hornblende.
S	Soil/fertilizer	Gypsum, Pyrite, Organic Matter
Fe	Soil/fertilizer	Hematite, Magenetite, Tourmaline, Pyrite, Augite, Biotite, Hornblende.
Cu	Soil/fertilizer	Augite, Biotite, Chalcopyrite, Olivine, Hornblende.
Mn	Soil/fertilizer	Magenetite, Olivine, Hornblende.
Zn	Soil/fertilizer	Augite, Biotite, Olivine, Hornblende, Sphalerite.
B	Soil/fertilizer	Tourmaline, Hematite, Magenetite, Pyrite, Augite, Biotite, Hornblende.
Mo	Soil/fertilizer	Olivine
Cl	Soil/fertilizer	Chlorapatite
Ni	Soil/fertilizer	Tourmaline

According to Mobility

(*a*) **In Soil**

1. **Mobile.** NO_3^-, SO_4^{2-}, BO_3^{3-}, Cl^- and Mn^{2-}
2. **Less mobile.** NH_4^+, K^+, Ca^{2+}, Mg^{2+} and Cu^{2+}
3. **Immobile.** $H_2PO_4^-$, HPO_4^{2-} and Zn^{2+}

(*b*) **In Plant**

1. **Highly mobile.** N, P and K
2. **Moderately mobile.** Zn
3. **Less mobile.** S, Fe, Mn, Cu, Mo and Cl
4. **Immobile.** Ca and B

According to Metal and Non Metal

1. **Metal.** K, Ca, Mg, Fe, Mn, Zn and Cu
2. **Non metal.** N, P, S, B, Mo and Cl

According to Cation and Anion

1. **Cation.** K, Ca, Mg, Fe, Mn, Zn and Cu
2. **Anion.** NO_3, H_3PO_4 and SO_4

TABLE 19.3. Major function and relative proportion in plants

Name	*Chemical Symbol*	*Relative% in Plant**	*Function in Plant*	*Nutrient Category*
Nitrogen	N	100	Proteins, amino acids	Primary
Phosphorus	P	6	Nucleic acids, ATP	macronutrients
Potassium	K	25	Catalyst, ion transport	
Calcium	Ca	12.5	Cell wall component	Secondary
Magnesium	Mg	8	Part of chlorophyll	macronutrients
Sulphur	S	3	Amino acids	
Iron	Fe	0.2	Chlorophyll synthesis	Micronutrients
Copper	Cu	0.01	Component of enzymes	
Manganese	Mn	0.1	Activates enzymes	
Zinc	Zn	0.03	Activates enzymes	
Boron	B	0.2	Cell wall component	
Molybdenum	Mo	0.0001	Involved in N fixation	
Chlorine	Cl	0.3	Photosynthesis reactions	

*Relative amounts of mineral elements compared to nitrogen in dry shoot tissue, may vary depending on plant species.

TABLE 19.4. Major indicator plants on the basis of nutrients and plant

On the basis of nutrients		*On the basis of plants*	
Nutrient	*Indicator plant*	*Plant*	*Nutrient deficiency/toxicity*
N	Maize, Small grains, Cereals, Mustered, Apple, Citrus	Oat	Mg, Mn and Cu deficiencies
P	Maize, Barley, Tomato	Wheat and barley	Mg, Cu and some times Mn deficiencies
K	Maize, Potato, Tobacco, Cotton, Beans	Sugar beets	B and Mn deficiencies
Ca	Lucerne, Barseam, Leguminous Crop	Maize	N, P, K, Mg, Fe, Mn and Zn deficiencies
Mg	Potato, Cauliflower	Potatoes	K, Mg and Mn deficiencies
S	Lucerne, Mustered	Rape	N, P and Mg deficiencies
Fe	Sorghum, Barley, Citrus, Peach	Brassica pecies	K and Mg deficiencies
Mn	Maize, Wheat Oat, Citrus, Pea, Apple, Cherry, Radish	Sudan grass	Fe and Mn deficiencies
Zn	Maize, Paddy, Onion, Citrus, Peach	Sunflower	B deficiency
Cu	Maize, Barley, Oat, Onion, Citrus, Tomato, Tobacco	Cauliflower	B and Mo deficiencies
B	Lucern, Turnip, Cauliflower, Apple, Peach	Flax	Zn deficiency
Mo	Leguminous, Cauliflower, Mustard, Citrus, Oat	Barley	B, Mn and Al toxicity
Cl	—	Cucumber	N and P excess
Ni	—	Sugar beets	Cu excess

FUNCTION OF ESSENTIAL PLANT NUTRIENT

Nitrogen (N)

Nitrogen is the first fertilizer element of the macronutrients usually applied in commercial fertilizers. Nitrogen is very important nutrients for plants and its seems to have quickest and most pronounced effect. Nitrogen is of special importance in the function of protein in plants. It is also present in chlorophyll, the green pigments that are receptors of light energy in photosynthesis.

Function of Nitrogen

- Nitrogen is a part of all living cells and is a necessary part of all proteins, enzymes and metabolic processes involved in the synthesis and transfer of energy.
- Nitrogen is a part of chlorophyll, the green pigment of the plant that is responsible for photosynthesis.
- Helps plants with rapid growth, increasing seed and fruit production and improving the quality of leaf and forage crops.
- Nitrogen often comes from fertilizer application and from the air (legumes get their N from the atmosphere, water or rainfall contributes very little nitrogen).

Phosphorus (P)

Phosphorus is the second fertilizer element and it is an essential constituent of every living cell and for the nutrition of plant and animal. It takes active part in all type of metabolism of plant. It is an essential constituent of enzyme and also structural component of membrane system of cell, the chloroplasts and the mitochondria. It is intimately associated with the life process.

Function of Phosphorus

- Like nitrogen, phosphorus (P) is an essential part of the process of photosynthesis.
- Involved in the formation of all oils, sugars, starches, etc.
- Helps with the transformation of solar energy into chemical energy act as 'energy currency' and proper plant maturation with standing stress.
- Effects rapid growth.
- Encourages blooming and root growth.
- Phosphorus often comes from fertilizer, bone meal, and super phosphate.
- Phosphorus makes tolerant to drought, insect, pest and disease.

Potassium (K)

Potassium is the third fertilizer element. Potassium acts as a chemical traffic policeman, root booster, stalk strengthen, food former, sugar and starch transporter, protein builder, breather regulator, water stretcher and as a disease retarder but it not effective without its co-nutrients such as Nitrogen and phosphorus.

Function of Potassium

- Potassium is absorbed by plants in larger amounts than any other mineral element except nitrogen and in some cases, calcium.

- Helps in the building of protein, photosynthesis, fruit quality and reduction of diseases.
- It improves the health and vigour of the plant, enable to certain disease and counteract the damaging effects of excess nitrogen.
- It necessary for the production of best quality of grains and fruits. Potassium plays a key role in production of quality vegetables.
- Potassium is an enzyme activator.
- It increases plumpness and boldness of grains and seeds.

Calcium (Ca)

Calcium as calcium pectate is an important constituent of cell wall and require in large amounts for cell division. It is a structural component of chromosomes. Excessive amounts of calcium can decrease the availability of many micronutrients.

Function of Calcium

- Calcium, an essential part of plant cell wall structure, provides for normal transport and retention of other elements as well as strength in the plant. It is also thought to counteract the effect of alkali salts and organic acids within a plant.
- It helps in translocate the sugar in the plants.
- It neutralizes organic acid which may become poisonous to plant.
- It is an essential to co-factor or an activator of a number of enzymes, for instance, lipase and apyrase.
- Calcium acts as a buffer in plant system, and ameliorates the toxic effect of other nutrients if they are toxic level in the plant.

The structure of having calcium becomes good and cation exchange capacity increases.

Magnesium (Mg)

Magnesium acts as essential constituent of chlorophyll. Several photosynthetic enzymes present in chlorophyll require magnesium act as activator. It is usually needed by the plants in relatively small quantities. Magnesium was provided through a number of sources such as magnesium chlorite.

Function of Magnesium

- Magnesium helps the formation of chlorophyll and thus imparts dark green colour to leaves. It is indispensable for photosynthesis by plants.
- It is usually needed by plants for formation of oil and fats
- It regulates the uptake of nitrogen and phosphorus from the soil.
- Magnesium may increase crop resistance to drought and disease.

Sulphur (S)

Sulphur exist two important essential amino acids methionine and cystenine, which are also components of protein. It has spacified role in initiating in synthesis of protein. Sulphur is an important nutrient for oil seed, cruciferae, sugar and pulse crops. As such, these crops grow best on sulphur rich soil, it is an essential constituent of many proteins, enzyme and certain non-volatile compound such as mustard oil.

Function of Sulphur

- Essential plant food for production of protein.
- Promotes activity and development of enzymes and vitamins.
- Helps in chlorophyll formation.
- Improves root growth and seed production.
- Helps with vigorous plant growth and resistance to cold.
- Sulphur may be supplied to the soil from rain water. It is also added in some fertilizers as an impurity, especially the lower grade fertilizers. The use of gypsum also increases soil sulphur levels.

Iron (Fe)

Iron is necessary for the synthesis of chlorophyll. But it is not a constituent of chlorophyll. Apple, banana, tomato, carrot and spinach contain high percentage of iron.

Function of Iron

- It is essential for synthesis of proteins contained in chloroplast.
- It has a catalyst role in the activities of several enzymes and it regulates respiration, photosynthesis, and reduction of nitrates and sulphates.

Manganese (Mn)

Manganese is a essential component of chlorophyll and also formation of oils and fats. Manganese influences uptake and utilization of other nutrients in plants. Manganese is an essential factor in photosynthesis, nitrogen metabolism, and respiration.

Function of Manganese

- Functions with enzyme systems involved in breakdown of carbohydrates, and nitrogen metabolism. It acts as catalyst in oxidation-reduction reaction with in the plant tissue.
- It helps in the protein synthesis in chloroplast.
- It also supports the movement of iron in plants

Zinc (Zn)

Zinc is widely distributed element that occurs in small but adequate amount in most soil and plants. The zinc ion (Zn^{++}) is strongly absorbed on the cation exchange site of silicate clay. Zinc functions in enzyme systems which are the necessary for important reactions in plant metabolism. It is associated with iron and manganese for synthesis of chlorophyll.

Function of Zinc

- Essential for the transformation of carbohydrates.
- Regulates consumption of sugars.
- Part of the enzyme systems which regulate plant growth.
- It has a positive role in photosynthesis and nitrogen metabolism.
- It is required for seed production and the rate of growth and also RNA synthesis.

Copper (Cu)

Copper is capable of acting as electron carriers in enzyme system which brings about oxidation reductions in plant. It is an essential constituent of enzyme.

Function of Copper

- Important for reproductive growth.
- Aids in root metabolism and helps in the utilization of proteins.
- It acts as a catalyst in respiration.
- It involved in respiration and utilization of iron.

Boron (B)

Normal plant leaves contain between 25 and 100 ppm boron. Most of available boron in soil is associated with organic matter.

Function of Boron

- Helps in the use of nutrients and regulates other nutrients.
- Adds production of sugar and carbohydrates.
- Essential for seed and fruit development.
- It helps in normal growth of plant and in absorption of nitrogen in soil.
- It helps in root development and flower and pollen grain formation.

Molybdenum (Mo)

Molybdenum and manganese have been found to be essential for certain nitrogen transformation in microorganism as well as in plants. Molybdenum is through to be essential for the process of nitrogen fixation both symbiotic and non-symbiotic.

Function of Molybdenum

- Helps in the use of nitrogen.
- It regulates the activities of several enzymes.
- It plays an essential role in the absorption and translocation of iron in plants.

Chlorine (Cl)

Chlorine to be an essential plant nutrients as root in top growth seem to suffer it is absent.

Function of Chloride

- Adds plant metabolism.
- Chlorine through the associated with the evaluation of oxygen during photosynthesis.

Nickel (Ni)

- Nickel is the metal component of urease that catalyzes the reaction

$$CO\,(NH_2)_2 + H_2O \longrightarrow 2NH_3 + CO_2.$$

- Nickel most benefited for legume crops.

Function of Nickel

- Nickel increase enzyme activity as well as molybdenum activity.
- It increase the germination in grain crops.

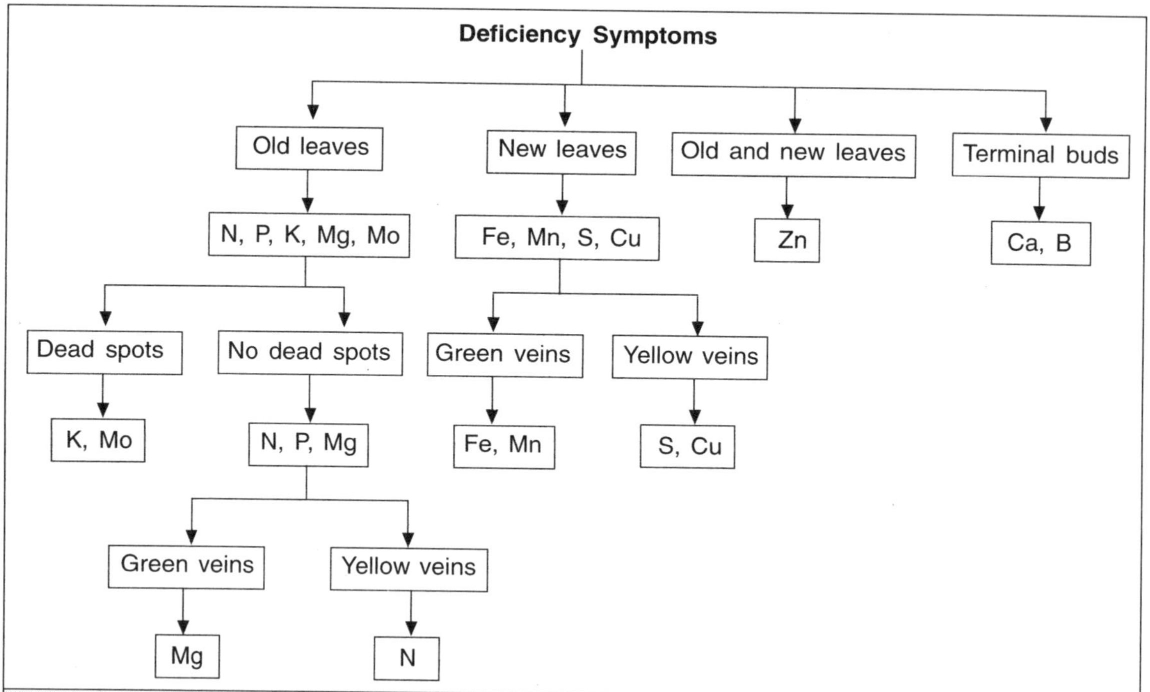

Fig. 19.1. Identification of deficiency symptoms

TABLE 19.5. Generalized symptoms of plant nutrient deficiency or excess

Plant Nutrient	*Type*	*Visual Symptoms*
N	**Deficiency**	1. Chlorosis, which starts from older leaves and progresses to younger leaves. 2. The leaves show mottled appearance of purple or red anthocyanin pigments over the vein. Examples: tomato, apple. 3. Lateral buds remain dormant. 4. There is little tillering in cereals. 5. Flower formation is either suppressed or only a few flowers are formed, which lead to the formation of small fruits and less viable seeds. 6. In potato, smaller and fewer tubers are produced.
	Excess	Dark green foliage which may be susceptible to lodging, drought, disease and insect invasion. Fruit and seed crops may fail to yield.
P	**Deficiency**	1. Leaves may develop purple coloration; stunted plant growth and delay in plant development. 2. Stunted growth. 3. Premature leaf fall. 4. Chlorosis appears later, which is of mottled type and is shown first by older leaves. 5. Necrosis in lamina, petiole and skin of soft fruits.

		6. Lateral buds show prolonged dormancy, but active buds are not affected. 7. Vascular tissues are poorly developed.
	Excess	Excess phosphorus may cause micronutrient deficiencies, especially iron or zinc.
K	**Deficiency**	1. Older leaves turn yellow initially around margins and die; irregular fruit development. 2. Leaves show chlorosis. 3. Necrosis at the leaf tip, margin or irregular patches. 4. Citrus leaves become bronzed and twisted. 5. Growth is stunted due to reduced apical activity. 6. Apical buds may die-Loss of apical dominance is a characteristic deficiency symptom of K^+ ions and it leads to bushy growth. 7. Cereals may show lodging.
	Excess	Excess potassium may cause deficiencies in magnesium and possibly calcium.
Ca	**Deficiency**	1. Reduced growth or death of growing tips; blossom-end rot of tomato; poor fruit development and appearance. 2. Fragility of chromosomes. 3. Roots become translucent and stop apical growth. 4. Young leaves show marginal and apical withering. 5. Flower and fruit stalks break premature falling.
	Excess	Excess calcium may cause deficiency in either magnesium or potassium.
Mg	**Deficiency**	1. Initial yellowing of older leaves between leaf veins spreading to younger leaves; poor fruit development and production. 2. Leaves show chlorosis. 3. Necrosis at the leaf tip, margin or irregular patches. 4. Citrus leaves become bronzed and twisted. 5. Growth is stunted due to reduced apical activity. 6. Apical buds may die. Loss of apical dominance is a characteristic deficiency symptom of K ions and it leads to bushy growth. 7. Cereals may show lodging.
	Excess	High concentration tolerated in plant; however, imbalance with calcium and potassium may reduce growth.
S	**Deficiency**	1. Initial yellowing of young leaves spreading to whole plant; similar symptoms to nitrogen deficiency but occurs on new growth. 2. Leaves show chlorosis. 3. Reduction in juice content of citrus fruits. 4. Fruit formation, in general is retarded. 5. "Tea yellow" in tea plant. 6. Premature germination of lateral buds, killing of young branches. 7. Smaller and chlorotic leaves.

		8. Necrosis of leaf margin and tip.
		9. Inward rolling of leaf margin and rapid defoliation.
	Excess	Excess of sulfur may cause premature dropping of leaves.
Fe	**Deficiency**	1. Initial distinct yellow or white areas between veins of young leaves leading to spots of dead leaf tissue.
		2. Chlorosis and interveinal chlorosis.
	Excess	Possible bronzing of leaves with tiny brown spots.
Mn	**Deficiency**	1. Interveinal yellowing or mottling of young leaves.
		2. Chlorotic patches are in the form of specks or reticulations in dicots and stripes in monocots.
		3. Necrosis may follow.
		4. Leaves show premature fall or do not develop at all.
		5. Both stem and root experience stunted growth. Their apices may die back.
		6. Flowers are often sterile.
		7. Grey spot disease in oat develops due to manganese deficiency.
Zn	**Deficiency**	1. Interveinal yellowing on young leaves; reduced leaf size.
		2. Interveinal chlorosis.
		3. Followed by necrosis.
		4. Terminal bud dies and leads to leaf rosettes.
	Excess	Excess zinc may cause iron deficiency in some plants.
B	**Deficiency**	1. Death of growing points and deformation of leaves with areas of discoloration.
		2. Causes disintegration of softer tissues.
		3. Browning of cauliflower.
		4. Heart rot of sugar beet.
		5. Reduced transpiration due to defunctioning of stomata.
	Excess	Leaf tips become yellow followed by necrosis. Leaves get a scorched appearance and later fall off.
Cl	**Deficiency**	1. Leaves become wilted.
		2. Chlorosis and then necrosis.
		3. Leaves develop bronze colour.
		4. Root growth is stunted.
Mo	**Deficiency**	1. Yellow spot disease of citrus fruits.
		2. Whiptail disease in crucifers like cabbage.
		3. Flowers show premature fall.
		4. In cauliflower the inflorescence loses its compact form.
Cu	**Deficiency**	1. Appearance of dark green colour in young leaves followed by chlorosis.
		2. In exanthema the tree barks show deep slits from which gum exudes.
		3. The reclamation disease is named so because of its widespread presence in reclaimed lands of Europe. Tips of leaves undergo chlorosis. Hence also known as the leaf-tip disease.

DISORDER/DISEASE CAUSED BY NUTRIENT DEFICIENCY

Nitrogen

(*i*) Red leaf in cotton
(*ii*) Bud opening in cotton
(*iii*) Firing of fruit in vegetable and grain crops
(*iv*) General starvation

Phosphorus

(*i*) Sickle leaves
(*ii*) Purple colouration in maize

Potassium

(*i*) Rosette in sugarbeat, carrot, cereal, pea and potato.
(*ii*) Dieback
(*iii*) Firing of potato and tomato leaf

Calcium (Ca)

(*i*) Tip hooking in cauliflower, tobacco and sugarbeat
(*ii*) Blossom and end rot disease of tomato

Magnesium (Mg)

(*i*) Send drown in tobacco

Sulphur (S)

(*i*) Tea yellow disease in tea
(*ii*) Akoichi disease in rice

Iron (Fe)

(*i*) Lime induces chlorosis

Manganese (Mn)

(*i*) Grey spike or grey spot in oat and wheat, barley, maize and mustard
(*ii*) Phahla disease in sugarcane
(*iii*) Mursespot in pea
(*iv*) Frunching in trunk tree (as citrus)
(*v*) Spiked yellow disease in sugarbeat

Molybdenum (Mo)

(*i*) Whiptail disease in brassica and cauliflower
(*ii*) Scaled in legume crops
(*iii*) Yellow spot disease in citrus and cauliflower

Zinc (Zn)

(*i*) Whiptail in brassica
(*ii*) Khaira in rice (first time observed by U.P. Agri. Uni. Pathologist Y.L. Nene 1965)
(*iii*) White bud in maize
(*iv*) Rosette in fruit trees
(*v*) Little leaf of mottled leaf in citrus

Copper (Cu)

(*i*) Exainthema in fruit trees
(*ii*) White tip or reclamation disease in cereal (oat) and vegetables
(*iii*) Dieback in shoot

Boron (B)

(*i*) Heart rot, crown rot, and dry rot in sugarcane and marigold
(*ii*) Cancer and internal black spot in garden pea
(*iii*) Hen and chicken in grape crops
(*iv*) Hallow heart disease in some crops
(*v*) Hard fruit of citrus
(*vi*) Cracking in tomato
(*vii*) Koeli/black tip/tip necrosis in mango
(*viii*) Brown rot in sugarbeat
(*ix*) Top rot in tobacco
(*x*) Brown and hallow stem in cauliflower
(*xi*) Internal necrosis of Aonla
(*xii*) Mango malformation

Oxygen (O_2)

(*i*) Black heart of Potato

Disorder/Disease Caused by Nutrient Toxicity

Ca—Green ear of Bajara

Mn—Crinkle leaf of potato

Absorption of Plant Nutrients by Plants

The solubility and availability of nutrients depend on various edaphic, climatic, and biotic factors. Nutrient uptake by plants requires an intimate root soil association. All field crops absorb nutrients through their roots. Most of the nutrients enter the plant roots as ions. The various forms in which different are absorbed by plant are listed in the table 19.1.

Nutrients are absorbed by the plants in the two ways as follows :

(*i*) Active absorption. Absorption of nutrients from the solution containing ion concentration compared to cell sap, by expending energy is called *active absorption.*

(*ii*) Passive absorption. Nutrients enter the plants along with transpiration stream without the use of energy is called *passive absorption.*

The process of active nutrient absorption requires an expenditure of energy by the plants which is derived mainly from the oxidation of carbohydrates and other plant substances in respiration activities. The plants are also capable of absorbing nutrients through their leaves. This method is known as foliar nutrition.

Plants obtain their nutrients from the various sources as follows :

(*i*) Soil solution. The water present in the soil contains dissolved salt and plant absorbs them through the roots.

(*ii*) Clay and Humus particles. Chief sources of nutrient to plants are clay and humus of the soil. Nutrient such as NH_4^+, K^+, Ca^{++}, Mg^{++} etc. are the held in the clay particles in an exchangeable and available from for use by plants. Soil organic matter serves as a principal storehouse for supply of anion such as $H_2PO_4^-$ or SO_4^{2-} to plants. The nutrients of organic matter are made available to plant after its decomposition by various microorganisms present in the soil. The nutrient absorbed by the plants are converted and built up into various complex substances such as carbohydrates, protein, fat, vitamins etc. in the plants.

(*iii*) Decomposable minerals. The water present in the soil contains dissolved salt and plant absorbs them through the roots.

(*iv*) Air. Plant absorbs some nutrients from air through the very small openings on the surface of the leaves called stomata.

FACTOR AFFECTING OF ABSORPTION OF PLANT NUTRIENTS

The essential nutrients are generally present in the soil. But the absorption of nutrients depends on several factors as follows:

1. External factor

(*i*) Oxidation and reduction state of nutrients. Nutrient uptake of plants requires intimate root soil association. The nutrients occur naturally in the oxidized state and this favored in absorption. But iron and manganese are more available to plants in their reduced form.

***(ii)* Concentration of nutrient.** The relative concentration of a nutrient absorption. Higher the concentration of a nutrient, greater is its availability.

***(iii)* Aeration.** Aeration respiration of root cells supplies energy for nutrient absorption and reactions with the cell membrane determine the rate at which any given element can be absorbed. Better aeration of the soil provides sufficient oxygen for the respiration of roots.

***(iv)* Moisture content in the soil.** Plant absorbs the nutrient from the soil in the form of solution. So moisture is an important factor that influences the absorption of nutrients. Water help in transport of nutrients to the root surface and promote absorption. Nutrient solubility is markedly affected by root exudates and by microbial activity in the vicinity of roots.

***(v)*Temperature.** Temperature effects the growth and development of crop and also availability of the microorganism. The microorganism has a role to increase the availability of nutrient to growing plants.

***(vi)* Soil pH.** Soil pH affects the availability of nutrient to plant. It also influences the absorption of nutrient from the soil.

2. Internal factor

***(i)* Cell wall.** Cell wall is differentially permeable and selectively absorbs particular cation and anions. But the cations have competitive advantage. Plant absorbs anions such as NO_3^-, HPO_4^{2-}, $H_2PO_4^-$, and SO_4^{2-} in large quantity.

***(ii)* Cell and its state of development.** The entry of inorganic material into xylem occurs at the root tips. The absorption of nutrients take place primarily by the cell of root hair may be effective for absorption just for a few days.

***(iii)* Transpiration.** Absorption is closely related with transpiration. The absorption of nutrients is more when the transpiration is high.

❑❑❑

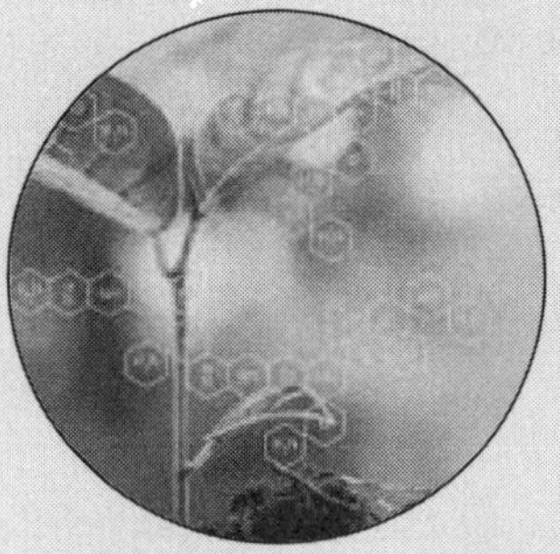

CHAPTER 20

Chemistry of Plant Nutrients

1. NITROGEN

The cheap source of N is the crop residues in temperate region. In tropical soils, the total N content is 0.03 - 0.1 %. Rainfall is also source of N at 4.6 kg of N / ha is received ha^{-1} yr^{-1}. It is converted to NO_3 during lighting addition of organic matter and fertilizer is other major sources. Nitrogen is an essential constituent of protein and also other non protein compounds of great physiological importance in plant metabolism. It is an integral part of chlorophyll, which is primary observer of light energy needed for photosynthesis. Nitrogen also imparts vigorous vegetative growth and governs the utilization of P, K and other elements.

Forms of soil nitrogen

Inorganic forms N

1. Ammonium NH_4^+
2. Nitrite NO_2^-
3. Nitrate NO_3^-
4. Elemental N (No)

Organic forms of soil

Amide form (NH_2)

Plant absorbs N as both

NH_4^-, NO_3^-.

Losses of Nitrogen

1. Crop removal
2. Leaching (or) drainage (11-18% loss)
3. Gaseous losses as NH_4 or elemental N_2
4. Volatilization.
5. Erosion (8 – 15 kg $ha^{-1}yr^{-1}$).
6. Ammonia fixation by clays
7. Immobilization in organic materials.

N transformations in soils

(*a*) N – Mineralisation

(*b*) Aminisation

(*c*) Conversation of urea

(*d*) N Immobilization.

(*e*) N factor

(*f*) Ammonification.

(*g*) Nitrification

(*h*) Denitrification

(*i*) Organic fixation

(*j*) Elemental N loss.

(*k*) Nitrogen cycle.

N transformations in soils

Nitrogen mineralization

Mineralization is the conversation of organic N to NH_4^+ as a result of microbial decomposition. Mineralization increases with a rise in temperature and is enhanced by adequate, although not excessive, soil moisture and a good supply of O_2. Mineralization of organic N involves in two reactions.

i.e (1) Aminisation (2) Ammonification.

Aminisation

Aminisation is the decomposition of proteins and the release of amines, amino acids and urea is called aminisation.

$$\text{Proteins} \xrightarrow[\text{Fungi } H_2O]{\text{Bacteria}} \underset{\text{Amino acid}}{R\text{–}\overset{\overset{NH_2}{|}}{\underset{\underset{H}{|}}{C}}\text{–}COOH} + \underset{\text{amines}}{RNH_2} + \underset{\text{Urea.}}{\overset{\overset{NH_2}{|}}{\underset{\underset{NH_2}{|}}{C}} = O} + CO_2 + \text{Energy}$$

The initial step in the decomposition of organic matter by the enzymatic digestion of proteins into amino acids like, peptones and amino acid. **Under aerobic** protolysis the major end products are CO_2 $(NH_4)_2$ SO_4 and H_2O. Under anaerobic conditions the end products are ammonia, amides, CO_2 and H_2S.

The organic compounds and proteins are mainly decomposed by various species of Pseudomonas, Bacilli, clostridium, serrotia, Micrococcus, Generally in the neutral and sodic soils, bacteria are active and in acidic soils fungi are active.

Conversion of urea

Urea is a product of ammonization. The hydrolysis of urea by the action of increases enzyme is effected by Bacilli micrococcus, Pseudomonas, clostridium, Aeromobactor and coryne bactor.

$$Co\,(NH_2) + H^+ + 2H_2O \longrightarrow 2NH_4^+ + HCO_3^-$$

$$NH_4^+ \longrightarrow NH_3 + H^+$$

$$2NH_3 + N_2\,CO_3 \longrightarrow (NH_4)_2CO_3 \longrightarrow NH_4^+ + CO_3^{2-}$$

The optimum H_2O holding capacity for these reactions is 50 – 75 and optimum temperature is 30 – 50°C.

The NH_4 can be utilized by microorganisams and root of higher plants. Some of the released NH_3 is fixed by clay especially illite. A major portion is oxidized to nitrate form. In the second reaction NO_2^- is further oxidized to NO_3^- by nitrobactor

$$2\,NO_2^- + O_2 \longrightarrow 2\,NO_3^-.$$

Nitrogen immobilization

"Immobilisation is the process of conversion of inorganic N (NH_4^+ or NO_3^-) to organic N and it is basically the reverse of N mineralization".

The Microorganisms accumulate NH_4 N and NO_3 – N in the form of protein, nucleic acid and other complexes. If C:N ratio is wider than 30, it favours immobilization and lesser C:N ratio encourage mineralization.

N factor

N factor is the No of units of in organic nitrogen immobilized for each 100 units of materials under going decomposition". The average values for the nitrogen factor vary from 0.1 or < to 1.3.

Ammonification

"Amines and Aminoacids produced during aminisation of organic N are decomposed by other heterotrophs with release of NH_4^+ is termed **Ammonifcation**"

$$R-NH_2 + H_2O \longrightarrow NH_3 + R-OH + \text{energy}$$

$$\searrow$$

$$H_2O \quad NH_4^+ + OH^-$$

Nitrification

Nitrification is the process of biological oxidation by which the ammonical form of N converts to nitrate form of N. There are two steps. (a) NH_4 is converted first to NO_2^- and then to NO_3^-.

$$2NH_4 + 3O_2 \xrightarrow{\text{Nitrosomonas}} 2NO_2^- + 2H_2O + 4H^+$$

Nitrosomonas are obligate autotropic bacteria that obtain their energy from the oxidations of N and their C from CO_2.

Others autotrophic bacteria *Nitrosolobus, Nitrospira* and *nitroso vibrio* and to some extend heterotrophic bacteria also can oxidize NH_4^+ and other N reduces, compounds to NO_3^-.

Losses of Nitrogen

The major losses of N from the soil are due to (1) crop removal and leaching, however under certain conditions inorganic N ions can be converted to gases and lost to the atmosphere. The primary pathway of gaseous N losses are

1. Denitrification
2. NH_3 volatilization.

Denitrification

Denitrification is the biochemical reduction of NO_3N or NO_2N to gaseous N, either as molecular Nitrogen or an oxide of Nitrogen. The most probable bio chemical pathway is

$$\underset{\text{Nitrate}}{NO_3} \longrightarrow \underset{\text{Nitrite}}{NO_2} \longrightarrow \underset{\text{Nitric oxide}}{NO} \longrightarrow \underset{\text{Nitrous oxide}}{N_2O} \longrightarrow \underset{\text{Nitrogen}}{N_2}$$

Nitrogen fixation

The conversation of elemental nitrogen to organic forms readily use able in biological process. Vermicullite and illite are capable of fixing NH_4^+ by a replacement of K^- or Na^+ for interlayer cations in the expended lattice of clay minerals. The radius of NH_4 ion 0.143°A. K^+ ion 0.133°A.

Because of NH_4 and K have more or less same charge, they easily replace each other in the exchange sites.

Organic fixation

It the soil has more organic matter the NH_4 will lockup as a complex. There complex are called **Chelates**. It release the nutrients only after its molecular break down. The facultative aerobic bacteria tiles pseudomonas, bacillus, porococcus are responsible for denitrification. It also depends upon the texture of soil. In heavy clay soils loss is upto 50% of added fertilizer.

Elemental N loss

It is due to chemical reduction. If chemical fertilizer containing amide (or) NH_4 form of N, it may be oxidized to elemental N and lost.

$$2NHO_2 + CO(NH_2)_2 \longrightarrow CO_2 + 3H + 2\,NH_2$$

Sources of N leading to N and NO_2 gaseous loss

1. **Denitrification:**

   $NO_3 \longrightarrow NO_2 \longrightarrow NO \longrightarrow N_2O \longrightarrow N_2$

2. **Nitrification:**

   $NH_4^- \longrightarrow NH_2OH \longrightarrow NO_2 \longrightarrow NO_3$

3. **Nitrates and ammonium:**

   $NH_4 + NO_2^- \longrightarrow N_2 + 2H_2O$

4. **Nitrates and amino acids:**

   $HNO_2 + RNH_2\, N_2 \longrightarrow ROH + 2H_2O$

5. **Lignin:**

   $HNO_2 + RNH_2 + \text{Lignin} \longrightarrow N_2 + N_2O + CH_3O\,NO$

6. **Phenols:**

   $\text{Phenol} \longrightarrow N_2 + N_2O + \text{Organic residue}$

7. **Decomposition of nitrous acid/reaction with metal cations:**

   $3HNO_2 \longrightarrow 2NO + 2HNO_3 + H_2O$

   $Mn^{2+} + HNO_2 + H \longrightarrow Mn^{3+} + NO + H_2O$

   $Fe^{2+} + HNO_2 + H \longrightarrow Fe^{3+} + NO + H_2O$

8. **NH_3 Gas**

9. **Urea:**

   $(NH_4)_2CO + H_2O \longrightarrow 2NH_3 + CO_2$

10. Ammonium Salts:

$NH_4 + OH \longrightarrow NH_3 + H_2O$

11. Decomposition of residues and manures

Release and volatilization of NH_3

Nitrogen cycle

The cycling of N in the soil – plant – atmosphere system involves many transformations of N between inorganic and organic forms.

The N cycle can be divided into—

1. N inputs or gains.
2. N outputs of losses
3. N cycling with in the soil.

1. N in plant and animal residues and N derived from the atmosphere through electrical, combustion, biological and industrial process is added to the soil.
2. N in the residues is mobilized as NH_4 by soil organisms as an end product of residue decomposition, plant roots absorb a portion of the NH_4.
3. Much of the NH_4 is converted to No_3^- by nitrifying bacteria in a process called nitrifications.
4. NO_3 is taken up by the plant roots and is used to produce the protein in crops that are eaten by humans or fed to live stocks.
5. Some NO_3 is lost to ground H_2O or drainage systems as a results of downward movement through the soil in perculating H_2O.
6. Some NO_3 is consorted by denitrifying bacteria in to N_2 and N_2O that escape into the atmosphere, completely the cycle.

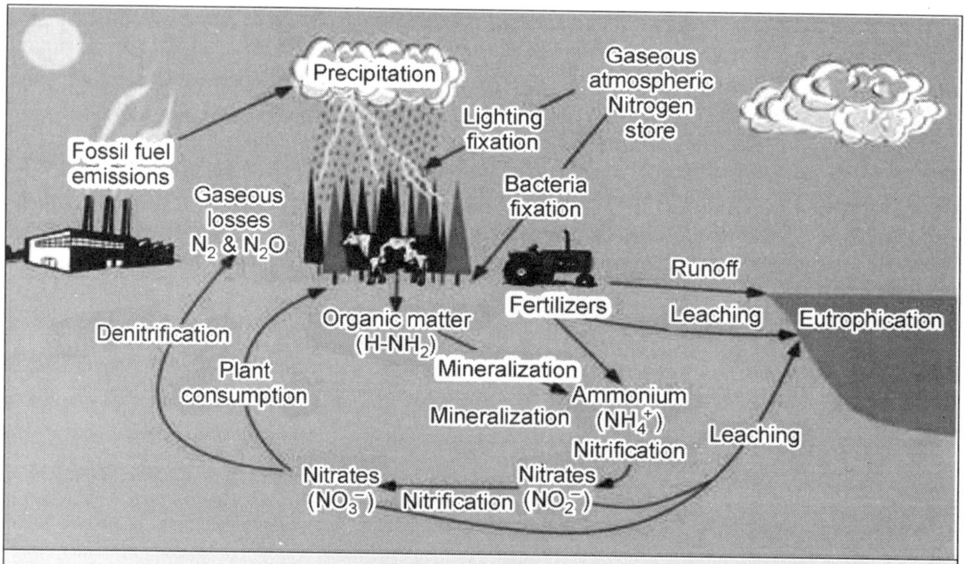

The nitrogen cycle

Important microorganisms in BNF

Organisms	Properties	Active location
Azotobacter	Aerobic, free living	Soil, water, rhizosphere, leaf surface
Azospirillum	Micro aerobic rhizobacteria; free fixers	Free living in Rhizosphere; Colonize roots of cereals and also gives phytotonic effect
Rhizobium	Symbiotic	Root nodules of legumes
Actinomycetes, Frankia, Beijerinckia	Symbiotic	Non leguminous forest tree roots, leaf surfaces
Cyanoba cteria	Photo autotrophic Anabaena - symbiotic	In wetland flood water; Anabaena associate with Azolla

Symbiotic N fixation

The symbiosis is the mutually beneficial relationship between host plant and bacteria. The location of association is in root or stem nodules, inside cavities, or by colonizing and penetrating plant tissue.

Legume (nodule forming)

Legumes and bacteria of the genera **Rhizobium** and **Bradyrhizobium** provide the major biological source of fixed N (40-60%) in agricultural soils. These organisms infect the root hairs and the cortical cells, ultimately inducing the formation root nodules that serve as the site of N fixation. The host plant supplies the bacteria with carbohydrates for energy and the bacteria reciprocate by supplying the plant with fixed N compound.

Effective nodules cluster on primary roots and have pink to red centers. The red colour of the nodule is attributed to the occurrence of **leghemoglobin**. The quantity of N fixed by properly nodulated legume averages about 75% of the total N used for the plant growth. The amount of BNF varies with Rhizobium strain, host plant, and environment.

Yield of non-legume crops often increase when they are grown following legumes (e.g. maize after soybean). Maximum N fixation occurs only when available soil N is at a minimum. When optimum conditions for N fixation is not prevailing, a legume crop can deplete soil N greatly, more than a cereal, if the legume grown is not incorporated into the same soil.

Fixer	Host plant
Rhizobium	Alfalfa, clover, peas, bean, soybean
	Gliricidia, Leuceana, Sesbania, Mimosa, Acacia
Bradyrhizobium	Cowpea, groundnut, red gram

Non-legume (nodule forming)

Roots of many species of angiosperm trees like casuarina in forests and wetlands form distinct nodules when infected with Actinomycetes of the genus **Frankia**.

Non-legume (non-nodule forming)

Azospirillum, **Azotobacter**, and **Azorhizobium**, dominant N fixers in cereals like rice, wheat, corn, sorghum, millets can grow on root surfaces and penetrate root tissues. The organisms use carbohydrates of root exudates as source of energy. They also induce crop growth by hormonal action. The organism **Beijerinckia** fixes N on leaf surfaces of tropical plants.

The **Anabaena** blue green algae (Cyanobacteria) inhabit cavities in the leaves of the floating water fern **Azolla** and fix quantities of N comparable to those of the better Rhizobium-legume complex. It could fix about 30-105 kg N/ season taking care of 75% N requirement of rice.

Nonsymbiotic N fixation

In wetland floodwater photoautotrophic **Cyanobacteria** independently do photosynthesis and fix N up to 20–30 kg N/ ha/ year. The excess ammonia is excreted in floodwater, which is beneficially absorbed by rice plants.

Free-living heterotroph bacteria like **Azotobacter** and **Beijerinckia** in aerobic upland soils and **Clostridium** in anaerobic wetland soils effectively fix N in pockets where O_2 supply is limited. Fixation depends upon the pH, soil N level, and source of organic matter.

Industrial fixation of N

Commercially produced N is the most important source of plant nutrient in agriculture. Industrial N fixation is by Haber-Bosch process, in which H_2 and N_2 gases react to form NH_3 under high temperature (1200°C) and pressure (500 atm). Anhydrous NH_3 can directly be used as fertilizer or combined to other ions as solid forms.

N additions from atmosphere

Ammonia escapes in to atmosphere from soils, manures, and industries because of volatilization. Organic N compounds remain in fine dust of air lifted from earth surface. Rainfall brings down to soil NH_3, NO_3^-, NO_2^-, N_2O, and organic N. About 10 to 20% of the NO_3^- in the rainfall is due to fixation of N_2 by energy of lightning.

2. PHOSPHORUS

Phosphorus is taken up by the plant in the form of $\mathbf{H_2PO_4^-}$ $\mathbf{HPO_4^{-2}}$ PO_4^{-3} through **diffusion** and **mass flow** action.

The P availability mainly depends on pH. In acid soils **(Al & Fe)** the presence of Al, Fe, Mn, P gets fixed as $AlPO_4$, $FePO_4$ and not available to the plants. Some times as $CaPO_4$. these are insoluble in H_2O.

Under hilly areas (or) high rainfall areas, all the cations will be leached leaving Fe, Al and Mn. The P availability will be reduced.

Ideal pH for available P = 6.5 - 7.5. If pH > 8.5 the fixation will be more. < 6.5 the fixation will be more.

Forms of P : Nucleic acid and Phospho lipids

Rock Phosphate - acid soluble. If the organic matter content is high the availability of P is more since it is soluble in acid. It is highly suited to **plantation crops.** Rock Phosphates is black in colour. Roots also exudates acids, which will solublises the P.

Fixation is high so the P_2O_5 deficiency is 15 – 35%.

P is present as Apatities

1. Chlor - $Ca_{10} (PO_4)_6Cl_2$.
2. Fluor - $Ca_{10}(PO_4)_6F_2$.
3. Carbonate - $Ca_{10}(PO_4)_6Co_3$.
4. Hydroxy - $Ca_{10}(PO_4)_6(OH)_2$.

Based on solubility the P fertilizers can be grouped into 4 groups.

1. H_2O soluble P : (*i*) SSP 16% P as H_2O soluble
   : (*ii*) TSP 45% P as H_2O soluble
2. Citrate soluble P : Dicalcium PO_4 34% P_2O_5.
   : Tricalcium PO_4 24%
3. Acid soluble P : Anhydrious Rock phosphate 16 - 18 %
4. Both H_2O and citrate soluble P : Kotka PO_4 25% P_2O_5.

   Rock phosphate is obtained in

Bihar	: Singlahe
Rajaithan	: Udaipur
Uttarakhand	: Mussoorri
Andhra Pradesh	: Kasi pattinam

Phosphorus occurs in most plants in concentrations between 0.1 and 0.4%. Plants absorb either $H_2Po_4^-$ or $H + PO_4^{2-}$ ortho PO_4 ions Absorption of $H_2PO_4^-$ is greatest at low pH values, where as uptake of HPO_4^{2-} is greater at higher values of soil pH, plant uptake of HPO_4^- is much slower than $H_2PO_4^-$.

Functions of P

1. It has a greater role in energy storage and transfer.
2. It is a constituent of nucleic acid, phytin and phospholipids
3. It is essential for cell division and development
4. P compounds act as energy currency within plants. The most common P energy currency is that found in ADP and ATP. Transfer of the energy rich PO_4 molecules from ATP to energy requiring substances in the plant is known as **"Phosphorylation"**
5. It stimulates early root development and growth and there by helps to establish seedlings quickly.
6. It gives rapid and vigorous start to plants strengthen's straw and decreasess lodging tendency.
7. It is essential for seed formation because larger quantities of P is found in seed and fruit-phytic acid is the principle storage from of phosphorus in seeds.
8. It increases the activity of Rhizobia and increases the formation of root nodules.

Soil P its origin and Nature

Soil P exists in many primary and secondary compounds. The **apatite** group of primary mineral is the original source i.e. 55% of soil P.

(*a*) **Aluminium and Iron Phosphates.** In the initial stages of acid weathering Po_4 becomes increasingly bound to Fe^{3+} and Al^{3+} ions released from silicate minerals by replacing OH^- from **hydroxyl minerals** or oxygen from **oxide minerals.** $FePO_4$ and $ZnPO_4$ has been found in H_2O logged or poorly drained soils, sand and silt fraction of some soils.

Calcium phosphates

The group of compounds form an important category in the young soils and the matured soils of **neutral** to **alkaline** pH ranges. The $CaPO_4$ found either in **stable** or **metastable** state in the soil fertilizer reaction zones.

Eg. Fluorapatite	-	$Ca_{10}(PO_4)_3 Fe$
Carbonate apatite	-	$Ca_{10}(PO_4)_3 Co_3$
Dlcalcium Po_4	-	$Ca HPO_4 2H_2O$
Monocalcium Po_4	-	$CaH_2PO_4 H_2O$.

Organic phosphates

It is derived secondarily by the addition of organic matter to the soil through the growth of plants and the deposition of plant residues. The soil micro organic synthesize organic PO_4 compounds and accumulate in the soil mixed with derived from plant tissues. It constitute 20 – 30% of total soil P. The major classes of organic compounds in soils are

1. Phospholipids (0.6 – 0.9%)
2. Phospho proteins of nucleic acid (0.6 – 2.4%)
3. Phosphorylated sugar
4. Phytin and Inositol PO_4

The ideal C : N : P : S ratio in soils are

(*a*) Calcarious	113	:	10	:	1.3	:	1.3
(*b*) Non calcarious	147	:	10	:	2.5	:	1.4
(*c*) Indian soils	144	:	10	:	1.4	:	1.8

Chemistry of solid phosphorus compounds and their equilibrium

The PO_4 concentration in soil solution is governed by the heterogenous equilibrium.

P adsorbed in soil $PO_4 \longrightarrow$ P in soil solution $\longrightarrow$ P' precipitated in soil solution.

The reactions involved in soil PO_4 equilibrium are **dissolution, precipitation, solubility product principle.**

By using radio active p^{32} Larsen (1952) characterized the total soil PO_4 into **Labile** and **Non labile** fractions and found the size of the labile pool primarily depended on soil properties and not a function of the total content of inorganic P. he correlated and equilibrium of Non labile soil P $\rightleftarrows$ Labile soil P $\rightleftarrows$ P in soil solution.

Fixation of phosphorus in soil

"It is the way of removal of PO_4 from solution by soil which reduces the amount that plant roots can absorb".

The factors affecting P fixation are:

1. **Clay minerals.** The PO_4 is fixed by clay minerals by reacting with soluble aluminum which originates from the exchanges sites or from lattice dissociation to from a highly **insoluble $AlPo_4$.**

2. **Iron and Aluminum (fixation in acid soils).** The formation of Iron and aluminium PO_4 in the soil results from the combination of P with these metals in solution and their oxides hydroxides in acid soil.

$$2Al + 3\ H_2Po_4 \_\ Al_2\ (PO_4)_3 + 2\ H_2O + 2H^+$$

3. **Exchange cations and calcium carbonate (Fixation alkaline soils).** In calcareous soils, free Ca CO_3 is a potent sources for 'P' fixation. P fixation in calcareous soil involved a rapid monolayer sorption of P in dilute concentration In $CaCO_3$ surfaces and form less soluble compounds of di and tricalcium PO_4.

$$Ca(H_2\ PO_4)_2 + 2\ CaCO_3\ Ca_3(PO_4)_2 + 2CO_2 + 2\ H_2O$$

4. **Organic matter.** Organic Po_4 can be fixed by soil organic matter also influences in Organic PO_4 fixation. The acids produced during the transformations of organic matter could decreases the pH and increases fixation by the solubilization of Fe and Al.

P Fixation in soil is affected by

1. Nature and Amount of soil minerals

Soils have high amount of Fe and Al oxides, crystalline hydrous metal oxides are usually capable of retaining more P than amorphous forms. P adsorbed to a greater extend by 1 : 1 than 2: 1 clays. The greater amounts P fixed by 1 : 1 clays is probably due to the higher amounts of Fe and Al oxides, associated with kaolinite clays that are predominate in highly weathered soils. Soils containing large quantities of clay will fix more P than soils with low clay content.

Soil pH

Fixation of P by Fe and Al oxides decreases with increasing pH. P availability is more in soils at a max in the pH range of 5.5 to 6.5. At low pH values, Fe and Al ions reacts with to from al Po_4 and $FePo_4$ oxides.

As the pH increases, the activity of Fe and Al decreases and the results of higher amount of P librates into soil solution.

Above pH 7.0, Ca^{2+} can precipitate with P as Ca $-PO_4$ mineral and P availability again decreases.

Cation effects. Divalent cations enhance the P fixation than monovalent cations.

Anion effects. Both organic and Inorganic anions can compete with P for adsorption sites, resulting in decreases the fixation of P.

Organic matter. Addition of organic matter to soils increased P availability by

- Formation of organoPo$_4$ complexes that are more easily assimilate by plants.
- Anion replacement of $H_2PO_4^-$ on adsorption sites.
- Coating of Fe and Al particles by humus to form a productive cover and thus reduce the P fixation.

Temperature. The rate of most chemical and biological reactions increases with increasing temperature. Mineralization of P from soil organic matter is dependent on soil biological activity an increases in temperature.

Flooding. In most soils there is an increases in available P after flooding largely due to conversion of Fe^{3+} PO_4 to soluble Fe^{2+} PO_4 and hydrolysis of Al PO_4 and thereby prevent the fixation of P in soils.

R_2O_3 : P_2O_5 (Ratio). "R_2O_3 : P_2O_5 (Ratio) is a measure of amount of P present in the soil". A wide ratio indicates a small P fixation and vice versa. When the ratio is narrow P fixation is more.

Addition of $ZnSO_4$. It may also cause P deficiency since it forms insoluble complex with P. This can be averted by addition of ZnSo$_4$ more and more.

P Cycle

"Process by which P moves form solid and liquid phase and transformation is called P cycle". P is taken mostly by diffusion in plants.

I. The decreases in soil solution P concentration with absorption by plants roots is buffered by both inorganic and organic fractions in soils.

Primary and secondary P minerals dissolve to re supply $H_2PO_4^-$ / $HPO_4^=$ in soluble.

Inorganic P adsorbed on mineral and clay surfaces as $H_2PO_4^-$ or $HPO_4^=$ (liable inorganic P) also can desorbs to buffer decreases in soil solution P. Numerous soil micro organic digest plant residues containing P and produce many organic plant compounds in soil and it can be mineralized through microbial activity to supply solution P.

H_2O soluble fertilizer P applied to soil readily dissolves and increases the concentration of soil solution.

II. In addition to uptake of P by roots, solution P can be adsorbed on minerals surfaces and precipitated as organic P and these organic P compounds are more resistant to microbial degradation.

Soil solution P is called **Intensity factor,** while organic and inorganic labile P fractions are collectively **Quantity factor.**

Maintenance of solution P concentration for adequate P nutrition in the plant depends on the ability of labile P to replace soil solution P. "The ratio of quantity to intensity factor in called the **capacity factor, "which express the relative ability of the soil to buffer changes in soil solution".**

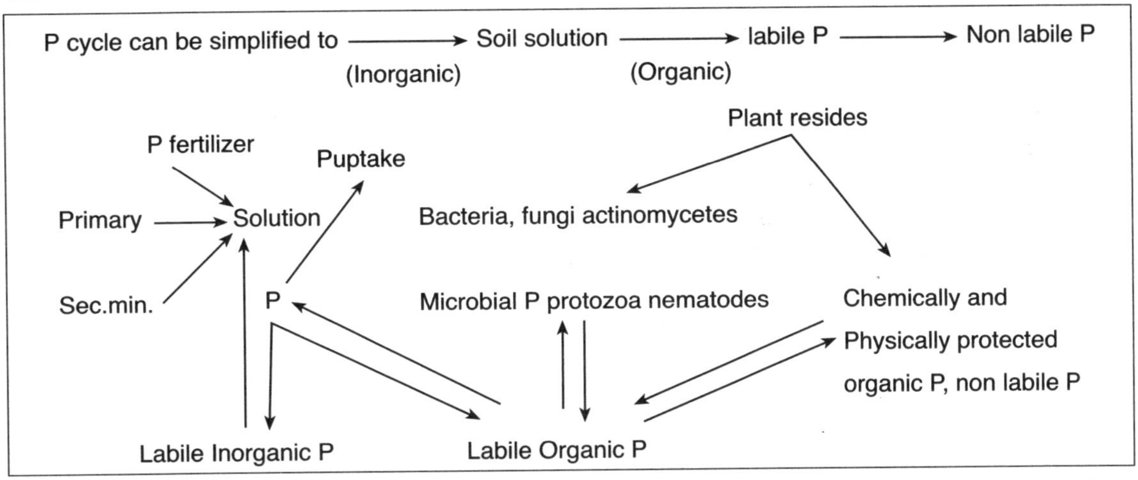

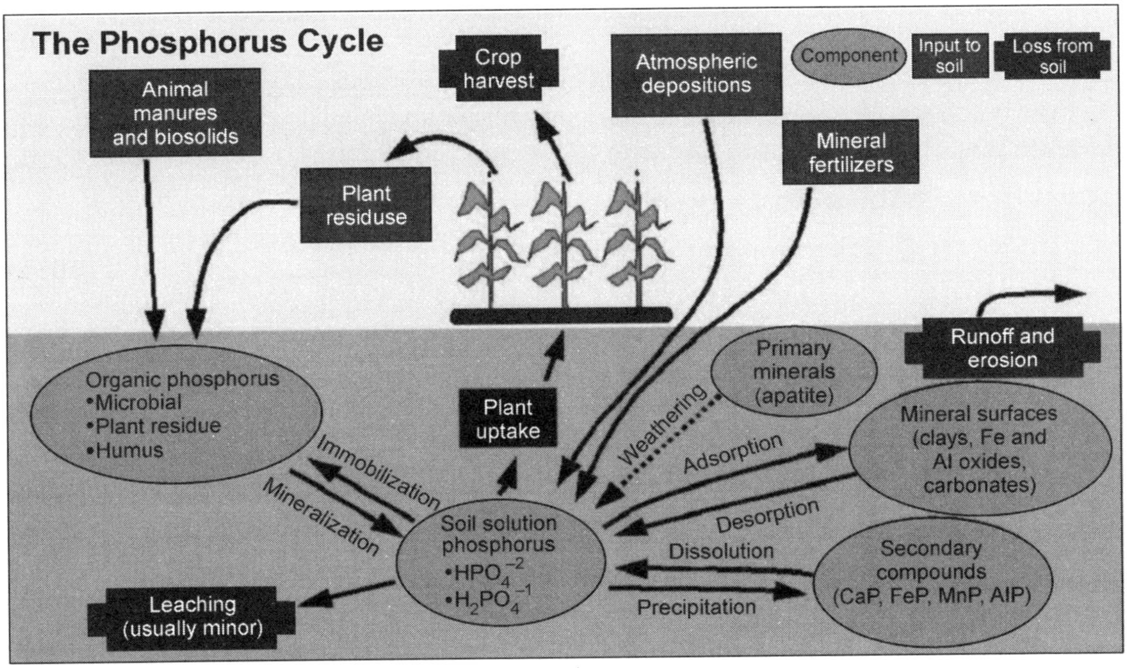

Y value / L value (Larsens Value)

Larsen measured the quantity of soil P involved in the isotopic dilution of applied radio active P during a growing season. It is used to calculate P supply of the soil.

$$L \text{ (or) } Y = K \times \frac{(Co - C)}{C}$$

Where,

L = Avail P in soil

Co = K × total P in the Plant

C = K × P taken by the plant

K = Proportionality constant.

Deficiency symptoms

P is mobile in plants and when a deficiency occurs it is translocated from older tissues to the active meristematic regions.

1. It arrests metabolism resulting in reduction of total N of Plants.
2. Reduced sugar content.
3. Premature leaf fall.
4. Develops necrotic area on the leaf petiole and in the fruit
5. Leaves will show characteristic bluish green colour.

Toxicity of phosphorus

(*a*) Profuse root growth i.e. lateral and fibrous root lets.

(*b*) It develops normal growth having green leaf colour.

(*c*) It may cause in some cases trace elements deficiencies i.e. **Zinc and Iron.**

3. POTASSIUM

The potassium ion (K^+) is actively taken up soil solution by plant roots. The concentration of K^+ in vegetative tissue ranges from 1 to 4% on dry matter basis.

Functions of potassium

1. Essential for photosynthesis, development of chlorophyll.
2. It improves vigour of the plants to enable to with stand adverse climatic conditions.
3. Reduces lodging in cereal crops.
4. It regulates stomata opening and closing.
5. It regulates the movement of ions with in the plants and hence it is called **traffic policeman** of the plant.
6. Activation of enzymes, enzyme synthesis, peptide bonds synthesis.
7. Regulates H_2O imbalance within the plant.

Sources of K

The micas and fieldspars constitute the major K bearing minerals which on weathering slowly release K to the soil.

(Muscovite and biotite)

(Orthoclase and microcline)

K–Feldspar: $KAlSi_3O_{10}$.

Forms of potassium in soils

(*a*) Water soluble K.

(*b*) Exchangeable K.

(*c*) Fixed or Non exchangeable K.

(*d*) Lattice or Mineral K.

The different forms are in **dynamic equilibrium** with one another and represented as follows.

$$\text{Fixed K} \overset{\text{Slow}}{\rightleftharpoons} \text{Exchangeable K} \overset{\text{fast}}{\rightleftharpoons} H_2O \text{ soluble K}$$

$$\nwarrow \qquad \nearrow$$

$$\text{Lattice Reserve K}$$

Water soluble K

The Concentration of H_2O soluble K in soil depends on (a) type of day (b) H_2O content (c) Intensity of leaching (d) Amount of exchange K (e) Kind and concentration of other ions.

The dilution of the soil, increases the concentration of H_2O soluble K and drying decreases it. The uptake of K is influenced by the presence of other cations, ie Ca^{2+} and Mg^{2+}, Al^{3+} (acidic soils) and Na^+ in salt affected soils.

The activity ratio (AR_e^K) $= \dfrac{\text{Activity of } K^+}{\sqrt{\text{activity of } Ca^{2+} \text{ and } Mg^{2+}}} = \dfrac{ak}{\sqrt{^{a}\text{Ca-Mg}}}$

Exchangeable K. The K adsorbed on soil clay complex and replaceable with neutral salts in relatively short time. The Cl reacts with soil Ca and form Ca Cl_2 which is leached by high rainfall. Hence **K is called** as

Decalcifier

Non exchangeable or Fixed K. Added K which is firmly bound by the soil and not immediately replaceable with neutral salts.

Lattice K or Mineral K. Muscovite, biotite and K feldspar. The capacity of soils to release lattice K by weathering depends on the content of K minerals and soil texture.

Potassium fixation

The important of K fixation is to regulate the supply of the soil a for the plants and protects it against loss through leaching.

In the dynamics of soil Potassium, the phenomenon of fixation of exchange K and the liberation of non-exchange K play an important role. K ions are relatively small to enter the silica sheets where they are held firmly by **electrostatic forces**. The presence of K^+ ions can block the release of fixed NH_4^+ and vice visa.

Factors affecting K fixation

1. **Soil texture:** Increases the texture grater will be fixation and vice visa.
2. **Wetting and drying:** Fixation is more under dry condition than wet condition.
3. **Type of day min:** Fixation is more in 2:1 type than 1: 1 type.
4. **Freezing and thawing:** Enhances the fixation of K depends their clay mineralogy and degree of weathering.
5. **Soil pH:** A decreases in pH reduces the K fixation either as result of competition of H_3O^+ for the inter layer exchange position. Liming also favors for the fixation of K. **Factors affecting K availability in plants**

(*a*) *Kind of clay minerals*: Soils containing vermiculite or montmorilonite will have more K than kaolinite clay soils.

(*b*) *Cation exchange capacity*: Increases texture soils having higher CEC and can hold more exchange K.

(*c*) *Amount of exchangeable K*: More K in soil solution leads to Higher fixation.

(*d*) *Subsoil K and rooting depth*: Low soil temperature may exhibit K release and diffusion, thus increasing crop response to K

(*e*) *Soil moisture*: fertilization increasing K levels or moisture contain will accelerate K diffusion.

6. **Soil temperature :** The reduced temperature slow down plant process plant growth and rate of K uptake.
7. **Soil aeration** : Under high moisture levels or incompact soils root growth is restricted, O_2 supply is lowered and absorptions of K is slowed.
8. **Soil pH :** In very acid soils, toxic amount of exchange Al^{3+} and Mn^{2+} create unfavorable root environment for uptake of K and other nutrients.
9. **Ca and Mg :** K uptake would be reduced as Ca^{2+} and Mg^{2+} are increased or uptake of these two cations would be reduced as the available supply of K is increased.
10. **Tillage:** Tillage is increased that K availability is reduced because of increases compaction, less aeration and lower temperature.

Plant factors affecting K availability

1. CEC of Roots : Higher root density, higher the removal of exchange K and soil solution available forms of soil K.
2. Root system and crop : Higher root density, higher the removal of exchange K and soil solution K. Fibrous root system absorbs more K than tap root system.
3. Variety or Hybrid : Hybrid absorbs more K than variety.
4. Plant population : Higher plant population and closer spacing increased the K removal.
5. Plant population : Higher plant population and closer spacing increased the K removal.

CALCIUM

Calcium is absorbed by plants as Ca^{2+} and its concentration ranges from 0.2 to 1.0% and it is supplied through mass flow method.

Functions of calcium

1. It is immobile in plants and hence the deficiency is observed in younger leaves.
2. It is a constituent of cell wall and increases in stiffness of plants.
3. Promotes root development and growth of plants, root elongation and cell division.
4. Helps to translocate the sugar in the plants.

5. It involves chromosome stability and that it is a constituent of chromosome structure.
6. Affects translocation of CHO in plants.
7. Encourages seed production.
8. Activates enzyme phosphate and kinease.
9. Accumulated protein during respiration by mitochondria and it increases their protein content.
10. It binds DNA to protein molecules.

Sources of soil calcium

Earth crust contains about 3.64%. The important source of calcium is **anorthite** (Ca Al_2, Si_2O_3). Generally arid region soils contain high amount of Ca regard less of texture, low rainfall and little leaching.

In arid and semiarid regions Calcite ($CaCo_3$); Dolomite (Ca, Mg, $(Co_3)_2$); Gypsum ($CaSo_4$, $2H_2O$)

In humid regions, even the soils formed from limestone are frequently acid in the surface layers because of the removal of Ca and other cations by leaching.

Calcium transformations in soils

In acid and humid region soils ca occurs largely in exchange form and as primary minerals. In most of these soils Ca^{2+}, Al^{3+} and H^+ dominates the exchange complex.

The forms of Ca are 1) Solution Ca^{2+} / Mg^{2+} 2) Exchangeable Ca/Mg 3) Mineral Ca/Mg.

The activity of solution Ca is decreased by leaching or plant removal. If solution Ca is increased, the equilibrium shifts in the opposite direction with subsequent desorption of some of the Ca^{2++} by the exchange complex. The rate of solution Ca is less complex than of K^+. It may be (a) Lost in drainage H_2O's. (b) absorbed by organisms (c) adsorbed on the CEC (d) Repricipitated as secondary calcium compound.

Factors affecting Ca^{2+} availability

1. Total Ca supply : Sandy acidic soils with low CEC having less Ca.
2. Soil pH: In acid soils Ca is not readily available to plants at low concentration.
3. CEC:Soils having low CEC might will supply more Ca^{2+}.
4. % Ca saturation:High Ca^{2+} saturation indicates favourable pH for plant growth and microbial activity.
5. Type of soil colloid: 2 : 1 type require higher Ca saturation than 1: 1 type.
6. Ratio of Ca^{2+} to other cations : Increasing the Al^{3+} conc. in soil solution reduces Ca uptake in plant.

MAGNESIUM

Magnesium is absorbed as Mg^{2+} and the concentration in crop varies between 0.1 and 0.6%.

It was taken by plant by *Mass flow and diffusion*.

Functions of Mg in plants

1. Primary constituent of chlorophyll
2. Imports dark green Colour in leaves.
3. Serves as a structural components in ribosomes and stabilizing the ribosome configuration for protein synthesis.
4. Involves numbers of physiological and biochemical function.
5. Activates phosphorylating enzymes in CHO metabolism.
6. Act as a cofactor for certain enzymes other than Po_4 transfer enzyme.
7. Increases in the oil content of oil seed crops.
8. Regulates the uptake of other nutrients.

Sources of soil Magnesium

It constitutes 1.93% of earth crust

Primarily minerals: (a) Biotite (b) Dolomite (c) Hornblende (d) olivine (e) serpentine. Secondary minerals: (a) Chlorite (b) Illite (c) Montmorillonite.

In arid region substantial amount of Mg present as **Epsomite** ($MgSO_4$ $7H_2O$)

Forms of Mg in the soil

1. It occurs predominately as exchange and solution mg.
2. Coarse text soil exhibits the greatest potential for Mg deficiencies.
3. Competition bet NH_4^+ and Mg^{2+} also lower the Mg^{2+} availability to crops.

Losses of Mg

It is leached by soils and it depends on the Mg content, rate of weathering, intensity of weathering and uptake of plants.

SULPHUR

Sulphur is absorbed by plant roots as SO_4^{2-} ions. Concentration of S in plants range between 0.1 and 0.4%.

Functions of sulphur

1. Essential for synthesis of sulphur containing amino acids cystine, cysteine and methionine.
2. Essential for synthesis of other metabolites including Co-enzyme A., Biotin, Thiamin of vitamin B and Glutothione.
3. Synthesis of chlorophyll.
4. It is a vital part of ferredoxins i.e Fe – S – protein occurring in the chloroplasts.
5. Responsible for the characteristic smell or odor and taste of mustard, onion and Garlic. (Puncy smell).
6. Enhances the oil formation in crops (Soya bean).

7. Increasing root growth.
8. Stimulate seed formation.
9. Promote nodule formation – Leguminous species.

Sources of sulphur

1. Amount has <0.05 ppm in the form of So_2.
2. Earth crust contains 0.06 to 0.10%.
3. Sulphur bearing minerals Gypsum - $CaSO_4$ $2H_2O$.
   Epsomite - $MgSO_4$, $7H_2O$
   Mirabilite - Na_2SO_4, $10H_2O$.
   Pyrite - FeS_2.
4. Silicate min contains <0.01 % S.
5. Igneous rocks 0.02 to 0.07% Sedimentary rocks 0.02 to 0.22%

Forms of sulphur in soil

Present both organic (90%) and Inorganic forms. The inorganic forms are

1. Solution SO_4^{2-}.
2. Adsorbed $SO_4^{=}$ Readily available fraction.
3. Insoluble $SO_4^{=}$
4. Reduced inorganic compounds.

Factors affecting S oxidation in soils

(*a*) Microbial population in soil.

(*b*) Characteristics of the 'S' source

(*c*) Soil environmental condition.

(*d*) **Soil micro flora.** Chemolithotropic S bacteria Thiobacilli utilized energy from oxide of Inorganic S for the fixation of CO_2 in Organic matter.

(*e*) **Soil temperature.** An increase in temperature increases the S oxidation rate in soil. Ideal temperature 25 –m 40°C.

(*f*) **Soil moisture and aeration.** S oxidizing bacteria are mostly aerobic and their activity will decline if O_2 is lacking due to H_2O logging. Favourable moisture is field capacity moisture.

(*g*) **Soil pH:** Optimum pH 4.0 or lower.

S transformation in soils

Numerous transformations of S in soil occur from inorganic to organic forms due to the presence of hetero tropic micro organic viz.,. Thiobacillus, chlorabium, Desulfotomaculam and Desulfovibrio.

When plant and animal residues are returned to the soil they are digested by microorganism releasing of the S as $So_4^{=}$. Most of the S remains in organic form and becomes part of soil humus. The S supply to plants in largely depend on the SO_4^{2-} released from the organic soil fractions and from the plant and animal residues.

S Mineralization and immobilization

Mineralization of "S" is the conversion of organic S to inorganic SO_4^{2-}.

Immobilisation is the conversion of SO_4^{2-} to organic S.

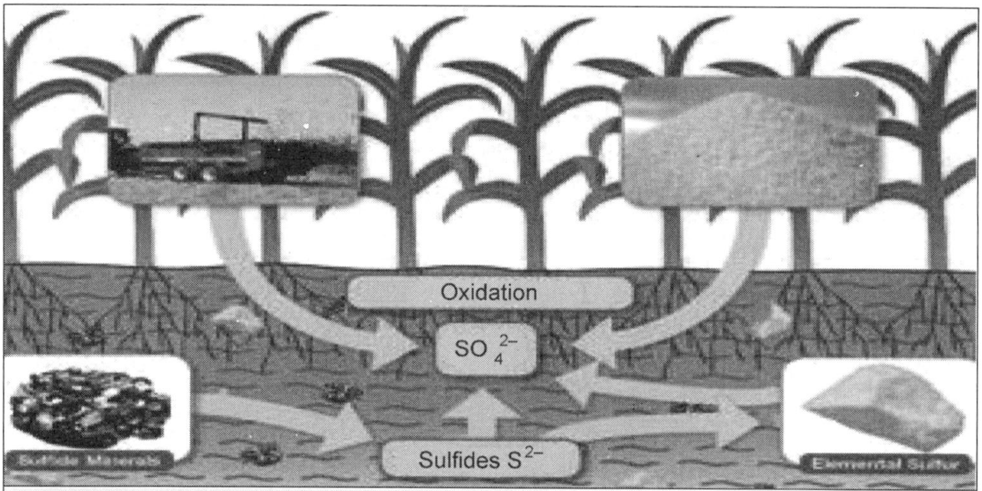

Sulphur cycle

Factor affecting of mineralization and Immobilization.

1. **S content of organic matter.** Mineralization of S depends on the S content of the decomposing material, smaller amounts of SO_4^{2-} are liberated from low S containing residue.
2. **Source of mineralizable sulphur.** Most of the available S removed by plants from the SO_4^{2-} fraction of labile S in soil Organic matter.
3. **Soil Temperature.** Mineralization of S is impeded @ 10°C increases with increasing temperature from 20°C to 40°C and decreases of temperature >40°C.
4. **Soil moisture.** Mineralization occurs in optimum moisture conditions.
5. **Soil pH.** S released is directly proportional to pH up to pH 7.5. Above 7.5 mineralization increases more rapidly.
6. **Absence or presence of plants.** Soils mineralization more S in the presence of growing plants than in their absence.
7. **Time and cultivation**
8. **S Volatilization.** Volatile S compounds are produced through microbial transformations under both aerobic and anaerobic conditions. The volatile compounds are **dimethyl sulfide (CH_3 SCH_3) (CS_2) Carbandi sulphide and mercaptons (CH_3SH).**

In low organic matter soils, S volatilization is negligible and increases with increasing organic matter content.

Practical aspects of S transformations.

1. Crops grown on coarse texture soils are generally more susceptible to S deficiency because these soils having low organic matter content and SO_4^{2-} leaching.
2. Leaching losses of SO_4^{2-} can occur highly on coarse texture soils under high rainfall. Under such conditions, SO_4^{2-} containing fertilizers maybe applied more frequently
3. **Immobilization** of added S can occur in soils having a high. **C/S or N/S ratio.** S mineralisation is favored in soils with a low C/S or N/S ratio. S availability generally increases with organic matter content.
4. Actual amount of S needed will depend on the balance between all soil additions of S by precipitation, air, irrigation H_2O, crop residues fertilizers, Agriculture Chemicals and all losses through crop removal. Leaching and erosion.

IRON

Fe is absorbed by plants roots as Fe^{2+}, Fe^{3+} and chelected irons. Sufficiency range of Fe in plant tissue is 50-250 ppm.

Functions of Iron

1. It helps in the synthesis of chlorophyll.
2. Structural component of porphyrin molecules like cytochromes, hematin, hemes, ferrichrome and hemoglobin. These substance are involved in oxidation-reduction reactors in respiration and photosynthesis.
3. Structural component of non hemine compounds like ferredoxins.
4. Constituent of enzyme systems Egl cytochrome oxidase, catalase, nitrogenase reaction in plants.
5. Component of flavoprotein like FMN = Flavin mono nucleotides
   FAD = Flavin Adinosine Dinudeotide.

Sources of iron

- Earth crust contains about 5%
- Primary and secondary minerals such as 1. Olivene, 2. Pyrite 3. Hematite, 4. Goethite, 5. Magrulite 6. Limestone

Forms of iron

Fe occurs in *Four* major forms in soil.

1. Primary and secondary minerals Fe
2. Adsorbed Fe
3. Organic Fe and
4. Solution Fe.

Soil solution Fe

It occurs primarily as $Fe(OH)^{+}_{2}$, Fe^{3+} concentration In solution is very low. In well-drained, oxidized soils, the solution Fe^{2+} concentration is less than that of the dominant Fe^{3+} in solution. The pH dependent relationship for Fe^{3+} is described as

$$Fe(OH)_3 \text{ (Soil)} + 3H^+ \longleftrightarrow Fe^{3+} + 3H_2O$$

For every increases in pH, Fe^{3+} concentration decreases 1000 fold. Oxidation - redn reactions, the result of change in O_2 partial pressure, exert considerable influence on the amount of soluble Fe in the soil solution. The insoluble Fe^{3+} form predominates in well drained soils, while levels of soluble Fe^{2+} increases significantly when soils become H_2O logged. In general, lowering Redox increases Fe^{2+} solubility, 10 fold for each unit decreases. in pH.

Over the normal pH range in soils, total solution Fe is not sufficient to meet plant requirements for Fe even in acid soils, where Fe deficiency Occur less frequently than in high pH and caleanous soils.

Schematic representation of Fe, Zn, Cu and Mn cycle

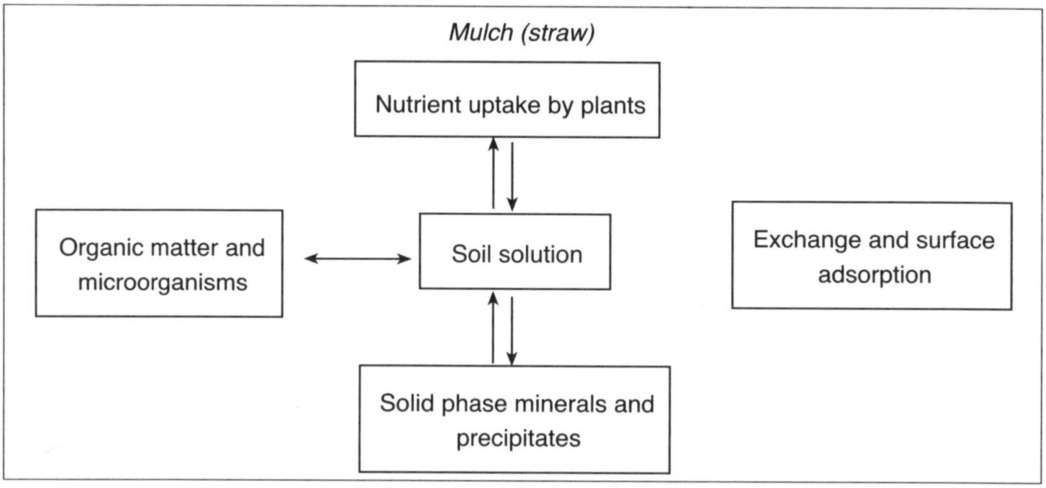

Chelates: "Is a term derived from a Greek and meaning "Claw".

Chelates are soluble organic compounds that bond with metals such as Fe, Zn, Cu and Mn increasing their solubility and their supply to plant roots.

"Natural organic cheleates in soils are products of microbial activity and degradation of soil organic matter and plant residues. Root exudates are capable complexing nutrients substantial quantities of organic completed. Fe can be cycled through crop residue and compounds of citric acid and oxalic acids have chelating properties.

Dynamics of chelation

"The dynamics of chelation increasing solubility and transport of micronutrients".

During active plant uptake, the concentration of chelated Fe or other micronutrient is grater in the bulk solution than at root surface the chelated Fe diffuses to the root surface in response to concentration gradient. After Fe^{3+} dissociates from the chelates and diffused due to concentration gradient. As the unchelated Fe^{3+} concentration decreases insolution because of chelation, additional Fe is desorbed from minerals surfaces or Fe minerals dissolved to resupply solution Fe.

Synthetic chelates

In soils synthetic chelates behave similarly to natural organic chelates. The choice of a chelate to use as chelate depends 1. specific micronutrient ii. Solubility of chelate in the soil. When synthetic or natural chelates are added to soils and they are readily complex with cations in soil solution.

Egl : Citric acid and Oxalic acids, two natural chelates complex Al^{3+} at low pH, but when pH increasess above 5 or 6, Ca^{2+} and Mg^{2+} are more readily completed.

Diethylene triamine penta acetic acid (DTPA) and EDTA (Ethylene diamine tetra acetic acid) readily chelate Fe at pH < 7 and pH <6.5 respects. The chelate EDDHA (Ethylene Diamine dihydroxy phenyl acetic acid) will strongly complex Fe and is stable over the entire pH range. As a result Fe EDDHA is commonly used as an Fe fertilizer because it provides more plant available Fe than other chelates.

Factors affecting Fe availability

1. Soil pH, Bicarbanate and Carbonates. Fe deficiency is most often observed in high pH and calcareous soils in arid regions, but it may occur an acid soils that are very low in total Fe.

Irrigation waters and soil high in HCO_3 may aggravate Fe deficiency Because of high pH levels associated with HCO_3^- accumulation.

In calcarious soils having pH range of 7.3 to 8.5 have Fe deficiency due to the lowest solubility of soil Fe and the formation of bicarbonate ion.

$$CaCO_3 + CO_2 + H_2O \text{ --\_ } Ca^{2+} + 2HCO_3^-$$

2. Excessive H_2O and poor aeration. Flooding and submergence of soils can improve Fe availability by increaseeasing Fe^{2+} canc. They actually buildup of toxic canc. of Fe^{2+} organic matter removed from the eroded portions of semi arid region calcareous net soils lime induced Fe deficiency will occur.

3. Organic matter. Additions of organic matter to well drained soils can improve Fe avail. Due to increases the Fe^{2+} solubility.

4. Interactions with other nutrients. Fe deficiency occur due to the accumulation of Cu, Mn, Zn, Mo and P. Fe availability decreasess when the soils are having more NO_3^- than NH_4^+ deficiency of K or Zn can reduce Fe translocation with in plants.

MANGANESE

Mn concentration in plant ranges from 20 to 500 ppm

Functions of Mn

1. Helps in chlorophyll formation
2. Involves in photosynthesis, particularly in evolution of O_2.
3. Involves in oxidation - reduction - process in decarboxylation and hydrolysis reactions.
4. Involves in enzyme systems and various enzyme reactions in the citric acid cycle.

5. It is a substitute for Mg^{2+} in many of the phosphorylating and group transfer reactions.

Sources of Mn

Earth crust contains 1000 ppm. Various oxides and hydroxides. Manganite MnO (OH) Braunite Mn_2O_3

Factors affecting Mn availability

1. **Soil pH and carbonates.** Liming to acid soils decreases solution and exch. Mn^{2+} due to precipitation Mn^{2+} as MnO_2.
2. **Excessive H_2O and poor aeration.** H_2O logging will reduce O_2 and lower redox potential will increases soluble Mn^{2+}. Poor aeration increases Mn availability.
3. **Organic matter.** Increases solution and exchangeable Mn.
4. **Climatic factor.** Increases soil temp during the growing season improves Mn uptake, because of greater plant growth and root activity.
5. **Soil microorganism.** Deficiency caused by soil organisms oxidizing Mn^{2+} to Mn^{4+}.

Forms of Mn

(*i*) Solution Mn^{2+}
(*ii*) Exchange Mn^{2+}
(*iii*) Organic bound Mn
(*iv*) Mn Mineral

ZINC

Normal concentration in plant 25 to 150 ppm Deficiency level is < 20 ppm Toxic level is > 400 ppm, Zn is present in all parts of the plants. In general root contain more zinc than fruits.

Cereals	: 27.8 ppm
Pulses	: 34.8 ppm
Vegetables	: 28.2 ppm
Fruits	: 36.6 ppm

Functions of Zn

- Essential to formation of growth harmones
- Helps in reproduction of certain plants.
- Stabilise rhibosomal fractions
- Influence the activity of dehydrogenase enzymes
- Involves in auxin metabolism like tryptophan synthetase.

Sources of zinc

Soil	: 10-300 ppm
Igneous rock	: >10 ppm
Sedimentary	: > 95 ppm

Forms of soil Zn

1. Solution Zn^{2+}
2. Adsorbed Zn^{2+}
3. Organically completed Zn^{2+}

Factors affecting Zn availability

1. Soil pH : Avail of Zn decrease with increase soil pH Zn def occur in neutral and calcareous soil. At soil pH, Zn precipitates as insoluble amorphous soil Zn, which reduces Zn^{2+} in soil.

   *Al and Fe oxides, OM and $CaCO_3$ increase with increasing pH.
2. Organic matter
3. Interaction with other nutrients

   *SO_4 and N can increase the Zn uptake in plants.

   *Higher the soil pH, poor aeration greater the Zn deficiency

COPPER

Copper is absorbed by plants as cupric ion Cu^{2+} Normal concentration in plants 5-20 ppm.

Functions of copper

1. Essential for the synthesis of vitamin A
2. Act as a catalyst in respiration
3. Act as a "electron carrier" in enzyme which bring about oxidation reduction reactions in plants.
4. Constituent of chlorophyll.

Sources of copper

1. Igneous rock 10-100 ppm of Cu.
2. Sedimentary rock 4-45 ppm
3. Primary minerals contains
   (*i*) Chalcopyrite
   (*ii*) Chalcocite
   (*iii*) Bornite
4. Sedimentary minerals Oxides, Carbonates, Silicates, Sulphates and Chlorides.

Forms of soil copper

1. Soil solution - ionic and completed
2. Cation exchange sites of clay and organic matter
3. Occluded and co-precipitated in soil oxide material
4. Specific adsorption sites
5. Inorganic matter and living organisms.

Factors affecting Cu availability

1. Soil texture
2. pH
3. CEC
4. Organic matter content
5. Hydrous oxides

Soil texture

Sandy soils contain lower amounts of Cu than silt and clay soils.

pH

The concentration of Cu in soil solution decreases with increase in pH.

Interaction with other nutrients

Application of NPK fertilizer induce Cu deficiency Increase N supply to crops reduce mobility of Cu in plants

High concentration of Zn, Fe and P in soil solution also can depress Cu absorption by plant roots.

BORON

B concentration in mono cotyledons and dicotyledons (20-60 ppm) varies between 6 and 18 ppm. It is absorbed by plants as undissociated boric acid (H_3BO_3).

Functions of boron

1. New cell development in meristematic tissue.
2. Pollination, fruit / seed set.
3. Translocation of sugars, starches, N and P
4. Synthesis of proteins and amino acids.
5. Nodule formation in legumes
6. Regulation of CHO metabolism.

Sources of boron

1. Non metal among the micronutrient
2. Low concentration in earth crust igneous rocks (<10 ppm)
3. Tourmaline and borosilicate contains B.

Forms of boron (Boron cycle)

B exists in 4 forms in soil.

1. Rocks and minerals.
2. Adsorbed on clay surface, Fe and Al oxides combined with O.M.
3. Boric acid (H_3BO_3) and $4B(OH)^-_4$ in soil solution.

Boron cycling between the solid and solution phase is very important because of the narrow range in solution concentration the separates deficiency and toxicity in crops.

Soil solution B

H_3BO_3 is the predominant species in soil solution at pH values ranging from 5-9. At pH > 9.2 $H_3BO_3^-$ can hydrolyse to $H_4BO_4^-$. It was taken by Massflow and Diffusion methods in plants.

Absorbed B

B adsorption and desorption can helps to reduce B leaching losses. Main B adsorption sites are

1. Broken Si - O and Al-O- bonds at the edge of clay min.
2. Amorphous hydroxide structure
3. Al and Fe oxides and hydroxides.

Factors affecting B availability

1. Soil texture : Fine text soils added B for longer period than coarse text soil. Plants can take up larger quantity of B from sandy soils than fine text soil at equal concentration of H_2O soluble B.
2. Type of clay : Mica > mont > kaolinite
3. Soil pH and liming : Less avail to plants with increase pH heavy liming lead to greater adsorption and reduced B uptake.
4. Organic matter : Available of B in surface soil is high compared to subsurface soil.
5. Interactions with other cations Occurrence of Ca in alkaline soil with restrict B availability. Increased K rates causes B toxicity.
6. Soil moisture

Restricted moist supply reduce the B availability in the root zone.

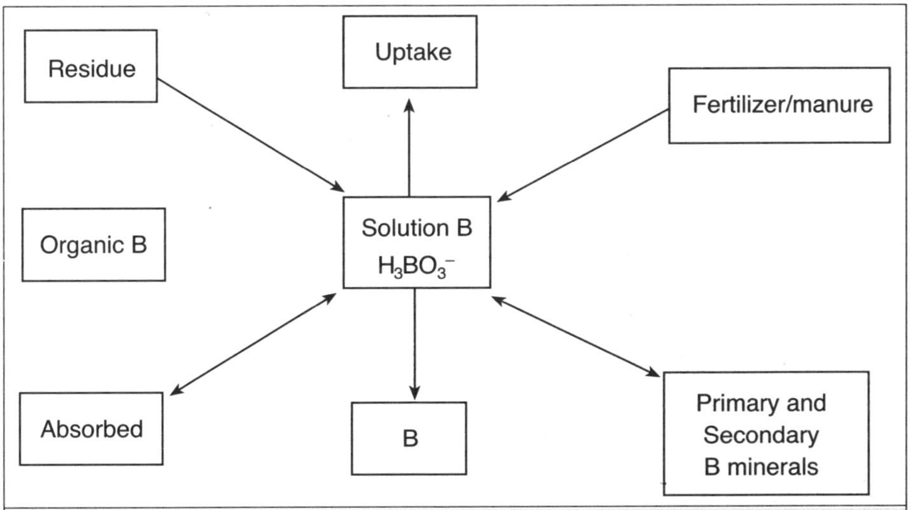

Boron cycle in soil Mulch (straw)

MOLYBDENUM

Non metal anion absorbed as molybdate (MoO_4). It is weak acid and form complex poly anions such as phosphomdybdate. Plant contains <1 ppm Mo.

Functions of Mo

1. Essential component of enzyme NO3 reductase, which catalyses NO_3^- to NO_2^-.
2. Structural component of nitrogenase enzyme - involved in N fixation.
3. Essential for absorption and translocation of Fe in plant 6.

Sources of Mo

Earth crust 2 ppm : and range from 0.2 to 5 ppm.

Forms of Mo

1. Non exchangeable Mo in primary and secondary minerals.
2. Exchangeable Mo held by Fe and Al oxides.
3. Mo in soil solution
4. Organically bound Mo.

Mo in solution occurs mainly as $Mo_4^{=}$, $HMoO_4^-$, H_2MoO_4.

Factors affecting Mo availability

1. Soil pH and liming. Mo availability increases with increasing pH. Liming to correct acidity will increase Mo avail. Mo avail decrease with application of acid forming fertilizer $(NH_4)_2SO_4$.

2. Reaction with Fe and Al. Strongly absorbed by Fe and Al oxides.

3. Interaction with other nutrients

- Mg and P enhances Mo absorption by plants. High level SO_4 decrease Mo absorption by plants. Cu and Mn decrease Mo uptake by plants.
- NO_3^-N encourages Mo uptake NH_4^-N reduces Mo uptake
- The beneficial effect of NO_3^- nutrition is related to the release of OH ions.

CHLORINE

Normal concentration in plant is about 0.2-2.0%. Absorbed by plants as Cl^- through roots and aerial parts.

Functions of chloride

1. Essential for biochemical reactions Osmotic cation neutralization reactors.
2. Act as a counter ion during rapid K fluxes.
3. Involves in the evaluation of O_2 in photosynthesis.
4. Creates disease resistant by increase osmotic pressure in cell sap.

Sources of Cl

(*i*) Igneous and metamorphic rocks

(*ii*) Soluble salts such as NaCl, $CaCl_2$ and $Mgel_2$.

(*iii*) Earth crust 0.02-0.05%.

It is mobile within the plant it can be rapidly recycled through soil systems.

COBALT

Normal concentration of Co in dry matter - 0.02 - 0.5 ppm.

Functions of cobalt

1. Essential for M.O. fixing atmosphere. N. It forms vit. B12 during growth and development of symbiotic M.O.
2. Improves growth, transpiration and photosynthesis.
3. Take parts in leg hemoglobin metabolism and Rhibonucliotide reductase.

Factors affecting: Co availability

1. Soil pH : Avail increase with increase in soil acidity, H_2O logging conditions.
2. Liming and drainage practices - reduce co availability.
3. Application $CoSO_4$ rectify the deficiency.

VANADIUM

Low concentration of Vanadium is beneficial for growth of Microorganisms. Vanadium substitute for Mo in N fixation by Rhizobia. Involves in Biological - oxidation-reduction reactions.

NICKEL

Nickel content in plant is 0.1 - 1.0 ppm dry matter basis. Taken by plant as Ni^{2+} High levels of Ni may induce Zn or Fe deficiency

1. Ni - metal component of urease that catalyse reaction.
   $CO(NH_2)_2 + H_2O$ _ $2NH_3 + CO_2$.
2. Essential for N metabolism.
3. Stimulates nodule weight and yield of crops.

SODIUM

Functions

1. Essential for maintaining turgor and growth of Plants.
2. Helps oxalic acid accumulation in Plants.
3. Helps in stomatal opening and regulate NO_3^- reductase activity.

Sources of Na

Earth crust 2.8% soils Minerals.

Forms of Na in soil

Solution, exchangeable Na and in silicate minerals.

In arid and semi arid soils Na exist in silicates, NaCl, Na_2SO_4

Na salts accumulating in poorly drained soils of arid and semi arid regions and causes soil salinity and sodicity.

Effect of Na on soil properties

Dispersing action of Na^+ on clay and organic matter reduces soil aggregation, permeability to air and H_2O, germination and root growth.

Sodium fertilizers

Sodium NO_3 : 25% Na Rhenania PO_4 12% NA

Abundant element in lithosphere and absorbed as monosilicic acid. Cereals and grass contain 0.2 - 2.0%.

SILICAN (SILICA)

Functions of silica

1. Contributes structure of cell wall.
2. Contributes drought tolerance to crops.
3. Regulates photosynthesis.
4. Deactivates invertase enzyme activity in sugarcane resulting grater sucrose production.
5. Larger amounts of Si are accumulated in intracellular deposits known as 'PLANT OPALS'.
6. Increased available P.
7. Responsible for plant disease resistance.

Sources of silicon

- Earth crust : 27.6% Most abundant element in earth crust. Soils 23-35%
- Primary and secondary mineral and quartz - major source.
- Quartz is the most common mineral in soil, comprising 90-95% of all sand and silt fractions.

Factors affecting Si availability

1. High H_2O content encourages Si uptake
2. Heavy application of N decreases Si concentration
3. Liming decreases Si uptake in plants.
4. Acidification increases Si uptake
5. Fe and Al oxides influence Uptake of Si by plants.

Si fertilizers

1. Calcium silicate slag ($CaAl_2\ Si_2O_4$) - 18.21% Si
2. Calcium silicate ($CaSiO_3$) - 31% Si.
3. Sodium metasilicate $NaSiO_3$ - 23% Si.

CHELATES

Chelate is a term derived from a Greek word meaning, "claw". Chelates are soluble organic compounds that bond with **metals ions** such as Fe^{3+}/Fe^{2+}, Zn^{2+}, Cu^{2+}, Mn^{2+}, and other, thereby *increasing their solubility and supply to plant roots*. It is important particularly in micronutrient availability.

Numerous natural organic compounds in soil, or synthetic compounds added to soils, are able to complex or chelate ions of micronutrients.

Natural organic chelates in soils are products of microbial activity and degradation of soil organic matter and plant residues. Root exudates also are capable of complexing micronutrients.

The concentration of metal ions in solution and the quantity transported to the root by mass flow and diffusion can be greatly increased through complexation with natural organic chelating compounds in soil.

Substantial quantities of organic-complexed metal ions can be cycled through crop residue, which remain available for the succeeding crop.

Many of the natural organic chelates have not been identified; however, compounds like citric and oxalic acids have chelating properties.

Common synthetic chelates are:

Ethylene diamine tetra acetic acid (EDTA) Diethylene triamine pentaacetic acid (DTPA)

Ethylene diamine di-o-hydroxy phenyl acetic acid (EDDHA)

❑❑❑

CHAPTER 21

Manure and Fertilizer

ORGANIC MANURES

The manures are organic in nature, plant or animal origin and contain organic mater in large proportion and plant nutrients in small quantities and used to improve soil productivity by correcting soil physical, chemical and biological properties.

Difference between manures and fertilizers

Manure	*Fertilizer*
1. Contains O.M. and hence improves soil physical properties	1. Do not contain O.M. and can not improve soil physical properties
2. Improves soil fertility as well as productivity	2. Improves soil fertility
3. Contains all plant nutrients, but small in concentration	3. Contains one or more plant, but in higher concentration
4. Required in large quantity bulky and costly	4. Required in less quantity concentrated and cheaper
5. Nutrients are slowly available upon decomposition	5. Nutrients are readily available.
6. Long lasting effect on soil and crop	6. Very less residual effect
7. No salt effect	7. Salt effect is high
8. No adverse effect	8. Adverse effects are observed when not applied in time and in proper proportion.

Bulky Organic Manures

Bulky organic manures include farm yard manure (FYM) or farm manure, farm compost, town compost, night soil, sludge, green manures and other bulky sources of organic matter. All these manures are bulky in nature and supply; (*i*) plant nutrients in small quantities and (*ii*) organic matter in large quantities; of the various bulky organic manures, farm yard manure, compost and green manure are most important and most widely used.

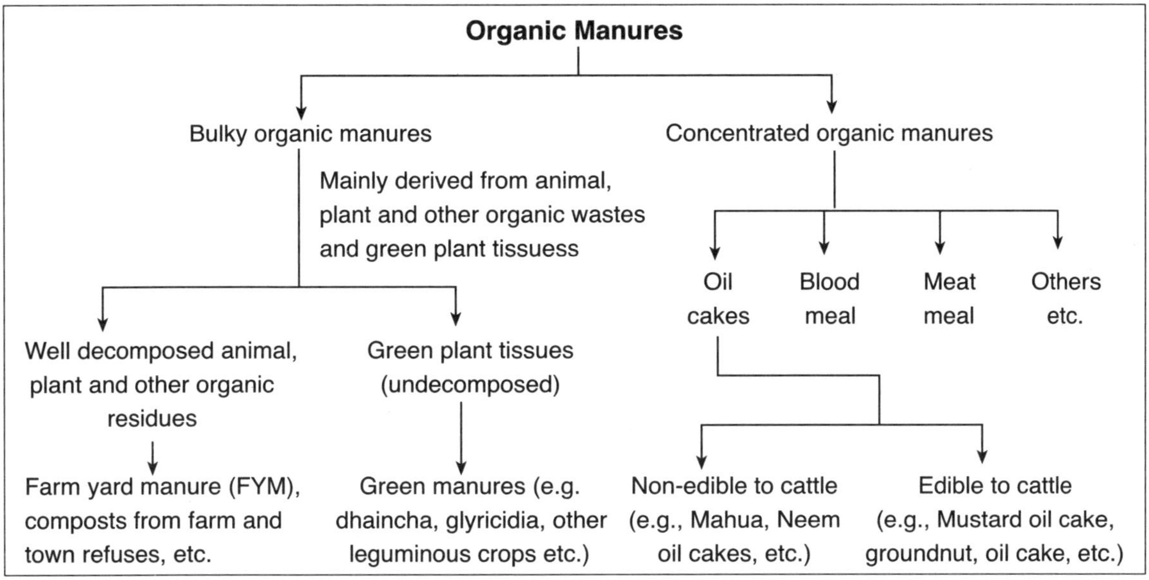

Effect of bulky organic manures on soil

(*i*) Direct effect on plant growth

(*ii*) Increase organic matter content and improve physical properties of soil. Increase humus content of soil and consequently WHC of sandy soil is increased and the drainage of clayey soil is improved.

(*iii*) Provide food for soil microorganisms. This increases activity of microbes which in turn helps in converting unavailable plant nutrients into available forms.

Farm Yard Manure (FYM)

It refers to the decomposed mixture of dung and urine of farm animals along with litter (bedding material) and left over material from roughages or fodder fed to the cattle. On an average well rotted FYM contains 0.5% N, 0.2% P_2O_5 and 0.5% K_2O.

TABLE 21.1. Average percentage of N, P_2O_5 and K_2O in the fresh excreta of farm animals

Excreta of		*Percentage of*		
		N	*P_2O_5*	*K_2O*
Cows and bullocks	Dung	0.40	0.20	0.10
	Urine	1.00	Traces	1.35
Sheep and goat	Dung	0.75	0.50	045
	Urine	1.35	0.05	2.10
Buffalo	Dung	0.26	0.18	0.17
	Urine	0.62	Traces	1.61
Poultry	—	1.46	1.17	0.62

FYM is one of the most important agricultural by products. Unfortunately, however nearly 50 per cent of the cattle dung production in India today is utilized as fuel and is thus lost to agriculture.

(*i*) Poultry manure is the richest of all

(*ii*) Urine of all animals contains more percentage of N and K_2O compared to the dung portion.

Factors Affecting Nutritional Build up of FYM

The following factors affect the composition of FYM :

1. Age of animal. Growing animals and cows producing milk retain in their system nitrogen and phosphorus required for productive purposes like making growth and producing milk and the excreta do not contain all the ingredients of plant food given in the feed. Old animals on the downgrade waste their body tissues and excrete more than what they do ingest.

2. Feed. When the feed is rich in plant food ingredients, the excreta produced is correspondingly enriched.

3. Nature of litter used. Cereal straw and leguminous plant refuse used as litter enriched the manure with nitrogen.

4. Ageing of manure. The manure gets richer and less bulky with ageing.

5. Manner of making and storage. In making and storage losses are in various ways.

Losses during Handling and Storage of FYM

(*a*) Losses during handling. FYM consists of two original components the solid or dung and liquid or urine. Both the components contain N, P_2O_5 and K_2O the distribution of these nutrients in the dung and urine is shown in figure below:

Approximately half of N and K_2O in the dung and the other half in urine. By contrast, nearly all of the P_2O_5 (96%) is in the solid portion. To conserve N, P_2O_5 and K_2O, it is most essential that both the parts of cattle manure are properly handled and stored.

(i) Loss of liquid portion or urine. Under Indian conditions the floor of the cattle shed is usually uncemented or Kachha. As such the urine passed by animals during night gets soaked into the Kachha floor. When the animals, particularly bullocks, are kept in the fields during the summer season, urine gets soaked into soil. But during remaining period cattles are kept in a covered shed and therefore the Kachha floor soaks the urine every day. Large quantities of nitrogen are thus lost through the formation of gaseous NH_3. The following reactions take place :

$$\underset{\text{Urea in urine}}{NH_2CONH_2 + 2H_2O} \longrightarrow \underset{\text{Ammonium carbonate}}{(NH_4)_2CO_3}$$

$$(NH_4)_2CO_3 + 2H_2O \longrightarrow 2NH_4OH + H_2CO_3$$

$$NH_4OH \longrightarrow \underset{\text{Gaseous Ammonia}}{NH_3\uparrow} + H_2O$$

The smell of NH_3 in the cattle shed clearly indicates the loss of N. No special efforts are made in India to collect the liquid portion of the manure.

(ii) Loss of solid portion or dung. It is often said that 2/3 of the manure is either utilized for making cakes or is lost during grazing, the remaining manure is applied to the soil after collecting in heaps. Firstly, the most serious loss of dung is through cakes for burning or for use as fuel-Secondly, when milk animals go out for grazing, no efforts are made to collect the dung dropped by them, nor is this practicable, unless all mulch animals are allowed to graze only in enclosed small size pastures.

(*b*) Loss during storage. Mostly, cattle dung and waste from fodder are collected daily in the morning by the cultivators and put in manure heaps in an open space outside the village. The manure remains exposed to the sun and rain. During such type of storage, nutrients are lost in the following ways:

(i) By leaching. Losses by leaching will vary with the intensity of rainfall and the slope of land on which manure is heaped. About half of portion of N and P_2O_5 of FYM and nearly 90% of K are water soluble. These water soluble nutrients are liable to get washed off by rain water.

(ii) By Volatilization. During storage considerable amount of NH_3 is produced in the manure heap from

(*i*) the decomposition of urea and other nitrogenous compounds of the urine and

(*ii*) the much slower decomposition of the nitrogenous organic compounds of the dung. As the rotting proceeds, more and more quantity of ammonia is formed. This NH_3 combines with carbonic acid to form ammonium carbonate and bicarbonate. These ammonium compounds are unstable and gaseous NH_3 may be liberated as indicated below :

1. Urea and other nitrogenous compounds in urine and dung $\xrightarrow[\text{decomposition}]{\text{microbial}} NH_3\uparrow$
2. $2NH_3 + H_2CO_3 \longrightarrow (NH_4)_2\,CO_3$
3. $(NH_4)_2\,CO_3 + 2H_2O \longrightarrow 2NH_4\,OH + H_2CO_3$
4. $NH_4OH \longrightarrow NH_3 + H_2O$

Loss of NH_3 increases with

(*i*) the increase in the concentration of ammonium carbonate

(*ii*) increase in the temperature and

(*iii*) air movement

Improved Methods of Handling FYM

It is practically impossible to check completely the losses of plant nutrients and organic matter during handing and storage of FYM. However, improved methods could be adopted to reduce such losses considerably.

Among these methods are described here under :

(*i*) Trench method of preparing FYM

(*ii*) Use of gobar gas-compost plant

(*iii*) Proper field management of FYM

(*iv*) Use of chemical preservatives

(*i*) Use of gobar gas compost plant

Methane gas is generated due to anaerobic fermentation of the most common organic materials such as cattle dung, grass, vegetable waste and human excreta. Gobar gas and manure both are useful on farms as well as in homes. A few advantages of this method are give below :

(1) The methane gas generated can be used for heating, lighting and motive power.

(2) The methane gas can be used for running oil engines and generators

(3) The manure which comes out from the plant after decomposition is quite rich in nutrients. N-1.5%, P_2O_5-0.5%, K_2O-2.0%

(4) Gobar gas manure is extremely cheap and is made by locally available materials.

TABLE 21.2. Superiority of gobar gas compost plant over traditional method

	1000 Kg fresh dung manure obtained by	
	Traditional method	*Gobar gas plant*
1. Loss of OM	500 Kg	270 Kg
2. Loss of N	1.25 Kg	Nil
3. Final manure	500 Kg	730 Kg
4. % N	0.5%	1.5%
5. Additional advantage	—	2000 Cu.ft. gas for cooking

(*ii*) Proper field management of FYM

Under field conditions, most of the cultivators unload FYM in small piles in the field before spreading. The manure is left in piles for a month or more before it is spread. Plant nutrients are lost through heating and drying. To derive maximum benefit from FYM, it is most essential that it should not be kept in small piles in the field before spreading, but it should be spread evenly and mixed with the soil immediately.

(*iii*) Use of Chemical Preservatives

Chemical preservatives are added to the FYM to decrease N losses. To be most effective, the preservatives are applied in the cattle yard to permit direct contact with the liquid portion of excreta or urine. This has to be done because the loss of N from urine starts immediately. The commonly used chemical preservatives are (*i*) Gypsum and (*ii*) Super phosphate.

The value of gypsum in preserving the N of manure has been known and it has been used for many years in foreign countries. The reaction of gypsum with ammonium carbonate (intermediate product from decomposition of urea present in urine) is :

$$(NH_4)_2 CO_3 + CaSO_4 \longrightarrow CaCO_3 + (NH_4)_2 SO_4$$

As long as the manure is moist, no loss of NH_3 will occur, but if the manure becomes dry, the chemical reaction is reversed and the loss of NH_3 may occur. As such, under Indian conditions, use of gypsum to decrease N losses, does not offer a practical solution.

Superphosphate has been extensively used as a manure preservative :

$$2CaSO_4 + Ca (H_2PO_4)_2 + 2(NH_4)_2 CO_3 \longrightarrow Ca_3 (PO_4)_2 + 2(NH_4)_2 SO_4 + 2H_2O + 2CO_2$$

In this reaction, tricalcium phosphate is formed which does not react with ammonium sulphate, when manure becomes dry. As such, there is no loss of NH_3. Since FYM becomes dry due to high temperature under Indian conditions, the use of superphosphate will be safely recommended as a preservative to decrease N losses.

Use of superphosphate as a chemical preservative will have three advantages

1. It will reduce loss of N as ammonium from FYM.
2. It will increase the percentage of P in manure thus making it a balanced one.
3. Since, tricalcium phosphate produced with the application of superphosphate to the FYM is in inorganic form, which is readily available to the plants; it will increase the efficiency of phosphorus.

It is recommended that one or two pounds of SSP should be applied per day per animal in the cattle shed where animal pass urine.

Supply of plant nutrients through FYM

On an average, FYM applied to various crops by the cultivators contains the following nutrients :

% N : 0.5 % P_2O_5 : 0.2 % K_2O : 0.5

Based on this analysis, an average dressing of 10 tonnes of FYM supplies about

50 Kg N 20 Kg P_2O_5 50 Kg K_2O

All of these quantities are not available to crops in the year of application, particularly N which is very slow acting. Only 1/3 of the N is likely to be useful to crops in the first year. About 2/3 of the phosphate may be effective and most of the potash will be available. This effect of FYM application on the yield of first crop is known as the direct effect of application. The remaining amount of plant food becomes available to the second, third and to a small extent to the fourth crop raised on the same piece of land. This phenomenon is known as the residual effect of FYM.

When FYM is applied every year, the crop yield goes on increasing due to direct plus residual effect on every succeeding crop. The beneficial effect is also known as cumulative effect.

COMPOST

Composting is largely a bio-chemical process in which microorganisms both aerobic and anaerobic decompose organic residue and lower the C : N ratio. The final product of composting is well rotted manure known as compost.

Rural compost

Compost from farm litters, weeds, straw, leaves, husk, crop stubble, bhusa or straw, litter from cattle shed and waste fodder, etc. is called rural compost.

Urban compost

Compost from town refuse, night soil and street dustbin refuse, etc is called urban compost.

Composition of town compost

Nitrogen (%N)	Phosphorus (%P_2O_5)	Potassium (%K_2O)
1.4	1.0	1.4

Compared to FYM, town compost prepared from Katchara and night soil is richer in fertilizer value.

Mechanical Composting Plants

Mechanical composting plants with capacities of 500-1000 tonnes per day of city garbage could be installed in big cities in India and 250 tonnes per day plants in the small towns. Refined mechanical compost contains generally about 40% mineral matter and 40% organic materials with organic carbon around 15%. The composition would vary depending on the feed but typically the nutrient content is about 0.7% N, 0.5% P_2O_5 and 0.4% K_2O. There are trace elements like Mn, B. Zn and Cu and the material has C : N ratio of nearly 15-17.

Decomposition

The animal excreta and litter are not suitable for direct use as manure, as most of its manurial ingredients are present in an unavailable form. However urine, if collected separately, can be used directly. The dung and litter have to be fermented or decomposed before they become fit for use. Hence, the material is usually stored in heaps or pits, where it is allowed to decompose. Under suitable conditions of water supply, air, temperature, food supply and reaction, the microorganisms decompose the material. The decomposition is partly aerobic and partly anaerobic. During decomposition the usual yellow or green colour of the litter is changed to brown and ultimately to dark brown or black colour; its structural form is converted into a colloidal, slimy more or less homogenous material, commonly known as humus. Well decomposed manure has a typical black colour and a loose friable condition. It does not show the presence of the original litter or dung.

Factors controlling process of decomposition

(1) Food supply to micro-organisms and C : N ratio. The suitable ratio of carbonaceous to nitrogenous materials is 40, if it is wider than this, the decomposition takes place very slowly and when narrow it is quick. C : N ratio of the dung of farm animals varies from 20 to 25, urine 1 to 2, poultry manure 5-10, litters cereals straw 50, and legume refuse 20.

(2) Moisture. About 60-70 per cent moisture is considered to be the optimum requirement to start decomposition and with the advance in decomposition, it diminishes gradually being 30-40 per cent in the final product.

Excess of moisture prevents the temperature form rising high and retards decomposition, resulting in loss of a part of the soluble plant nutrients through leaching and drainage. Hence, in regions receiving heavy rainfall, it is advisable to store the manure or prepare compost in heaps above ground level.

(3) Aeration. Most of the microbial processes are oxidative and hence a free supply of oxygen is necessary.

Reasons for poor aeration in pit/heap

(*i*) Excessive watering

(*ii*) Compaction

(*iii*) Use of large quantities of fine and green material as litters

(*iv*) High and big heaps or deep pits.

(4) Temperature. Under the optimum conditions of air moisture and food supply, there is a rapid increase in the temperature in the manure heap or pit. The temperature usually rises to 50°–60°C and even to 70°C. The high temperature destroys weed seeds, worms, pathogenic bacteria, etc; which prevents fly breeding and makes the manure safe from hygeinic point of view.

(5) Reaction. The microorganisms liberate certain organic acids during the course of decomposition, which, if allowed to accumulate, retards fermentation and some time even stop it completely. Hence, it is necessary to control the reaction of the material.

A neutral or slightly alkaline reaction between pH 7.0 and 7.5 is considered the most suitable. The addition of alkaline substances like lime and wood ashes neutralized the excess acidity. Since in the preparation of FYM it is a common practice to add household ashes to the manure pit, it is not necessary to add additional alkaline substances.

Heap V/S Pit decomposition

Heap	*Pit*
1. Aerobic	1. Anaerobic
2. Turning is required	2. No turning is required
3. Physical disintegration	3. Very little physical disintegration
4. Quick oxidation	4. Slow rate of decomposition
5. High temp. 60°-70°C. Kill weed seeds and pathogenic organisms	5. High temp. is not developed but weed seeds and micro-organism destroyed due to toxic products of decomposition.
6. Loss of OM is about 50%	6. Loss is about 25%
7. If not properly protected, moisture loss is high. Watering is necessary	7. Moisture loss is minimized. No watering is necessary
8. If rainfall is high, leaching takes place	8. Protected form leaching but anaerobic condition occurs.

Night Soil

Night soil is human excrement *i.e.* solid and liquid.

Night soil is richer in N, P_2O_5 and K_2O as compared to FYM or compost. On oven dry basis, it has an average chemical composition of:

N%	P_2O_5%	K_2O%
5.5.	4.0	2.0

In India it is applied to a limited extent directly to the soil. Pits or trenches of 10 to 12 ft. long, 2 to 3 ft. wide and 9 inches to 1 foot deep are made. In these pits, night soil is deposited and covered over on top with layers of earth or Katchara. This is known as the Poudrette

System. Since the material formed in the above trenches after they become dry, is known as **poudrette.**

Improved methods of handling night soil

Since night soil is important bulky organic manure, supplying a good deal of organic matter and plant nutrients to the soil, it is important that night soil is used by the following improved methods :

1. Night soil should be protected from flies and fly breeding should be controlled.
2. It should be stored in such a way that it does not pollute the supply of drinking water.
3. Pathogens, protozoa, cysts, worms and eggs should be destroyed before the night soil is applied to the land.
4. Attempts should be made to compost the night soil with other refuse in urban centers by municipal or town authorities and in rural areas by the farmer himself.

Sewage and Sludge

In the modern system of sanitation adopted in cities, water is used for the removal of human excreta and other wastes. This is called the sewage system of sanitation. In this system, there is a considerable dilution of the material in solution and in dispersion in fact, water is the main constituent of sewage, amounting often to 99.0%.

In general sewage has two components, namely

(*i*) Solid portion, technically known as sludge and

(*ii*) Liquid portion, commonly known as sewage water.

Both the components are used in increasing crop production as they contain plant nutrients. Both components of sewage as separated and are given a preliminary fermentation and oxidation treatments to reduce the bacterial contamination, the offensive smell and also to narrow down the C : N ratio of the solid portion.

(*i*) Sludges. In the modern system of sewage utilization, solid portion or sludge is separated out to a considerable extent and given a preliminary treatment (*i.e.* fermentation and oxidation) before its use as manure. Such oxidized sludge is also called activated **sludge** which is of inoffensive smell and on dry weight basis contains up to 3 to 6 per cent N, about 2 per cent P_2O_5 and 1 per cent K_2O in a form that can become readily available when applied to soil.

(*ii*) Sewage irrigation. When raw sewage is treated to remove the solid portion or sludge the water, technically known as **treated effluent**, is used for irrigation purpose. Such a system of irrigation is known as sewage irrigation.

Thus, both the activated sludge and the effluent can be used with safely for manuring and irrigating all field crops except the vegetables which are eaten raw or uncooked.

GREEN MANURING

Practice of incorporating undecomposed green plant tissues into the soil for the purpose of improving physical structure as well as fertility of the soil.

Types of green manuring

Broadly two types of green manuring can be differentiated.

(*i*) Green manuring *in-situ* and

(*ii*) Green leaf manuring

(*i*) Green manuring *in-situ*. In this system green manure crops are grown and buried in the same field, either as a pure crop or as intercrop with the main crop. The most common green manure crops grown under this system are Sannhemp, dhaincha and guar.

(*ii*) Green leaf manuring. Green leaf manuring refers to turning into the soil green leaves and tender green twigs collected from shrubs and trees grown on bunds, waste lands and nearby forest areas. The common shrubs and trees used are Glyricidia, Sesbania (wild dhaincha), Karanj, etc.

The former system is followed in northern India, while the latter is common in eastern and central India.

Advantages of Green Manuring

1. It adds organic matter to the soil. This stimulates the activity of soil micro-organisms.
2. The green manure crops return to the upper top soil, plant nutrients taken up by the crop from deeper layers.
3. It improves the structure of the soil.
4. It facilitates the penetration of rain water thus decreasing run off and erosion.
5. The green manure crops hold plant nutrients that would otherwise be lost by leaching.
6. When leguminous plants, like sannhemp and dhaincha are used as green manure crops, they add nitrogen to the soil for the succeeding crop.
7. It increases the availability of certain plant nutrients like phosphorus, calcium, potassium, magnesium and iron.

Disadvantages of green manuring. When the proper technique of green manuring is not followed or when weather conditions become unfavorable, the following disadvantages are likely to become evident.

1. Under rainfed conditions, it is feared that proper decomposition of the green manure crop and satisfactory germination of the succeeding crop may not take place, if sufficient rainfall is not received after burying the green manure crop. This particularly applies to the wheat regions of India.
2. Since green manuring for wheat means loss of kharif crop, the practice of green manuring may not be always economical. This applies to regions where irrigation facilities are available for raising kharif crop along with easy availability of fertilizers.
3. In case the main advantage of green manuring is to be derived from addition of nitrogen, the cost of growing green manure crops may be more than the cost of commercial nitrogenous fertilizers.

4. An increase of diseases, insects and nematodes is possible.
5. A risk is involved in obtaining a satisfactory stand and growth of the green manure crops, if sufficient rainfall is not available.

Green manure crops

Leguminous	Non-leguminous
1. Sannhemp	1. Bhang
2. Dhaincha	2. Jowar
3. Mung	3. Maize
4. Cowpea	4. Sunflower
5. Guar	
6. Senji	
7. Khesari	
8. Berseem	

Selection of Green manure crops for Situ

Certain green manure crops are suitable for certain parts of the country. Suitability and regional distribution of important green manure crops are given below :

Sannhemp. This is the most outstanding green manure crop. It is well suited to almost all parts of the country, provided that the area receives sufficient rainfall or has an assured irrigation. It is extensively used with sugarcane, potatoes, garden crops, second crop of paddy in South India and irrigated wheat in Northern India.

Dhaincha. It occupies the second place next to sannhemp for green manuring. It has the advantage of growing under adverse conditions of drought, water-logging, salinity and acidity. It is in wide use in Assam, West Bengal, Bihar and Chennai with sugarcane, Potatoes and paddy.

Guar. It is well suited in areas of low rainfall and poor fertility. It is the most common green manure crop in Rajasthan, North Gujarat and Punjab.

Technique of Green Manuring in Situ

The maximum benefit from green manuring can not be obtained without knowing :

(*i*) When the green manure crops should be grown,

(*ii*) When they should be buried in the soil and

(*iii*) How much times should be given between the burying of a green manure crop and the sowing of the next crop.

(*i*) Time of sowing. The normal practice usually adopted is to begin sowing immediately after the first monsoon rains. Green manure crops usually can be sown/broadcast preferably giving some what higher seed rate.

(*ii*) Stage of burying green manure crop. From the results of various experiments conducted on different green manure crops, it can be generalised that a green manure crop may be turned in soil at the stage of flowering. The majority of the green manure crops take about six to eight weeks from the time of sowing to attain the flowering stage. The basic principle which governs the proper stage of turning in the green manure crops, should aim at maximum succulent green matter at burying.

***(iii)* Time interval between burying of green manure crop and sowing of next crop.** Following two factors which affect the time interval between burring of green manure crop and sowing of next crop.

1. Weather conditions
2. Nature of the buried green material

In paddy tracts the weather is humid due to the high rainfall and high temperature. These favour rapid decomposition. If the green material to be buried is succulent there is no harm in transplanting paddy immediately after turning in the green manure crop. When the green manure crop is woody, sufficient time should be allowed for its proper decomposition before planting the paddy.

Regions not suitable for green manuring

The use of green manures in dry farming areas in arid and semiarid regions receiving less than 25 inches of annual rainfall is, as a rule, impracticable. In such areas, only one crop is raised, as soil moisture is limited. Such dry farming areas are located in Punjab, Maharashtra, Rajasthan, M.P. and Gujarat.

On very fertile soils in good physical condition, it is not advisable to use green manures as a part of the regular rotation.

In areas where rabi crops are raised on conserved soil moisture, due to lack of irrigation facilities, it is not practicable to adopt green manuring. If green manuring is followed in these areas, there is danger of incomplete decomposition of the green matter and as such less moisture for the succeeding crop.

CONCENTRATED ORGANIC MANURES

Concentrated organic manures are those that are organic in nature and contain higher percentages of major plant nutrients like N, P_2O_5 and K_2O compared to bulky organic manures like FYM and compost. These concentrated manures are made from raw materials of animal or plant origin. The common concentrated organic manures are oil cakes, blood meal, fish manure, meat meal and wool waste.

Oil cake

Oil cake is the residue left after the oil is extracted from oil bearing seeds. It contains varying quantities of oil depending upon the process of manufacture employed in treating the oil seed as shown below :

Process of manufacture	Oil (per cent)
Country ghani	10-15
Hydraulic press	8-10
Expeller	5-8
Solvent	1-2

Oil cakes are of two types

(1) Edible Oil cake

(2) Non Edible Oil cake

Edible oil cakes are valued more as cattle feed and seldom used as manure, except when it becomes mouldy or rancid and unfit for feeding to cattle. Non edible oil cakes are used as manure.

Characteristics

1. Quick acting organic manures as C : N ratio is usually narrow (5-15).
2. Oil prevents rapid conversion of N.
3. Nearly 50-80% of its N is made available in 2-3 months and rate of availability varies with the type of cake and nature of soil.
4. Castor cake contain **Ricin**, Mahuva cake contains **Saponin** and Neem cake contains **Nimbidin** which are responsible for slow nitrification of their N due to effects of alkaloids on soil microorganisms.
5. Castor cake has also good vermicidal effect against white ants.
6. Groundnut cake has the highest nitrification rate.
7. Mahua cake is very poor in N and takes a long time to nitrify. When used as manure it has got to be applied to the soil two to three months before sowing/planting of crop.

TABLE 21.3. Average nutrient contents of principal oil cakes

Name of the oil cake	*Percentage composition*		
	N	*P_2O_5*	*K_2O*
Non edible oil cakes			
Castor cake	4.3	1.8	1.3
Cotton seed cake [Undecorticated]	3.9	1.8	1.6
Karanj cake	3.9	0.9	1.2
Mahua cake	2.5	0.8	1.8
Neem cake	5.2	1.0	1.4
Safflower cake [Undecorticated]	4.9	1.4	1.2
Edible oil cakes			
Coconut cake	3.0	1.9	1.8
Cotton seed cake (decorticated)	6.4	2.9	2.2
Groundnut cake	7.3	1.5	1.3
Linseed cake	4.9	1.4	1.3
Rape seed cake	5.2	1.8	1.2
Safflower cake(decorticated)	7.9	2.2	1.9
Sesame or til cake	6.2	2.0	1.2

Precautions in using oil cakes

1. It should be powdered before use.
2. Apply during last ploughing in short duration crop.
3. It is best used as a topdressing after the plants have established themselves.
4. Use only when there is sufficient moisture in the soil.
5. If Mahua cake is to be used, apply before 2-3 months before planting or decompose in a pit and than apply or treat with ammonium sulphate.

Blood meal. Dried blood or blood meal contains 10-12% N and 1-2% P_2O_5. Blood meal is prepared from the blood collected from slaughter house treating with copper sulphate, dried, powdered and bagged and sold as bloodmeal.

Blood meal is quick acting manure and is effective for all crops on all soils. It should be applied like oil cakes.

Meat meal. Bones and meat are cooked in special type of pan for 2-3 hours. Bones are separated and meat is dried and powdered. It is quick acting and used like oil cakes. It contains 10.50% N and 2.5% P_2O_5.

Fish manure. Fish and fish waste is dried and powdered. It is quick acting organic manure and used like oil cakes for all crops on all types of soils. Fish manure or fish meal contains 4 to 10% N, 3 to 9% P_2O_5 and 0.3 to 1.5% K_2O.

Horn and hoof meal. Horn and hoof cooked in bone digester, dried and powdered. It contains 13% N.

Transformation Reactions of Organic Manures in Soils

It is found that both bulky and concentrated organic manures contain some amount of plant nutrients including macro-and micro-nutrients, of which organic nitrogen content is likely to be dominant. The organic forms of soil nitrogen occur as consolidated amino acids, proteins, amino sugars etc. When Organic manures like FYM, composts, oil cakes, green manures etc. are added to the soil, the microbial attack to these materials takes place and results complete disappearance of the organic protein with the remainder of the nitrogen being changed into inorganic form of nitrogen through the process of mineralization.

$$\text{Proteins} \longrightarrow R\text{-}NH_2 + CO_2 + \text{energy} + \text{other products}$$

(Present in organic manures)

$$R\text{-}NH_2 + HOH \longrightarrow NH_3 + R\text{-}OH + \text{energy} + H_2O$$

$$\downarrow$$

$$NH_4^+ + OH^-$$

(release of ammonium in the soil)

The released ammonium (NH_4^+) is subject to following changes

(1) It may be converted to nitrites and nitrates through the process of nitrification carried out by microorganisms,

$$NH_4^+ + 3O_2 \xrightarrow[\text{oxidation}]{\text{enzymic}} 2NO_2^- + 2H_2O + 4H^+ + \text{energy}$$

$$2\,NO_2^- + O_2 \xrightarrow[\text{oxidation}]{\text{enzymic}} 2NO_3^- + \text{energy}$$

(2) It may be absorbed directly by the plants.

(3) It may be utilized by hetero-trophic organisms in further decompising organic carbon residues.

(4) It may be fixed in the lattice of certain expanding type of clay minerals.

(5) It could be slowly released back to the atmosphere as elemental nitrogen.

Mineralization and immobilization of nitrogen or any other nutrient elements occur continuously in microbial metabolism and the magnitude and direction of the net effect are greatly influenced by the nature and amount of organic manures added. Normally organic manures are applied to the soil as a source of fertilizer nitrogen should contain about 1.5 to 2.0 per cent of the dry weight of the manures in order to meet the needs of the soil microorganisms, otherwise little or no nitrogen will be released for the use of plants.

Role of Organic Manure

1. Organic manure binds soil particles into structural units called aggregates. These aggregates help to maintain a loose, open, granular condition. Water infiltrates and percolates more readily. The granular condition of soil maintains favorable condition of aeration and permeability.
2. Water-holding capacity is increased by organic matter. Organic matter definitely increases the amount of available water in sandy and loamy soils. Further, the granular soil resulting from organic matter additions, supplies more water than sticky and impervious soil.
3. Surface run off and erosion are reduced by organic matter as there is good infiltration.
4. Organic matter or organic manure on the soil surface reduces losses of soil by wind erosion.
5. Surface mulching with coarse organic matter lowers soil temperatures in the summer and keeps soil warmer in winter.
6. The organic matter serves as a source of energy for the growth of soil microorganisms.
7. Organic matter serves as a reservoir of chemical elements that are essential for plant growth. Most of the soil nitrogen occurs in organic combination.
8. Fresh organic matter has a special function in making soil phosphorus more readily available in acid soils.
9. Organic acids released from decomposing organic matter help to reduce alkalinity in soils.

10. Fresh organic matter supplies food for such soil life as earthworms, ants and rodents. These macro-organisms improve drainage and aeration. Earthworms can flourish only in soils that are well provided with organic matter.
11. Organic matter on decomposition produces organic acids and carbon dioxide which help to dissolve minerals such as potassium and make them more available to growing plants.
12. Humus (highly decomposed organic matter) provides a storehouse for the exchangeable and available cations—potassium, calcium and magnesium. Ammonium fertilizers are also prevented from leaching because humus holds ammonium in an exchangeable and available form.
13. It acts as a buffering agent. Buffering checks rapid chemical changes in pH and in soil reaction.

FERTILIZERS

Fertilizer is any material dry or liquid added to the soil in order to supply one or more plant nutrients. The term fertilizer is generally applied to commercially manufactured materials other than lime and gypsum.

Nitrogen Fertilizers

Nitrogen is present in soil as (*i*) Organic form and (*ii*) inorganic form. Inorganic form includes ammonical (NH_4^+), Nitrite (NO_2^-) and Nitrate (NO_3^-). Plant absorbs N in the form of NO_3^- and NH^+_4 forms by paddy in early stages. Nitrogen in NH_4^+ form goes on exchange complex on clay and organic colloids and hence, this part is not lost due to leaching, while NO_3^- is lost due to leaching as it does not go on exchange complex under neutral to higher pH values of soil. But it goes on exchange under highly acidic conditions. The nitrate fertilizers are hygroscopic in nature, it is for this reason, nitrate fertilizers are not commonly used even though plant absorbs N as NO_3^-. Therefore, organic form (urea) and fertilizers of NH_4^+ form like ammonium sulphate are widely used.

Most of Indian soils are low in N and the requirement of N by crop is throughout its growing period, therefore N should be applied in such a way that plant gets it throughout its life period. It becomes absolutely necessary to apply nitrogenous fertilizers to every soil and crop. For this, the total quantity of nitrogenous fertilizers requirement is more compared to fertilizers of other nutrients.

Commercial Nitrogenous Fertilizers

Commercial nitrogenous fertilizers are those fertilizers that are sold for their nitrogen content and are manufactured on a commercial scale.

Classification of Nitrogenous Fertilizers

Nitrogenous fertilizers may be classified into four groups on the basis of the chemical form in which nitrogen is combined with other elements with a fertilizer.

Nitrogenous Fertilizers

- Nitrate Fertilizers
- Ammonical Fertilizers
- Nitrate and Ammonical Fertilizers
- Amide Fertilizers

(1) Nitrate Fertilizers. Nitrogen is combined as NO^-_3 with other elements. Such fertilizers are

(*i*) Sodium nitrate or Chilean nitrate ($NaNO_3$)—16% N

(*ii*) Calcium nitrate [$Ca(NO_3)_2$]—15.5% N.

Out of these, sodium nitrate is an imported commercial fertilizer.

(2) Ammonical Fertilizers. In these fertilizers, nitrogen is combined in ammonical (NH_4) form with other elements. Such fertilizers are

(*i*) Ammonium sulphate [$(NH_4)_2SO_4$]—20% N

(*ii*) Ammonium Chloride (NH_4Cl)—24 to 26% N

(*iii*) Amhydrous ammonia—82% N

(3) Nitrate and Ammonical Fertilizers. These fertilizers contain nitrogen in the form of both nitrate and ammonical. Such fertilizers are :

(*i*) Ammonium nitrate (NH_4NO_3)—33 to 34% N

(*ii*) Calcium ammonium nitrate—26% N

(*iii*) Ammonium sulphate nitrate—26% N

(4) Amide fertilizers. These fertilizers contain nitrogen in amide or cynamide form. Such fertilizers are

(*i*) Urea [$CO(NH_2)_2$]—46% N

(*ii*) Calcium cynamide ($CaCN_2$)—21% N

General characteristics of four groups

(1) Nitrate fertilizers. Most of the field crops except paddy in early stages of their growth, take up nitrogen in nitrate form as such,

(*i*) Nitrate fertilizers are readily absorbed and utilized by these crops. Nitrate fertilizers are very often used as top and side dressings.

(*ii*) The great mobility of the nitrate ion in the soil has the advantage that, even by broadcasting the fertilizer on the surface of the soil, the nitrogen reaches the root zone quickly.

(*iii*) On the other hand, there is also the increased danger of leaching of these fertilizers. On dry soils, nitrate fertilizers are superior to the other forms of nitrogenous fertilizers.

(*iv*) All nitrate fertilizers are basic in their residual effect on the soils and their continued use may play a significant role in reducing soil acidity. Sodium nitrate, for example, has a potential basicity of 29 pounds of calcium carbonate per 100 pounds of fertilizer material.

(2) Ammonical Fertilizers

(*i*) Ammonical fertilizers are water soluble.

(*ii*) It is less rapidly used by plant than NO^-_3, as it is to be changed to NO^-_3 before use by crop.

(*iii*) It is resistant to lost due to leaching as being cation goes on exchange complex.

(*iv*) Any fertilizer which contain N as NH^+_4 or which is changed as NH^+_4 produced acidity in soil due to production of HNO_3.

(*v*) Ammonium (NH^+_4) of fertilizer goes on exchange complex, used by crop like paddy.

(*vi*) Used by microorganisms nitrified to NO_3 and lost due to volatilization from soil.

(3) Nitrate and Ammonical Fertilizers

(*i*) Fertilizers of this group are soluble in water.

(*ii*) Nitrate part can readily be used by crop.

(*iii*) NH^+_4 can go on exchange and hence, this is best type but did not over take ammonium sulphate and urea, as they are hygroscopic in nature.

(*iv*) They are acidic in their residual effect on soil.

(4) Amide Fertilizes

(*i*) Fertilizers of this group are readily soluble in water. They are easily decomposed by microorganisms due to presence of oxidisable carbon.

(*ii*) They are quickly changed to NH^+_4 then in to NO^-_3.

Manufacturing process of ammonium sulphate and urea

Most of the nitrogenous fertilizes like ammonium sulphate, urea, ammonium nitrate, ammonium sulphate nitrate and even DAP are manufactured by using NH_3^- as one of the important compound. Most of the commercial NH_3^- is prepared by Haber's process by the fixation of atmospheric N by means of H_2.

The reaction is :

$$N_2 + 3H_2 \xrightarrow[\text{at } 550°\text{C temp. Fe}]{\text{200 atm. Pressure}} 2NH_3 + 24.4 \text{ KCal}$$

and Mo as catalysts

Ammonia can also be obtained from natural gas, coal gas and nephtha. Therefore, cost of fertilizer production in fertilizer factory installed near a petrochemical will be low.

The NH_3 gives ammonium sulphate with sulphuric acid, NH_4Cl with HCI; NH_4NO_3 with HNO_3; urea with CO_2; MAP and DAP with H_3PO_4. Thus, NH_3 is chief compound for most of the nitrogenous fertilizers.

(*i*) Preparation of Ammonium sulphate (A/S). It is prepared by

(*a*) reacting NH_3 with H_2SO_4

(*b*) gypsum process

(*c*) by-product of coal and steel industries.

(a) NH_3 with H_2SO_4. NH_3 is reacted with H_2SO_4 giving A/S. The liquid is crystallized and crystals of A/S are obtained.

$$2NH_3 + H_2SO_4 = (NH_4)_2\,SO_4$$

Since the sulphur used in sulphuric acid is to be imported, the source of H_2SO_4 becomes costlier and hence, gypsum a cheaper source of sulphur is used in gypsum process.

(b) Gypsum process. The main raw material required in gypsum process is NH_3, pulverized gypsum, CO_2 and water. NH_3 is obtained by Haber's process. This NH_3 when reacts with CO_2, gives $(NH_4)_2\,CO_3$. The ground gypsum when reacts with $(NH_4)_2\,CO_3$ solution gives $(NH_4)_2\,SO_4$ and $CaCO_3$. The reactions are :

$$N_2 + 3H_2 \rightarrow 2NH_3$$
$$2NH_3 + H_2O + CO_2 = (NH_4)_2\,CO_3$$
$$(NH_4)_2\,CO_3 + CaSO_4 = (NH_4)_2\,SO_4 + CaCO_3$$

(*ii*) Preparation of Urea. Urea is manufactured by reacting anhydrous ammonia with CO_2 under higher pressure in presence of suitable catalyst. The intermediate unstable product ammonium carbamate is decomposed to urea:

$$N_2{+}3H_2 = 2NH_3$$
$$2NH_3 + CO_2 \xrightarrow[\text{30 atm (Amm. Carbamate)}]{} NH_2COONH_4$$

$$NH_2COONH_4 \longrightarrow \underset{\text{Urea}}{NH_2CONH_2} + H_2O$$

During the preparation of urea, biuret is formed which is harmful. This biuret is formed when two molecules of urea are reacted eliminating NH_3.

$$\underset{\text{Urea}}{NH_2.CO.N\,(H_2} + \underset{\text{Urea}}{H.N)\,HCO.NH_2} = \underset{\text{Biuret}}{NH_2CO.NH.CONH_2} + NH_3$$

In urea biuret should not be more than 1.5%.

Now a day's urea is used as fertilizer more compared to other nitrogenous fertilizers due to the following reasons :

(*a*) Higher N content (44 to 46 per cent).
(*b*) Good physical conditions.
(*c*) Less acidic in residual effect compared to A/S.
(*d*) Less cost per unit of N in production, storage and transport.
(*e*) Lack of corrosiveness.
(*f*) Suitable for foliar application.
(*g*) It is having of equal agronomical value compared to other nitrogenous fertilizers.

Transformations of Nitrogenous Fertilizers

Ammonical nitrogenous fertilizers are ionized to give $NH^+{}_4$ ion and enters in the exchange complex. Fertilizers containing NO_3^-. N can not be retained on the exchange complex. Leaching of NO_3^- is more in light textured soils. Urea is an organic fertilizer and its dissociation in water is only slight. So it can not be retained by soil particles in the same manner as ammonical fertilizers unless it is converted into ammonium carbonate.

(1) Urea

Urea hydrolysis. When urea is added to the soils, it is hydrolysed to ammonium carbonate. The reaction which is brought about by the enzyme urease can be represented by the following :

$$NH_2CONH_2 + 2H_2O \xrightarrow{\text{Urease}} (NH_4)_2CO_3$$

The rate of urea hydrolysis is 25 to 175 ppm per day *i.e.* 56 to 350 Kg N/ha/day at 25°C. Thus, 3 days (72 hrs) under normal field condition.

(2) Nitrification

The ammonium formed as a result of hydrolysis of urea is transformed into NO_2^- and NO_3^-. The conversion from NH_4^+ to NO_3^- is a biological oxidation and can be completed within 2 to 4 weeks, depending upon (1) moisture (2) temperature (3) pH (4) Organic matter content (5) Soil type and (6) rate of application. It is also an acid producing fertilizer.

It is a two step process :

(1) Ammonium first converted to nitrite NO_2^- by a group of autotrophic bacteria known as nitrosomonas, nitrosococcus

$$2NH_4^+ + 3O_2 \xrightarrow[\text{Nitrosococcus}]{\text{Nitrosomonas}} 2NO_2^- + 2H_2O + 4H^+$$

(2) The nitrite is convertd to nitrate by second group of autotrophic bacteria known as nitrobacter.

$$2NO_2^- + O_2 \xrightarrow{\text{Nitrobacter}} 2NO_3$$

(3) $(NH_4)_2SO_4$ (Ammonium Sulphate)

A/S when added to soil is first solubilized in water in soil. NH_4^+ and SO_4^{2-} ions are ionized in soil solution. Firstly, NH_4^+ ion goes on exchange complex replacing basic material Ca^{2+}. This Ca^{2+} will combine with SO_4^{2-} forming $CaSO_4$ which is lost due to leaching or absorbed by plant and hence continued removal of Ca lowers the pH of soil. It is, therefore, an acid producing fertilizer. Secondly, NH_4^+ ion is nitrified to NO_3^- :

$$2NH_4^+ + 3O_2 \xrightarrow[\text{Nitrosococcus}]{\text{Nitrosomonas}} 2NO_2^- + 2H_2O + 4H^+$$

$$2NO_2^- + O_2 \xrightarrow{\text{Nitrobacter}} 2NO^-_3$$

Reaction releases H^+ ion which produces acidity in soil. Continued use of this fertilizer will result in lowering of soil pH. Within about a month or so most of A/S is changed to nitrate in soil.

Denitrification

Nitrate fertilizers applied under waterlogged soil. Under waterlogged condition of soils, anaerobic decomposition of NO_3^- takes place.

$$2HNO_3 \xrightarrow[-2H_2O]{+4H^+} 2HNO_2 \xrightarrow[-2H_2O]{+4H^+} H_2N_2O_2$$

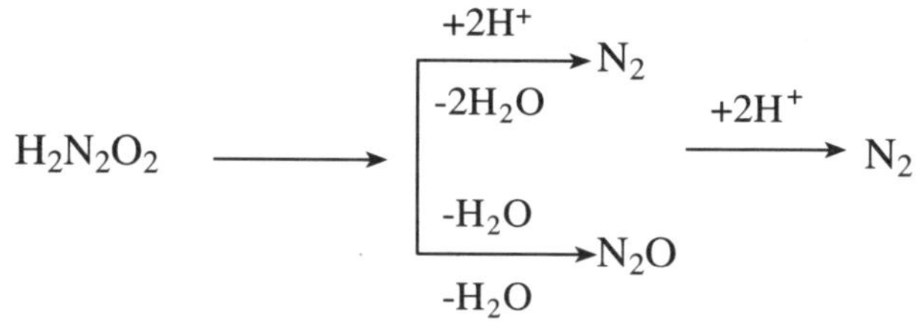

The organisms responsible for denitrification are the species of the genera Pseudomonas and Bacillus. Several autotrophs also capable of reducing nitrate i.e. Thiobacillus denitrificans.

The rate is affected by soil pH, moisture level, partial pressure of the oxygen in the soil air and to a certain extent by the amount of organic matter present. These losses are about 12 to 60 per cent in low land paddy soil.

Volatilization of ammonia

When ammonical fertilizers are applied to the calcareous soils, considerable losses of ammonia through volatilization may occur. The reaction in calcareous soil may be represented as :

(I) $$(NH_4)_2SO_4 + CaCO_3 + 2H_2O \longrightarrow CaSO_4.2H_2O + \underset{\text{unstable}}{(NH_4)CO_3}$$

Ammonium carbonate formed is unstable and decomposed easily to give $NH_3 + CO_2 + H_2O$ such losses of N are 20% when ammonium sulphate is surface broadcasted.

(II) Ammonical fertilizes in alkaline medium (Soil) react as follows :

$$NH^+{}_4 + H_2O + OH^- \longrightarrow NH_3 + 2H_2O$$

When urea is broadcasted on surface soil, the nitrogen may loss by volatilization. The rate of volalilization depends upon temperature and air movement.

$$NH_2CONH_2 + 2H_2O \longrightarrow (NH_4)_2CO_3$$
$$(NH_4)_2CO_3 + 2H_2O \longrightarrow 2NH_4\,OH + H_2CO_3$$
$$NH_4OH \longrightarrow NH_3\uparrow + H_2O$$

Ease of storage, handling and residual effect of nitrogenous fertilizers in soil

The nitrogenous fertilizers differ in their ability to become moist or hygroscopic and as such they have to handle carefully in rainy season. The main features of nitrogenous fertilizers from storage view point are as follows :

(A) Ease of storage and handling

S. No.	Fertilizer	Ease of storage and handling
(i)	A/S	Storage property good, no difficulty in handling and storage.
(ii)	Ammonium chloride	Storage property excellent, no difficulty in handling and storage.
(iii)	Ammonium Nitrate	Storage property satisfactory but it is hygroscopic, so the bag should be firmly tied. As it is fire hazardous, handle carefully.
(iv)	Sodium nitrate	Storage property good, no difficulty in handling and storage.
(v)	Ammonium sulphate nitrate	Storage property satisfactory, slightly hygroscopic, store in dry condition.
(vi)	Calcium ammonium nitrate	Storage property satisfactory but it is hygroscopic. Use entire bag in one lot. Store bags in dry place. Tie half way used bag firmly when it is to be used.
(vii)	Urea	Storage property satisfactory. It is hygroscopic. Use entire bag in one lot and store in a dry place.

(B) Residual effect of nitrogenous fertilizers in soil. (On lime basis)—Nitrogenous fertilizers differ in their residual effect. Fertilizrs which contain $NH^+{}_4$ ions or which poroduce $NH^+{}_4$ ion in soil, produce acidity in soil or cause loss of lime. While other fertilizers being basic in reaction save lime. Among several nitrogenous fertilizes, except $NaNO_3$ and calcium ammonium nitrate are acid producing. Sodium Nitrate is basic in residual effect as it save lime, while CAN is neutral.

The amount of lime lost or saved when nitrogenous fertilizes are added to soil is as under :

S. No.	Fertilizer	Pounds of $CaCO_3$/100 lbs of fertilizers when added to soil for	
		Equivalent acidity (lime lost)	Equivalent basicity (lime saved)
1.	Ammonium Sulphate	110	—
2.	Ammonium chloride	128	—
3.	Ammonium Nitrate	60	—
4.	Ammonium Sulphate Nitrate	93	—
5.	Urea	80	—
6.	CAN	Neutral	Neutral
7.	Sodium nitrate	—	29
8.	Potassium Nitrate	—	26
9.	Calcium Nitrate	—	21
10.	Calcium Cynamide	—	63

Slowly Available Nitrogenous Compounds and Nitrification Inhibitors

Firstly, the N requirement of growing plant is less in early stages of growth, maximum during its grand growth period and very low at the subsequent stages up to harvest. It is thus, seen that N is required through out the growth period.

Secondly, the nitrogenous fertilizers in general high analysis nitrogenous fertilizer in particular, give out the entire amount of added N through fertilizer in available form in very short period. The crop is unable to use the entire available amount in such a short period.

Thirdly, the N not used by a crop is either lost due to leaching and volatilization or fixed as NH_3 by clay particles and immobilization by micro-organisms.

In general, the crop recoveries of N seldom exceed 60 to 70% of that added as fertilizers. Under the circumstances, one should be careful for the use of nitrogenous fertilizers. Therefore, the nitrogenous fertilizers should be used or manufactured or made to act in soil in such a way that there should be minimum loss, maximum recovery and availability should be through out the growth period as per requirement of crop.

Attempts have been made in this direction to over come the problem by four ways :

(*i*) Proper agronomic practices

(*ii*) Preparing large size granules

(*iii*) Preparing slow release nitrogenous compounds

(*iv*) Use of nitrification inhibitors

(*i*) Proper Agronomic Practices. There are two established agronomic practices (*a*) application of fertilizers N to a crop in two or more splits to coincide with the important growth stages (*b*) Placement of N 3 to 5 cms below soil surface at the time of sowing/planting, which permits better contact with soil particles to retain NH_4–N and also prevent losses due to volatilization.

(*ii*) Preparing large size granules and briquettes. By preparing large size granules like urea super granules and briquettes of varying in weight from 1 to 3 gram, increase efficiency of fertilizers, by slower rate of hydrolysis, increase in the rate of downward diffusion and low volatilization loss as NH_3.

(*iii*) Preparing slow release nitrogenous compounds. By the formation of slow release compounds which are ranging from quite soluble to completely insoluble but slowly available form Nitrogenous fertilizers which have few dissolving rates and release their nitrogen slowly are known as slow release nitrogenous fertilizers. These fertilizers are classified into two groups :

(*a*) Chemical compounds with inherently slow rate of dissolution. E.g. Urea formaldehyde compound, Isobutylidene Diured (IBDU), Crotonylidene Diurea (CDU), Oxamide ($CONH_2$) and

(*b*) Material formed by coating to conventional N fertilizers, *e.g.* sulphur coated urea, lac coated urea, neem cake coated urea, plastic coated urea.

(*iv*) Nitrification Inhibitors. These materials decrease the activity of nitrifying bacteria (organisms) and slow rate of nitrification. These compounds are :

(*a*) AM (2 amino chloro-6-methyl pyrimidins).

(*b*) N-serve or Nitrapyrin (2-chloro-6-trichloromethyl pyridine)

(*c*) Thiourea

PHOSPHATIC FERTILIZERS

The phosphorus (P) nutrient of all phosphatic fertilizers is expressed as P_2O_5. In soil, P is present as (*i*) Organic P and (*ii*) Inorganic P. The forms of inorganic P are $H_2PO^-{}_4$; $HPO^{-2}{}_4$; and $PO^{-3}{}_4$; out of which, H_2PO_4 and HPO_4 ions are available to plant. In soil, water in is changed to $HPO^{-2}{}_4$ and $PO^{-3}{}_4$ ions with increase in pH.

$$H_2PO^-{}_4 \xrightarrow{-H^+} HPO^{-2}{}_4 \xrightarrow{-H^+} PO^{-3}{}_4$$

Firstly, the P in soil is immobile or slightly mobile around one cm diameter and therefore, they should be applied in root zone.

Secondly, the requirement of P is maximum in the initial stages. The crop takes up 2/3 of total P when the crop gains 1/3 of total dry matter and hence, the entire quantity should be applied at one time that is at the time of sowing as a basal dose.

Thirdly, water soluble-P is changed to insoluble form as Fe and Al—PO_4 (Phosphate) under acidic and calcium phosphate in calcareous or high Ca content or in higher pH soils and hence, there is no danger for the loss due to leaching and volatilization. The applied P remains as in available form in less quantity while greater quantity is changed to insoluble form.

Chemistry of P compounds

Phosophorus when burns gives P2O5 and with water, it forms HPO3 (Metapohosphoric acid) and H_3PO_4 (orthophosphoric acid) $P_2O_5 + H_2O = 2HPO_3$; $HPO_3 + H_2O = H_3PO_4$. These H_3PO_4 is important in agriculture as it forms three compounds (salts) by replacing one hydrogen every time hydrogen every time.

$$H_3PO_4 \xrightarrow{-H^+} H_2PO^-{}_4 \xrightarrow{H^+} HPO^{-2}{}_4 \longrightarrow PO^{-3}{}_4$$

When H_3PO_4 combines with calcium, it forms three salts.

They are :

(*i*) $Ca(H_2PO_4)_2$ Monocalcium phosphate

(*ii*) $CaHPO^-{}_4$ Dicalcium phosophate

(*iii*) $Ca_3\ (PO_4)^-{}_2$ Tricalcium phosophate

Classification of phosphatic fertilizers

The phosphatic fertilizers are classified into three classes depending on the form in which H_3PO_4 combined with Ca.

Phosphatic fertilizers

I **Water soluble P containing**	II **Citric acid soluble P containing**	III **Citrate and water insoluble-P containing**
Super phosphate (SSP) (16 to18% P_2O_5)	Basic slags (14 to 18% P_2O_5)	Rock phosphate (20 to 40% P_2O_5)
Double Super phosphate (DSP) (32 to 36% P_2O_5)	Dicalcium phosphate (34 to 39% P_2O_5)	Raw bone meal (20 to 25% P_2O_5 and 3 to 4% N)
Triple Super phosphate (TSP) (46 to 48% P_2O_5)	Rhenania phosphate (23 to 26% P_2O_5)	
Mono ammonium phosphate (20% N and 20% P_2O_5)	Steamed bone meal (22% P_2O_5)	
Diammonium phosphate (18% N and 46% P_2O_5)	(Part of P_2O_5 soluble in citric acid)	

(*i*) Characteristics and conditions for the use of water soluble P containing fertilizer :

(*a*) They contain water soluble-P as H_2PO_4 ion which can be absorbed quickly and available to plants when root system is not fully developed.

(*b*) Water soluble-P is rapidly transformed into water insoluble form in soil and hence there is no danger of loss due to leaching.

(*c*) These fertilizers should be used on slightly acidic, neutral to alkaline soils but not on acidic soils as the water soluble-P is changed to unavailable Fe and A1-PO_4.

(*d*) These fertilizers are applied when a crop requires quick start and for short duration crops.

(*ii*) Characteristics and conditions for the use of citric acid (1%) soluble P containing fertilisers :

(*a*) They contain citrate soluble-P and hence this P is less available than water soluble-P.

(*b*) They are suitable for moderately acid soils because it gets converted into water soluble form. They are basic in reaction and Ca content.

(*c*) There are less chances of getting fixed by Fe and Al.

(*d*) They are suitable for long term crops and where immediate and quick start to crops is not important.

(*iii*) Characteristics and conditions for the use of citrate and water insoluble P fertilizers :

(*a*) They are suitable for strongly acidic soils.

(*b*) They contain insoluble P and hence not available to crops.

(*c*) The P is available when ploughed with green manuring crop or organic residues.

(*d*) They are used for long duration crops and in large quantity 500 to 1000 kg/ha.

(*e*) They are used where immediate effects are not important.

Manufacturing of P fertilizers

(*i*) Single super phosphate (SSP). SSP is manufactured by mixing equal amounts of rock phosphate and concentrated H_2SO_4 (approximately 70%) and allowing to react for one minute in mechanical rotators. It is left for 12 hrs to harden and to cool down. It is then matured and after some weeks, it becomes ready for use. Due to free H_2SO_4 present in it, it is responsible for destroying gunny bags and hence first fill in polythene bags and then in gunny bags.

$$Ca_3(PO_4)_2 + H_2SO_4 + 5H_2O = Ca(H_2PO_4)_2.H_2O + 2CaSO_4.2H_2O$$

It contains two part by weight Ca $(H_2PO_4)_2$ monoalcium phosphate (16 to 18% water soluble-P) and three parts by weight gypsum. The formula of superphosphate is $Ca(H_2PO_4)_2$. H_2O, $CaSO_4$. $2H_2O$. Superphosphate supplies P, Ca and S and due to gypsum, it improves physical conditions of soil when added to soil.

In double superphosphate, there is no separate process but gypsum is removed and when the P_2O_5 per cent of the content comes to 32 to 36, it is called double super phosphate.

In triple super phosphate, phosphoric acid is used instead of H_2SO_4 with calcium phosphate.

(*ii*) Diammonium phosphate (DAP). DAP or monoammonium phosphate is prepared by reacting phosphoric acid (H_3PO_4) with NH_3. In this if one H^+ ion of H_3PO_4 reacts with NH_3 if forms MAP ($NH_4H_2PO_4$) and NH_3 reacts with two H^+ ions of H_3PO_4 forms DAP [$(NH_4)_2$ HPO_4].

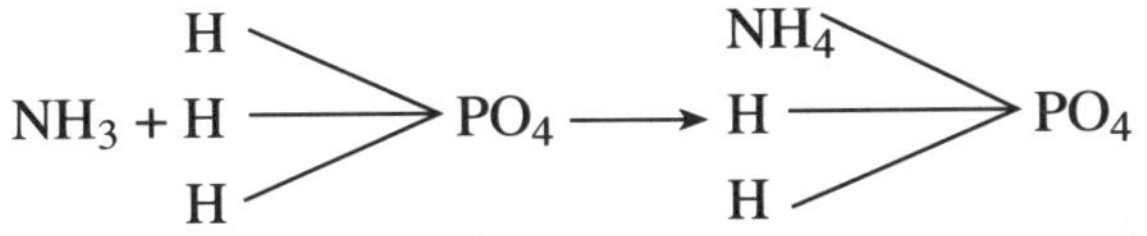

Mono ammonium phosphate

(NH_4 H_2PO_4)

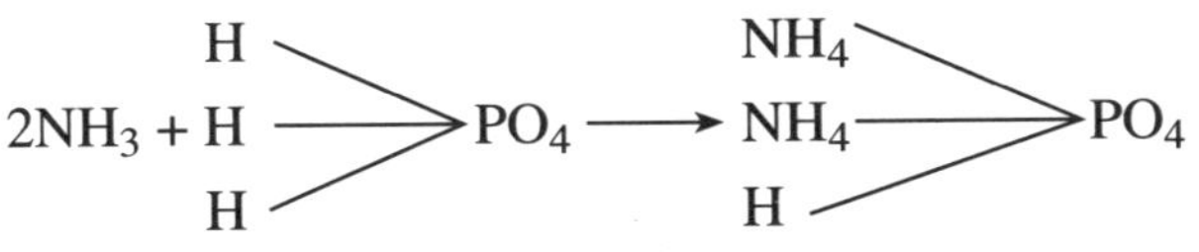

DAP $(NH_4)_2$ HPO_4)

Behavior of P fertilizes in soil. (SSP and ammonium phosphate)

(*i*) Super phosphate (Mono Calcium Phosphate). When superphsphate (normal or triple) is applied to soil, water vapour moves rapidly into each granules. The saturated solution of mono and dicalcium phosphates is formed and a residue of dicalcium phosphate remains at the site of original granules and saturated solution which moves out contain Ca and P and is extremely acidic (pH 1.8). This saturated acid solution reacts with different constituents of soil under different conditions. In acid soil; it dissolves Fe, Al and Mn and with them reacts with forming their insoluble Fe, Al and Mn phoshpates. In calcareous soil, it reacts with Ca forming insoluble $Ca_3(PO_4)_2$. The reactions are as follows :

(*a*) In slightly acid or calcareous (alkaline) soils :

$$Ca(H_2PO_4)_2 + Ca(HCO_3)_2 = 2\ CaHPO_4 + 2H_2CO_3$$

$$Ca(H_2PO_4)_2 + 2Ca(HCO_3)_2 = Ca_3(PO_4)_2 + 4H_2CO_3$$

Slowly the water soluble Ca $(H_2PO_4)_2$ is changed to $CaHPO_4$ and then insoluble $Ca_3 (PO_4)_2$.

(*b*) In markedly acid soils :

$$2Ca(HCO_3)_2 + Fe_2O_3 = 2FePO_4 + 2CaHPO_4 + 3H_2O$$

The phenomenon is diagrammatically shown below :

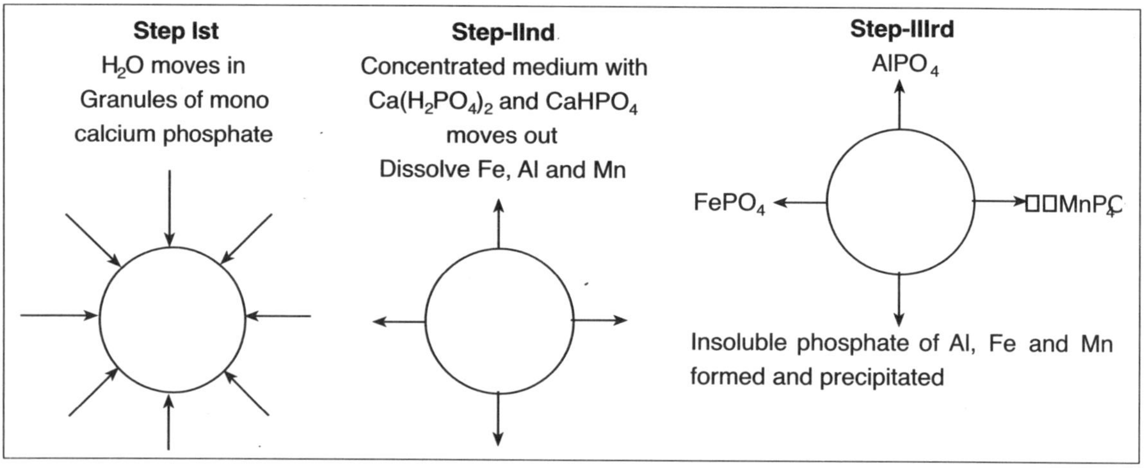

(*ii*) Ammonium phosophate (MAP and DAP). Ammonium phosphate when applied in soil the water vapour moves rapidly inside the granules and form saturated solutions. The saturated solution of MAP has pH-4.0 and DAP 9.0. All salts of ammonium are soluble in water and hence the entire granules of ammonium phosphate are dissolved by soil water. No residue is left at the site of granule because of absence of Ca in fertilizer. After it is dissolved, it reacts with calcium particularly in a soil containing large amount of exch. Ca. One of the reaction products is $CaHPO_4$. The other reactions are similar to that of superphosphate.

POTASSIC FERTILIZERS

Potassium (K) is present in soil as

(*i*) Readily available forms as in soil solution and as exchangeable. These forms are available and plant absorbs these K forms as K^+ ion.

(*ii*) Slowly available form as non-exchangeable *i.e.* fixed

(*iii*) Relatively unavailable in the form of minerals (feldspars and micas etc.)

Firstly, the potash behaves partly like N and partly like P. From view point of the rate of absorption, it is required (absorbed) upto harvesting stage like N and like P, it becomes slowly available. Therefore, the entire quantity is applied at sowing time.

Secondly, potash being cation adsorbed on clay complex and hence leaching loss reduces. Leaching is greater in light soils than heavy textured soils. Therefore, like N, some time split application of K is desirable in sandy soil.

Thirdly, even though the soil contains enough potash or does not give response to crops, it becomes necessary to apply for the following reasons:

(*a*) Maintaining K status of soil.

(*b*) For improving burning quality of tobacco.

(*c*) For neutralizing harmful effects of chloride in plant.

(*d*) For sugars or starch producing crops like potato, sweet potato, sugar cane, sugar beet, banana etc. for formation of sugar and starch.

(*e*) For fibrous crops like sann, flex etc. to give strength to fibre.

(*f*) For the formation of pigments in crops like tomato, brinjal etc for quality purpose and it improves the luster and gives more colouration to the fruits of these crops.

Chemistry of K compounds

Potassium is not found in free state in soil. As metal, it reacts with CO_2 forming K_2O and K_2O with H_2O gives KOH. For this reason, K in elemental form is not used as fertilizer. It must be combined with other element like chlorine or group of elements.

Classification of potassic fertilizers

Potassic fertilizer

Fertilizer containing

E.g. KCl (Muriate of potash 58% K_2O). This is cheaper fertilizer and used extensively by cultivators for all crops except where chlorine is not desired in fertilizer

Chlorine Fertilizer containing other than chlorine

E.g. Sulphate of potash (K_2SO_4 48% K_2O)
Potassium Nitrate (KNO_3 44% K_2O, 13% N)
Sulphate of potash and magnesium (double salt of K and Mg, (Schoenite) K_2SO_4, $MgSO_4$ (25 to 30% K_2O)

Properties of Potassic fertilizers

Muriate of Potash (KCl). It is commonly marketed as a commercial fertilizer in granular form. However, it is also available in powder form. It is easily soluble in water. On application to the soil, it ionizes to dissociate into K^+ and Cl ions. K^+ like NH_4^+ gets attached or absorbed on the soil complex. As such, though muriate of potash is readily soluble in water, it is not leached.

Potassium sulphate (K_2SO_4). It is water soluble. On application to the soil, it separates into K^+ and SO_4^{-2} ions. K^+ is absorbed by growing plants or is absorbed on the soil complex. As such, though potassium sulphate is readily soluble in water, it is not lost by leaching.

SECONDARY AND MICRONUTRIENT FERTILIZERS

The secondary nutrients fertilizers: The secondary plant nutrients are Ca, Mg and S. Out of these, three nutrients, Ca and Mg are added indirectly in soil through fertilizes and soil amendments. Soil contains Ca and Mg as exchangeable and as $CaCO_3$ and dolomite. Normally, it is not necessary apply Ca and Mg fertilizers in soils of India.

Formerly, the use of FYM, A/S and superphosphate sources of S were used and now their use is either restricted or their replacement by other fertilizers which are devoid of S. Therefore, sulphur now becomes necessary to apply in soil because of the following reasons :

(*i*) A/S a source of S is replaced by urea.

(*ii*) Another source of S, superphosphate is replaced by DAP.

(*iii*) Use of KCl instead of K_2SO_4.

(*iv*) Decrease in the use of FYM.

(*v*) Use of high yielding varieties which absorb more quantity of nutrients.

The soils deficient in sulphur are supplied with the sources of S like elemental S. Elemental S when applied to soil, it is changed to $SO_2 \rightarrow SO_3$ and H_2SO_4. This H_2SO_4 with basic material of soil gives its sulphate salt. Plant absorbs S as SO_4^{-2}.

Micronutrients or Trace Elements

The micro-nutrients are zinc (Zn), iron (Fe), copper (Cu), Manganese (Mn), Boron (B), Molybdenum (Mo) and Chlorine (Cl). These nutrients are present in available forms in soil in very small quantity and the requirement by crops is also less.

Application of micronutrient fertilizers now becomes necessary as their deficiencies are observed in soil. The deficiency of micronutrients was observed in soil because of the following reasons.

(*i*) Due to increase in irrigation facility, the number of crops taken in a year is increased.

(*ii*) Use of hybrid varieties which absorb more nutrients.

(*iii*) Intensive cultivation.

(*iv*) Reduction in the use of organic manures like FYM, which supply these nutrients,

(*v*) Use of high analysis fertilizers which are devoid of these nutrients.

Out of these micronutrients, chlorine is not applied as its fertilizer because it is indirectly applied through irrigation water. Mo is required in very small quantity and is also present in sufficient in some of seeds and soils and hence generally its fertilizers are not used. Boron is found to be deficient in calcareous soil as it is changed to calcium borate which is insoluble and hence boron is applied as its fertilizers. All these nutrients are present as anions.

These four micronutrients are generally applied both soil and foliar as their sulphates at the time of deficiency. Now a days the micronutrient carriers which contain all two to three in one.

The micronutrient limits of the deficiency in soil, quantity and type of fertilizers added by soil and foliar application is given below:

S. N.	Element	Rating (ppm)			Soil application	Foliar application (200 to 300 lit/ha)
		Low	Medium	High		
1.	Iron	< 2	2 to 5	> 5	10 ppm Fe as $FeSO_4$ *i.e.* 100 Kg $FeSO_4$/ha	Mix.0.4% $FeSO_4$ solution with 0.2% lime solution
2.	Managanese Exchange Reducible	<3 <100	3 to 5 100 to 200	>5 >200	10 ppm Mn as $MnSO_4$ *i.e.* 80 Kg $MnSO_4$/ha	Mix.0.6% $MnSO_4$ Solution with 0.3% lime solution
3.	Zinc	< 0.5	0.5 to 1.0	>1.0	5 ppm Zn as $ZnSO_4$ *i.e.* 45 kg $ZnSO_4$/ha	Mix 0.6% $ZnSO_4$ with 0.3% lime solution
4.	Copper	< 0.2	0.2to 0.5	> 0.5	5 ppm Cu as $CuSO_4$ *i.e.* 40 Kg $CuSO_4$/ha	Mix 0.4% $CuSO_4$ solution with 0.2% lime solution
5.	Boron	< 0.1	0.1 to 0.5	> 0.5	0.2 ppm B as Borax *i.e.* 15 Kg Borax/ha	0.2% Borax solution
6.	Molybdenum	< 0.05	0.05 to 0.1	> 0.1	0.05 ppm Mo as ammonium molybdate *i.e.* 1.8 kg/ha	0.05% ammonium molylbdate solution.

The micronutrients are soon changed to insoluble forms when they are added to soil and hence chelates are used as one of the sources. Chelates (meaning "Claw") is a compound in which metallic cation is bounded to an organic molecule. In chelates form, the cations are protected from reactions with inorganic constituents that would make them unavailable for uptake.

The common chelating agents are :

EDTA : Ethylene Diamine Tetra Acetic Acid

DTPA : Diethylene Triamine Penta Acetic Acid

HEDTA : Hydroxy Ethylenthylene diamine Triacetic Acid

NTA : Nitricotriacetic acid

FERTILIZER MIXTURES (MIXED FERTILIZERS)

For application of individual nutrient, fertilizers of the nutrients were also applied separately which increased labour cost, transport and storage cost. In order to avoid the said difficulty the fertilizer mixtures were used.

Fertilizers Mixtures

A mixture of two or more straight fertilizer materials is referred to as fertilizer mixture. The term complete fertilizer refers to these fertilizers that contain three major (N, P and K) nutrients.

Advantages of fertilizer mixtures

(1) Less labour is required to apply a mixture than to apply its components separately.

(2) Use of fertilizer mixture leads to balanced manuring.

(3) The residual acidity of fertilizers can be effectively controlled by the use of proper quantity of lime in fertilizer mixture.

(4) Micronutrients can be incorporated in fertilizer mixture.

(5) Mixture has better physical condition.

Disadvantages of fertilizer mixtures

(1) Use does not permit individual nutrient application which oat specific growth stage of crop.

(2) Unit cost of plant nutrients in mixtures is usually higher than those of straight fertilizers.

(3) Farmers use mixtures without careful study of their needs.

Materials and methods of preparing fertilizer mixtures

The type of grade of fertilizer mixture to be prepared should be decided. The straight fertilizers are chosen according to compatibility in mixture. The quantity of each fertilizer is calculated for the preparation of desired quantity of preparing fertilizer mixture. It happens that there is a gap in weight of fertilizers taken on the basis of nutrient content and the total weight of fertilizer mixture. The gap is filled by using **filler**. A filler is the make weight material added to a fertilizer mixture. The common fillers used are: sand, soil, ground coal, ash and other waste products. It is also necessary to add the **conditioners** to avoid caking. For this low grade organic materials like tobacco stem, peat, groundnut and paddy hulls are added at the rate of 100 lbs/ton of mixture. If the fertilizers used leave acidic residual effect when it is added in soil then liming materials like lime stone, dolomite etc. are added.

The fertilizer materials can be mixed without using special equipments. Mixing should be done on cement floor and it preferably on the date of application or a day before its application.

Incompatibility in fertilizer mixtures

1. Fertilizers containing NH_3 should not be mixed with basically reactive fertilizers, otherwise there will be loss of N as NH_3.
2. All water soluble phosphatic fertilizers should not be mixed with those fertilizers that contain free lime, otherwise a portion of soluble phosphate is converted into an insoluble form.
3. Easily soluble and hygroscopic fertilizers tend to cake or form slums after mixing. Such fertilizers should be mixed shortly before use.

Fertilizer mixtures available in the market

1. Sufla (15 : 15 : 15)
2. Sufla (20 : 20 : 0)
3. Lakshmi (12 : 12 : 12)
4. Lakshmi (8 : 8 : 8)
5. IFFCO-1 (10 : 26 : 26)
6. IFFCO-2 (12 : 32 : 16)

Considering the incompatibility, the chart is given below which can be used while preparing fertilizer mixture.

1	2	3	4	5	6	7	8	9	10	11	
✓	✓	×	×	*	✓	✓	✓	×	✓	✓	1. Muriate of Potash
✓	✓	×	×	*	✓	✓	×	×	✓	✓	2. Sulphate of potash
×	×	✓	✓	*	×	*	*	✓	✓	✓	3. Sulphate of ammonia
×	×	✓	✓	*	×	*	*	✓	✓	✓	4. Calcium amm. nitrate
*	*	*	*	*	*	*	*	*	*	*	5. Sodium nitrate
✓	✓	×	×	*	✓	*	×	×	×	*	6. Calcium cynamide
✓	✓	*	*	*	*	✓	✓	✓	*	*	7. Urea
✓	×	*	*	*	×	*	✓	✓	*	*	8. Superphosphate single or triple
×	×	✓	✓	*	×	*	✓	✓	✓	✓	9. Ammon. Phosphate
✓	✓	✓	✓	*	✓	*	*	✓	✓	✓	10. Basic slag
✓	✓	✓	✓	*	*	*	*	✓	✓	✓	11. Calcium carbonate

Guide for mixing fertilizers

✓ Fertilizer which can be mixed

* Fertilizer which may be mixed shortly before use

× Fertilizer which can not be mixed

COMPLEX FERTILIZERS

Due to uneconomical and labour cost of using individual fertilizer, the fertilizer mixtures were prepared and they were used. These fertilizer mixtures were not homogenous, containing less quantity of N, P, K and many times inferior quality of material were used. For these difficulties, complex fertilizers have been prepared. These complex fertilizers contain the nutrients of grade mentioned, homogenous, granular and good physical conditions.

Complex Fertilizers

Commercial complex fertilizers are those fertilizers which contain at least two or three or more of the primary essential nutrients. When it contains only two of the primary nutrients, it is designated as incomplete complex fertilizer. While those contain three nutrients are designated as complete complex fertilizers. At present, the complex fertilizers obtained by chemical reaction are more important than fertilizer mixtures.

Complex fertilizers being manufactured in India are

(*i*) Nitrophosphate

(*ii*) DAP and

(*iii*) Ammonium phosphate sulphate

Characteristics of complex fertilizers

(1) They usually have high content of plant nutrients more than 30 kg/100 kg of fertilizer. As such they are called **high analysis fertilizers.**

(2) They usually have uniform grain size and good physical condition.

(3) They supply N and P in available form in one operation. Nitrogen is present as NO^{-3} and $NH^{+}{}_{4}$ forms and P as water soluble form upto 50 to 90% of total P_2O_5.

(4) They are cheaper compared to individual fertilizer on the basis of per Kg of nutrient.

(5) Transport and distribution cost is reduced on the basis of per kg of nutrients.

Time and Method of Fertilizer Application and Balanced Fertilizetion

To obtain the maximum benefit from fertilizers, it is most essential that fertilizes to be applied at the proper time and at the proper place. The fertilizers to be applied, possess different qualities with regard to solubility in water and movement in to the soil solution. Similarly, soils are of different nature, sandy to clayey. The nature of the soil governs the movement of applied fertilizers. Again, the requirement of plants for different plant nutrients varies to their stage of growth. For example, nitrogen is absorbed by the plants throughout the growth period. While phosphorus is absorbed at a faster rate during the early growth period. Thus, the time and method of fertilizers application will vary in relation to :

(1) The nature of fertilizer

(2) The soil type and

(3) The difference in nutrient requirement and nature of field crops.

Principles governing selection of proper time for application of fertilizers

1. Nitrogen is required throughout the crop growth. As such, it is absorbed by the plant at the same rate as that of its growth. All plants grow at a slow rate in the beginning. Then follows a rapid increase in the growth rate. Near the harvest time, the rate of growth again slows down. Accordingly, nitrogen is taken up by the plant slowly in the beginning, rapidly during the grand growth period and again slowly as it nears maturity. In other words, the nitrogen requirement of a growing plant is less in the early stages of growth, maximum during its grand growth period, and very low at the subsequent stages upto harvest. It is thus seen that nitrogen is required throughout the growth period.
2. Nitrogenous fertilizers are soluble in water. They are mobile and move rapidly in all directions within the soil. As such nitrogen is easily lost through leaching.
3. Phosphorus is required during the early root development and early plant growth. As such, crop plants utilize 2/3 of the total requirement of phosphorus when the plants accumulate 1/3 of their dry weight. In other words, plants require more of phosphorus during the early growth period.
4. On the one hand, phosphorus is required in greater quantities during the early growth period; while on the other, all phosphatic fertilizers become available to the growing plants slowly. As such, it is always recommended that the entire quantity of phosphatic fertilizers should be applied before sowing or planting.

5. Potash behaves partly like nitrogen and partly like phosphorus. From the point of view of the rate of absorption, it is like nitrogen, being absorbed up to the harvesting stage. But potassic fertilizers, like phosphatic fertilizers, become available slowly. As such, it is always advisable to apply the entire quantity of the potash at sowing time.
6. Leaching is greater from sandy soils than from heavy textured soils. This means that more frequent applications or split application of nitrogenous fertilizers, and sometimes of potassic fertilizers, is desirable on sandy soils.

Practical recommendations based on the principles guiding the time of application of fertilizers can be summed up as follows

1. Nitrogenous fertilizers should be applied in two split doses to crops of four to five months duration, in three splits to crops of 9 to 12 months duration, and in four to five splits when crops are of still longer duration, like **adsali** crop of sugarcane.
2. On sandy soils or light textured soils more frequent or split application of nitrogenous fertilizers is desirable, compared to heavy textured soils, like clayey soils. This is important for reducing losses due to leaching.
3. The entire quantity of water soluble phosphatic fertilizers should be applied in one dose at sowing time. In acid soils, it is advisable to apply bone meal or rock phosphate a week or fortnight prior to sowing.
4. Potassic fertilizers also should be applied in one dose at planting time.

Principles involved in selecting the correct methods of fertilizer application

1. Nitrogenous fertilizers are easily soluble in water and move rapidly in all directions from the place of application. In other words, nitrogenous fertilizers applied on the soil surface reach the plant roots easily and rapidly. As such, these fertilizers are broadcasted on the soil surface just before sowing.
2. Since nitrogen is liable to be lost by leaching, it is applied at different stages of plant growth. Since nitrogenous fertilizers move rapidly in moist soil, application of nitrogenous fertilizers on the soil surface followed by irrigation is good enough to meet the nitrogen requirement at the critical stage of plant growth. In other words, nitrogenous fertilizers are suitable for topdressing and side dressing.
3. Since phosphorus moves slowly from the point of placement it should be placed where it will be readily accessible to the plant roots.
4. Progressive fixation of phosphates by soil clays continues to diminish their efficiency for a considerable period following application. Fixation refers to any chemical or physical interaction between the applied plant nutrients and the soil whereby the nutrients become less available to crops. To reduce the fixation of phosphate, phosphatic fertilizers should be so placed that they come into minimum contact with the soil particles and are closer to the plant roots. In other words, localized placement of phosphatic fertilizers near the seeds or seedling roots should be practiced.
5. Since potassic fertilizers move slowly in the soil; they should also be placed near the root zone.

Balanced Fertilization

Plants contain 90 or more elements, only 16 of which are currently known to be essential. The elements essential for plant growth are carbon, hydrogen, oxygen, phosphorus, potassium, nitrogen, sulphur, calcium, iron, magnesium, boron, manganese, copper, zinc, molybdenum and chlorine. On practical point of view, generally application of nitrogenous, phosphatic and potassic fertilizers are considered as balanced fertilization.

Unbalanced fertilization has led to decrease in the yield of crops and also deteriorate the physical condition of the soil. The growing of crops by using only nitrogen fertilizer has depleted the reserve of available phosphoric acid, potash, and other nutrients in the soil. The result is that subsequent additions of nitrogen fertilizer do not result in increased yields because some other essential elements such as phosphorus and potash are now a limiting factor.

Balanced application of fertilizers enhances the efficiency of nutrients. For example, the efficiency of a nutrient like nitrogen is greatly enhanced when it is used in conjunction with phosphorus. For instance, when a dose of 30 Kg of nitrogen was applied in the filed, only 14 to 30% of nitrogen is utilized by the crops. On the other hand, when 30 Kg of nitrogen was applied along with 30 Kg of phosphoric acid, the recovery of added nitrogen varied from 23 to 50%. This clearly shows that phosphoric acid contributed to the better utilization of the nitrogen. Just as phosphoric acid helps in the better utilization of nitrogen, potash also helps in the better assimilation of nitrogen and phosphoric acid.

Balanced fertilizer application, particularly, phosphorus and potash makes plants more drought resistant and winter hardy. Balanced fertilization imparts plant vigor and resistance to certain diseases.

A certain balance among the various nutrients is essential if the greatest efficiency in the use of fertilizer is to be obtained.

METHODS OF FERTILIZER APPLICATION

An important item in efficient use of fertilizer is that of placement in relation to plant.

(1) Solid fertilizers

Broadcasting is the method of application of fertilizer uniformly over the entire field. It may be at planting or in standing crop as top dressing.

(*i*) **Broadcasting at planting** is adopted under certain conditions.

1. Soils highly deficient, especially in nitrogen,
2. Where fertilizers like basic slag, dicalcium phosphate, bone meal and rock phosphate are to be applied to acid soils, and
3. When potash fertilizers are to be applied to potash deficient soils.

(*ii*) **Top dressing** is application of fertilizer to the standing crop. Usually, nitrate nitrogen fertilizers are top dressed. Depending on the duration of the crop and soil type, top dressing may be more than one to meet the crop needs at times of greatest need of the crop.

***(iii)* Placement.** Fertilizers are placed in the soil either before sowing or after sowing the crop.

(*a*) ***Plough-sole placement*** consists of placing the fertilizer in a continuous band at the bottom of the furrow during the process of ploughing, which is usually covered by the next furrow adjacent to it.

(*b*) ***Deep placement*** is application of fertilizers, especially in N, in the reduced zone to avoid N losses in low land rice.

(*c*) ***Localized placement.*** In this method fertilizer are applied close to the seed or plant. It is usually adopted when relatively small quantizes of fertilizers are applied.

(*d*) ***Contact placement or drill placement*** refers to drilling seeds and fertilizer simultaneously at sowing. Care must be taken to place the seed and fertilizer at different depths to avoid salt injury to the germinating seed.

(*e*) ***Band placement*** consists of applying the fertilizer in continuous bands, close to the seed or plant. This method is ideal for crops grown in wide space *i.e.,* cotton, castor, sugarcane, tobacco, maize etc.

(*f*) ***Pellet placement*** is application of fertilizer, especially nitrogen in pellet from in the low land rice avoid nitrogen loss from applied fertilizer.

(2) Liquid Fertilizers

***(i)* Starter solution.** These are solutions of fertilizers prepared in low concentrations used for soaking seed, dipping roots or spraying on seedlings for early establishment and growth.

***(ii)* Foliar application**

- This method, nutrients are applied are to the standing crops in the form of spray for quick recovery from the deficiency. It avoids fixation of nutrients in the soil.
- In the case of calcium, transport from roots to fruit is limited, so foliar applications are the best method we know of go get more calcium into fruit tissue to reduce post harvest disorders.
- If soil pH limits nutrient availability, and ground applied fertilizes are not taken up, foliar fertilizers may be a valid option. In this case, a soil sample should be taken to determine pH, and a leaf tissue sample taken to determine the need for addition foliar fertilization. In some cases poor root health from compaction, replant disease, crown rot, mouse damage, water logging or other problem may warrant foliar feeding of trees.
- However, the fertilizer in the required amount cannot be phototoxic as a foliar spray, and uptake must have been demonstrated with the product under consideration.
- Zinc uptake deserves special attention. In our soils zinc is largely immobile and it is difficult to supply roots with adequate amounts of available Zn. As a result of limited soil availability, zinc is applied as a foliar spray. Research has shown that only a small amount of Zn can be taken up by leaves, however foliar application are still more successful than soil applied Zn.

***(iii)* Soil application.** Liquid fertilizer such as anhydrous ammonia is applied directly to the soil with special injecting equipment. Liquid manures such as urine, sewage water and shed washing are directly let into the field.

***(iv)* Fertigation.** This is the application of fertilizer in irrigation water in either open or closed system. The open system includes lined and unlined open ditches and gated pipes that are used for furrow and flood irrigation.

- Sprinkler and trickle systems are main closed systems. Nitrogen and sulphur are the principal nutrients applied by fertigation.
- The fertigation allows applying the nutrients exactly and uniformly only to the wetted root volume, where the active roots are concentrated. This remarkably increases the efficiency in the application of the fertilizer, which allows reducing the amount of applied fertilizer. This not only reduces the production costs but also lessens the potential of ground water pollution by fertilizer leaching.

Other advantage of the fertigation is

(1) the saving of energy and labor,

(2) the flexibility of the moment of the application (nutrients can be applied to the soil when crop of soil conditions would otherwise prohibit entry into the field with conventional equipment),

(3) convenient use of compound and ready-mix nutrient solutions containing also small concentrations of micronutrients which are otherwise very difficult to apply accurately to the soil, and

(4) The supply of nutrients can be more carefully regulated and monitored. When fertigation is applied through the drip irrigation system, crop foliage can be kept dry thus avoiding leaf burn and delaying the development of plant pathogens.

CHAPTER 22

Soil Amendment

SOIL AMENDMENT

To amend soil means to improve it with additional materials. These soil amendments or soil conditioners improve the physical nature of soil. They reduce compaction, aerating the soil to allow water and nutrients to more easily move through it and reach plant roots. Some soil amendments also add nutrients to the soil, help retain moisture and help maintain the correct pH balance.

Soil amendment includes all inorganic and organic substances mixed into the soil for achieving a better soil constitution regarding plant productivity. Soil amendment does not include mulching, which includes substances lying on top of the soil. There are different substances for different soils and plants to optimise the soil conditions. A very common amendment is the addition of organic matter like compost, due to its low production costs.

Advantages

- Soil amendments improve the physical properties resulting in better con-ditions for water storage, root development and soil ecosystems
- Soil amendments enhances soil aeration
- Soil amendments can be produced locally, especially organic amendments (e.g. compost), which are cheap to produce
- Soil amendments can be applied almost everywhere by almost anybody

Disadvantages

- Wood products can tie up nitrogen in the soil
- The incorporation of the soil amendment (especially of organic amendments) can be time consuming

- If too many nutrients or organic matter are put into the soil, they can be released and cause an outflow of nutrients into the groundwater and sur-rounding rivers and lakes, which can result in water pollution

Why use of Amendment?

The reason for soil amendment is to provide a better environment for roots and plant growth: this includes the improvement of the soil structure and water holding capacity, the availability of nutrients, and the living conditions for soil organisms, which are important for the plants to grow. Furthermore, a better soil texture and better root growth avoids **soil degradation** during heavy rains or in windy regions. It also supports the **nutrient cycle** when organic amendments are used (e.g. manure). Beside soil amendment, there are several methods to provide soil moisture conservation such as **soil cover and reforestation** (living plants), **mulching** or several **tillage techniques**. Of course it is also very important that a **crop** is planted which is suitable for the given climate. Basically, any organic or inorganic material that is added to the soil and improves its quality can be considered as soil amendment. The type of amendment chosen depends entirely on how the soil needs to be changed. By using soil amendment, almost every type of soil can be made fertile.

Both inorganic and organic substances can be added into the soil. Organic substances consist of material derived from living things (e.g. plants), whereas inorganic substances are mined or man-made.

Inorganic Amendments

Inorganic substances are vermiculite, perlite, tire chunks, pea gravel and sand. In general, they must be bought, which makes them more expensive than organic amendments. Additionally, the industrial production process needs a great deal of energy. Therefore, these substances do not have the same degree of sustainability as organic amendments. Most are relatively sterile (with regard to plant pathogens) and many are relatively inert. Inorganic amendments are used to :

- increase aeration
- increase drainage
- decrease excessive water holding capacity
- decrease or increase weight.

Organic Amendments

Organic growing medium amendments usually are derived from plants or plant products that occur naturally (peat moss from peat bogs), or are the by-products of processing plants or mills (sawdust, cedar chips, bark, bagasse, rice hulls) or waste disposal plants (compost, processed sewage sludge, biosolids). The main purpose of using organic amendments is to loosen the soil and create large pores to increase :

- aeration
- drainage
- usable water holding capacity
- nutrient holding capacity
- decrease growing medium weight (compared to soil)

By far, the most important organic soil amendments worldwide are compost and animal dung (e.g. chicken, cow). **Compost** and animal dung are most often easily available and economically affordable.

In professional agriculture, the most commonly used organic amendment is peat moss (e.g. sphagnum peat moss which is the highest quality, but also hypanaceous or domestic peat). Other organic amendments include wood chips, grass clippings, straw, compost in general (produced in **large** or **small scale** facilities), manure (see also **use of compost**, **use of dehydrated faeces** or **terra preta**), processed sewage sludge (biosolids), sawdust, etc. Normally, there are more organic substances available than inorganic substances and generally they are cheaper. Practising good crop rotations and choosing the correct **crop** improves soil amendment.

Before incorporating into ground beds, most organic amendments, especially sawdust, cedar chips, bark and bagasse, should be composted or aged, and sterilised before use if possible. All of these amendments have a high C:N ratio. Use of amendments which are not composted and have a high C:N ratio will deplete N from the soil, may cause a salt or an ammonia/ammonium burn, or may cause damage due to heat build up.

Amendments with a low C:N ratio will release N upon further decomposition, thus act as an organic fertiliser. However, organic matter with a low C:N ratio also should be composed to avoid rapid ammonia/ammonium release and toxicity.

Advantages of Organic Amendments

Humic acid is a principal component of humic substances, which are the major organic constituent of organic soil amendments. Organic soil amendments (humus) have been known by farmers to be beneficial to plant growth for longer than recorded history. It was supposed that humus was used directly by plants, but it was shown later that plant growth depends upon inorganic compounds. Therefore, many soil scientists held the view that organic matter was useful for fertility only as it was broken down with the release of its constituent nutrient elements into inorganic forms. At the present time, soil scientists hold a more holistic view and at least recognise that humus influences soil fertility through its effect on the water-holding capacity of the soil: the spongy structure of organic matter is able to bind water and some inorganic molecules which act as micro- or macro-nutrients. Consequently, humic acids also slow water evaporation from soils. This is especially important in soils where clay is not present or in a low concentration, in arid areas, and in sandy soils without the capability to hold water. The oxygen end of another water molecule bonds with the hydrogen end of another, until the evaporation rate is reduced by 30%.

An additional benefit of organic amendments is also the fact that organic matter feeds soil microbes, which in turn release nutrients into the soil, thereby increasing soil fertility.

Factors to Consider When Choosing an Amendment

There are at least four factors to consider in selecting a soil amendment:

- How long the amendment will last in the soil
- Soil texture

- Soil salinity and plant sensitivities to salts
- Salt content and pH of the amendment

Laboratory tests can determine the salt content, **pH** and organic matter of organic amendments. The quality of bulk organic amendments for large-scale landscape uses can then be determined. The amendment you choose depends on your goals.

- Are you trying to improve soil physical properties quickly? Choose an amendment that decomposes rapidly.
- Do you want a long-lasting improvement to your soil? Choose an amendment that decomposes slowly.
- Do you want a quick improvement that lasts a long time? Choose a combination of amendments.

TABLE 22.1. Permeability and water retention of various soil types. This can be changed by adding an amendment.

Soil texture	Permeability	Water Retention
Sand	high	low
Loam	medium	medium
Silt	low	high
Clay	low	high

TABLE 22.2. Depending on crops, permeability and water retention of soils (table 1) can be adjusted.

Amendment	Permeability	Water Retention
Fibrous:		
Peat	low-medium	very high
Wood chips	high	low-medium
Hardwood bark	high	low-medium
Humus:		
Compost	low-medium	medium-high
Aged manure	low-medium	medium
Inorganic:		
Vermiculite	high	high
Perlite	high	low

Cost Considerations

Most inorganic amendments are mined from natural deposits and further processed to yield the final product. Heavy machinery and technical know-how is necessary to produce such amendments. These facts cause higher costs in production. In the other hand, organic amendments have high self-help compatibility, because farmers can produce them on-site. There are numerous methods that help to produce organic amendments and support a sustainable handling of the local **nutrient** and **water cycle. Composting toilets**, **terra preta toilets**, **fossa alternas** or **arborloos**, **UDDT** are toilet systems that generate organic amendments. There are more organic substances available than inorganic, and they are generally cheaper.

Environmental Effects

Soil amendments have to be handled carefully. Soil does not have the capacity to bind substances ad infinitum without releasing them. If too many nutrients or organic matter are put into the soil, they can be released and cause an outflow into the groundwater and surrounding rivers and lakes, which can cause **water pollution**.

Applicability

Soil amendments, if managed carefully, can be applied everywhere. Care has to be taken in choosing the appropriate soil amendment depending on the initial soil conditions. Especially organic amendments can be produced locally. Mixture into the soil can be time consuming only very few soils are "by nature" ideal substrates for plant growth. Much effort has been devoted to improving "problem" soils. Generally, the chemical properties of soils are easier to improve than are the physical ones. With increasing intensity of cropping, many methods of soil improvement have become available and proved profitable. Of the chemical soil properties, the soil reaction (pH) of many soils must be optimized in order to create favourable conditions for plant growth, nutrient availability and to eliminate the harmful toxic substances. Optimizing soil pH is a precondition for the success of nutrient management for crop production. It entails either raising the pH of acid soils or lowering the pH of alkaline soils. Among the soil physical properties, the improvement of soil structure is of great concern to farmers. The texture of sandy, clayey or stony soils may also be improved but to a very limited extent. Therefore **Gypsum** and **Lime** two basic and important soil amendment for the improving the soil.

Working Principle	**Organic** or inorganic substances are mixed into the soil to improve the physical properties. The goal is a better environment for roots, water infiltration, and holding capacity.
Capacity/Adequacy	Each soil type has different needs for soil amendments.
Performance	Intelligent management leads to moisture conservation and a good harvest. Too much addition of amendments leads to polluted water due to nutrient wash-out.
Costs	Depending on the infrastructure, it can either be more or less expensive to buy inorganic substances than to produce organic substances.
Self-help Compatibility	**Organic** substances can be produced by oneself from animal waste, plant debris or with the approach of different toilet systems.
O&M	It can be very time consuming to mix soil amendments with the soil. If organic amendments are produced locally or on-site, the adopted technique (e.g. composting toilet) must be used properly.
Reliability	Reliable, old method. Carefully applied, regular soil amendment can improve soil quality immensely.
Main strength	Even minor improvement of the physical properties of the soil can generate a much better soil condition for plants.
Main weakness	Too much input of substances results in an output mainly in surrounding water bodies, which is an environmental damage.

Application of Lime ($CaCO_3$)

Soil acidity is reflected primarily in an increase in H^+ ions and a corresponding decrease in the basic cations. Carbonates (lime), hydroxides and some other basic acting substances are able to neutralize soil acids. The purpose of liming is primarily the neutralization of the cause of soil acidity (H^+ ions and Al^{3+} in very acid soils), thus raising the pH value.

Ca and Mg compounds are mainly used for the amelioration of acid soils. Most liming materials are obtained from limestone deposits that were formed in seas of earlier geological periods. The resulting limestone may be from inorganic precipitates or from carbonate shells. It can range from physically very soft material to very hard rock. Limestone reserves are immense in the form of calcitic and dolomitic mountains. However, there may be regional deficiencies of liming materials as many tropical regions that need them are distant from such deposits.

Liming materials:

Common liming materials are:

- Calcium carbonate. It generally contains 75–95 percent $CaCO_3$, corresponding to 42–53 percent CaO (the reference basis for lime effect). A magnesium carbonate ($MgCO_3$) concentration of more than 5 percent is useful. The particle size of hard limestone must be less than 1 mm and that of soft material (chalk) less than 4 mm.

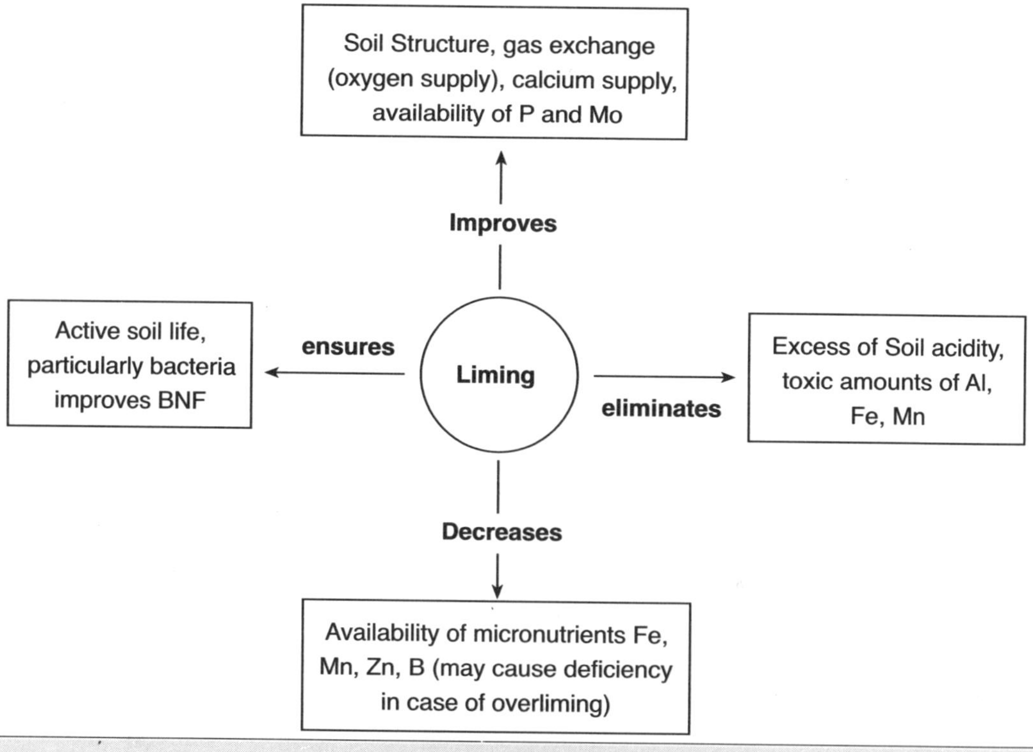

Fig. 22.1. Effect of Liming on Soil Properties

- Calcium magnesium carbonate (dolomite). Its different types contain 15– 40 percent $MgCO_3$ and 60–80 percent $CaCO_3$. These products are suitable for acid soils that are also Mg deficient.
- Quicklime (CaO) and slaked lime $Ca(OH)_2$. These are quick-acting amendments for the neutralization of soil acidity, but they are generally more expensive than natural limes. They have a special role in certain applications, e.g. creating a well-structured soil surface layer for sowing sugar-beet seeds.

Application of Gypsum

Intentional acidification to lower the soil pH may be required on alkaline soils for various reasons. These include removal of negative factors such as micronutrients deficiencies, and removal of excess Na. Soils that have been overlimed may require acidification to improve the availability of Fe, Mn and Zn. Other situations may require an acidic environment for certain crops such as tea. As already mentioned, a certain degree of acidification can be obtained by using N fertilizers that produce an acidic effect where these are cost-effective. However, on soils with a high buffering capacity, this effect may be small.

Amendments for effective acidification are either acids or those that produce acids after decomposition in soil. The most effective substance is diluted sulphuric acid, but its use is technically difficult, costly and inconvenient. In alkali (sodic) soils, the objective is to remove excess exchangeable sodium ions (Na^+) from the root zone and the undesirable soil dispersion in order to create a favourable environment for plant growth. Common amendments are:

- ferrous sulphate ($FeSO_4$), which yields acid after hydrolysis with water;
- elemental S, which yields acid after oxidation by bacteria to sulphate;
- iron pyrite (FeS_2), which yields sulphuric acid after decomposition (also used for alkali soils);
- calcium sulphate or gypsum ($CaSO_4.2H_2O$), for alkali soils.

The amount of acidifying amendments required depends on the lime content of the soil and other properties. One tonne of S decomposes about 3 tonnes of calcium carbonate. A special test for acidity requirement is recommended in order to avoid unwanted damage. The amount of amendments required for reclaiming alkali soils depend on soil pH and soil texture, with higher amounts needed in soils with very high pH (10 and above) and a high clay content. It is now known that reclamation of only the top 10–15 cm of alkali soils is sufficient. This results in considerable savings in terms of the cost of amendments, water and labour.

SOIL CONDITIONER

A **soil conditioner** is a product which is added to soil to improve the soil's physical qualities, usually its fertility (ability to provide nutrition for plants) and sometimes its mechanics. In general usage, the term "soil conditioner" is often thought of as a subset of the category **soil amendments** (or **soil improvement**, **soil condition**), which more often is understood to include a wide range of fertilizers and non-organic materials.

Soil conditioners can be used to improve poor soils, or to rebuild soils which have been damaged by improper soil management. They can make poor soils more usable, and can be used to maintain soils in peak condition.

Composition

A wide variety of materials have been described as soil conditioners due to their ability to improve soil quality. Some examples include biochar, bone meal, blood meal, coffee grounds, compost, compost tea, coir, manure, straw, peat, sphagnum moss, vermiculite, sulfur, lime, hydroabsorbant polymers and biosolids.

Many soil conditioners come in the form of certified organic products, for people concerned with maintaining organic crops or organic gardens. Soil conditioners of almost every description are readily available from online stores or local nurseries as well as garden supply stores.

Purpose

Soil structure. The most common use of soil conditioners is to improve soil structure. Soils tend to become compacted over time. Soil compaction impedes root growth, decreasing the ability of plants to take up nutrients and water. Soil conditioners can add more loft and texture to keep the soil loose.[6]

Soil nutrients. For centuries people have been adding things to poor soils to improve their ability to support healthy plant growth. Some of these materials, such as compost, clay and peat, are still used extensively today. Many soil amendments also add nutrients such as carbon and nitrogen, as well as beneficial bacteria.

Additional nutrients, such as calcium, magnesium and phosphorus, may be augmented by amendments as well. This enriches the soil, allowing plants to grow bigger and stronger.[7]

Cation exchange. Soil amendments can also greatly increase the cation exchange capacity (CEC) of soils. Soils act as the storehouses of plant nutrients. The relative ability of soils to store one particular group of nutrients, the cations. The most common soil cations are calcium, magnesium, potassium, ammonium, hydrogen, and sodium.

The total number of cations a soil can hold, its total negative charge, is the soil's cation exchange capacity. The higher the CEC, the higher the negative charge and the more cations that can be held and exchanged with plant roots, providing them with the nutrition they require.[8][9]

Water retention. Soil conditioners may be used to improve water retention in dry, coarse soils which are not holding water well. The addition of organic material for instance can greatly improve the water retention abilities of sandy soils and they can be added to adjust the pH of the soil to meet the needs of specific plants or to make highly acidic or alkaline soils more usable.[10] The possibility of using other materials to assume the role of composts and clays in improving the soil was investigated on a scientific basis earlier in the 20th century, and the term soil conditioning was coined. The criteria by which such materials are judged most often remains their cost-effectiveness, their ability to increase soil moisture for longer periods, stimulate microbiological activity, increase nutrient levels and improve plant survival rates.

The first synthetic soil conditioners were introduced in the 1950s, when the chemical hydrolysed polyacrylonitrile was the most used. Because of their ability to absorb several hundred times their own weight in water, polyacrylamides and polymethacrylates (also known as hydroabsorbent polymers, superabsorbent polymers or hydrogels) were tested in agriculture, horticulture and landscaping beginning in the 1960s.

Interest disappeared when experiments proved them to be phytotoxic due to their high acrylamide monomer residue. Although manufacturing advances later brought the monomer concentration down below the toxic level, scientific literature shows few successes in utilizing these polymers for increasing plant quality or survival. The appearance of a new generation of potentially effective tools in the early 1980s, including hydroabsorbent polymers and copolymers from the propenamide and propenamide-propenoate families, opened new perspectives.

Application. Soil conditioners may be applied in a number of ways. Some are worked into the soil with a tiller before planting. Others are applied after planting, or periodically during the growing season. Soil testing should be performed prior to applying a soil conditioner to learn more about the composition and structure of the soil. This testing will determine which conditioners will be more appropriate for the available conditions.

Ecological concerns. While adding a soil conditioner to crops or a garden can seem like a great way to get healthier plants, over-application of some amendments can cause ecological problems. For example, salts, nitrogen, metals and other nutrients that are present in many soil amendments are not productive when added in excess, and can actually be detrimental to plant health. (See fertilizer burn.) Runoff of excess nutrients into waterways also occurs, which is harmful to the water quality and through it, the environment.

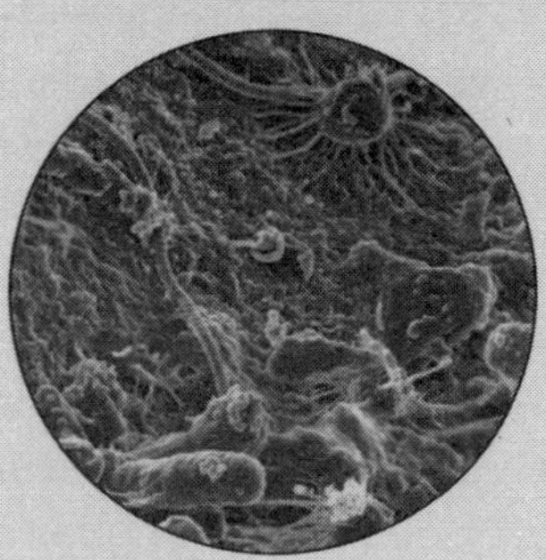

CHAPTER 23

Soil Organism and Biofertilizer

The soil is not dead mass it contains living things like plant roots, insects, protozoa, nematodes, algae, actinomycetes, bacteria, etc. Microbial activities enhance the availability of nutrients and stabilize soil aggregates

CLASSIFICATION OF ORGANISMS

1. Bacteria

They are one celled organisms and are of two types :

(*a*) Autotrophic

(*b*) Heterotrophic

(*a*) Autotrophic. They are capable of getting their energy from oxidation of inorganic constituents such as NH_4, S, Fe and other substances and C from CO_2. They can multiply in absence of organic matter. This group of bacteria oxidizes ammonia, nitrite, sulphur, iron, manganese, hydrogen and methane. Among these mainly they oxidizes :

$$NH_4 \xrightarrow{\textit{Nitrosomonas}} NO_2 \xrightarrow{\textit{Nitrobacter}} NO_3$$

(*b*) Heterotrophic. This group of bacteria obtains their energy by the decomposition of organic matter present in the soil. Organic matter of soil is generally made up of celluloses, hemicelluloses, sugars, proteins, fats and waxes. Due to decomposition of organic matter

Autotrophic	*Heterotrophic*
1. Obtain their energy from oxidation of inorganic material.	1. Get their energy by decomposition of organic matter
2. They utilize N, P, S and other inorganic nutrients and oxidize it to convert into available form.	2. They utilize organic matter and number of nutrients is released by various processes.
3. They do not require organic matter.	3. Organic matter is essential for them.
4. Oxidize $NH_4 \rightarrow NO_2$ (*Nitrosomonas*) $NO_2 \rightarrow NO_3$ (*Nitrobacter*)	4. Bacteria of this group : (*i*) N-fixers and (*ii*) Non-N fixers

essential plant nutrients like N, P and others are transformed into available form. The bacteria of this group are :

(*i*) N fixing bacteria (symbiotically and non-symbiotically)

(*ii*) Non-nitrogen fixing bacteria

2. Fungi

Fungi having filamentous structure, they are in less number as compared to bacteria. They do not have chlorophyll hence cannot use carbon from CO_2. In a soil, fungi remain as parasite or saprophyte or symbiotic organism.

(*a*) ***Parasitic fungi :*** Causing plant diseases, *e.g.* root rot of cotton, wilt, rust, blight and smut.

(*b*) ***Saprophytic fungi :*** Decomposes organic matter to get energy.

(*c*) ***Symbiotic fungi :*** Live on the roots of certain pants and both fungus and plants are mutually beneficial.

Fungi are especially useful in the soil because

(*i*) They break down the substances like lignin, cellulose, wax, etc. which are difficult to decompose.

(*ii*) They decompose speedily the substances like sugar, starch and protein.

3. Actinomycetes

These are the transitional organisms in between bacteria and fungi, as they are having cells like bacteria and filaments like fungi. They give bad smell to soil, because of this only during cultivation of soil particular smell is given out. The functions of actinomycetes are :

(*a*) Conversion of lignin, cellulose, hemicellulose and protein into simple substances.

(*b*) Humus is as very difficult to decomposing substance, it is decomposed by actinomycetes and produce N, which is never available to plants become available to plant.

Actinomycetes are sensitive to pH. They cannot survive at low pH and hence potato scab disease can be controlled by maintaining the pH below 5.

4. Algae

Algae are chlorophyll-bearing organism. Algae fix atmospheric N or by symbiotic relationship with *Azotobacter*. They develop well in fertile soil. After application of fertilizers some time green colour appears, which is due to algae.

Effect of algae on plant growth

(1) They add organic matter in soil through chlorophyll.

(2) Improve soil aeration particularly in paddy field. They benefits the plant by giving oxygen.

5. Protozoa

This group of microorganisms feed on some bacteria thereby reduces the bacterial population, *e.g.* when they feed on N microorganisms, the population of N microorganisms reduces and the N supply to plant also reduces and adversely affect the plants growth. This is a harmful activity. At the same time they are also having beneficial activity, *e.g.* they also feed on pathogens and thereby reduce the diseases.

6. Nematodes

They are just like thread and occur in almost all the soils. They are more in irrigated soils. The nematodes, which feed on plant roots, enter in the plant by puncturing plant roots, through this puncture, other pathogenic bacteria can enter easily. Hence this is a harmful effect of nematodes.

7. Earthworms

Earthworms allow passing soil from their own body, due to which soil is digested properly and by this digestion, the essential nutrients became an available one. They mix up the soil well and they mostly bring up the lower soil to surface. They pass through soil by virtues of holes, due to which it improves leaching of water and soil aeration.

The important reactions carried out by microorganisms (bacteria)

(1) Aminization. The process of converting substances containing protein and organic N into amino group is called as aminization.

$$\text{Protein and organic N containing substance} \xrightarrow{\text{Enzyme}} \text{Amino acid} + CO_2 + \text{energy}$$

(2) Ammonification. This is the process in which amino group (NH_2) is converted first into NH_3 (ammonia) and the into NH_4 (ammonium) by *Bacillus, Clostridium* and *Pseudomonas* bacteria.

$$R\text{-}NH_2 + H_2O \xrightarrow{\text{Bacteria}} R\text{-}OH + NH_3 + \text{energy}$$

$$2NH_3 + H_2CO_3 \xrightarrow{\text{Bacteria}} (NH_4)_2CO_3 + 2NH_4 + CO_3$$

(3) Nitrification: The process in which NH_4 is a converted into NO_2 and NO_3 is called as nitrification. This reaction takes place in two parts.

[I] $$NH_4 \xrightarrow{\text{Bacteria}} NO_2$$

[II] $$NO_2 \xrightarrow{\text{Bacteria}} NO_3$$

This process is carried out by *Nitrosomonas, Nitrosococus* and *Nitrobacter* bacteria.

$$2NH_4 + 3O_3 \xrightarrow{\textit{Nitrosomas, Nitrosococus}} 2NO_2 + 2H_2O + 4H + \text{energy}$$

$$2NO_2 + O_2 \xrightarrow{\textit{Nitrobacter}} 2NO_3 + \text{energy}$$

There are intermediate products, *e.g.*

$$NH_4 \longrightarrow \underset{\text{Hyponitrus}}{NH_2OH} \longrightarrow H_2N_2O_2 \longrightarrow NO_2 \longrightarrow NO_3$$

Mineralization. Conversion of organic N to inorganic N is called mineralization. It depends on C : N ratio of organic complex. If C : N ratio is < 20 : 1, mineralization take place, but of total nitrogen, only 2 to 3% is mineralized, Suppose total N is 0.05% but of this only 20 to 30 lbs/ac will be mineralized which is very less and total nitrogen content of soil is not important.

Immobilization.

Simple compound ⟶ Complex compound
i.e. inorganic form change to *i.e.* organic N

i.e., $NO_3 \longrightarrow$ protein (protein in plants or microorganism body)

If C : N ratio > 30 : 1 there is immobilization, between 20 : 1 and 30 : 1 neither mineralization nor immobilization.

Denitrification. This is the reverse process of nitrification in which the reduction of NO_3 take place and converted mostly as elemental nitrogen or its oxides or NH_3.

This process take place when

(*i*) Presence of NO_3 or is in large amount
(*ii*) Absence of O_2
(*iii*) Large quantities of decomposable organic material

This process is carried out by *Bacillus denitrificans* and *Micrococus denitrificans*.

$$NO \longrightarrow N_2O \longrightarrow N_2 \text{ gas}''$$
$$NH_4OH \longrightarrow NH_3 \text{ gas}''$$

This process takes place under anaerobic condition for long time *e.g.* in rice field, nitrate fertilizers should not be used in rice fields.

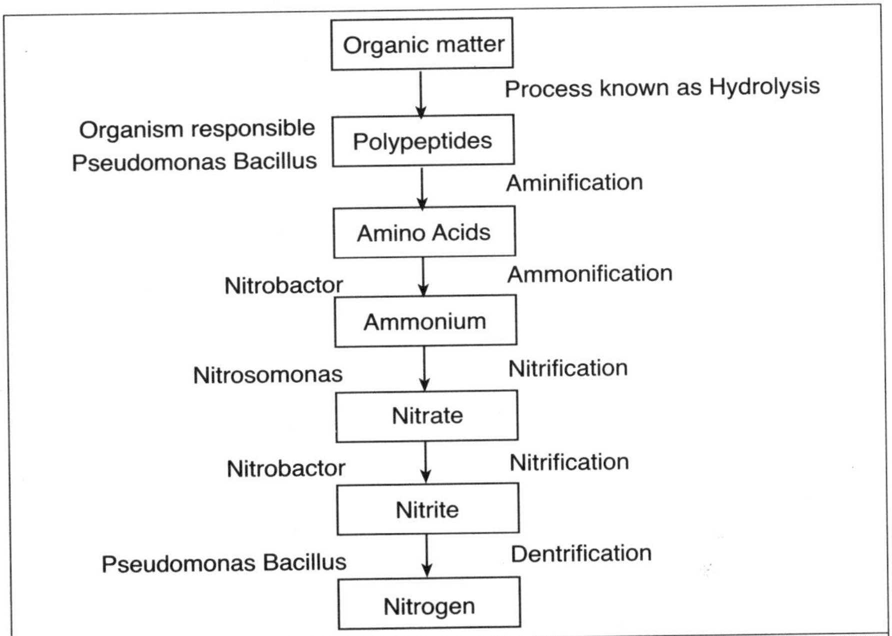

Fig. 23.1. Flow chart showing organism involved in mineralization of nitrogen

It also takes place in heap of manures. If the heap is loose then protein at the surface gets decomposed and NO_3 is formed. This NO_3 is carried down at the bottom in monsoon season, where anaerobic condition exists, NO_3 is changed to N_2 and NH_3 which are lost in atmosphere and hence the manure heap should be compact in order to avoid the loss of nitrogen.

Biological Nitrogen Fixation

There are two main classes of organism, which involved in the fixation of atmospheric N;

1. Non-symbiotic microorganisms (Free living N fixing organism *i.e.* heterotrophic bacteria)

(*a*) *Azatobacter* spp. (aerobic)

(*b*) *Clostridium* spp. (anaerobic)

They utilize carbon by decomposing plant residues for their energy and fix atmospheric N, *Azotobacter* is favored by

(*a*) Neutral pH

(*b*) Ample P

(*c*) Aerobic condition

(*d*) Moist and well-drained soils.

Clostridium is less efficient than *Azotobactor*. It fixes N under anaerobic condition and soil having lower pH.

2. Symbiotic nitrogen fixation. The leguminous crops can fix atmospheric nitrogen through symbiotic nitrogen fixation process. On an average in the world, the amount of nitrogen fixed by this way is 100 $mg/m^2/year$.

The fixation of nitrogen is carried out by the group of bacteria called *Rhizobium* spp. These organisms are present in soil and if a new leguminous crop is introduces in the area for the first time, then these organisms are introduces in the soil through culture.

The organism come in contact and enters in plant through root hairs of legume crops. After few hours of infection, thread is formed which grows from root hair into root tissues. The cell through which thread passes is enlarged and division of cell takes place. The cell division becomes localized and the initiation of nodule formation takes place. The curling growth and branching of root hairs are the first response to *Rhizobium* infection. The fully matured red colour has the ability to fix atmospheric N. The *Rhizobium* passes into five stages till the nodule is fully matured. The organism use carbohydrates of plant for their food and supply the nitrogen which is fixed by them to the plant. Thus plant gets benefit of nitrogen and the organism for the food. So the process is called symbiotic nitrogen fixation.

Mechanism of Nitrogen Fixation

The central reaction according to which biological nitrogen fixation proceeds and the enzyme responsible for the reaction are the same in all organisms (Symbiotic and non-symbiotic).

$$N_2 + 6e^- + 8H^+ + 12ATP \longrightarrow 2NH_4 + 12ADP + 12pi$$

A molecule of nitrogen gas reduced to ammonia requires energy to proceed. It is estimated that 12 moles of ATP are required for 1 molecule of N_2, which is reduced to 2 molecules of ammonium.

The enzyme responsible for nitrogen fixation is called **Nitrogenase**. It consists of two proteins (*i*) Iron protein also called Azoferredoxin or Component II or Azofer (*ii*) Molybdenum iron protein also called molybdo-ferredoxin or Component I or Azofermo. The individual component does not catalyse any reaction only the combined system of both proteins is regarded as an enzyme.

Both of the nitrogenase proteins are Iron-sulphur components. The iron protein is the smaller of the two with molecular weight ranging from 50,000-70,000. It is rapidly but reversibly inactivated by oxygen. The molecular weight of molybdenum iron protein range from 100,000-300,000 and also reversibly inactivated by oxygen.

Factors influencing nitrogen fixation

Biological factors

1. There has to be appropriate organism-host relationship or compatibility, because not all rhizobia can form nodules in all legume roots.
2. The plant should be nutritionally healthy to carry out optimal photosynthesis so as to obtain enough carbon for itself and the organism.
3. Infection by other organisms should be minimal, *e.g.* infection of roots by nematodes.

Chemical factors

1. High soil nitrogen content discourages nitrogen fixation.
2. Soil pH has a profound influence on the process, soil pH of 6-7.5 favor nitrogen fixations.

Physical factors

Aeration is important as most of the organisms involved are heterotrophic and aerobes. However, the presence of oxygen could retard the process, since it is a reduction process.

The presence of a pigment called **Legume hemoglobin** salvages the problem by binding O_2 thereby rendering it inactive, to be released only when needed. A cross section of an active nodule is reddish brown due to the presence of legume hemoglobin.

Agronomic importance of nitrogen fixation

1. In symbiotic nitrogen fixation the organisms live inside plant root, nitrogen fixed is immediately assimilated into products needed by plants such as amino acids, amines etc. In non-symbiotic fixation, the nitrogen is fixed into soil and absorbed by plants.
2. When ploughed in as green manure or incorporated as crop residues, the nitrogen synthesized into organic N can be mineralized as nitrates and be of benefit to crops that will be subsequently grown in the soil.
3. In mixed cropping, when legumes and non-legumes are grown in mixture, the non-legume benefit from nitrogen fixed by legumes.
4. Nitrogen fixation is so important that where it is suspected that the appropriate strains of rhizobia are not present in the soil, legume seeds are inoculated with such strains.

How legume crops do helps to fertility

Legume crops though have more nitrogen (protein) content require less nitrogen. Thus it saves fertilizers. Secondly they fix atmospheric nitrogen and amount of 10% of this fixed nitrogen is thrown back in soil.

The advantages of legume crop is obtained only if we;

(*i*) Do not remove the roots and allow it to decay in soil, and

(*ii*) Burry the whole plant in soil for organic matter, generally we do not follow these two procedure and hence little advantage is obtained. The best advantage is only that it is nitrogen saver.

Non-Symbiotic Nitrogen Fixation

Organisms live independently in soil. They utilize carbon of CHO and plant residue for energy. They have the enzyme nitrogenase in the soil which activates nitrogen and convert into NH_3 (procedure same as mentioned in symbiotic fixation). This NH_3 inside the body of organism is changed to protein which is called bacterial non-symbiotic N fixation.

Rhizosphere

The vicinity of roots can be distinguished into many microhabitats shown in Fig. 23.2. The term Rhizosphere was introduced in 1904 by German scientist Hiltner to denote that

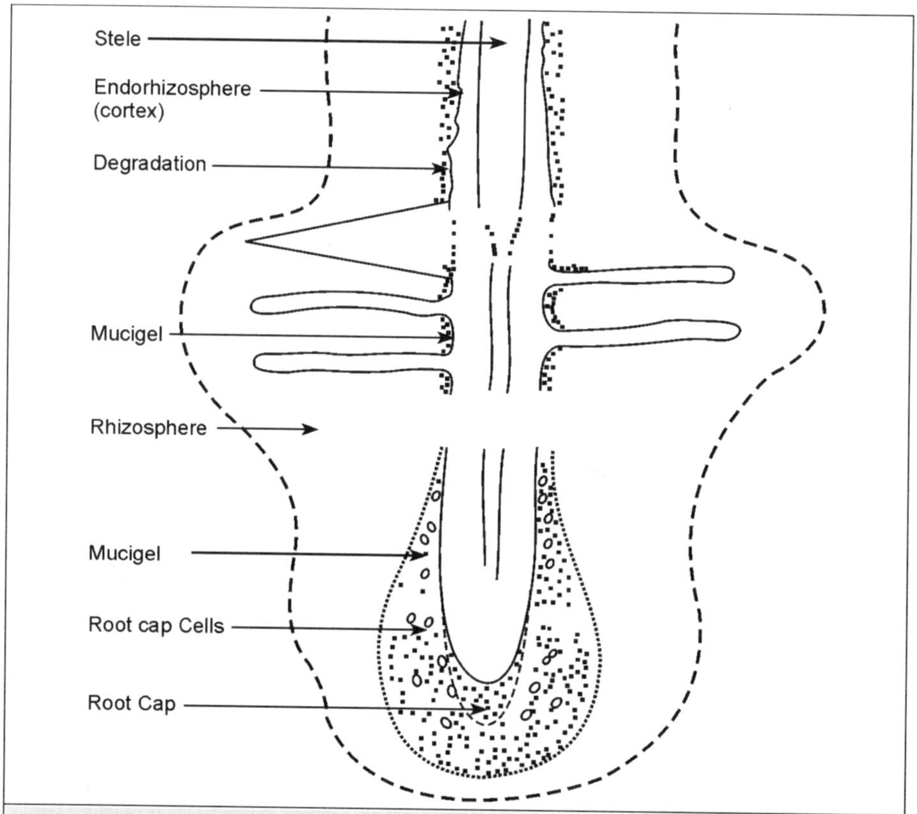

Fig. 23.2. A generalized diagramatic view of the root region of a growing plant

region of the soil which is subject to the influence of plant roots. Rhizosphere characterized by greater microbial activity depends on distance to which exudations from the root system can migrate. It is clearly established that greater number of bacteria fungi and actinomycetes are present in the rhizosphere effect. It has also been demonstrated that the rates of metabolic activity of rhizosphere microorganisms are different from those of the non-rhizosphere soil. Wide ranges of enzyme of plant and microbial origin present in rhizosphere catalyze the breakdown of organic materials.

Rhizosphere effect

Greater rhizosphere effect is seen with bacteria (R : S values ranging from 10 to 20 or sometimes more) than with actinomycetes or fungi. Only negligible change is noted with regard to protozoa and algae.

1. Microorganisms may favour the growth of higher plant by affecting the availability of various nutrient elements essential for plant growth, most especially carbon, nitrogen and phosphorus.
2. The production of CO_2 in the rhizosphere and the formation of organic or inorganic acids aid in the solubilization of inorganic plant nutrients. This is particularly so with insoluble phosphate containing compounds.
3. At the same time, the vast population of microorganisms demands some anions and cations for their own development leading to immobilization of N and P.
4. Aerobic bacteria remove O_2 from the environment and add CO_2 and either of these processes may reduce root elongation and development or diminish the rate of nutrient and water uptake.
5. Microorganisms may favour plant growth through the production of specific growth stimulating or growth regulating substances such as auxins and phytohormones *e.g.*, indole acetic acid, gibberelins and cytokinins.
6. Some microorganisms are parasitic to plants or produce certain toxic substances which are injurious to plants.
7. Antibiotics may be produced in the rhizosphere and this may affect the growth of root pathogens and even the development of diseases in the above tissues if translocated to stem and intravascular system. Antibiotics are also known to affect the physiology of plant.
8. Some groups of microorganisms form symbiotic relationship with higher plant, *e.g.* certain fungi form mycorrhizal association with higher plants and the numbers of free living nitrogen fixing organisms are quite high on the root surface.

Phyllosphere

Plant is especially leaves are exposed to dust and air currents resulting in the establishment of typical flora on their surface aided by cuticle, waxes and appendages which help in the anchorage of microorganisms. These microorganisms may die, survive or proliferate on leaves depending on the extent influence materials in leaf diffuseness of exudates. Leaf diffusive or leachates have been analyzed for their chemical constituents. The principle nutritive factors are amino acids, glucose, fructose and sucrose. If the catchments areas on leaves or leaves sheaths are significantly substantial, such specialized habits may provide niches for nitrogen fixation and secretion of substances capable or promoting the growth of plants.

Leaf surface has been termed 'phylloplane' and the zone of leaves inhabited microorganism as 'Phyllosphere'. In general, apart from nitrogen-fixing bacteria like *Azatobactor*, other genera such as *Psuedomonas* , *Pseudobacterium*, *Phytomonas*, *Erwinia*, *Sarcina* and other undefined one have been encountered on plant surface, especially on leaf surface.

Biochemical reaction in the Phyllosphere

Leaf surface microorganisms perform an effective function in controlling the spread of air-borne pathogens inciting plant disease. The presence of spores of a pathogen on the surface of leaves and pods results in the formation of a substance referred to as 'phytoalexin'. Alternatively, the phytoalexin may be normally present in plants and the concentration of such a substance may rise markedly in response to microbial infection. The term phytoalexin meaning warding-off compound

MYCORRHIZA

This is the symbiotic association between fungi and root of higher plants, the association is beneficial to most organisms. Mycorrhizas are classified into several groups;

Ectomycorrhiza

This association consists of septate fungal cells infecting roots of trees and shrubs. The fungi form compact mantle or sheath over the root surface and penetrate between the cells of the root cortex to form a complex intercellular system called the Hartig net. The ectomycorrhizal fungi produce auxins responsible for some morphological differences between mycorrhizal and nonmycorrhizal roots. Many fungi from classes Basiodiomycetes, Ascomycetes, Zygomycetes and Mushrooms form ectomycorrhiza. It is usually difficult and sometimes impossible to plant seedlings of trees in grassland soils or other new areas, particularly in forest establishment without introduction of the fungi partner.

Ectendomycorrhiza

This is similar to ectomycorrhiza except that the external mantle of fungi sheath may be much reduced or absent, the Hartig net is well developed and the hyphae also penetrate the host cells.

Ericaceous mycorrhizas

These include the mycorrhizas associated with Arbutus, Ericales and Monotropaceae;

Arbutoidmycorrhizas are formed as mantle which serve as storage organ, when Hartig net is present it penetrates the outer layer of the cortical cells. The septet hyphae form intracellular coils that eventually disintegrate within the cell.

Ericoid mycorrhiza occurs between the ericaceous plants and a fungus called *Pezizella*. The fungus forms multiple coils within the cells and up to 42% of the root cells can be occupied by the fungal hyphae.

Monotropoid mycorrhiza a member of the Basidiomycetes called *Boletus* infects both the monotropa and the roots of neighboring trees. The seed of monotropa is very small it will initiate germination but will not develop further until infected with *Boletus*. Phosphate and glucose can be translocated by the fungi over a distance of 1 to 2 m to the tissue of monotropa.

Functions of Mycorrhiza

1. The major contribution of the fungus is in nutrient uptake and translocation, especially of phosphorus and sometimes nitrogen.
2. Mycorrhizal plants have the capacity to withstand or tolerate drought better than non mycorrhizal plants.
3. The plants are protected from pathogens, nematodes and heavy metal concentrations in the rooting zone.
4. The fungi partners obtain carbon from the plant.
5. Mycorrhizal fungi have aggregating effect especially on coarse soil.
6. The production of phyto-hormones such as cytokinins may have positive effect on plant growth.

BIOFERTILIZER

Biofertilizers are microbial inoculants which are capable of

(*i*) Fixing atmospheric nitrogen

(*ii*) Solubilise plant nutrients like P

(*iii*) Stimulate plant growth through synthesis of growth promote substances.

Importance of Biofertilizer

Fertilizer cost is increasing day by day and there is a acute shortage of energy sources like neptha (natural gas) and sulphur. In our country imports of fertilizers to meet growing demand impose a heavy foreign exchange burden. Moreover, the continuous widening gap between supply of mineral fertilizer and the existing low purchasing power of millions of small and marginal farmers are at present the major constraints for the use of mineral fertilizers. Thus it seems that biofertilizer assume great importance in present day of agriculture because,

(1) They form nodules in the pulses and fix the atmospheric N.

(2) Help in break down of O.M. which enhances the soil properties and nutrition to the plant.

(3) Solubilise the insoluble phosphate *e.g. Bacillus megatherium* var. phosphaticum.

(4) Increase N_2 in soil as *Azolla pinnata* in rice.

(5) Can be multiplied in farm, so they are less expensive.

However, it must be realized that biofertilizer would never be able to substitute chemical fertilizers in modern agriculture system, but can be considered only complimentary and supplementary source of plant nutrients.

Classification of Biofertilizers

Biofertilizer

N-fixing Bacteria or Biological N-fixer

Symbiotic N-fixing bacteria

A. With nodule forming legume
   e.g. Rhizobium spp.

B. With nodule forming not legume
   e.g. Actinomycetes 50-150 kg N $ha^{-1}year^{-1}$

C. Without nodule
   e.g. Blue green algae 10-20 kg N $ha^{-1}year^{-1}$

Non symbiotic N-fixing bacteria

(Free living micro-organism exist in the soil and water are able to fixed molecular N from the air without any symbiotic process)

e.g. ***Azatobactor*** **:** for cereals mainly in maize crop

Clastridium **:** hetrotropic, aenarobic, N fixed 3-15 kg ha^{-1}

Azatospirillum **:** for wheat, sugarcane, sorghum, bajara

Azolla. for low land paddy, 100-150 kg N ha^{-1}

BGA. for paddy 20-30 kg N ha^{-1}

Nutrient Solubility Bacteria

1. P-Solublising bacteria
   - *Psuedomonas straita*
   - *Bacillus polymexa*
   - *Bacillus mycoid*
   - *Bacillus megatherium*
   - *Bacillus cercullans*
   - *Bacillus subilitis*
2. P-solublising fungi
   - *Penicillim degilatum*
   - *Aspergilus awamorii*
   - *Aspergilus niger*
   - *Aspergilus nodulation*
3. P-absorbing & mobility fungi
   - VAM—*vasicular arbuscular mycorrhyza* (ecto and endo)
4. K solublizing bacteria
   - *Bacilluscelecius*
5. Fe oxidizing bacteria
   - *Ferrobacillus ferro-oxidense*
   - *Ferribcterium, leptothrix*
6. S-oxidizing bacteria
   - *Thiobacillus theo-oxidence*
   - *Thiobacillus thioparas*
   - *Thiobacillus denitrificance*
   - *Desulfovibrio*
7. Cellulose and lignin degredating bacteria
   - *Aspergilus awamorii*
   - *Tricoderma visidi*
   - *Tricoderma ressie*

Rhizobium

Among different micro inoculants, rhizobia are most important biofertilizer. They are present in legume root nodules and they function in association with the host plant and help in fixing atmospheric nitrogen. Rhizobium isolates, show a certain degree of specificity in nodulation, and therefore specific rhizobium culture should be inoculated to a given legume.

One type of *Rhizobium* group cannot work on all the types of leguminous crops, but the different species can work on the specified group of legume crops.

Group of Crop	Rhizobium spp.	N-Fix (Kgha^{-1})	Crops
1. Pea group	*R. leguminosaram*	80-150	Pea, Vetch, Lentil
2. Soybean group	*R. japonicum*	50-100	Soybean
3. Alfalfa group	*R. meliloti*	150-250	Alfalfa, Indian Clover (Barseam), Fenugreek
4. Bean group	*R. phaseoli*	30-50	Garden Bean, Kidney Bean
5. Clover group	*R. trifoli*	100-150	Egyptian Clover, Ladino Clover
6. Bean and vetch group	*R.* spp.	30-50	Cowpea, Arhar, Peanut
7. Lupine group	*R. lupini*	50-100	Lima Bean, Velvet Bean
8. Lotus spp.	*R. loti*	—	Lotus
9. Cowpea, Luciana,	*R. NGR-234*	—	Cowpea, Luciana

Results of multiplication experiments revealed that the effect of rhizobium inoculation on the grain yield of various legumes is variable. In majority cases, positive responses are observed but zero or negative results are also not uncommon. The poor response of rhizobia cultures may be due to

(*i*) Use of wrong strain of bacteria,

(*ii*) Unfavorable environmental conditions, and

(*iii*) Improper handling and storage of Rhizobia culture which lead to deterioration in quality.

Carriers of legume inoculants

For better survival and longivity of Rhizobia, some carriers *viz*. lignite, peat, charcol, soil in combination with cellulose powder, leaf manure, rice husk powder, press mud, pelleting of gypsum, Calcium carbonate etc. are used.

Directions for use of Rhizobium cultures

Producers of Rhizobium culture are supposed to mention the following details on the packets containing the cultures.

(*i*) Type of carrier material used

(*ii*) Net quantity

(*iii*) Crops to be inoculated

(*iv*) Manufacturing and expiry dates

Besides this information, the following directions for the use of cultures should also be given on the packets :

1. The contents of the packet are sufficient for seeds to be sown in 0.4 ha (acre).
2. Use only for leguminous crops mentioned before the expiry date and do not expose it to direct sunlight or heat.
3. Mix the inoculants uniformly with the seeds gently with minimum amount of water taking care to avoid damage to seed coat. Dry the inoculated seeds under shade over clean paper or gunny bag and sow immediately.

4. This is not a chemical fertilizer and hence do not mix inoculated seeds or Rhizobium inoculant with chemical fertilizer.

Non-symbiotic N fixers

Azotobacter. Azotobacter is the most important and well known free living nitrogen fixing bacterium for its role in agriculture. Positive as well as negative responses of different crops like cotton, wheat, rice, sorghum and pearl millet to inoculation of Azotobacter cultures have been reported. Azotobacter is an important culture containing cells of *Azotobacter chroococcum* on agar.

Azospirillum. Use of Azospirillum in crop plants is of recent origin. The effect of Azospirillum on gramineae family of cereals in both greenhouse and field conditions has been extremely variable from negative or zero to significant increase in the crop yield.

Blue Green Algae. They use sunlight as a source of energy and water as a source of reductant for photosynthesis and nitrogen fixation. Most of N fixing blue green algae of rice field is filamentous, consisting of chain of vegetative cells including specialized cells called Heterocyst which function as a sort of "micro nodule" for synthesis and N_2-fixing machinery.

Blue green algae is stated to be capable of contributing 25-30 kg N/ha for rice crop. However, the actual benefits depend mainly on the suitability of soil and environment for the growth and multiplication and activity of blue green algae.

Azolla. Nitrogen fixed by Azolla becomes available to the rice plant through decaying of Azolla crop in the form of biofertilizers. Availability of 5-10 cm standing water 25-30°C temperature, neutral pH and 4-8 kg available P_2O_5/ha are important inputs for proper growth of Azolla. Promising results with 5.6 t/ha Azolla application in rice fields at various locations have been observed.

The main constraints in using Azolla as biofertilizer are availability of water for azolla multiplication. The temperature range for Azolla is 25-30°C and it begins to die as the temperature crosses 40°C. Thus, high temperature of summer and low temperature of winter in northern part of country is a constraint in the use of Azolla as a biofertilizer. About 12 t/ha of fresh Azolla increased rice yields equivalent to 20-30 kg N/ha.

Constraints in extension and promotion of biofertilizers

The following factors have been identified for poor promotion and extension of biofertilizer;

(*i*) Lack of training to extension workers and farmers for use of biofertilizer
(*ii*) Inadequate demonstrations
(*iii*) Lack of production programme of biofertilizers on large scale
(*iv*) Improper storage facilities
(*v*) Absence of quality standard
(*vi*) Lack of co-ordination and basic support

❑❑❑

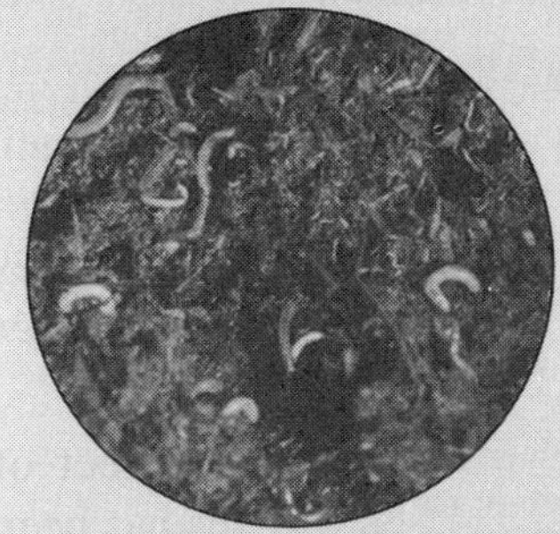

CHAPTER 24

Soil Organic Matter and Humus

Organic matter in the soil comes from the remains of plants and animals. As new organic matter is formed in the soil, a part of the old becomes mineralized. The original source of the soil organic matter is plant tissue. Under natural conditions, the tops and roots of trees, grasses and other plants annually supply large quantities of organic residues. Thus, higher plant tissue is the primary source of organic matter. Animals are usually considered secondary sources of organic matter. Various organic manures, that are added to the soil time to time, further add to the store of soil organic matter.

Composition of plant residues

Composition of organic residues have un-decomposed soil organic matter (mainly plant residues together with animal remains, i.e. animal excreta etc.) The moisture content of plant residues varies from 60 to 90% (average 78%) and 25% dry matter (solid). Plant tissues (organic residues) may be divided into (1) organic and (2) inorganic (elemental) composition. The compounds constituting the plant residues or undecomposed soil organic matter is shown in the following diagram

Organic Residues
(Un-decomposed organic matter)

- **Organic**
  - **Nitrogenous**
    - ***Insoluble***: protein, peptides, starch, hemicelluloses, pectin, mucilage etc.
    - ***Water-soluble***: Nitrates, ammonical compounds etc.
  - **Non-nitrogenous**
    - ***Carbohydrates.*** Cellulose (insoluble), Peptones etc. (Hydrolysable); sugars (soluble)
    - ***Ether soluble.*** Fats, oils, waxes, resins, steroids compound etc.
    - ***Miscellaneous***. Lignin, tanin, essential oils, organic acids
- **Inorganic** (mineral matter or ash)
  S, P, Cl, CO_3, Ca, Mg, Na, K, Fe, Zn, Cu, Mn, etc.

Type and Forms of Soil Organic Matter

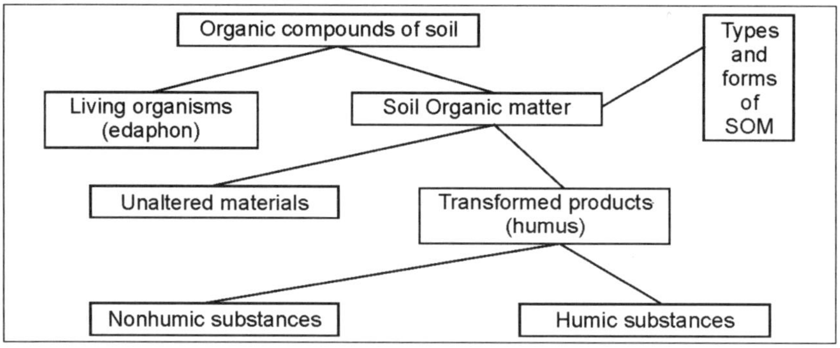

Relative Percentage of Compound in Plant Material

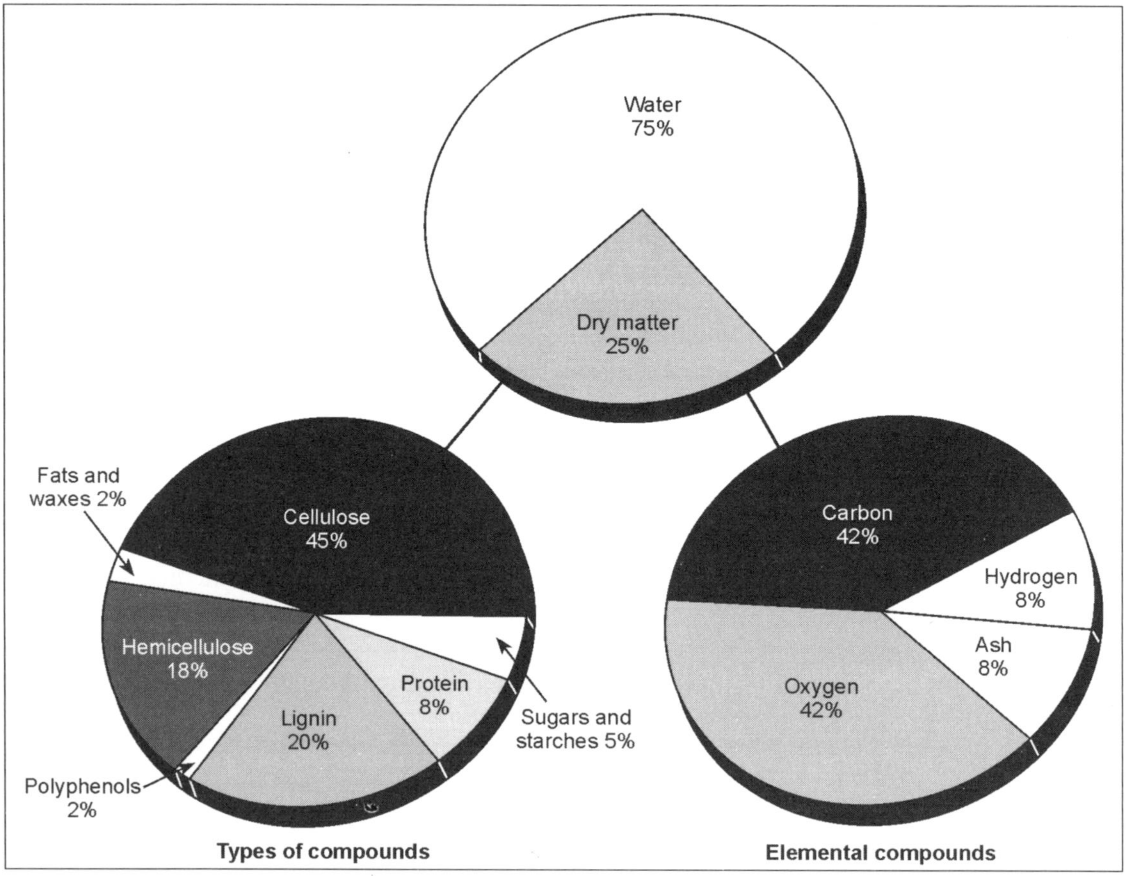

Decomposition of Organic Matter

The organic materials incorporated in the soil do not remain as such very long. They are at once attacked by a great variety of microorganisms, worms and insects present in the soil especially if the soil is moist. The microorganism for obtaining their food, break up the various constituents of which the organic residues are composed and convert them into new substances, some of which are very simple in composition and others highly complex. The whole of the organic residues is not decomposed all at once or as a whole. Some of the constituents are decomposed very rapidly, some less readily and others very slowly.

(A) Decomposition of soluble substances

Sugar and water-soluble nitrogenous compounds are the first to be decomposed as they offer a very readily available source of carbon, nitrogen and energy for the microorganisms. Thus, when glucose is decomposed under aerobic conditions the reaction is as under :

$$\text{Sugar} + \text{Oxygen} \xrightarrow[\text{condition}]{\text{aerobic}} \text{Carbon dioxide} + \text{Water}$$

(1) Ammonification. The transformation of organic nitrogenous compounds into ammonia is called ***ammonification***. During the course of action under aerobic conditions by heterotrophic organisms, oxygen is taken up and carbon dioxide is released. Ammonification process involves a gradual simplification of complex compounds. The ammonification occurs as a result of action of enzymes produced by microorganisms. Their action is chiefly hydrolytic and oxidative (in presence of air).

Organic nitrogen $\longrightarrow$ NH_3 or protein $\longrightarrow$ polypeptides $\longrightarrow$ amino acids $\longrightarrow$ ammonia or salts

(2) Nitrification. The process of conversion of ammonia to nitrite (NO_2) and then to nitrate (NO_3) is known as ***nitrification***. The production of nitrate is more rapid than that of nitrite, while the formation of ammonia is the slowest process. That is why soil usually contains more nitrate nitrogen than nitrite at any time. Nitrification is an aerobic process involving the production of nitrates from ammonium salts. It is the work of autotrophic bacteria.

$$\underset{\text{Ammonia}}{NH_3} \xrightarrow{\textit{Nitrosomonas}} \underset{\text{Nitrite}}{NO_2} \xrightarrow{\textit{Nitrobacter}} \underset{\text{Nitrate}}{NO_3}$$

The net reactions are as follows :

$$NH_4^+ + O_2 \longrightarrow NO_2^- + 2H^+ + H_2O + \text{energy (66 kcal)}$$

$$NO_2^- + O_2 \longrightarrow NO_3^- + \text{energy (18 kcal)}$$

The process which involves conversion of soil nitrate into gaseous nitrogen or nitrous oxide is called ***denitrification***.

$$\text{Nitrate} \xrightarrow{\textit{Pseudomonas/Bacillus}} \text{Nitrogen gas}$$

Water logging (*e.g.*, rice field) and high pH will increase nitrogen loss by denitrification.

(B) Decomposition of insoluble substances

(1) Breakdown of protein. Proteins are complex organic substances containing nitrogen, sulphur, and sometimes phosphorus, in addition to carbon, hydrogen and oxygen. During the course of decomposition of plant materials, the proteins are first hydrolyzed to a number of intermediate products, e.g., proteoses, peptones, peptides, etc., collectively known as ***polypeptides***.

$$\text{Proteins} \xrightarrow{\text{Hydrolysis}} \begin{matrix}\text{Proteoses}\\ \text{Peptones}\\ \text{Peptides}\end{matrix} \begin{matrix}\nearrow & \text{amino acids} & \searrow \\ & \longrightarrow & \\ \searrow & \text{Amides} & \nearrow\end{matrix} \text{Ammonia}$$

The process of conversion of proteins to amino acids is known as ***aminization***.

(2) Breakdown of cellulose. Cellulose is the most abundant carbohydrate present in plant residues. The microorganisms break up cellulose into cellobiose and glucose. Glucose is further attacked by organisms and converted into organic acids.

$$\text{Cellulose} \xrightarrow[\text{(Cellulase)}]{\text{Hydrolysis}} \text{Cellobiose} \xrightarrow[\text{(Cellobiase)}]{\text{Hydrolysis}} \text{Glucose}$$

$$\text{Glucose} \xrightarrow{\text{Oxidation}} \text{Organic acids} \xrightarrow{\text{Oxidation}} CO_2 + H_2O$$

The decomposition of cellulose in acid soils proceeds more slowly than in neutral and alkaline soils. It is quite rapid in well-aerated soils and comparatively slow in those poorly-aerated.

(3) Breakdown of hemi-cellulose. When subjected to microbial decomposition, hemicelluloses are first hydrolyzed to their component sugars and uronic acids. The sugars are further attacked by microorganisms. They are converted to organic acids, alcohols, carbon dioxide and water. The uronic acids are broken down to pentose and carbon dioxide. The newly synthesized hemicelluloses thus form a part of the humus. Hemicelluloses decompose faster than cellulose.

(4) Breakdown of starch. Chemically it is glucose polymer. It is first hydrolyzed to maltose by the action of enzymes (amylases). Maltose is next converted to glucose by another enzyme (maltase). Glucose being soluble in water is utilized for growth and other metabolic activities.

(C) Decomposition of ether-soluble substances

Fats are first broken down by microorganisms through the agency of enzyme lipase into glycerol and fatty acids. Glycerol is next oxidized to organic acids which along with the other fatty acids are finally oxidized to carbon dioxide and water.

(D) Decomposition of lignin

Lignin is deposited on the cell wall to impart strength to the skeleton framework of plant. Lignin decomposes slowly, much slower than cellulose. Complete oxidation of lignin gives rise to carbon dioxide and water.

(E) Simple decomposition products

As the enzymic changes of the soil organic matter proceed, simple products begin to manifest themselves. Some of these, especially carbon dioxide and water, appear immediately. Others such as nitrate-nitrogen accumulate only after the peak of the vigorous decomposition is over. The more common simple products resulting from the activity of the soil microorganisms are as follows :

Carbon : CO_2, CO_3^{2-}, HCO_3^-, elemental carbon
Nitrogen : NH_4^+, NO_2^-, NO_3^-, gaseous nitrogen
Sulphur : S, H_2S, SO_3^{2-}, SO_4^{2-}, CS_2
Phosphorus : $H_2PO_4^-$, HPO_4^{2-}, PO_4^{3-}
Others : H_2O, O_2, H_2, H^+, OH^-, K^+, Ca^{2+}, Mg^{2+} etc.

Mineralization of organic sulphur. Many organic compounds especially those of a nitrogenous nature, carry sulphur. Heterotrophic bacteria simplify the complex organic compounds, and then autotrophic bacteria (sulphur bacteria) oxidize it into sulphate form.

$$\underset{\text{Sulphur}}{S + 2O_2} \xrightarrow[\text{Oxidation}]{\text{Enzymic}} \underset{\text{Sulphate}}{SO_4^{2-}}$$

Mineralization of organic phosphorus. A large proportion of the soil phosphorus is carried in organic combinations. Upon attack by microorganisms the organic phosphorus compounds are mineralized; that is, they are changed to inorganic combinations. It depends upon soil pH. As the pH goes up from 5.5 to 7.5 the available phosphorus changes from $H_2PO_4^-$ to HPO_4^{2-}. Both of these forms are available to higher plants.

Humus

Humus is a complex and rather resistant mixture of brown or dark brown amorphous and colloidal substances that results from microbial decomposition and synthesis and has chemical and physical properties of great significance to soils and plantThe humic and non-humic compounds collectively make up humus.

(A) The *humic substances* comprise about 60-80 per cent of the soil organic matter. Humic substances are dark in colour, amorphous and have high molecular weight. Humic substances can be classified into three chemical groups. (*i*) *Humin* : The highest in molecular weight, dark in colour, insoluble in both acid and alkali and more resistant to microorganism attack (*ii*) *Humic acid*: medium in molecular weight, medium in colour, soluble in alkali but insoluble in acid, intermediate resistant to microbial degradation and (*iii*) *Fulvic acid* : lowest in molecular weight, light in colour, soluble in both acid and alkali and most susceptible to microorganism attack

(B) The *non-humic group* make up of about 20-30 per cent of the soil organic matter. Non-humic substances consists *polymers, polysaccharides, polyuronides*. Polysaccharides are especially effective in enhancing soil aggregate stability. Non-humic substances are less complex and less resistant to microbial attack than humic sunstances.

Humus is more resistant to decay and may present in soils even hundreds of years. This resistant property of humus is important in maintaining organic matter level in soils and protect nitrogen and other essential nutrients that are founs in humus complex.

Humus fractions

The humified fractions are considered as the most active part of humus which consists of a series of highly acidic, yellow to black coloured, high molecular weight polyelctrolytes known humic acid, fulvic acid and so on.

Based on the solubilities, the group is generally divided into three classes : (*i*) fulvic acid, which is thought to be of the lowest molecular weight and is alkali and acid soluble, (*ii*) humic acid, which is of medium molecular weight, alkali soluble and acid insoluble, (*iii*) humin, which is apparently of the highest molecular weight and is insoluble in both alkali and acid except under most drastic conditions.

The classical method of fractionation of humic substances is based on difference in solubility of the constituents in aqueous acidic and alkaline solutions and ethanol. The steps in the separation and fractionation of soil organic matter is shown here under :

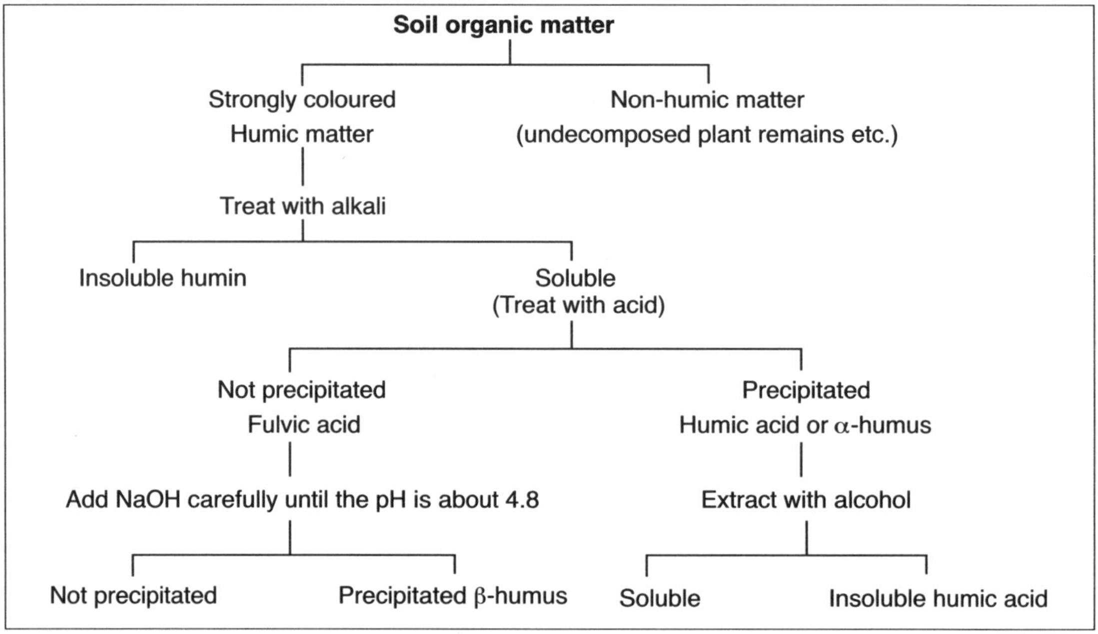

Carbon cycle

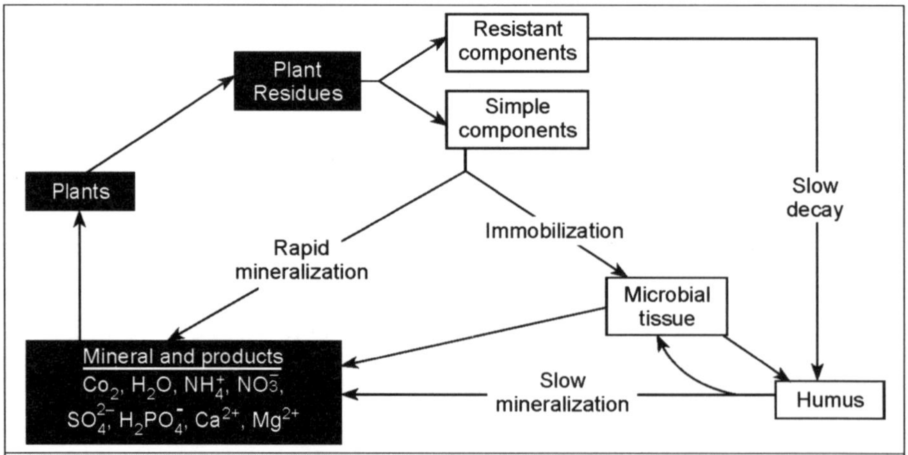

Fig. 24.1. Carbon cycle

Role of Organic Matter

The effects of organic matter on fertility are as follows :

(1) Organic matter binds soil particles into structural units called aggregates. These aggregates help to maintain a loose, open, granular condition. The granular condition of soil increase water infiltration and percolation.

(2) Water holding capacity is increased by organic matter. The granular soil resulting from organic matter additions, supplies more water than sticky and impervious soil.

(3) Surface runoff and erosion are reduced by organic matter as there is good infiltration.

(4) Organic matter on the soil surface reduces losses of soil by wind erosion.

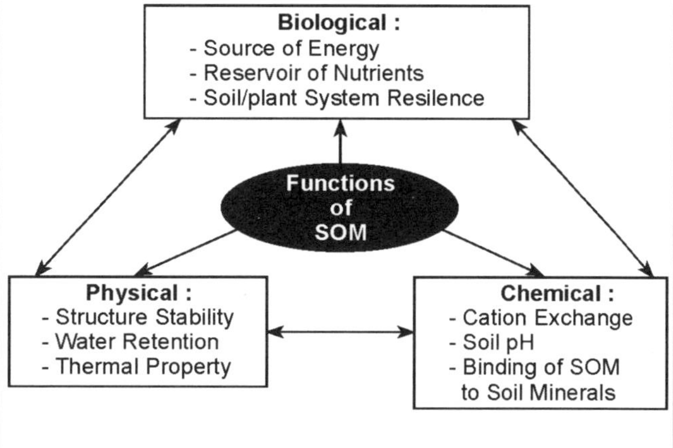

Fig. 24.2. Role of Soil Organic Matter

(5) Surface mulching with coarse organic matter, lower soil temperatures in the summer and keep the soil warmer in winter.

(6) The organic matter serves as a source of energy for the growth of soil micro-organisms.

(7) Organic matter serves as a reservoir of chemical elements that are essential for plant growth. Upon decomposition, organic matter supplies the nutrients needed by growing plants, as well as many hormones and antibiotics.

(8) Fresh organic matter has a special function in making soil phosphorus more readily available in acid soils.

(9) Organic acids released from decomposing organic matter help to reduce alkalinity in soils.

(10) Fresh organic matter supplies food for such soil life as earthworms, ant, and rodents. These microorganisms improve drainage and aeration.

(11) Organic matter upon decomposition produces organic acids and carbon dioxide which helps to dissolve minerals such as potassic and make them more available to growing plants.

(12) Humus (highly decomposed organic matter) provides a storehouse for the exchangeable and available captions potassium and magnesium. Ammonium fertilizers are also prevented from leaching because humus holds ammonium in an exchangeable and available form.

(13) It acts as a buffering agent. Buffering checks rapid chemical changes in pH.

Maintenance of Organic Matter in Soil

Normally in the country like India, it is difficult to increase/maintain organic matter in soil. Due to high temperature in summer, carbon is lost as CO_2 and hence, there is reduction of O.M. There is relation between C : N *i.e.* 10 : 1. So if we can keep more nitrogen in the soil, more carbon will remain in soil and hence more o.m. Therefore, we should use or add such a crop with high N or proportion content *i.e.* Material with low C : N ratio means legume crops. Therefore, we should use legume crops (low C : N ratio material) to increases/maintain O.M. in soil. Secondly use cereal-legume crop rotation, so that more nitrogen will remain in soil and hence more carbon/O.M.

Relationship among organic carbon, N and O.M.

Organic matter contains 58%C.

Therefore, 58 g C = 100 g O.M.

Organic Matter in Relation to Soil Fertility (Humus)

Definition of humus. It is a complex resistant mixture of fats, waxes, polysaccharides, polyuronides, lignin, lignoproteinate having brown to dark brown color, amorphous and colloidal in nature, which is transferred from original plant/microbial tissues.

What is Humus ?

1. As decompodzsition of O.M. is continued the digestible material *i.e.* exhausted and the resistant material like, fat, waxes, lignin and polysaccharides remains as uncomposted material.
2. As the easily oxidizable carbon reduces the activity of organisms is decreased. Finally they are die and the microbial tissue containing polyuronides resistant material will be part of humus.
3. Protein combines with lignin forming lignoproteinate compound (humic acid and humate). This being resistant to decomposition also becomes a part of humus.
4. Some of the proteins combine with clay forming protein, clay combination and this protein is not decomposed and hence it becomes a part of humus.

Thus at the end of decomposition, resistant mixture of dark brown, colloidal, amorphous which contains resistant. Polysaccharide from plant, tissues, polyuronides from microbial tissues and lignoproteinate complex resistant to decomposition material is obtained and this material is called humus.

Humus. lignoproteinate + other dark brown partly/fully decomposed organic/microbial tissue.

Properties and functions of humus:

1. It is light, bulky, amorphous, dark brown in color.
2. It has high WHC (water holding capacity) 100 parts of humus absorb 181 parts of water compared to 70 parts by clay and 25 parts by sand.
3. It possesses high plasticity, cohesion and adhesion than sand and low in these properties compared to clay. Because of these properties it is able to bind the sand particles and it reduces the movement of water and increases WHC of sand soil.

While with this low property, it cannot bind the clay particles but is helps to form aggregates and hence improves physical conditions of clayey soil.

4. It has 4 to 6 time more high CEC than silicate clay, CEC of humus is 150 to 300 meq/100 g.
5. It has negative charge due to carboxyl and phenolic group.
6. It acts as buffering agent.
7. It is a source of plant nutrients.

Source of Humus

The major source of organic matter is plant tissues generally leaves, branches, grasses etc. becomes the source of O.M. All above sources when buried in soil decomposition occurs and o.m. is obtained. Apart from this when the organisms die, the o.m. is added in the soil. Lastly the insects (ants, earthworms) also become the source of organic matter.

Composition of plant tissues

1. Water : 75%
2. Carbon : 11%
3. Oxygen : 10%
4. Hydrogen : 2%
5. Ash (mainly N) : 2%

Composition of humus

Lignin	:	55%
Amino acid	:	35%
Carbohydrate	:	15%
Hemicelluloses	:	7%
Fat, wax	:	3%
Other	:	5%

Rate of decomposition:

1. Sugar, starches and simple proteins — rapidly decomposed
2. Crude proteins
3. Hemicelluloses
4. Cellulose
5. Lignin, fats, waxes, etc. — very slowly decomposed.

(↓ from rapidly decomposed to very slowly decomposed)

Sugars, starches and water soluble protein are examples of readily available energy sources for soil organisms. Lignin is very resistant source of food.

When organic tissues are added to soil, three general reactions take place.

1. Organic material $\xrightarrow{\text{Oxidation}}$ $CO_2 + H_2O$ + Energy
2. The essential elements N, P and S are released and/or immobilized by a series of specific reactions relatively unique for each element.

3. Compound resistant to microbial action are formed either through modification of compounds or by microbial synthesis.

Simple decomposition products

The more common simple products resulting from the activity of the soil microorganisms may be listed as follow :

(1) Carbon. CO_2, CO_3^{2-}, HCO_3^-, CH_4, elemental carbon

(2) Nitrogen. NH_4^+, NO_2^-, NO_3^-, N_2.

(3) Sulphur. S, H_2S, SO_3^{2-}, SO_4^{2-}, and CS_2.

(4) Phosphorous. $H_2PO_4^-$, HPO_4^{2-}.

(5) Others. H_2O, O_2, H_2, H^+, OH^-, K^+, Ca^{2+}, Mg^{2+}, etc.

Classification of Humus

According to Mulder Scientist, on the basis of solubility in water as well as alkali humus is classified in three groups :

(i) **Soluble in water.** Crenic acid, Apocreic Acid

(ii) **Soluble in Alkali.** Almic (Black), Humic acid (black)

(iii) **Insoluble in alkali.** Almin, Humin acid

According to Oden scientist, on the basis of behavior and colour, humus is classified in four groups :

(*i*) Humic coal

(*ii*) Humic acid

(*iii*) Humatomelenic acid

(*iv*) Fulvic acid

TABLE 24.1. Impotent Properties of humus fraction

Properties	Water	Behavior			Remark
		Alcohol	Alkali	Colour	
Humus coal	Insoluble dispersion	Insoluble	Insoluble but able blossom or swelling	Black	From alkali consecution convert to humic acid
Humic acid	Low soluble but by dispersion make suspension	Insoluble but partially dispersed	Soluble	Dark brown in color with red spot	Soluble in base (pH 10) intermediate molecular weight (< 10,000) more resistant
Hematomelenic acid	Low solubility by dispersion make colloid suspension	Make the true solution	Soluble	Brown colour with yellow spot	C = 26%
Fulvic acid	Make true solution	-do-	-do-	Golden or fade yellow colour	Soluble in acid (pH 2) Lowest molecular weight (<1,000) Least resistant to decay

Mineralogical Significance of Humus

Extensive studies have shown that not much of the humic substances in soil is in free state but much is bound to colloidal clay.

The ways in which humic substances are combination with mineral portion of soil as follows :

1. As salts of low-molecular organic acids (acetate, oxalate, lactate and others).
2. As salts of humic substances with alkaline cations-humate, fulvate.
3. As chelate with metal ions.
4. As substances held on clay mineral surfaces.

Salts of low-molecular organic acids

Salts of low-molecular acids forms in result of action of acids (acetic acid, oxalic acid, fumaric acid, lactic acid) on minerals (magnesite, calcite, siderite and others) or salts of mineral acids with Ca, K and others cations.

Salts of humic substances with alkaline cations

Salts of humic substances with alkaline cations comprehensive of compounds:

- humate (salts of humic acids)
- fulvate (salts of fulvic acids)

They are the most characteristic compounds of soil humic substances. The alkaline cations (Na^+, K^+, Ca^{2+}, Mg^{2+}) are held primarily by simple cation exchange with COOH groups (RCOONa, RCOOK etc.). The humate and fulvate occur in soil largely as mixture with hydroxide of Fe and Al.

Chelate with metal ions

A chelate complex is formed when two or more coordinate positions about the metal ion are occupied by donor groups of a single ligand to form an internal ring structure. In soil role of ligands fulfilment simple organic compounds and functional groups of humic substances.

The order of decreasing affinity of organic groupings for metal ions is approximately as follows :

—O—	>	$—NH_2$	>	—N=N—	>	=N	>	—COO—	>	—O—	>	C=O
enolate		amine		azo		ring N		carboxylate		ether		carbonyl

The order of decreasing ability of metal ions to chelating is as follows :

$$Fe^{3+} > Cu^{2+} > Ni^{2+} > Co^{2+} > Zn^{2+} > Fe^{2+} > Mn^{2+}$$

The complexing ability of humic and fulvic acids results largely from their content of oxygen-containing functional groups, such as COOH, phenolic OH and C=O group.

Soil organic constituents form both soluble and insoluble complexes with metal ions and thereby play a dual role in soil. Low-molecular-weight compounds (biochemicals, fulvic acids) bring about the solubilization of metal ions and affect their transport to plant roots. In contrast, high-molecular-weight compounds (*e.g.* humic acids) function as a "sink" for polyvalent cations. Natural complexing agents are of considerable importance in weathering processes and in the movement of sesquioxides into the subsoil.

Clay–organic complexes

The interaction of organic substances with clay has a multitude of consequences that are reflested in the physical, chemical and biological properties of the soil matrix. Several mechanisms are involved in the adsorption of humic substances by clay minerals, the main ones being :

(*i*) Van der Waals' forces
(*ii*) Bonding by cation bridging
(*iii*) H-bonding
(*iv*) Adsorption by association with hydrous oxides
(*v*) Adsorption on interlamellar spaces of clay minerals

(*i*) Van der Waals' forces

Van der Waals' forces operate between all molecules, but are rather weak. Essentially, these forces result from fluctuations in the electric charge density of individual atoms. An electrically positive fluctuation in one atom tends to produce an electrically negative fluctuation in a neigh-boring atom and net attractive forces results. Attractive forces resulting from these fluctuations are every pair of atoms or molecules.

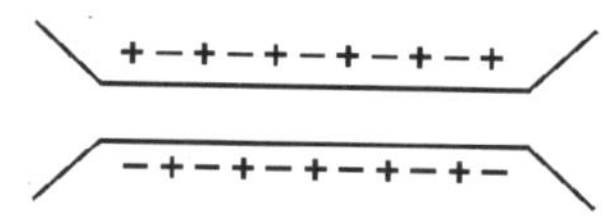

Van der Waal's forces

Adsorption caused by van der Waals' forces can be of considerable importance in the adsorption of neutral polar and non polar molecules, particularly those which are high in molecular weight.

(*ii*) Bonding by cation bridging

Since organic anions are normally repelled from negatively charged clay surfaces, adsorption of humic and fulvic acids by clay minerals such as montmorillonite occurs only when polyvalent cations are present on the exchange complex.

Unlike Na^+ and K^+, polyvalent cations are able to maintain neutrality at the surface by neutralizing both the charge on the clay and the acidic functional group of the organic matter (*e.g.* COO^-).

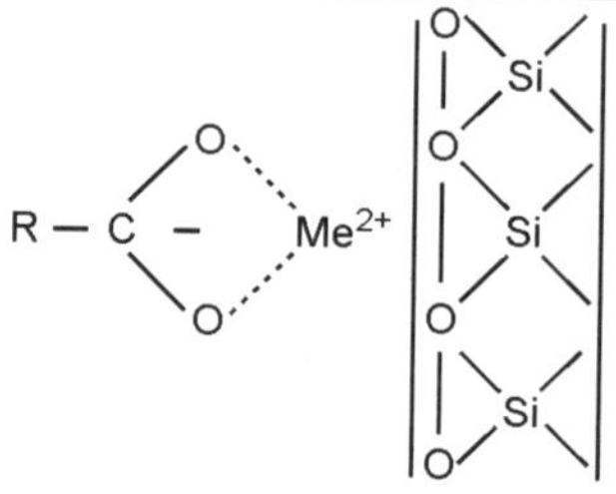

Cation bridgine

The main polyvalent cations responsible for the binding of humic and fulvic acids to soil clays are Ca^{2+}, Fe^{3+} and Al^{3+}. The divalent Ca^{2+} ion doesn't form strong coordination complexes with organic molecules. In contrast Fe^{3+} and Al^{3+} form strong coordination complexes with organic compounds. The polyvalent cations act as a bridge between two charged sites.

(iii) H–Bonding

This is a linkage between polar groups of the organic molecule and adsorbed water molecules or oxygens of the silicate surface through bonding with a single H^+ ion. The strength of an individual bond is small, but they are additive thus total adsorption energy can be appreciable. Rigorous drying, such as by desication at the soil surface or consumption of available moisture by plant roots, will tend to increase the bonding between humic material and clay by eliminating hydration water and bringing the humic matter in contact to the clay.

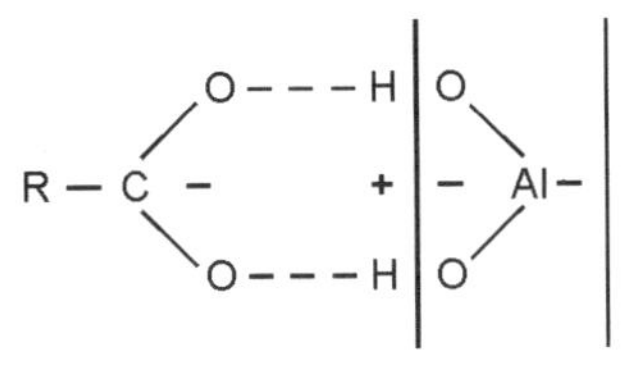

H - bonding

(iv) Adsorption by association with hydrous oxides of Fe and Al

For many soils, hydrous oxides are equal in importance to mica-type surfaces in sorbing humic substances. When clay minerals are coated with layers of hydrous oxides their surface reactions are dominated by these oxides rather than the clay. Organic anions can be associated with the oxides by simple coulombic attraction. Anion associated with clay in this manner is readily removed by increasing the pH or by leaching with NaCl or NH_4Cl. The fact that very little humic material can be recovered from soils by these treatments suggests that most of the adsorbed organic matter is retained by supplementary mechanisms.

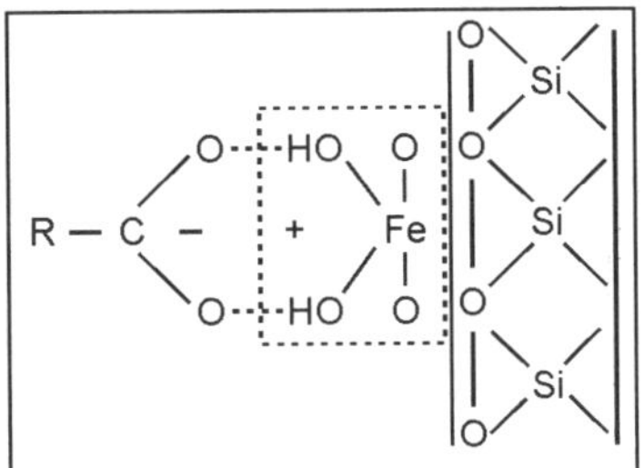

Bond by hydrous oxides

Coordination or ligand exchange occurs when the anionic group penetrates the coordination shell of Al or Fe and becomes incorporated with the surface OH layer. The sorption of fulvic acid on oxide surfaces is accompanied by displacement of OH groups by COO^- ions. The organic anion is not easily displaced with simple salts, although adsorption is pH sensitive.

As was the case with organic cations on clay mineral surfaces, a very strong bond will result if more than one group on the humic molecule participates.

(v) Adsorption on interlamellar spaces of clay minerals

An important mechanisms for retention of proteins and charged organic cations by expandable-layer silicates is through adsorption on interlamellar spaces. Considerably contrversy exist as to whether humic and fulvic acids are bound in this way in the natural soil.

C : N Ratio (Carbon to Nitrogen ratio). The C : N ratio of in the organic matter of arable soil ranges from 8 : 1 to 15 : 1. The average being 10 : 1 or 12 : 1.

1. The ratio is lower in arid region soils than humid regions.
2. It is also lower in warmer regions than cooler one.

C : N ratio in plants and microbes. It is varies from 4 : 1 to 9 : 1 for bacterial tissues, 20 : 1 to 30 : 1 for legumes and farm yard manures and 100 : 1 for straw and 400 : 1 for saw dust.

General principles for decomposition of C and N in relation to microbial population and use of these two elements

1. Microbes require carbon for energy. This carbon must be easily oxidizable (like carbon of glucose, sucrose etc.)
2. As the plant is in younger stage, there is more easily oxidizable carbon. This carbon will be used by the organisms. They will get more energy and hence, their activities and total number will be increased. As the available carbon is slowly reduced both the number and activity will also be reduced and finally for want of carbon organisms die.
3. Microbes also require available N for their tissues (body) building.
4. As the activity and number are increased they will require more available N for their tissue formation. Therefore, they will use original available soil nitrogen. So during the period of high activity, available N will be minimum in the soil and most of the N is tied up in microbial tissue as bacterial protein.
5. Under this situation, either mineralized or immobilization of nitrogen take place. If C : N ratio of material added to soil is :
   (*a*) 20 : 1 there will be mineralization
   (*b*) 30 : 1 there will be immobilization.
   (*c*) Between 20 : 1 and 30 : 1 there will be neither mineralization nor immobilization of nitrogen.

Carbon : Nitrogen (C : N) ratio

The ratio of the weight of organic carbon (C) to the weight of total nitrogen (N) in a soil (or organic material), is known as C : N ratio. When fresh plant residues are added to the soil, they are rich in carbon and poor in nitrogen. The content of carbohydrates is high. This results in wide carbon-nitrogen ratio which may be 40 to 1. Upon decomposition the organic matter of soils changes to humus and have an approximate C : N ratio of 10 : 1.

Matter/Substance	*C : N Ratio*
Microorganism	4-9 : 1
Bacteria	5 : 1
Actinomycetes	6 : 1
Fungi	4 : 1
Humus	10-12 : 1
Organic Matter	12-40 : 1
Green Legumes	12 : 1
Alfa alfa	13 : 1
Clovers	20 : 1
Manures	20 : 1
FYM	20-30 : 1

Matter/Substance	*C : N Ratio*
Barseem	21 : 1
Hay (Green grasses)	25 : 1
Maize Stalk	40-50 : 1
Sugarcane Buggasse	40-50 : 1
Wood Burada	350 : 1
Wheat straw	124 : 1
Paddy Stover	80-90 : 1
Saw dust (flyash)	400-500 : 1
Cultivated/General soil	8-15 : 1
Mineral soil	10-12 : 1
Waterlogged soil	10-12 : 1

The ratio of carbon to nitrogen in the arable (cultivated) soils commonly ranges from 8 : 1 to 15 : 1. The carbon-nitrogen ratio in plant material is variable, ranging from 20 : 1 to 30 : 1. Low ratios of carbon to nitrogen (10 : 1) in soil organic matter generally indicate an average stage of decomposition and resistance to further microbiological decomposition. A wide ratio of C : N (35 : 1) indicates little or no decomposition, susceptibility to further and rapid decomposition and slow nitrification.

Significance of C : N Ratio

(1) Keen competition for available nitrogen when organic residues (with high C : N ratio) are added to soils. When organic residues with a wide C/N ratio (50 : 1) are incorporated in the soil, decomposition quickly occurs. Carbon dioxide is produced in large quantities. Under these conditions, nitrate-nitrogen disappears from the soil because of the instant microbial demand for this element to build up their tissues. And for the time being, little (or no) nitrogen is an available to plants. As decomposition occurs, the C/N ratio of the plant material decrease since carbon is being lost and nitrogen conserved. Nitrates-N again appear in quantity in the soil, thus, increases plant growth (Fig. 24.3).

(2) Consistency of C : N Ratio as the decomposition processes continue, both carbon and nitrogen are now subject to loss the carbon as carbon dioxide and the nitrogen as nitrates which are leached or absorbed by plants. At a point carbon-nitrogen ratio, becomes more or less constant, generally stabilizes at 10 : 1 or 12 : 1.

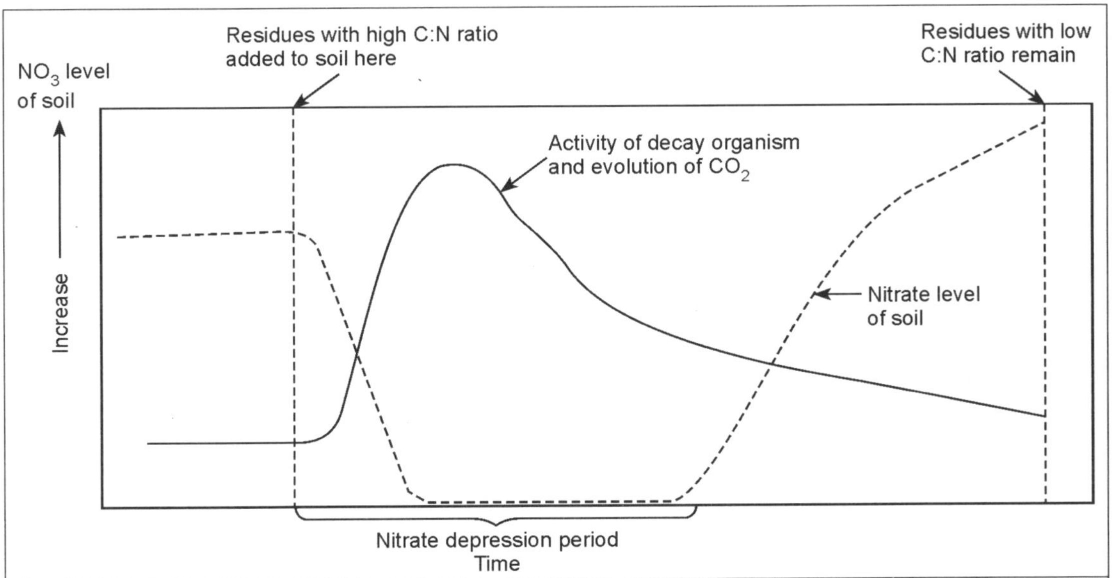

Fig. 24.3. Relationship between stage of decay of organic residues and presence of nitrate nitrogen in soil

It has always been considered profitable to mix the highly carbonaceous material like straw with a small quantity of ammonium sulphate. With this available source of nitrogen from ammonium sulphate, the decomposition of fresh organic material is hastened and thus, the release of available nitrogen is affected in a shorter period of time.

What will happen if materials of different C : N ratios material is added to soil

Before adding material, levels of CO_2, NO_3 and activity of organisms remain the same, when materials containing high C : N say 50 : 1 are added to soil, the organisms become active and use carbon as source of energy. They multiply rapidly and yield CO_2 in large quantities. Under this condition due to increase in activities and number of organisms, they require more NO_3—N for their body building so they take N from soil hence NO_3 is reduced in soil. This situation is continued until decomposition near completion. At this stage (time) activity of organisms gradually over subsides due to lack of carbon. There number decrease, CO_2 formation reduces, organisms do not form their tissues and hence do not use nitrogen. Therefore from this stage nitrification can be proceeding and NO_3 is accumulated.

Reasons for the Constancy of C : N Ratio in Soil

As the decomposition starts initially C is lost at the faster rate than nitrogen. When the C : N ratio comes nearly 10 : 1 or 15 : 1 the loss of carbon, nitrogen is the same rates of 10 : 1 *i.e.* loss every 10 carbons, there will be loss of nitrogen. So there will total loss of both C and N but it will remain constant in the neighbourhood of soil.

Low C : N material is added to soil when material containing low C : N ratio say 20 : 1 high proteineous material is added to soil, first activity of Mo increases. Mineralization of nitrogen is continued and only a few quantity of this nitrogen is used by organisms as the number and activity are small, protein is exhausted because of liberation of NO_3 from soil. The mass of microbial tissue is approximately equal to initial and the content of NO_3–N in soil is high.

❑❑❑

CHAPTER 25

Soil Health and Soil Quality

STRATEGIES FOR MANAGING SOIL HEALTH FOR SUSTAINABLE AGRICULTURE

Integrated Plant Nutrient Management (IPNM)

- The basic concept underlying IPNS is the maintenance of soil fertility, sustainable agricultural productivity and improving farmers' profitability through judicious and efficient use of fertilizers, organic manures, crop residues, bio-fertilizers, etc.
- Soil testing is an important component of nutrient management. Integrated nutrient supply, including the use of chemical fertilizers with organic sources like green manure, FYM, crop residues, bio fertilizers help not only in bridging the existing wide gap between nutrients removal and addition but also ensuring balanced nutrient proportions, in enhancing nutrients response efficiency and maximizing crop productivity of the desired quality.
- For maintenance of sustained soil fertility in intensive cropping systems, greater, importance has assigned to the organic waste management and its availability.
- Long Time Fertilizer Experiment (LTFE) experiments in different agro-ecological zones of India showed that full application of recommended dose of NPK failed to sustain soil health and crop productivity.
- Results of long-term experiments indicate that with the use of 10-15 t FYM/ha annually along with 100% recommended dose of NPK, additional yields of different crops as compared to chemical fertilization at the recommended rate could be realized.
- In some of the other long-term experiments, application of NPK alone or substitution with organic sources could save fertilizers to the tune of 25 to 50% and sustained soil health. Most of the Indian soils require N fertilization for optimum crop productivity.
- This costly plant nutrient (N) can be supplied through the inclusion of legumes in crop rotation through biological N fixation and harvesting residual effect on succeeding cereal crop.

Balanced Use of Fertilizers

- The average N : P_2O_5 : K_2O consumption ratio was 6.9 : 2.7 : 1 in 2003-04, while in 2010-11 the average N : P_2O_5 : K_2O consumption ratio is 5.3 : 2.1 : 1. Which is considered quite wide compared to the projected average ideal ratio of 4 : 2 : 1. The large scale usage of high analysis chemical fertilizers with only one or two nutrient elements has caused increased deficiencies of several secondary (Mg, S) and micronutrients (Zn, Mn, Fe, B and Cu).
- It is reported that more than 50% of soils are deficient in Zn, 12% in Fe, 5% in Mn, 3% in Cu and 33% in B. Regular nutrient monitoring of different production systems under agro ecological situations and employment of timely corrective measures are imperative to maintain good soil health for sustained high productivity.

Microbiological Approach

- Biofertilizers enhance soil fertility as well as crop production by fixing atmospheric N, mobilizing sparingly soluble P and by facilitating the release of nutrients through decomposition of crop residues.
- *Azotobacter*, free living heterotrophic N fixing bacteria, not only provides N but also produces a variety of growth promoting substances.
- *Azospirilla* are mesophylic and have been reported to fix N in association with crops grown on soils with acidic to alkaline range, It is claimed that blue green algae (BGA) in rice field contributes 20-30 kg N ha^{-1} per season and may increase grain yields by 5-14%.
- However, under soil conditions when P availability is considerably reduced due to fixation and limited mobility.
- Inoculation with Vesicular Arbuscular Mycorrhizae (VAM) could be an advantageous. Field trials conducted on high P fixing Vertisols have shown that by using VAM, 15 kg fertilizers P ha^{-1} can be saved.

Soil Fertility Appraisal through Soil Testing

- Soil testing work should be expanded along with modernization of analytical facilities. Vital linkages should be established between soil test laboratories and research organizations.
- Recent moves to establish soil test laboratories in each of Krishi Vigyan Kendra (KVK) and also to support the creation of soil and water analysis facilities at agri-clinics would go a long way in soil testing service.
- These new soil testing laboratories should be, at least, capable of testing soils for primary, secondary and micronutrients besides, having greater analyzing capacities. Soil testing laboratories at the division level should be upgraded as soil health clinics.

CONCEPTS OF NUTRIENT AVAILABILITY

Liebig Law of Minimum. This law states "the nutrient present in least relative amount is the limiting nutrient" in its extreme from, it implies that "even if all but one of the essential elements be presents, the absence of that one constituent renders the crop barren."

Mitscherlich's Law. Mitscherlich's law of physiological relationships states that the "yield can be increased by each single growth factor even when it is not present in the minimum a long as it not present in the optimum". As per Mitscherlich's growth law "increase in yield of a crop as a result of increasing a single growth factor is proportional to the decrement from the maximum yield obtainable by increasing that particular growth factor"

Law of Minimum of Wallance and Wallance. This law state that "when the need is fully satisfied for every factor required in the process, the rate of the process can be at its maximum potential, which is greater than the sum of the individual parts because of the sequentially additive interactions".

These basic laws have been used while developing the concepts of nutrient availability.

Bray's Concept of Availability (1938)

I. The available amount of the nutrient in the soil is that portion, whose variation is mainly responsible for the variation in the yield and the response to the added fertilizer.

   The first condition. Content of the available nutrient in a soil is high; it should not be respond to fertilizer application.

   The second condition. Available nutrient content is low it should be response to the applied fertilizer.

II. Fraction of the total content, which is susceptible to absorption by plants during its growth.

Selection of Methods

Bray (1948) proposed that a good soil test should meet the following three criteria.

1. The extractant used should extract all or a proportionate part of the available form or forms of a nutrient from soils with variable properties.
2. The amount of nutrient extracted should be measured with reasonable accuracy and speed.
3. The amount extracted should be correlated with the growth and response of each crop to that nutrient under various conditions.

A, E and L Values through Radio Tracer Technique

The use of radioisotope in soil fertility research is being done widely and the concept of "A", "E" and "L" values have come in to use.

***(i)* "A" Value Concept.** Fried and Dean (1952) have presented the concept that a plant having two sources of a nutrient will absorb its nutrients from each of these sources in direct proportion to the amount available. The mathematical expression of this relationship is as follow :

$$A = B\frac{(1 - Y)}{Y}$$

where, A = amount of nutrient available in the soil.

B = amount of nutrient in the standard.

Y = proportion of the nutrient in the pant derived from the standard.

The method simply involves the introduction of a known quantity of a standard source of the nutrients under consideration into soil, growing the desired crop, determining the proportion of the total nutrient absorbed that was derived from the standard source and calculating the amount of available nutrient in the soil, "A", by using the above equation.

The advantages of the method over non-isotopic procedure are :

(1) Its independency from the amount of nutrient applied *i.e.* one rate of fertilizer application is sufficient and curved need not be established.

(2) Plants do not have to be grown under abnormal condition of severe nutrient stress,

(3) The amount of growth does not affect the results,

(4) Size of plot does not affect the results, and

(5) The value obtained is not extrapolated value and thus the error of estimate is not appreciably increased.

***(ii)* "E" Value Concept.** This was proposed by Russell and his colleagues. The "E" value is considered to be the amount of phosphate in the soil *i.e.* exchangeable in a certain time with the element in solution to which phosphate has been added. In this method, the difficulty of measuring a small amount of phosphorus in the soil solution is overcome by adding a high carrier level of tagged phosphate. The "E" value (often measured after the added phosphate has been shaken with the soil for 24 hours) can be calculated from the following equation by the application of the isotopic dilution principle :

$$E = b\,\frac{S^*_o}{S^*_e} - 1$$

where, b = amount of carrier phosphate added/unit of soil

S^*_o = Specific activity of the radioactive phosphate solution added to the soil

i.e., $$S^*o = \frac{P^{32}}{P^{31}}\text{ fertilizer.}$$

S^*e = Specific activity of the Phosphate in solution after equilibrium

$$S^*e = \frac{P^{32}}{P^{31}}\text{ solution}$$

***(iii)* "L" value concept.** Sigurd Larsen suggested that when labeled phosphatic fertilizer was added to soil at different rates and plants were grown, the specific activity analysis of the plant material would give a constant value if isotopic dilution of the added chemical was assumed to take place in the soil system. Larsen assumed that reason for the constant value obtained was that equilibrium had been reached between added phosphate salt and the exchangeable phosphate in the soil. He tested this by the formulae.

$$L = B\,\frac{(1 - Y)}{Y}$$

where, L = amount of labile phosphorous

B = amount of radio active fertilizer applied

Y = fraction of phosphorous in the plant *i.e*. derived from the fertilizer.

$$Y = \frac{S^*\text{ plant}}{S^*\text{fertilizer}}$$

In practice, the most suitable form of the equation is :

$$L = B \times \frac{\frac{P^{32}}{P^{31}}\text{ in fertilizer}}{\frac{P^{32}}{P^{31}}\text{ in crop}} - 1$$

The "L" value can be considered as an "E" value in which the plant is being used as the means of sampling the soil solution upon equilibration of added P with exchangeable soil P. The "E" value has the advantages that it can be easily and quickly measured but where the parameter is to be related to plant uptake of phosphorus, the "L" value is the more relevant measurement.

Different workers have established the "A" value for majority of nutrients, while "E" and "L" values were primarily for determining P supplying capacity of a soil.

Limitation of these methods

(1) Handling of radioactive materials which requires special care, training and special equipments.

(2) They are costly.

Hence, they are not used for routine analysis purpose but they are certainly used at centralized laboratories for standardizing the routine chemical methods.

SOIL FERTILITY

Soil is a dynamic natural body composed of mineral and organic materials and living forms in which crops grow to feed and clothe the world.

There are two basic concepts of soil, which have been developed through scientific study of soil *viz*., Pedological and Edaphological.

From the Greek word *pedon*, this means soil or earth. Pedology involved the origin of soil, its classification and description. It considers the soil as a natural body and does not focus primarily on soils immediate practical utilization. Edaphology (from the Greek word edaphos which also means soil or ground) is the study of the soil from the standpoint view of higher plants. It considers various soil properties as they relate to plant production.

Soil, in general, has three-fold function to perform (*a*) Physical (*b*) Chemical and (*c*) Biological.

Physically the soil serves as the mechanical support for crops to stand erect. The nutrient supply for the plant is fulfilled by chemical functions. Biological functions depend on physical and chemical condition of the soil. It serves as the seat of teeming microorganisms.

The word 'fertile' means bearing abundantly and a fertile soil is considered to be one that produces abundant crops under suitable environmental conditions. Soil fertility is vital to a productive soil. But a fertile soil is not necessarily a productive soil. All fertile soils may or may not be productive. Poor drainage, insects, drought and other factors can limit production, even when fertility is adequate. To fully understand soil fertility, one must know other factors which support or limit productivity.

Soil Fertility. The status of a soil with respect to the amount and availability of essential nutrients to plants which are necessary for growth.

Soil Productivity. The capacity of a soil for producing a specified plant or sequence of plants under a specified system of management.

In other words, productivity is defined as the response to management in term of yield per hectare.

The soil is said to be productive when good yields are obtained. Productive soils are those, which contain adequate amounts of all essential nutrients in readily available forms to plants are in good physical condition to support plants and contain just the right amount of water and air for desirable root growth. Thus, soil fertility, good management practices, availability of water supply and a suitable climate contribute towards soil productivity. Therefore, a soil can be highly fertile, yet it may be unproductive, even a soil has readilly supply of nutrients but has an in sufficient water supply, presence of toxic substances or physical properties. For a soil to be productive, it must of necessity be fertile. Soil fertility denotes the status of plant nutrients in the soil while soil productivity denotes the resultant of various factors influencing crop production both within and beyond the soil. Thus, soil productivity is a function of environmental factors combined with soil fertility or more correctly, in combination with environmental factors and management practices constitutes soil productivity. The factors that affect the plant growth are following :

1. Internal or Genitical factors
   (*a*) Plant genetics
   (*b*) Physiology
2. External or Environmental factors
   (*a*) Soil Factors :
      (*i*) Mechanical support (*ii*) Nutrients
      (*iii*) Air (*iv*) Water
      (*v*) Temperature
   (*b*) Above ground factors
      (*i*) Light (*ii*) Temperature/Heat
      (*iii*) Insect and disease (*iv*) Cultural practices

In a discussion on soil fertility, only those factors are of importance that are within the influence of man and the judicious control of which determines the maximum crop yields in any given soil situation in a particulars climatic condition.

Man has little control over air, light and temperature, but can influence the supply of plant nutrients in the soil. He may increase the supply of available nutrient by modifying soil condition through good management or by making additions in the form of fertilizers.

With the advancement in scientific knowledge of plant nutrition and soil science as a result of the impact of the basic science of physiology, chemistry, physics and biology in the field of agricultural research, basic concepts on soil fertility have come in to sharper focus. It is now known that fertility in the soil is the result of the presence of essential plant nutrients in adequate amount and in available forms. According to present state of our knowledge, 17 mineral elements are considered to be essential for plant growth of the 17 essential elements, plant obtained 14 nutrient elements *viz*., N, P, K, Ca, Mg, S, Fe, Cu, Mn, Zn, Mo, B, Cl and Ni from the soil that are usually limiting plant growth.

Besides, the inorganic plant nutrients indicated above, organic matter in the soil is another very vital factor that control soil fertility. It serves as the principal store house for soil N and other plant nutrients and through its decomposition by microorganisms like bacteria, fungi, actinomycetes, etc., it gives life to the soil. Without organic matter, in a process of decay, with its millions of microorganisms, the soil will be the dead soil. Thus, a study of the inorganic plant nutrients in the soil, its organic matter content and the microbiological status should enable an appraisal of its fertility. These studies in turn, will help us to determine how one can augment from outside their supplies to increase fertility or impair their action to help plant growth. Such a treatment of the subject is very fundamental to understand wise soil management and to assist for increasing crop production.

Soil productivity is basically an economic concept and not a soil property. Three things are involved :

(*i*) Inputs (a specified management system)

(*ii*) Outputs (Yield of particular crops)

(*iii*) Soil type

The different soils have different capâcities to absorb inputs for profit maximization. Second, different crops have different capacities to absorb management inputs for profit maximization on a given soil type. These are illustrated as follow :

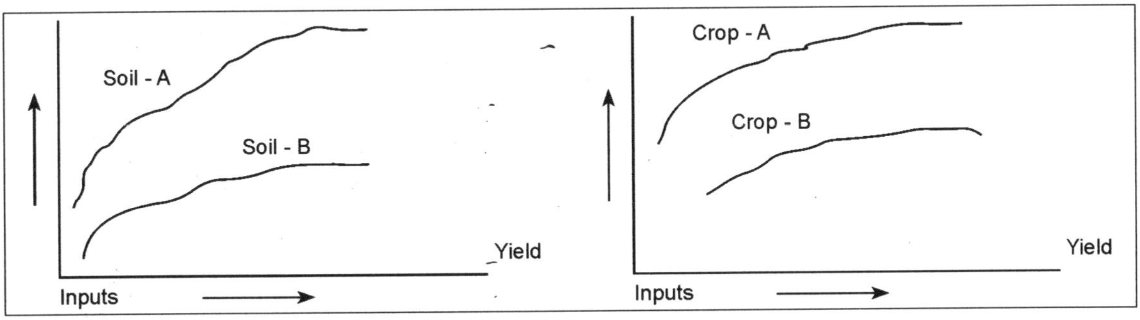

On increasing inputs, the yield from soil A increases more rapidly than from soil B. Thus, soil A is a more productive than soil B.

The soil represented is more productive for crop A than crop B. Thus, crop A has a greater profit potential than crop B.

By assigning costs and prices, net profit can be calculated and used as a basis for determining land value, which is important in loan appraising and tax assessment.

Thus, soil fertility is the most valuable assets of a nation. It should be maintained where it is high, improved where it is low and developed where it is lacking. Soil fertility is of two kinds *viz.*, permanent fertility and temporary fertility. Permanent fertility is inherent in the soil itself and temporary fertility is acquired by suitable management practices.

SOIL FERTILITY EVALUATION

- The proper rate of plant nutrient is determined by knowing nutrient requirement of the crop and nutrient supplying power of soil. Hence, the evaluation of soil fertility becomes important.
- Soil fertility evaluation is essential for balanced nutrition of the crops. Balance nutrients use refers to the application of essential plant nutrients in right amounts and proportions using correct methods and time of application for specific soil-crop-climatic situations.
- Several techniques are commonly employed to asses the fertility status of the soils.
- A proper evaluation of fertility of soil before planting of a crop helps in adopting appropriate measures to make up for the shortcoming and ensuring a good crop production. The diagnostic techniques are
  1. Nutrient deficiency symptoms of plant
  2. Analysis of tissues from plant growing on the soil
  3. Biological tests in which the growth of higher plants or certain micro-organisms are used as a measure of soil fertility
  4. Soil testing

1. Nutrient deficiency symptoms of plant

There are some indicator plants which shows the nutrient deficiencies or excess. Some of them are given as follows :

Plant		Nutrient deficiency/toxicity
Oat	:	Mg, Mn and Cu deficiencies
Wheat and barley	:	Mg, Cu and some times Mn deficiencies
Sugar beets	:	B and Mn deficiencies
Maize	:	N, P, K, Mg, Fe, Mn and Zn deficiencies
Potatoes	:	K, Mg and Mn deficiencies
Rape	:	N, P and Mg deficiencies
Brassica species	:	K and Mg deficiencies
Sudan grass	:	Fe and Mn deficiencies
Sunflower	:	B deficiency
Cauliflower	:	B and Mo deficiencies
Flax	:	Zn deficiency
Barley	:	B, Mn and Al toxicities
Cucumber	:	N and P excess
Sugar beets	:	Cu excess
Sugar beet, Turnip	:	Na deficiency
Cereals	:	Si deficiency

2. Analysis of tissues from plant growing on soil

- Plant analysis in a narrow sense is the determination of the concentration of an element or extractable fraction of an element in a sample taken from a particular part or of a crop at certain stage of morphological development.
- Plant analysis is complementary to soil testing. In many situations, total or available content of an element in soil fails to correlate with the plant tissue concentration or the growth and yield of crop.
- This can be ascribed to many reasons including the physico-chemical properties of the soils and the root growth patterns.
- On the other hand, the concentration of an element in the plant tissue is, generally, positively correlated with the plant health.
- Therefore, the plant analysis has been used as a diagnostic tool to determine the nutritional cause of plant disorders/diseases.

(A) The plant analysis constitutes

(1) The collection of the representative plant parts at the specific growth stage.

(2) Washing, drying and grinding of plant tissue.

(3) Oxidation of the powdered plant samples to solubilize the elements.

(4) Estimation of different elements.

(5) Interpretation of the status of nutrients with respect to deficiency/sufficiency/toxicity on the basis of known critical concentrations.

(B) Plant analysis has many applications such as

(1) Diagnosis of nutrient deficiencies, toxicities or imbalances.

(2) Measurement of the quantity of nutrients removed by crops to replace them in order to maintain soil fertility.

(3) Estimating overall nutritional status of the region or soil types.

(4) Monitoring the effectiveness of the fertilizer practices adopted.

(5) Estimation of nutrient levels in the diets available to the live stock.

(C) Collection and Preparation of plant samples

- Plant scientists have been able to standardize the procedures for collection of samples of plant tissue with respect to the plant part and growth stage, which reflect the nutrient concentrations corresponding to the health of the growth because the concentrations of different nutrients vary significantly over the life cycle of a plant.
- Generally, the recently matured fully expanded leaves just before the onset of the reproductive stage are collected and put in perforated paper bags.
- The plant samples are often contaminated with dust, dirt and residues of the sprays, *etc*. and need to be washed first under a running tap water followed by rinsing with dilute HCl (0.001N), distilled water and finally in deionized water.
- The washed samples are dried in a hot air oven at 60 ± 5°C for a period of 48 hours and ground in a stainless steel mill to pass through a sieve of 40/60 mesh.

(D) Oxidation of plant material

The objective of oxidation is to destroy the organic components in plant material to release elements from their combinations. The plant materials can be oxidized by dry ashing at a controlled high temperature in a muffle furnace or wet digestion in acid or mixture of two or more acids.

(i) Dry-ashing

- The powdered plant materials in tall form silica crucibles are ashed at 500°C in a muffles furnace for 3-4 hours. High temperatures are result in the loss of some volatile elements but with adjusting the time of muffling between 2-72 hours, any significant effect on the analytical results can be avoided.
- Nitrogen and sulphur, being highly volatile, are lost more or less completely during dry ashing even at 500°C but at higher temperatures, elements like K are also to be lost. Thus, temperature is an important in dry ashing.
- The ash is dissolved in 2ml of 6N HCl, heated on a hot plate to near dryness and taken in 10 ml dilute HCl (0.01N) or 20% aqua-regia before making up the final volume with distilled water.
- These extracts contain different amounts of insoluble materials, mainly silica.
- These insoluble materials settle down for sometime or can be separated by filtration before estimation of different elements.
- All elements, except N and S, can be estimated in these extracts by any technique.
- In general, the results obtained by this method, are quite satisfactory and comparable to those obtained by wet digestion procedures. Moreover, B can only be determined by dry ashing since it is volatilized during wet digestion with di- or tri-acid mixtures.

(ii) Wet Digestion. Wet oxidation digestion reagents and their applicability

Reagents	*Applicability to organic manure*	*Remarks*
1.H_2SO_4/HNO_3	Vegetable origin	Most commonly used
2.H_2SO_4/H_2O_2	Vegetable origin	Not very common
3.HNO_3	Biological origin	Easily purified reagent, short digestion time, temperature 350°C
4.$H_2SO_4/HClO_4$	Biological origin	Suitable only for small samples, danger of explosion
5.$HNO_3/HClO_4$	Protein, carbohydrate	Less explosive
6.$HNO_3/HClO_4/H_2SO_4$	Universal (also fat and carbon black	No danger with exact temperature control

Procedure

- The powdered plant samples can be dissolved by digesting in acids, usually HNO_3, $HClO_4$ and H_2SO_4.
- These acids are used either singly or in combinations of two or three acids, *e.g.* di-acid combination is HNO_3 and $HClO_4$ (in 4 : 1 ration) or a triple acid is a mixture of HNO_3, $HClO_4$ and H_2SO_4 (in 10 : 4 : 1 ration).

- A triple acid combination destroys the organic matter in a shorter time without any hazard.
- But the method is unsatisfactory for plant materials with high Ca and in cases where S is one of the test elements. The insoluble sulphate renders the method unsuitable because of adsorption of different element ions on precipitate & exclusion of Ca from analysis.
- The use of perchloric acid in the di-or triple acid digestion mixtures results in the formation of sparingly soluble potassium per chlorate, resulting in lower estimates of K, especially when the plant material contains K, more than 1%.
- As such for multi element analysis, the plant materials should be digested in nitric acid alone.

(E) Interpretation of results

- The basis for plant analysis as a diagnostic technique is the relationship between nutrient concentration in the plant and growth and production response.
- This relation should be significant to complete interpretation in term of deficient, adequate and excess nutrient concentration in the plant.
- Curves representing the relationship between nutrient concentration and growth response vary in shape and character depending on both the nutrient concentration in the growth medium and the plant species.
- When nutrients are in deficiency range, plant growth and yield are significantly reduced and foliar deficiency symptoms appear. In this range, application of nutrient results in sharp increase in growth.
- In marginal range, growth or yield is reduced, but plant does not show deficiency symptoms.
- The marginal range is also called transition zone. Within the marginal or transition zone lies the critical level or concentration.
- The critical level can be defined as that concentration at which the growth or yield begins to decline significantly.

3. Rapid tissue tests

These tests are rapid and are qualitative. The nutrients are absorbed by roots and transported to those parts of plants where they are needed. The concentration of cell sap is usually good indication of how well the plant is supplied at the time of testing. The plant parts, usually leaves are removed and plant sap is extracted. The plant sap is usually tested for nitrate, phosphorus and potassium. The use of specific reagent for each nutrient to be tested develops the colour. The intensity of colour is a qualitative measure of the content of the nutrient.

DRIS approach. Recently Diagnosis Recommendation Integration System (DRIS) is suggested for fertilizer recommendation. Plant samples are analyzed for nutrient content and they are expressed as rations of nutrients with others. Suitable ratios of nutrients are established for higher yields from experiments and plant samples collected from farmer's fields. The nutrients whose ratios are not optimum for high yields are supplemented by top dressing. This approach is generally suitable for long duration crops, but it is being tested for short duration crops like soybean, wheat etc.

4. Biological tests in which the growth of higher plants or certain micro-organisms is used as a measure of soil fertility

The biological methods consist of raising a crop or a microbial culture in a field or in a sample of the soil and estimating its fertility from the volume of crop or microbial count. Although these methods are direct estimates of soil fertility, they are time consuming and therefore, not well adapted to the practice of soil testing.

(*i*) **Field tests.** The field plot technique essentially measures the crop response to nutrients. In this, specific treatments are selected, randomly assigned to an area of land, which is representative of the conditions. Several replications are used to obtain more reliable results and to account for variation in soil. Field experiments are essential in establishing the equation used to provide fertilizer recommendation that will optimize crop yield. Maximum profitability, and minimize environment impact of nutrient use.

(*ii*) **Pot culture tests.** The pot culture test utilize small quantities of soil to quantify the nutrient supplying power of a soil. Selected treatments are applied to the soils and crop is planted and evaluated.

(*iii*) **Laboratory tests**

(*a*) ***Neubauer seedling Method:*** The neubaur technique is based on the uptake of nutrient by growing a large number of plants on a small amount of soil. The seedlings (plants) exhaust the available nutrient supply within short time. The total nutrients removed are quantified and tables are established.

(*b*) ***Microbial methods:*** The absence of nutrients, certain microorganisms exhibits behavior similar to that of higher plants, *e.g.* growth of Azotobacter or Aspergillus niger reflects nutrient deficiency in the soil. The soil is rated from very deficient to not deficient in the respective elements, depending on the amount of colony growth. In comparison with methods that utilize higher plants, microbiological methods are rapid, simple and require little space. These laboratory tests are not in common use in India.

5. Soil testing

Soil testing is the chemical analysis that provides a guideline for amendments and fertilizer needs of soils. The primary advantage of soil testing when it is compared to the plant analysis is its ability to determine the nutrients status of the soil before the crop is planted

The soil testing is done with following objectives :

1. Soil fertility evaluation for making fertilizer recommendation.
2. Prediction of likely crop response to applied nutrient.
3. Classification of soil into different fertility groups for preparing soil fertility maps of a given area.
4. Assessment of the type and degree of soil related problems like salinity, sodicity, acidity etc., and suggesting appropriate reclamation measures.

The following steps are involved in soil analysis

1. Sampling
2. preparation of samples
3. Analytical procedure
4. Calibration and interpretation of the results
5. Fertilizer recommendation

Analytical procedure. A suitable method is one which satisfied following three criteria:

(*i*) It should be fairly rapid so that the test results can be obtained in a reasonably short period.

(*ii*) It should give accurate and reproducible results of a given samples with least interferences during estimation.

(*iii*) It should have high predictability *i.e.*, a significant relationship of test values with the crop performance.

Calibration and interpretation of the results

For the calibration of the soil test data, a group of soils ranging in soil fertility from low to high in respect of the particular nutrient are selected and the test crop is grown on these soils with varying doses of particular nutrient with basal dose of other nutrients. The most common method is to plot soil test values against the percentage yield and to calculate the relationship between soil test values and per cent yield response

$$\text{Percent yield} = \frac{\begin{pmatrix}\text{Crop yield with}\\ \text{adequate nutrient}\end{pmatrix} - \begin{pmatrix}\text{Yield of control without addition}\\ \text{of particular nutrieint under study}\end{pmatrix} \times 100}{\text{Crop yield with adequate nutrient}}$$

FERTILIZER RECOMMENDATION

(*i*) Blanket Recommendation

Based on the fertilizer experiments conducted in different regions with improved varieties, fertilizer dose is recommended for each environment. This approach does not consider soil contribution. However, it is suitable for recommendation of nitrogen since residual effect of fertilizer N applied to previous crop is negligible and soils are generally low in nitrogen content.

Problem. Recommended fertilizer dose for low land rice 120, 60, 40 kg N, P_2O_5 and K_2O per hectare, respectively. The amount of fertilizer required in the form of urea, SSP and MOP is calculated as shown below :

(*i*) **Urea contain 46% N**

To supply 46 kg N, 100 kg urea is necessary

Urea (kgha^{-1}) =120 × 100/46 = 260.85

(*ii*) **SSP contain 16% P_2O_5**

To supply 16 kg P_2O_5, 100 kg SSP is necessary

SSP kg ha^{-1} = 60 × 100/16 = 375 kg SSP/ha

(*iii*) MOP contain 60% K_2O

To supply 40 kg K_2O, 100 kg MOP

MOP kg $ha^{-1} = 40 \times 100/60 = 68.9$ or 69 kg MOP/ha

(*ii*) Response Equations

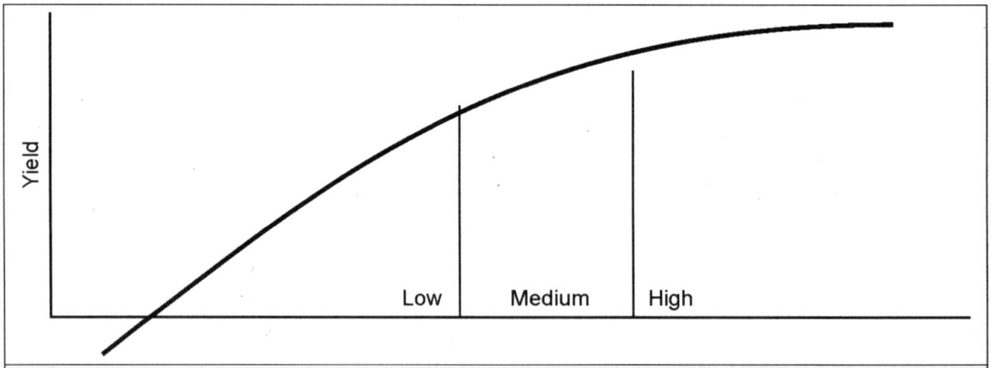

Fig. 25.1. Availability of nutrients

When plotting the soil test data and per cent yield, the resultant graph should be curvilinear. After partitioning the graph, the straight line yield increase considered as low, yield increase parallel to X axis considered as high soil test value. Intermediate considered as medium. Based on it categorization of different nutrient into low, medium and high has been suggested.

TABLE 25.1. Categorization of available nutrients

Nutrients	*Category*		
	Low	*Medium*	*High*
1. Alkaline $KMnO_4$-N (kg/ha)	< 250	250-500	> 500
2. Olsens-P_2O_5 (kg/ha),	< 28	28-56	> 56
3. Neutral N NH_4OAc-K_2O	< 140	140-280	> 280
4. 0.15% $CaCl_2$ -S (mg/kg)	< 10	10-20	> 20
5. DTPA extractable Fe (mg/kg)	< 5	5-10	> 10
6. DTPA extractable Mn (mg/kg)	< 5	5-10	> 10
7. DTPA extractable Zn (mg/kg)	< 0.5	0.5-1.0	> 1.0
8. DTPA extractable Cu (mg/kg)	< 0.2	0.2-0.4	> 0.4
9. Hot water soluble B (mg/kg)	< 0.1	0.1-0.5	> 0.5
10. Hot water soluble Mo (mg/kg)	—	—	—

This classification indicated that low class of soil would respond to added fertilizer means add 25% more fertilizer than recommended dose. Medium class soil may or may not respond to added fertilizer, add recommended dose of fertilizer. High status soils do not respond to added fertilizer, add 25% less recommended dose.

Problem. In above example, fertilizer dose of paddy is 120, 60, 40 kg N, P_2O_5 and K_2O per hectare, respectively. The recommendation of fertilizer is given below:

Nutrient application			
Category	***N***	***P_2O_5***	***K_2O***
Low	150	75	50
Medium	120	60	40
High	90	45	30
Fertilizer application			
Category	***Urea***	***SSP***	***MOP***
Low	326	469	86
Medium	261	375	69
High	196	281	52

(*iii*) Soil Test Crop Response (STCR) Approach

In this approach, soil contribution and yield level are considered for recommending fertilizer dose. This approach is also called as rationalized fertilizer prescription. From the soil test crop response experiments, following parameters are available.

Nutrient requirement (kg nutrient/q of grain)

$$= \frac{\text{Total uptake of nutrient (kg/ha)}}{\text{Grain yield (q/ha)}}$$

% contribution from soil (CS)

$$= \frac{\text{Total uptake of nutrient in control plot (kg/ha)}}{\text{Soil test value of nutrient in control plot (kg/ha)}} \times 100$$

Contribution from fertilizer (CF)

$$= \left(\begin{matrix}\text{Total uptake of nutrient}\\ \text{in treated plot}\end{matrix}\right) - \left(\begin{matrix}\text{Soil test value of nutrient}\\ \text{in treated plot (kg/ha)}\end{matrix}\right) \times \frac{\text{CS}}{100}$$

% Contribution from fertilizer

$$= \frac{\text{CF (kg/ha)}}{\text{Fertilizer dose}} \times 100$$

Fertilizer dose (kg/ha)

$$= \frac{\begin{matrix}\text{Nutrient requirement in}\\ \text{kg/a of grain} \times 100\end{matrix}}{\text{\% contribution from fertilizer}} \times T - \frac{\text{\% contribution from soil}}{\text{\% contribution from fertilizer}} \times \text{STV (kg/ha)}$$

Fertiliser dose (kg/ha) = Constant (kg/ha) × T (q/ha) – Constant × STV (kg/ha)

Based on this, fertilizer recommendations are developed for different regions. One such equation developed to recommend P and K, fertilizers for sugarcane in south Gujarat is given below:

Dose of P_2O_5 (kg/ha) = 2.24T-3.97 × STV for available P_2O_5

Dose of K_2O (kg/ha) = 2.67T-0.383 × STV for available K_2O

Based on above equation schedule of P_2O_5 and K_2O addition for plant sugarcane for targeted yields

Phosphorus

Available (Olsen's) P_2O_5 (kg/ha)	*Targeted millable cane yield*		
	100	*125*	*150*
	P_2O_5 to be added (kg/ha)		
10	184	249	296
20	145	201	257
30	105	161	217
40	65	121	177
50	26	82	138
57	—	54	110

Potash

Available (Neutral N NH_4OAc extractable) K_2O (kg/ha)	*Targeted mill able cane yield*		
	100	*125*	*150*
	K_2O to be added(kg/ha)		
200	190	257	324
300	152	219	286
400	114	181	247
500	76	142	209
600	37	104	171
700	—	66	132

Problem. Recommend fertilizer dose for rice using soil-test crop response equation from the data given below :

Assume that soil available N (Potassium permanganate method) is 250 kg/ha, soil available P_2O_5 (Olsen's method) 35 kg P_2O_5 per ha, soil available K_2O (ammonium acetate method) 350 kg K_2O per ha and targeted yield is 5 t/ha. Convert P_2O_5 and K_2O into P and K respectively as soil phosphorus and potassium are considered in elemental form in the equation.

$$\text{Soil N} = 250 \text{ kgha}^{-1}$$
$$\text{Soil P} = 35 \times 0.43 = 15.05 \text{ kgha}^{-1}$$
$$\text{Soil K} = 350 \times 0.83 = 290.5 \text{ kgha}^{-1}$$
$$\text{Targ. yield} = 5 \text{ t/ha} = 50 \text{ qha}^{-1}$$

Substitute T, SN SP and SK in the equation

$$\text{FN} = 4.39\text{ T} - 0.6723\text{ SN}$$
$$= (4.39 \times 50) - (0.6723 \times 250)$$
$$= 219.50 - 168.07 = 51.43 \text{ kg N/ha}$$

$$FP_2O_5 = 2.83\ T - 6.11\ SP$$
$$= (2.83 \times 50) - (6.11 \times 15.05)$$
$$= 141.50 - 91.95 = 49.55 \text{ kg } P_2O_5 \text{ /ha}$$
$$FK_2O = (1.41 \times 50) - (0.329 \times 290.5)$$
$$= 70.50 - 95.57 = -25.07 \text{ kg } K_2O\text{/ha}$$

Conclusion

- Thus for a 5 t crop of rice, with soil test values of 250 kg N/ha, 35 kg P_2O_5/ha and 350 kg K_2O /ha, the fertilizer recommended dose is 51.43 kg N, 49.55 kg P_2O_5 and 0.0 K_2O hectare soil contains sufficient quantities of K in soil.
- If the recommendation is compared with blanket recommendation of 100 : 60 : 60 kg N, P_2O_5, K_2O /ha, lot of fertilizers are applied unnecessarily for a 5t crop by blanket recommendation approach.
- The drawbacks of STCR approach are that these equations are not available for different crops and regions and development of these involves cost and time.
- These equations are suitable when available N P K is estimated by potassium permanganate, Olsen and ammonium acetate methods respectively.

Critical level approach

- Instead of grouping the soil into 3 or more classes, one critical value is being fixed and it groups the data only in two classes *viz*. responsive and non responsive.
- In this graphical technique, vertical and horizontal lines are super imposed on scatter diagram so there are maximum numbers of observation in upper right hand and lower left hand. The point where the vertical line intersects the X axis is termed as critical. Response is expected when fertilizer applied in soils having soil test value below critical limit. If soil is low to medium in nutrient status, apply recommended dose of fertilizer and high status apply half dose of recommendation.

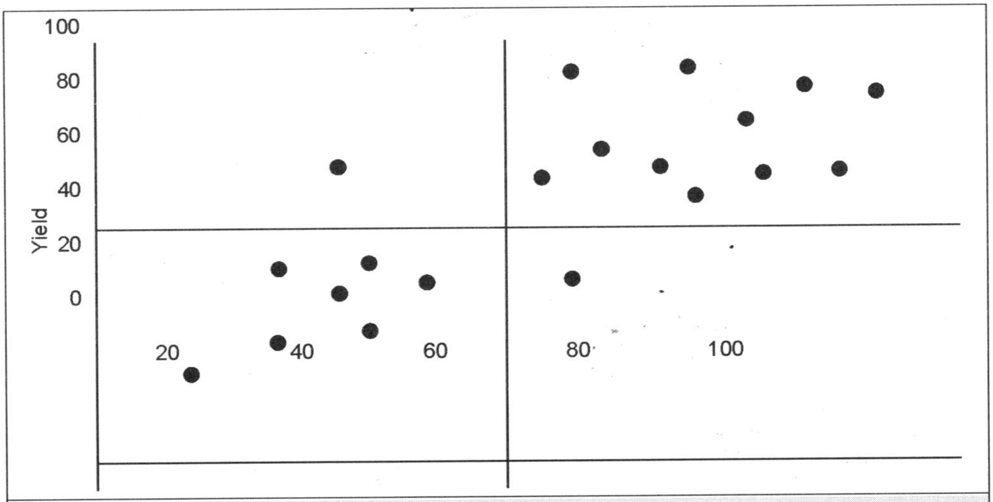

Fig. 25.2. Available nutrients

- The main disadvantage of this approach is that it can not give the idea about how much fertilizer is to be added.

Factors influencing nutrient use efficiency

The proportion of the added fertilizer actually used by plants is a measure of fertilizer efficiency.

(A) Soil characteristics,

(B) Crop characteristics and

(C) Fertilizer management techniques are the major factors that determine fertilizer efficiency.

(A) Soil characteristics

(1) Nutrient Status of Soil

- The response of any crop to added nutrient depends largely upon the inherent capacity of soil to supply that nutrient as per the requirement of crop.
- In a low nutrient soil, the crop responds remarkably to its application.
- On the other hand, in a high nutrient soil, the crops may show little or no response.
- In medium test soil, the response is intermediate. Soil testing helps in adjusting the amount of fertilizer and thus improves the efficiency of fertilizers use. By demarcating the areas responding differently to different plant nutrients, right type and proper amount of fertilizers can be applied to them.

(2) Nutrient Losses and Transformations. The amount of nutrients estimated by soil tests may not be entirely available to plants because of their **leaching, volatilization, denitrification** and **transformations** to unavailable forms.

Leaching. Leaching losses are important for nitrate nitrogen because it is not held by exchange sites in the soil, it is lost. Such losses are of particular significance in sandy soils and in situations if heavy rain or irrigation follows its application. In acid soils, leaching losses of Ca, SO_4, K and Mg are more common.

Volatilization. Volatilization of ammonia in high pH surface soils is considerable when urea is applied at the surface.

Denitrification. Denitrification loss of nitrogen mainly occurs under waterlogged conditions prevailing during rice cultivation, particularly under higher temperatures and in the presence of easily decomposable organic materials.

Transformations to unavailable forms

- The conversion of a portion of available nutrients into insoluble mineral forms is also important. Thus, the efficiency of added phosphorus is 20 to 30 per cent.
- Microbial immobilization also converts temporarily the soluble forms of nutrients into unavailable forms. Similarly, efficiency of zinc applied to soil is less than 3%.
- Soil reaction (pH) is one of the important soil properties that affects plant growth. The harmful effects of soil acidity are more due to secondary effects except in extreme case. The important secondary effects of high acidity or low pH in a soil are

the inadequate supply of available calcium, phosphorus and molybdenum on one hand and the excess of soluble aluminum, manganese and iron on the other.

- Likewise, in saline-alkali soil, the deficiency of Ca, Mg, P, Zn, Fe and Mn is very common.
- The main aim of liming of acid soils and addition of gypsum to alkali soils is to change the soil pH suitable for the availability of most plant nutrients.

(3) Soil Organic Matter

- Soil organic matter content is generally considered as the index of soil fertility and sustainability of agricultural systems.
- It improves the physical and biological properties of soil, protects soil surface from erosion and provides a reservoir of plant nutrients.
- In tropics, the maintenance of soil organic matter is very difficult because of its rapid decomposition under high temperatures.
- The cultivation of soils generally decreases its organic carbon content because of increased rate of decomposition by the current agricultural practices.
- LTFE shown that the integrated use of organic manures and chemical fertilizers can maintain high productivity and sustainable crop production. The application of FYM, compost and cereal residues effectively maintains the soil organic matter.
- Yields are, however, low in residue incorporated treatments due to wide C : N ratio of the residues. This ill effect, however, can be avoided if the rice straw is incorporated at least 20 days before seeding wheat.

(4) Soil moisture

- Fertilizer application facilitates root extension into deeper layers and leads to grater root proliferation in the root zone. Irrigated wheat fertilized with nitrogen used 20-38 mm more water than the unfertilized crop on loamy sand and sandy loam soils and increased dry matter production.
- Soil moisture also affects root growth and plant nutrient absorption. The nutrient absorption is affected directly by soil moisture and indirectly by the effect of water on metabolic activities of plant, soil aeration and concentration of soil solution. If soil moisture becomes a limiting factor during critical stage of crop growth, fertilizer application may adversely affect the yield.

(5) Physical Conditions of Soil

- Unfavorable physical conditions resulting form a combination of the size, shape, arrangement and mineral composition of the soil particles, may lead to poor crop growth and activity of microorganisms.
- Soil nitrogen generally increases as the texture becomes finer. The basic requirements for crop comes finer.
- The basic requirements for crop growth in terms of physical conditions of soil are adequate soil moisture and aeration, optimum soil temperature and freedom from mechanical stress.

- Tillage, mulching, irrigation, incorporation of organic matter and other amendments like liming of acid soils and addition of gypsum to sodic soils are the major field techniques that aim at creating soil physical environment suitable for crop growth.
- Tillage affects water use by crops not only through its effect on root growth but also affects the hydrological properties of soils.
- Mulching with residues, plastic film etc., influences evaporation losses from soil by modifying the hydro-thermal regime of the soil and affects root growth and rooting pattern.
- Use of organic mulch also decreases maximum soil temperature in summer and increases minimum soil temperature in winter and help in the conservation of soil moisture.

(B) Crop Characteristics

(*i*) Nutrient Uptake

- The total amount of nutrients removed by a crop may not serve as an accurate guide for fertilizers recommendations, it does indicate the differences in their requirement among crops and the rate at which the nutrients reserves in the soil are being depleted.
- The nutrient uptake may vary depending upon the crops and its cultivars, nutrient level in the soil, soil type soil and climatic conditions, plant population and management practices.
- It is estimated that 8t of rice grain remove 160 kg N, 38 kg P, 224 kg K, 24 kg S and 320 g Zn as compared to a removal of 125 kg N, 20 kg P, 125 kg K, 23 kg S and 280 g Zn by 5t of wheat from one hectare field.

(*ii*) Root Characteristics

- Roots are the principal organs of nutrient absorption. The absorption of nutrients depends upon the distribution of roots in soil. The shallower the root system, the more dependent the plant is on fertilizers. Hence, any soil manipulation, which encourages deep rooting, will encourage better utilization of fertilizers.
- It is well known that some plants are better scavengers of certain nutrients than others. This is mainly because of the preferential absorption of these nutrients by the roots of those plants.
- For example, legumes have a marked preference for divalent cations like Ca^{2+} whereas grasses feed better on monovalent cations like K^+.
- The efficiency of the applied fertilizer can be improved considerably if the rooting habits of various plants during early growth stages are known. This is particularly true for relatively immobile nutrients and for situations where the fixation of applied nutrients is very high.
- If a plant produces tap root system early, fertilizer can best be placed directly below the seed. On the other hand, if lateral roots are formed early, side placement of fertilizer would be helpful.

- Mycorrhizal fungi often associated with plant roots, increase the ability of plants to absorb nutrients particularly under low soil fertility. However, fertilizer additions generally reduce their presence and activity.

Crop Rotation

- Crops are known to differ in their feeding capacities on applied as well as native nutrients. The crops requiring high levels of fertilizers such as maize, potato may not use the applied fertilizers fully and some amount of the nutrient may be left in the soil which can be utilized by the succeeding crop. Phosphorus, major nutrients, is worthy of consideration because only less than 20 per cent of the applied phosphatic fertilizer is utilized by the first crop. Similarly, less than 3% of the applied zinc is used by the first crop.
- The magnitude of the residual effect is, however, dependent on the rate and kind of fertilizer used, the cropping and management system. Crops have a tendency of luxury consumption of N and K and may not leave any residual effect. On the other hand, if sub-optimal doses of fertilizers are applied to a crop, they may leave the soil in a much exhausted condition and requirement of the succeeding crop may increase.
- The legumes leave nitrogen rich root residues in the soil for the succeeding crop and thus reduce its nitrogen requirement.

(C) Fertilizer Characteristics and Management Techniques

The efficiency of a fertilizer varies to a large extent on the **type of fertilizer, time of application** and **method of application.**

Type of Fertilizer

- Fertilizers differ in both their nutrient content and form. In the case of nitrogenous fertilizers, the nutrient may be present in ammonium, nitrate or amide form.
- Similarly, in the case of phosphatic fertilizers, phosphorus may be present in water soluble, citrate soluble or citrate insoluble form. The nutrient content of a fertilizer may also differ largely.
- Thus, the total nitrogen content of calcium ammonium nitrate is 25% as compared to 46% of urea, 20.5% of ammonium sulphate and 82% of anhydrous ammonia. Nitrogen may also be present as one of the components of the combined fertilizer sources such as 18% in diammonium phosphate and 13% in potassium nitrate.
- Similarly, single super phosphate will supply only 16% P_2O_5 as compared to 46% P_2O_5 supplied by diammonium phosphate and triple super phosphate. The K_2O content of potassium chloride is 60 per cent.
- Nitrate fertilizers have high water solubility and are subject to leaching in high rainfall areas or due to heavy irrigation, as these do not interact with soil and thus move to greater depths.
- Generally, all sources of fertilizer N have been shown to equally efficient in upland soils, but ammonical and amide forms of N are more efficient as compared to nitrate sources of N for submerged rice soils.

- Phosphatic fertilizers containing phosphorus in water-soluble form like diammonium phosphate, single super phosphate have been found superior for most of the crops in neutral or alkaline soils as compared to citrate soluble or citrate insoluble form.
- Both single super phosphate and diammonium phosphate proved equally efficient on the basis of equivalent phosphate content but single super phosphate has the advantage in soils low in available sulphur and p for sulphur loving crops like oilseeds and pulses.
- Rock phosphate which has phosphate in water insoluble form has proved useful in acid soils, rice soils or for long duration legumes.
- Nitro phosphates more than 60% water soluble P have shown promise as efficient sources of P in alkaline soils.
- Most of the fertilizer K used in Indian agriculture is imported largely in the form of muriate of potash and only about 1% as sulphate of potash. In highly leached acid soils where sulphate deficiency is expected, potassium sulphate should be preferred. For certain crops like tobacco which are chloride sensitive, potassium sulphate should be applied.
- Straight micronutrient carriers like zinc sulphate, ferrous sulphate, manganese sulphate and copper sulphate have been found to be superior and economical as compared to other sources of micronutrient cations.

Time of Application

- Time of fertilizer application is important particularly for those nitrogenous fertilizers which tend to leach with irrigation water or rainfall.
- Split application of nitrogen is the most common and widely accepted practice for almost all crops. The basic concept is to apply nitrogen in two or more splits to coincide with peak period of nitrogen requirements of the crop.
- Nitrogen application in split doses is particularly beneficial on light textured soils in increasing the efficiency of applied nitrogen.
- In general, crops grown in rainy season should receive nitrogen fertilizers in split doses so that the leaching of the nutrient during heavy rains may be avoided and supply of the nutrient at critical stages is ensured.
- In the case of phosphatic and potassic fertilizers as well as for zinc and copper among micronutrient cations, all the quantity applied at sowing gives the best results with most of the crops.
- However, in the case of iron and manganese where foliar sprays of these nutrients are recommended, initiation of foliar sprays is very important.
- In the case of manganese, foliar sprays initiated 2-3 days before the first irrigation to wheat have been found to be significantly superior to their application after the first irrigation.

Method of Application

- Various techniques have been developed to improve the efficiency of applied nutrients. Since nitrates are easily leached and lost by denitrification, retardation of nitrification of ammonium containing or ammonium producing fertilizers by using nitrification inhibitors in rice fields subjected to intermittent flooding helped in increasing the nitrogen use efficiency.

- Chemical nitrification inhibitors and indigenous materials such as *neem* (*Azadirachta indica*) and *karanj* (*Pongamia glabra*) cakes have been successfully used except on highly coarse textured soils of Punjab. Also some release nitrogen materials like urea form, isobutylidene, diurea as well as coated fertilizers such as sulphur coated urea, lac coated urea, have used to reduce the nitrogen losses.
- Root zone placement of urea super granules appears to be a better way of placing N (although it presents some difficulties) in rice fields for reducing volatilization losses as ammonia, particularly in high pH soils.
- In coarse textured soils of Punjab, urea applied in three equal splits has shown a better performance than urea super granules and neem coated urea applied.
- Single application of sulphur coated urea has been found to be more efficient than urea application in three splits. Placement of fertilizer N in both summer and winter crops is superior to its broadcast application in increasing yield of crops. Placement of N prevents volatilization losses.
- Foliar application of nitrogen as a supplement to soil application has been found useful under rainfed conditions.
- The placement of water soluble phosphatic fertilizers is better than its broadcast as it reduces its fixation. However, phosphates of low water solubility react slowly in soil and are usually more effective as a source of phosphorus when broadcast. When rock phosphate is used in rice culture, it should be mixed with soils a fortnight or a month before rice planting.
- Split application of potassium is expected to increase its efficiency in situations where leaching losses are considerable either because of light texture of the soil or long duration of the crop. Beneficial effects of split application have been observed in sugarcane and rice. For fruit crops, 2-6 splits have been recommended depending upon the crop.
- Application of sulphur in neutral to calcareous soils is equally efficient in correcting its deficiency whether broadcast, drilled or applied in split doses. In standing crop of wheat, top dressing of ammonium sulphate is beneficial.
- For efficient utilization of applied zinc, the best time of its application for wheat and rice is at seeding or transplanting of the crop.

Among different methods, broadcasting and mixing zinc is more efficient than its drilling or band placing and top dressing 60 days after seeding. Application of zinc sulphate @ 25-50 kg/ha to soil is superior to foliar sprays of 0.5% zinc sulphate solution neutralized with lime.

Other methods of zinc application such as coating or soaking of seeds in zinc solution, dipping rice seedling roots in ZnO suspension and transplanting zinc enriched nursery have proved either inferior to or at par with soil application of zinc. Foliar sprays of 0.5 to 1.0% manganese sulphate solution has been found more effective and economical as compared to soil application (20 kg Mn/ha) of manganese in manganese deficient sandy loams of Punjab.

ESSENTIAL OF PLANT GROWTH

Growth

Growth is defined as the progressive development of an organism. It may be refer to the development of some specific organ or organs or to the plant as a whole. Growth may be expressed in terms of dry weight, length, height or diameter.

Factors affecting the plant growth

[A] Genetical factors or heredity or internal factors

[B] Environmental factors or external factors

[A] Genetical factors

The important of genetics in the growth of agricultural crops is clearly shown by the increase in yields that have been obtained by the use of improved seed. UK has incorporated many desirable characteristics in to their hybrids and varieties. The following outlines gives at least of useful characters which are considered as desirable breeding aims, although it may not be possible to compile all these useful properties in a single variety.

1. High yield under given environmental condition
2. Early maturing
3. Better resistance to insects, pests
4. Better resistance to lodging
5. Drought, flood and salinity tolerance
6. Chemical composition of grain *i.e.* oil, protein
7. Quality of final out put (grain → fineness, coarseness)
8. Quality for straw (sweetness, juiciness, etc.)

The increased yield and other desirable characters are related to the genetic makeup of the plant. These characters are inherent in each individual and are transmitted from one generation to other by genes.

[B] Environmental factors

1. Climatic
2. Adaphic
3. Biotic
4. Physiographic
5. Man (Anthrophic)

1. Climatic. The atmospheric factors, which affect the growth of plant, are called climatic factors. The main climatic factors are listed as under :

(*i*) Precipitation
(*ii*) Temperature
(*iii*) Humidity
(*iv*) Solar radiation
(*v*) Wind velocity
(*vi*) Atmospheric gases

(i) Precipitation. Precipitation occurs in many ways such as rainfall, hail, etc. Besides there may be fog, drip and dew that may contribute to moisture.

Rainfall is one of the most important factors influence the vegetation of a place. The yearly precipitation, both in total amount and seasonal distribution greatly affects the choice of cultivated crops of a place. Low and ill distributed rainfall are common feature at dry land farming, where in drought resistant crops like sorghum and pearl millet are commonly grown, on the other hand in places of heavy and regular rainfall areas such as in the western ghats of India, crops like rice are grown in flat areas, while tea, coffee, rubber, etc. are grown in the slopes.

(ii) Temperature. The range of maximum growth for most agricultural plants is between 15 and 40°C. *i.e.* 59 to 140°F. Plant community has its own maximum, optimum and minimum temperature which are known as their cardinal points.

TABLE 25.2. Cardinal temperature of certain crops in °F

Crops	*Minimum*	*Optimum*	*Maximum*
Wheat	39-40	77	86-90
Barley	39-40	68	82-86
Maize	46-50	89	104-111
Oats	39-41	77	86
Sorghum	46-50	89	104
Rice	50-53	90	97-101
Tobacco	55-57	82	95

Apart from the reduction in yield, many injuries on the plants and adverse effect on soil conditions occur under both extremes of temperature. These injuries are :

(*a*) ***Cold injury***. Plants are injured due to cold temperature in following ways :

- Chilling
- Freezing
- Suffocation

(*b*) ***Heating injury.*** Very high temperatures often stop growth. The general effects of excessive heat are :

- Defoliation
- Premature dropping of fruits
- In extreme case death of plant

(*iii*) ***Humidity***. Water is always present in the atmosphere in the form of invisible water vapour. This is normally known as humidity of the air. In unsaturated conditions the water vapour contents of air is usually expressed as relative humidity, which is the ratio between the actual humidity present and the saturation humidity possible at the temperature.

The relative humidity of a place, besides being affected by temperature and pressure, is also affected by wind exposure, vegetation and water content of soil.

Transpiration of crop plants increase with temperature but decrease with high relative humidity affecting the quantity of irrigation water. Moisture of air favor the growth of many fungi and bacteria and these affect seriously the crop. Similarly many kinds of insect parasites as aphids and jassids well developed under moist conditions.

(iv) Solar radiation. Solar radiation provides two essential needs of plants :

1. Light requirement for photosynthesis and for many other functions of the plant
2. Thermal conditions require for the normal physiological function of the plant.

Light affects the plant in following ways :

(1) Light intensity

(2) Quality of light

(3) Duration of light

(1) ***Light intensity.*** Very low light intensity reduced the rate of photosynthesis and may even results in the closing of the stomata. This results in reduced vegetative growth of the plants in many ways. It increases the rate of respiration and thus disturbs the photosynthesis-respiration balance. It causes rapid losses of water, resulting in the closure of stomata. Depending upon the nature of the crop, such as helophytes (sun loving) and sciophytes (shade loving). The dry matter production is affected.

(2) ***Quality of light.*** The principal wave lengths absorbed in photosynthesis are in the violet blue (400-435 mm), blue (435-490 mm) and orange (595-626 mm) and red (626-750 mm) regions. Among the short rays beyond the violet such as X-rays and gamma rays and longer rays beyond red such as infrared are detrimental to growth. Red light seems to be the most favorable light for growth followed by violet blue.

(3) ***Duration of light.*** The response of plants to the relative length of day and night is known as photoperiodism.

Plant which develops and produces normally when the photoperiod is more than 12 hours is called long day plants.

Those plants develop normally when photoperiod is less then 12 hours is called short day plants.

Some plants are found to be unaffected by photoperiod are called as neutral plants.

(v) Wind velocity. Its action on plants may be direct or indirect.

As a direct effect higher velocity of wind tears the plant's leaves and higher velocity may be up rooted the plant and blown away. Higher velocity of wind resulted in lodging of crop. In desert, high velocity of wind causes the constant erosion of soil and this make difficult to grow the plant.

Wind is also responsible for causing the rainfall to a very large extent. Wind has a very powerful effect on humidity and atmospheric pollution.

Important function of wind is for plant growth is in pollination of flowers and dispersal of seed, fruits and microorganisms.

As an indirect effect, velocity of winds differs the rate of transpiration in plants. Much damage in crops by hot dry winds at the time of flowering.

(vi) Atmospheric gases. The atmosphere surrounding the earth contains a mixture of gases *viz*., CO_2 (0.03%), O_2 (20.95%), nitrogen (78.09%) argon (0.93%) and miscellaneous gases (0.02%).

The proportion variation from this may be found over industrial plants/units, which release large quantity of toxic gases as CO_2, CO, SO_2, as well as water vapor and mineral particles, which inhibit the plant growth.

2. Adaphic factor

The factors affects the crop growths through the soil are called the adaphic factors. They are listed as under :

(*i*) Soil moisture
(*ii*) Soil air
(*iii*) Soil temperature
(*iv*) Soil mineral
(*v*) Soil organic matter
(*vi*) Soil organism
(*vii*) Soil reaction

(*i*) Soil moisture. Plant tissue constitute about 90% of the moisture, lost through transpiration is made only by absorbing water from the soil. Soil moisture is playing a very dynamic role for plant growth. High free water table reduced the plant growth and decreased the absorption of water and mineral through the root. Optimum soil moisture is favorable for growth of root ultimately increases the plant growth.

(*ii*) Soil air. In well-aerated soil, the absorption of water and nutrients becomes rapidly. While it greatly retarded rate in soils deficient in oxygen supply in poorly aerated soil and CO_2 gets accumulated and is determinates the water absorption process of the plant.

(*iii*) Soil temperature. The maximum metabolic activity of plant and maximum absorption of water by roots take place generally between 20 to 30°C. Soil temperature below 20°C resulted in reduction of rate of absorption by roots.

Soil temperature is one of the major factors for the activity and growth of soil micro-organism, which are related with nitrogen fixing and phosphorus solubilising in soil.

(*iv*) Soil mineral matter. The total amount of elements contains in soils depends partly on the nature of the rock from which they are formed and partly on their age and the extent to which soluble products have been leached away.

Loamy soils are the best one for the better growth. As they contain coarse sand as well as fine silt and clay particles, loamy soils have a good aeration, good water infiltration as well as water holding capacity in which water movement in soils becomes easy. In such soil, the root penetration is also become easier.

(*v*) Soil organic matter. The organic matter of the soil is very essential source of mineral nutrients for the growth of plant. During decomposition, the humus is mineralized and it increases the water holding capacity to its contents of organic colloids. Organic matter is a unique source for soil microorganisms. CEC is also become higher due to soil organic matter.

(*vi*) Soil organism. A large number of bacteria, fungi bring about the decay of organic substances during the mineralization, which released the variety of nutrients for plant to absorb in available form ultimately increased the plant growth. Number of bacteria *viz. Rhizobium, Azotobacter* fixes the atmospheric nitrogen in soils and they can be utilized as biofertilizers. BGA is also helpful to supply nitrogen in paddy land for paddy crop.

There are a large number of bacteria; fungi are also present in soil, which are the main cause for the diseases, which ultimately reduced the plant growth.

The larger organisms like, earthworms, rodents etc. improve the aeration of soil. They play a key role in the weathering of rocks and mineral and in the formation of soils.

***(vii)* Soil reaction**. Soil may be acidic, alkaline or neutral depending upon their content of base, salt and acidic components. Neutral soil is the best one for plant growth of most of the crops.

Soil acidity beyond a particular unit is injurious for plant growth due to following reasons:

(1) High aluminum content is toxic and major cause for higher acidity.

(2) In acidic soil P_2O_5 is fixed which cannot be absorbed by plant.

(3) High acidity affects the absorption of nutrients *viz*., K, Ca, and Mg.

(4) Due to higher acidity the activity of microorganisms is reduced and decomposition of organic matter is decreased and activity of nitrogen fixing bacteria is checked.

In the same fashion high alkaline soils adversely affected crop growth due to higher content of Na. Na interfere with nutrients and water absorption.

3. Biotic factors

Beneficial or harmful effects are caused by other plants and animal on the growth of crops are called biotic factors. They are grouped as follows.

(*i*) Plants
(*ii*) Weeds
(*iii*) Parasites
(*iv*) Animals

***(i)* Plants.** Competitive and complementary effects of plants are being observed. Closer spacing reduced the yield of individual plants; wider spacing will reduce the total yield. Hence, optimum spacing is important. In case of mix cropping, there is mutual benefit resulting in better yield of cereal crops due to it mixed with legumes and hence, it is very commonly practiced in the world.

***(ii)* Weed competition.** In non-irrigated areas the competition between weeds and crops is mainly for water. In irrigated areas the competition is done for the nutrients. Weeds in fallow land, depute the soil for both moisture and nutrients.

***(iii)* Parasite.** Parasite like, fungi, bacteria, virus causes different kind of disease on crops.

Symbiosis. Certain organisms are normally found associated with other to form a community. In the community the different organisms have mutual relationship with each others and with the prevailing environment of the place. This biological interrelationship among the organism is termed as symbiosis. (A mutual beneficial association of two different types of organisms).

(iv)* Animals**. ***Soil animals. Protozoa, nematodes, snails and insects constitute highly important part of the environment for plants roots. Among these, insects and nematodes cause considerable damage as crop pest.

Beneficial organisms. Many crops are pollinated primarily by insect. Bees and wasp are probably pollinators of greatest importance. Earthworms are influencing in changing soil conditions.

Small animals. Rabbits and rats constitute an important factor.

Large animals. Domesticated animals like cattle, goats, sheep and horses as well as elephant, pigs do considerable damage to crops plants by their grazing and browsing habits.

4. Physiographic factors

The geological status of a place and topography affects the crop considerably.

5. Anthrophic factors

Man and woman have produced changes in plant environment. Improvements affected by plant breeder towards increasing the crop yield, introduction of exotic plants, etc. have greatly influenced crop growth.

SOIL QUALITY

Soil quality is the capacity of the soil to function within the ecosystem boundaries to sustain biological productivity, maintain environmental quality, and promote plant and animal health. In this course, state-of-the-art studies on soil quality and the principles, assessment and management of soil quality are examined with respect to biological production, plant and animal health, food security, and environmental quality.

Definition and Concepts

What is soil quality ? Soil quality is the capacity of the soil to function within the ecosystem boundaries to sustain biological productivity, maintain environmental quality, and promote plant and animal health. Soil quality is a measure of the conditions of soil relative to the requirement of one or more species and/or to any human need or purpose. Soil quality consists of physical, chemical, and biological components.

Definition of Soil Quality. The capacity of a soil to sustain biological production maintain environmental quality, and promote plant and animal health.

Development of soil quality concept. Soil quality concerns are not new; evaluations of soil characteristics for crop growth appeared in the first written literature and certainly predate those records. The soil quality concept per se was introduced by Warkentin and Fletcher (1977) as an approach to facilitate better land use planning for the various functions that soil must accommodate. Early efforts to define soil quality were followed by more formalized definitions (Larson and Pearce 1991, Karlen *et al.*, 1997), selection of indicators (Doran and Parkin 1994), and specific strategies to enhance soil quality.

The concept is not without its critics. Recently, there have been several research editorials that recommend moving away from subjective efforts to develop an index of soil quality. Letey *et al.* (2003) suggest a move toward utilizing available technical information to motivate and educate farmers on management practices that optimize the combined goals of high agricultural production, low environmental degradation, and a sustained soil resource. Sojka and Upchurch (1999) reported that quality of soil management rather than soil quality management should be the goal of soil science.

Research efforts to monitor and index soil quality indicators need to be balanced with efforts to better define relationships between the status of soil quality indicators and soil functions. In addition, consideration must be given to the simultaneity of diverse and sometimes conflicting nature of soil functions. Greater relevance to research efforts may be achieved under a broader context that first defines strategies to enhance agricultural and natural resource sustainability, and then uses indicators encompassing all aspects of agroecosystem performance.

Why do we need soil quality concept ? The importance of developing the concept of soil quality was enhanced because of the need to apply soil science to address the problems of nonagricultural uses of soil (*e.g.*, mineland restoration, urban uses and disposal of urban wastes, soil contamination and pollution by industrial activities, athletic and recreational uses of soil, and environmental regulatory functions with particular reference to water quality and the greenhouse effect). A strong need, therefore, arose to develop appropriate indicators of soil quality in relation to specific soil function (*e.g.*, agricultural, urban, industrial, recreational, athletic, environmental, and waste disposal).

Tools for assessing soil quality

Our ability to assess soil quality is complicated by many physical, chemical, and biological processes and their interactions in time, space and intensity. It is not usually possible to directly measure the rate of soil processes; instead they can be inferred by measuring specific soil properties that are indicative of these rates. These measurements then can be used in simulation models to predict future changes in process rates and, in turn, soil quality. The properties measured are termed indicators of soil quality. The best soil quality indicators are those that integrate the combined effects of several properties and processes. Sets of basic soil quality indicators should :

(1) Encompass ecosystem processes and relate to process oriented modeling.

(2) Integrate soil physical, chemical and biological properties and processes.

(3) Be accessible to many users and applicable to field conditions.

(4) Be sensitive to variations in management and climate.

(5) Be part of existing soil data bases (where possible).

Efforts to assess soil quality have resulted in the development of tools to evaluate the impact of management practices on the soil and environment. The soil quality kit (reviewed by Cramer 1994) and soil quality scorecard (USDA-NRCS-SQI 1999) are examples of two tools used to quickly evaluate soil properties and processes with simple equipment and relatively limited experience.

An important role for soil scientists is to determine appropriate indicators for various management goals or land uses. Doing so will ensure that assessments of soil quality will be useful and understandable to farmers and other land managers who are the stewards of soil quality.

Indicators for Soil Quality Evaluation

What are indicators ? Soil quality indicators are physical, chemical, and biological properties, processes, and characteristics that can be measured to monitor changes in the soil.

The types of indicators that are the most useful depend on the function of soil for which soil quality is being evaluated. These functions include :

1. providing a physical, chemical, and biological setting for living organisms;
2. regulating and partitioning water flow, storing and cycling nutrients and other elements;
3. supporting biological activity and diversity for plant and animal productivity;
4. filtering, buffering, degrading, immobilizing, and detoxifying organic and inorganic materials;
5. Providing mechanical support for living organisms and their structures.

Why are indicators important ? Soil quality indicators are important to

1. focus conservation efforts on maintaining and improving the condition of the soil;
2. evaluate soil management practices and techniques;
3. relate soil quality to that of other resources;
4. collect the necessary information to determine trends;
5. determine trends in the health of the Nation's soils;
6. Guide land manager decisions.

TABLE 25.3. Basic soil quality indicators and rational for its use

Indicator	*Rationale for its use*
Physical	
Texture	Retention and transport of water and chemicals
Depth of soil and rooting	Estimate of productivity potentials and erosion normalizes landscape and geographic variability
Infiltration and soil bulk density	Potential for leaching productivity and erosion
Water holding capacity	Related water table retention, transport and erosivity
Chemical	
Total soil organic matter	Defines carbon storage potentially fertility, and stability
Active organic matter	Defines structural stability and food for microbes
pH	Defines biological and chemical activity thresholds
EC	Defines plant and microbial activity
Extractable N, P, K	Plant available nutrients and potential for N loss, productivity and environmental quality indicators
Biological	
Microbes biomass C and N	Microbial catalytic potential and early warning of management effect on organic matter
Potentiality mineralizable N	Soil productivity and N supply potential
Specific respiration	Microbial activity per unit of microbial biomass
Microorganism numbers	Potential influence of such organism as earth warms

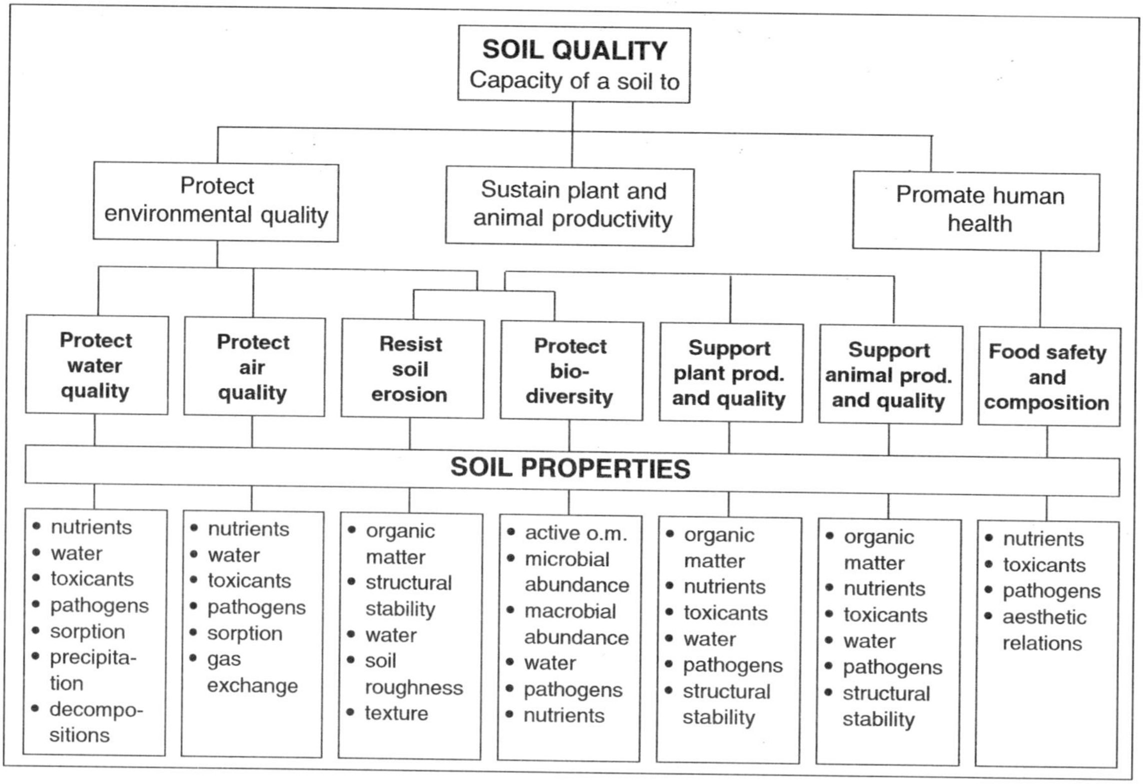

Physical indicators are related to the arrangement of solid particles and pores. Examples include topsoil depth, bulk density, porosity, aggregate stability, texture, crusting, and compaction. Physical indicators primarily reflect limitations to root growth, seedling emergence, infiltration, or movement of water within the soil profile.

Chemical indicators include measurements of pH, salinity, organic matter, phosphorus concentrations, cation-exchange capacity, nutrient cycling, and concentrations of elements that may be potential contaminants (heavy metals, radioactive compounds, etc.) or those that are needed for plant growth and development. The soil's chemical condition affects soil-plant relations, water quality, buffering capacities, availability of nutrients and water to plants and other organisms, mobility of contaminants, and some physical conditions, such as the tendency for crust to form.

Biological indicators include measurements of micro and macro-organisms, their activity, or byproducts. Earthworm, nematode, or termite populations have been suggested for use in some parts of the country. Respiration rate can be used to detect microbial activity, specifically microbial decomposition of organic matter in the soil. Ergo sterol, a fungal byproduct, has been used to measure the activity of organisms that play an important role in the formation and stability of soil aggregates. Measurement of decomposition rates of plant residue in bags or measurements of weed seed numbers, or pathogen populations can also serve as biological indicators of soil quality.

Visual indicators may be obtained from observation or photographic interpretation. Exposure of subsoil, change in soil color, ephemeral gullies, ponding, runoff, plant response, weed species, blowing soil, and deposition are only a few examples of potential locally determined indicators. Visual evidence can be a clear indication that soil quality is threatened or changing.

How are indicators selected ?

Soil quality is estimated by observing or measuring several different properties or processes. No single property can be used as an index of soil quality. The selection of indicators should be based on :

1. the land use;
2. the relationship between an indicator and the soil function being assessed;
3. the ease and reliability of the measurement;
4. variation between sampling times and variation across the sampling area;
5. the sensitivity of the measurement to changes in soil management;
6. compatibility with routine sampling and monitoring;
7. the skills required for use and interpretation.

When and where to measure ?

The optimum time and location for observing or sampling soil quality indicators depends on the function for which the assessment is being made. The frequency of measurement also varies according to climate and land use. Soil variation across a field, pasture, forest, or rangeland can greatly affect the choice of indicators. Depending on the function, such factors as the landscape unit, soil map unit, or crop growth stage may be critical. Wheel tracks can dramatically affect many properties measured for plant productivity. Management history and current inputs should also be recorded to ensure a valid interpretation of the information. Monitoring soil quality should be directed primarily toward the detection of trend changes that are measurable over a 1 to 10 year period. The detected changes must be real, but at the same time they must change rapidly enough so that land managers can correct problems before undesired and perhaps irreversible loss of soil quality occurs.

What does the value mean ?

Interpreting indicator measurements to separate soil quality trends from periodic or random changes is currently providing a major challenge for researchers and soil managers. Soils and their indicator values vary because of differences in parent material, climatic condition, topographic or landscape position, soil organisms, and type of vegetation. For example, cation exchange capacity may relate to organic matter, but it may also relate to the kind and amount of clay. Establishing acceptable ranges, examining trends and rates of change over time, and including estimates of the variance associated with the measurements are important in interpreting indicators. Changes need to be evaluated as a group, with a change in any one indicator being evaluated only in relation to changes in others. Evaluations before and after, or with and without intervention, are also needed to develop appropriate and meaningful relationships for various kinds of soils and the functions that are expected of them. The overall goal should be to maintain or improve soil quality without adversely affecting other resources.

Soil Components and Basic Soil Quality Properties for evaluating soil quality

The different components are as under

Inorganic components. 1. Primary minerals; 2. Clay minerals; 3. Oxides;

Organic components. 1. Organic matter; 2. Humus; 3. Soil organisms

General soil quality attributes. 1. Soil texture; 2. Soil reactions; 3. Soil charges; 4. Ion exchange; 5. Buffering capacity; 6. Adsorption-desorption; 7. Microbial turnover; 8. Nutrient cycling

Measurements of Soil Quality Indicators

Physical Parameters. Likes Soil texture; Depth of soil and rooting; Soil bulk density and filtration; Water holding capacity; Water retention characteristics; Water content

Chemical Parameters. Total organic C and N; pH; Electrical conductivity; Labile nutrients and metals; Labile contaminants

Microbiological and Biochemical Parameters. Microbial biomass C and N; Potentially mineralizable N; Soil respiration; Enzyme activity; Microbial quotient; Microbial respiration quotient

Soil Quality Management for Plant Production

1. Objectives of soil quality management
2. Management strategies
3. Management criteria
4. Land use and soil quality
5. Soil quality indexing of plant production
6. Soil erosion
7. Quality restoration of eroded soils
8. Soil acidification
9. Quality improvement of acid soils

Effect of Soil Quality on Nutrient Efficiency

Nutrient efficiency is a measure of how much crop is produced per unit of nutrient supplied. The higher the efficiency, the more products is produced per unit of nutrient. The quality of soil affects nutrient use efficiency. Soil quality is measured or evaluated by a number of indicators. This technical note will discuss how 13 indicators relate to nutrient efficiency.

1. Soil Quality definition with regards to nutrients. A healthy soil functioning at nearly full capacity stores and cycles nutrients and allows crops to grow and use nutrients efficiently. In a healthy soil, nutrients become available when the plants need them. There is little risk for crop nutrients to move below the root zone through leaching, off the edge of field by runoff and erosion, or above the crop canopy by volatilization. Crop nutrients that move beyond the crop's zone of uptake could potentially contaminate the environment.

2. Erosion. Erosion and runoff are both detrimental to nutrient management. Nutrients contained in the topsoil, along with soil organic matter, can be carried away by erosion or washed out with runoff water. The organic matter is the first to be transported by water or wind because of its lower specific gravity. Additional nutrients are required to maintain productivity lost when topsoil is carried away by erosion.

3. Deposition of Sediment. Sediment additions in the field can be good or bad. Some sediment, especially the finer clay particles and organic matter, bring in nutrients. The coarser sediments, like sands, do not have a high nutrient content and tend to cover the topsoil that is in place. Coarser textured soils also lack moisture-holding and pesticide-retention capacity.

4. Compaction. Compact soils restrict the movement of roots. Less root volume in the soil prevents nutrient uptake. Compaction also restricts the diffusion and flow of nutrients in the soil. Few roots and limited nutrient movement can result in stunted growth because the plant is unable to take up the nutrients in the soil. Compacted soils retard air movement and gas exchange in the root zone. This can lead to nutrient losses, like denitrification or toxic gas build-up near the roots.

5. Soil Aggregation at the Soil Surface. Good soil aggregation means better water and nutrient movement through the soil. More aggregation means more of the surface areas of the soil particles have capacity for adsorbed nutrients. Surface aggregation allows pore space for water infiltration and gas exchanges. Good soil aggregation is closely tied to the amount of active organic matter and to biological activity. Thus soil aggregation is connected to nutrient cycling.

6. Infiltration. Plants require water. Nutrients move with the water through the soil pores and are absorbed into the plant. When nutrients are applied to the soil surface, as in no-till systems, water is required to move the nutrients down into the root zone. Good soil infiltration permits this to happen. Nutrients that are not carried into the root zone are susceptible to runoft. Percolating water carries the nutrients deeper into the root zone and also removes harmful salts that may accumulate there.

7. Soil Crusting. Crusting seals the soil surface and restricts water infiltration and gas exchange. If not allowed to infiltrate, surface applied nutrients on crusted soils are susceptible to runoff and wind transport. Crusting also reduces seed germination and seedling survival which directly has an effect on the plant population and the amount of nutrients necessary for the crop.

8. Nutrient Loss or Imbalance. Nutrients need to be applied according to the crop and soil requirements. Soil and plant analyses are a good way to determine the amount of nutrients needed. Over-application of nutrients can lead to plant toxicity, poor pH reaction, and excess nutrients susceptible to runoff, leaching, and volatilization. A deficiency in nutrients will not sustain optimum plant growth.

9. Pesticide Carryover. Pesticides with residual soil activity can stunt growth of subsequent crops. If roots are affected, their ability to absorb nutrients will be lessened. Any effect on plant photosynthesis will reduce nutrient uptake and metabolism. Without pesticide or weed control, weeds can utilize nutrients in competition of the crop. The weed residue may not decompose and recycle plant nutrients for the subsequent crops.

10. Organic Matter. Soil organic matter is a very valuable component of the topsoil. Organic matter stores nutrients, feeds soil organisms that decompose organic material, and return the basic nutrients to the soil. Organic matter holds soil moisture for plant use. Soil organic matter is developed by combining of carbon, oxygen, and nitrogen plus other nutrients in the soil. Nitrogen and other nutrients must be available to soil microorganisms for development of organic matter.

11. Biological Activity. A healthy soil has a diverse set of macro and micro organisms that assure a well functioning soil food web. Microorganisms decompose organic material, store nutrients in their bodies, and as they decay or become food for other organisms, they release nutrients. Some small animals like insects and crustacea carry organic material and related nutrients into the soil and aid in its decomposition. Some microorganisms have a symbiotic relationship with plants such as mycorrhiza. Mycorrhiza lives in plant roots and help the plants assimilate water and nutrients.

12. Weeds and Pathogens. Nutrients can be used by crops or by weeds. Weeds utilize nutrients, but fail to produce a marketable commodity. So, the nutrients are not efficiently used to grow crops. The same is true for crops that are attacked by disease and insects. Efficient utilization means nutrients are converted to a harvestable product.

13. Extreme Soil Moisture Conditions. The amount of soil moisture impacts nutrient cycling. A dry soil does not promote root extension in the root zone. And, since nutrients are carried by water, plants are unable to obtain adequate nutrition. Waterlogged soils affect the transformation of nutrients. Phosphorus becomes more mobile and less attached to minerals in waterlogged conditions. Nitrate nitrogen is denitrified by changing form from a liquid to a gas which can be lost to the atmosphere. Roots consume oxygen and respire carbon dioxide. Because gases are transported much more slowly through water (about one ten thousand slower) than air, some gases such as carbon dioxide can accumulate in the soil and be toxic to roots.

INDICATORS OF AGRICULTURAL SUSTAINABILITY

Agriculture is a complex of processes taking place within biophysical, socio-economic and political constraints, which control the sustainability of the farming activities. The concept of sustainable agriculture combines characteristics such as long-term maintenance of natural systems, optimal production with minimum input, adequate income per farming unit, fulfillment of basic food needs, and provision for the demands and necessities of rural families and communities. All definitions of sustainable agriculture promote environmental, economic and social harmony in an effort to attain the meaning of sustainability.

The most relevant issue today is to design suitable technologies, as well as compatible strategies from the social, economic and ecological viewpoints that will bring about the necessary behavioral changes to achieve the objectives of sustainable agriculture. Sustainability is a concept and cannot be measured directly. Appropriate indicators must be selected to determine levels and duration of sustainability. An indicator of sustainability is a variable that allows describing and monitoring the processes, states and tendencies of systems at the farm, regional, national or worldwide levels. An indicator of sustainability must be sensitive to temporal and spatial changes, predictable, measurable and interactive.

In the present study, the concept of indicator was extended to system statistics that measure or reflects system status or change in condition, with emphasis on the national agricultural systems. Indicators are selected on the basis of diagnostic criteria that permit the discrimination of factors, causes and effects controlling a system. The definition of criteria

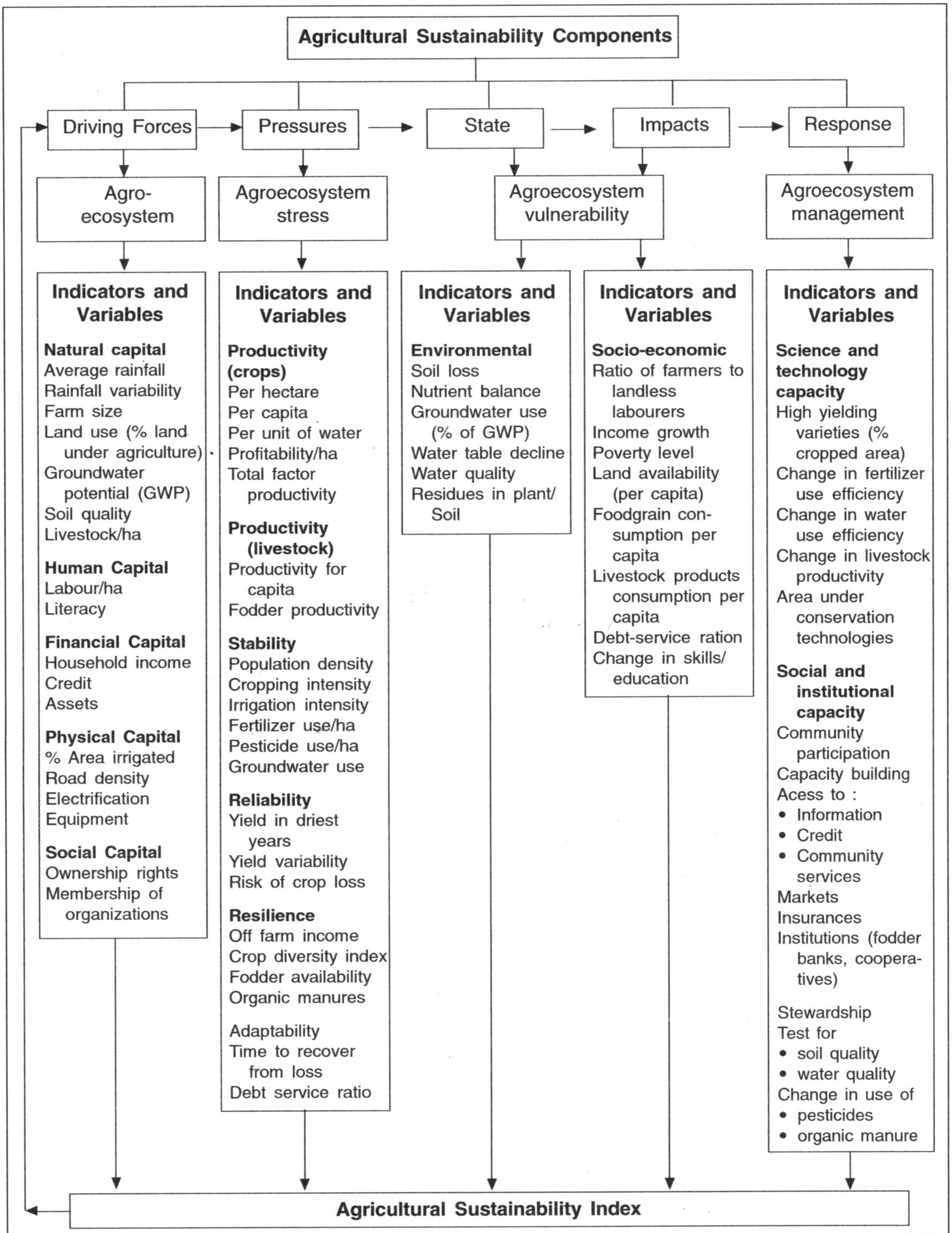

Fig. 25.3. Agricultural sustainability assessment framework

may be broadened to standards or rules that govern judgments on system condition, instead of only environmental condition. Agricultural systems can be analyzed at various hierarchical levels. For land evaluation and farming systems analysis, FAO (1992) distinguishes: cropping systems, farm systems, sub-regional systems, regional systems and national systems. Consider geographical domains of sustainability and include continental and global levels. The objective of this study was to describe and assess criteria and indicators of agricultural sustainability at the national level, taking the case of Venezuela as example.

Agricultural Sustainability Indicators

Sustainable agriculture is defined as a practice that meets current and long-term needs for food, fibre, and other related needs of society while maximizing net benefits through conservation of resources to maintain other ecosystem services and functions, and long-term human development. This definition emphasizes multidimensional (economic, environmental and social) goals of sustainable agricultural development. Thus, while green-revolution agriculture addressed mainly productivity issues, sustainable agriculture must not only address productivity issues more intensively, but do so keeping multidimensional (economic, environmental and social) concerns of sustainability in sight. As a result there are differing approaches, guided by local priorities and practices, and only limited attempts at developing systematic frameworks.

❑❑❑

CHAPTER 26

Soil Erosion and Conservation

Soil and water conservation term is similar to the conservation of energy, momentum and mass. It applied for conserving the soil and the water against several atmospheric agents such as water and wind. Soil conservation as a separate field, is a recent origin say around 1930 or so, but the basic problem undertaken by this subject are as old as mankind.

The 'erosion' word was derived from Latin word '*erodere*' which meaning is to eataway or to excavate. The erosion word was firstly used in geology for describing the term hollow, created by water. In addition to the erosion, several other terms were also introduced to express geomorphological process caused by water and wind. These are corrosion, corrasion, abrasion, denudation etc.

Definition

"Detachment and transportation of soil mass from one place to another by wind action or water action or beating action of raindrop."

"The wearing away of land surface by running water, wind, ice or other geological agents, including such the processes as gravitational creep."

"Detachment and movement of soil or rock by water, wind, ice or gravity."

Problems Caused by Erosion

Apart from several damages caused by water and wind erosion, there are following other Problems are also created by erosion :

1. Damage to sea coast and formation of sand dunes.
2. Disease and public health hazards.
3. Spent of money on water purification work.
4. Siltation of irrigation channels and reservoirs.
5. Silting of rivers.
6. Problems in crop irrigation and consequent need of conserving the water. All these problems are described as under.

Soil Conservation in India

In India about 81 million hectare lands are affected by erosion problem out of total geographical area of 326.8 m hectares. In other term out of net cultivated area of 185.8 m ha, 56.7 m ha lands are suffering from erosion either due to water or wind. Out of these about 40 m ha lands are badly affected and needed immediate control measures.

The dominating factors which are responsible for producing the problems of soil erosion in India are the excessive deforestation, overgrazing, faulty agricultural practices and occurrence of flood.

In order to maximize the net cultivable area, importance is now given to the soil conservation work in our country. In the first five year plan, the urgency has been given for making the nation wide policy, dealing with various existing problems. This resulted into the reorganization of soil and water conservation work plan. In the first five year plan *(Le,* 1954 to 1956) the soil conservation schemes were approved in three heads; these are the immobilizing of deserts, bunding and terracing on hilly land and afforestation of ravines and severely eroded areas. In whim, about 2.8 lakh hectares land were used for bunding and terracing practices in the first five year plan. In addition, eight regional training cum research centers were also established to study the soil conservation problems of the country. During this, Central Arid Zone Research Institute, Jodhpur was established to undertake the studies of the desert problems existing in the state of Rajasthan. The Central Soil and Water Conservation Research and Training Institute Dehradun as one of the ICAR institute were also established in 1954 as a central body to conduct different activities regarding the soil conservation and subsequently were recognized into a central institute in the year of 1974. This institute has 8 regional research centers all over the country, located at Chandigarh to tackle the Shivalik foothill problems, Agra, Kola, Vasad, Bellary, Ooatachamund, Koraput and Datia.

Soil Conservation Research and Training Centers

In India, the research soil and water conservation was started around in the thirties century. For the purpose, in 1953 the Government of India set up a Soil Conservation Board, which chairman is Union Agriculture Minister and other members are appointed from different departments and organizations. The main function of this board is to coordinate the soil conservation research programme running throughout the country. This board also set up different regional research centers, demonstration is training Centres for pursuance of different objectives related to soil conservation. The different research centres and their research problems being dealt are given as under :

The all above soil conservation centres were transferred to ICAR in Oct., 1967. Central Soil and Water Conservation Research Demonstration and Training Centre, Hyderabad became as headquarter of AICRP for dryland agriculture, which is now named ICRIDA. In 1952 at Jodhpur a desert afforestation research station was also established, which was designated as desert afforestation and soil conservation station in 1957, but now it is CAZRI.

The establishment dates of different Soil Conservation Research, demonstration and Training Centres in India are given in following table 26.1.

TABLE 26.1. Soil conservation research centre and problems of different regions of India

Research centers (Established year)	*Region*	*Problem to deal*
1. Dehradun (Uttarakhand), 1954	North-Western Himalayan region	Erosion problem in the Himalayan mountain, gullies and torrent control, stabilization of landslides, development of technology for better practices, trials of the establishment of forest and pasture grown on severely degraded lands falling in Himalayan region.
2. Kota (Rajasthan), 1954	Ravine bank of Chambal river	Survey, classification and reclamation of ravines of Chambal river, establishment of pasture and forest in the areas which have been reclaimed
3. Ootachmumd (Tamilnadu),1954	Southern hilly high rainfall region	Conservation of soil and water of Nilegiris and Western Ghat region, development of models for construction of dense terraces suitable for cultivation, evolution of suitable techniques, study of hydrological condition under different vegetative covers, development of pasture and tree plantation.
4. Bellary (Karnataka), 1954	Black soil region (semi arid)	Soil and water conservation in the track of black cotton soil of peninsular India, development of suitable bunding techniques evaluation of suitable method of cotton cultivation together with soil and water conservation measures.
5. Valsad (Gujarat), 1955	Ravine problems on the bank of river Mahi (Gujarat)	Control of ravines associated with the catchment of Mahi river, productions of crop, forage and forestry in the ravines.
6. Chandigarh (Punjab and Hariyana), 1957	Sub mountain tracks in Nourth Western regions of India with special references to Shiwalik hills	Erosion control in Shiwalik hills, survey of streams having stream bank erosion and measures to prevent then from overlarging.
7. Agra (UP), 1957	Ravine problem on the bank of river Yamuna	Survey, classification and implementation of control measures in the ravine of Ymuna river, measures for the production of cereals and fodder, afforestation of the reclaimed land.
8. Ibrahimpatnam (AP), 1962	Red soil region (semi arid)	Problem related to soil and water conservation in red soil regions, dry land farming systems.

Erosion Problems in India

The water and wind (*i.e.* air in motion) are the two main natural agents, causing soil erosion. The erosion pronounced by water is termed as water erosion and erosion resulted by wind is denoted as wind erosion. The erosion term indicated the meaning of soil removal from one place and depositing them to some another place. The happening of soil removal creates a very serious problem to perform agricultural activities and thereby causes reduction in crop yield too. Apart from this, a large quantity of nutritive contents of the soil which make it fertile, are also washed away during erosion Consequence, as a result the potentiality of soil to return good yield, gets reduced.

The consequence of water erosion is pronounced particularly in humid areas, where rainfall is more and intense, while wind erosion is common in arid and semi-arid areas, where rainfall is less and temperature and wind velocity are high. In India, the wind erosion is more effective in arid areas of Rajasthan, coastal areas and semi-arid tropics covering the areas of Haryana, Gujarat, U.P. and Punjab, adjacent to arid areas of Rajasthan.

In India, comparatively water erosion is occurring in higher percentage than the wind erosion. The serious soil erosion problem in our country is mainly in the form of sheet erosion, in which top soil is removed in the form of layer through overland flow from the soil surface. The red soils covering area of 69 Mha and lateritic soils of denuded hills of octachamund containing rolling or undulating topography are suffering from this type of soil erosion, as these are located in the regions of relatively higher rainfall. The black soils which are normally cultivated and kept fallow during rainy seasons are also affected by serious water erosion problem.

Further more, the gullied lands along banks of the river like Yamuna, Chambal, Mahi and other river in Gujarat have serious water erosion problem. The mountainous regions of the Himalaya are in highly deteriorated conditions due to deforestation, mining and adoption of cultivation practices.

TABLE 26.2. Effect of various soil conservation measures on detachment and transportation of soil practices

Measures	*Control over*					
	Rainsplash		*Runoff*		*Wind*	
1. Agronomic measure	*D*	*T*	*D*	*T*	*D*	*T*
• covering soil surface	sc	sc	sc	sc	sc	sc
• increase surface roughness	nc	nc	sc	sc	sc	sc
• increase surface depression storage	mc	mc	sc	sc	nc	nc
• increasing infiltration	nc	nc	mc	sc	nc	nc
2. Soil management						
• fertilizers, manure	mc	mc	mc	sc	mc	sc
• sub soiling, drainage	nc	nc	mc	sc	nc	nc
3. Mechanical measures						
• contouring, riding	nc	mc	mc	sc	mc	sc
• terracing	nc	nc	mc	sc	nc	nc
• shelterbelts	nc	nc	nc	nc	sc	sc
• water ways	nc	nc	nc	sc	nc	nc

D-detachment T-transportation, nc-no control, sc-strong control, mc-moderate control

Soil and water conservation is essential to protect the productive lands of the world. In our country, where droughts and floods cause crop damage almost every year, soil conservation will not only increase crop yields but also prevent floods and further deterioration of land. In India, a chain of 9 Soil Conservation Research Demonstration and Training Centers were established at Dehradun, Chandigarh, Ootacamund, Bellary, Kota, Valsad, Agra, Hyderabad and Chattra.

TABLE 26.3. Land degradation status in India

Type of degradation (mha)	*Area*
1. Water erosion	
(*i*) Loss of top soil	148.9
(*ii*) Terrain defoliation	132.5
2. Wind erosion	**13.5**
(*i*) Loss of top soil	6.2
(*ii*) Loss of top soil/terrain defoliation	4.6
(*iii*) Terrain formation/overflowing	2.7
3. Chemical deterioration	**13.8**
(*i*) Loss of nutrient	3.7
(*ii*) Salinization	10.1
4. Physical deterioration (waterlogging)	**11.8**
Total degraded area	**187.8**

A brief account of the work done on soil and water conservation in India is being highlighted below, broadly as identification and description of the problem, some results of practical value, and projection of the problem.

This was necessary to enable transfer of certain type of conservation practices established for a particular location to another location associated with similar situations. This gave rise to sub-dividing country's land into land resource regions and areas and other classifications based on their characteristics and other similarities.

Land resources regions and areas of India

Based on the information's available on soil, water, climate, topography, vegetation and land use, etc India has been divided into 20 land resource regions. The twenty land resource regions are as given below :

1. Northern Himalayas snow cold region
2. Northern Himalayas alpine grass and meadow region
3. Northern Himalayas forest region
4. Punjab, Haryana alluvial plains region
5. Upper Gangetic alluvial plains region
6. Lower Gangetic alluvial plains region
7. North-eastern Himalayas alpine grass and meadow region
8. North-eastern forest region
9. Assam valley region
10. Rajasthan desert region
11. Run of Kutch region
12. Gujarat alluvial plains region
13. Mixed yellow red black soil region
14. Black soil region
15. Eastern red soil region
16. Gangetic delta region
17. Western delta region
18. Southern red soil region

19. Eastern coastal region
20. Andaman-Nicobar and adjoining islands regions

The eight Central Soil and Water Conservation Research Centres are serve the land resource regions of the country are Dehradun, Chandigarh, Agra, Kota, Valsad, Bellary, Hyderabad and Ootacamund.

Soil Erosion

"Soil erosion generally refers to detachment and transport of soil and soil material by water, wind, ice or gravity water and wind being the major factors". Large flood plains and coastal plains are formed due to wearing of mountains. However, this steady and slow process of nature is non-destructive, and is, therefore, known as 'natural erosion" or 'geological erosion'. Geological erosion is not detrimental to man's well being and is wholly beyond his control.

Type of Soil Erosion

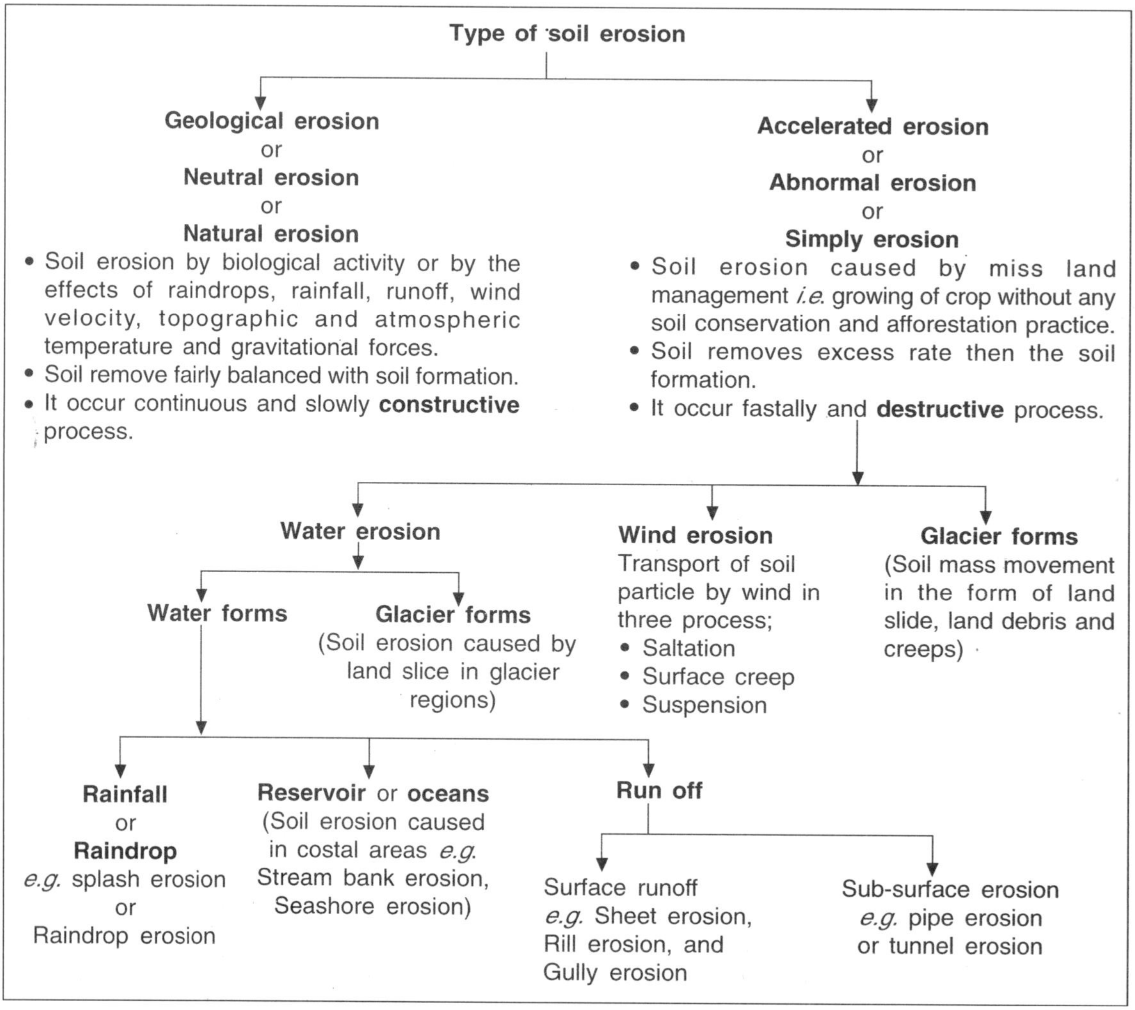

1. Neutral Soil Erosion

Such erosion is said to be in equilibrium with the soil forming process. It occurs under protective cover of natural vegetation, completely undisturbed by biotic interference. This long time, slow eroding process has developed the present topographic features like stream channels, valleys, canyons, through tile effect of water, wind, temperature changes and living organisms.

This is a normal feature of any landscape, Geologic erosion takes place steadily but so slowly that ages are required for it to make any marked alteration in the major features of the earth's surface. There is always equilibrium between the removal and formation of soil, so that unless the equilibrium is disturbed by some outside agency, the mature soil preserves more or less, a constant depth and character indefinitely.

2. Accelerated Soil Erosion

When there is a disturbance in the existing equilibrium condition in nature then accelerated erosion takes place. The agencies responsible for such disturbance are man or animals, Man or animals interfere with natural equilibrium through activities like wrong land management, over exploitation of forests and natural vegetation, over grazing etc. The removal of the surface soil from areas denuded (uncover, bare, remove) of their natural protective cover as a result of human and animal interference takes place at a much faster rate than that at which it is built up by the soil forming process. This accelerated detachment rapidly ravages (damage, destruction, ruin, depredation) the land and it is with this type of soil erosion that vie are so seriously concerned, Nature requires, on an average, about 1000 years to build up 2.5 cm of top soil, but wrong farming methods may take only a few years to erode it from lands of average slope.

Erosion consists of : (*i*) detachment of soil particles from the surface, and (*ii*) their transportation, that requires a source to carry the detached particles away.

Agencies responsible for erosion

The main agencies responsible for soil erosion are water and wind. On the basis of agencies responsible for erosion there are two type of erosion as describe below :

WIND EROSION

Wind erosion is the erosion of soil by the action of wind which dislodges the soil particles, transports from one place to another and deposits them there.

Erosion by wind, although most common in arid and semi-arid regions, occurs to some extent in humid regions as well. It is essentially a dry weather phenomenon and is accelerated wherever: (1) the soil is loose, dry and reasonably finely divided; (2) the soil surface is relatively smooth and vegetative cover is either absent or sparse; (3) the field is sufficiently large; and (4) the wind is sufficiently strong to initiate soil movement. Wind takes up soil from one place and deposits at another. If unprotected, the wind would slowly remove organic matter, fine silt and clay fructions leaving sand and gravel behind. This sorting action leads to more erodible and less productive soil.

Although wind has been active as an erosive agent throughout geologic times, it has become much more destructive because of defective methods of handling the land. As in water erosion, the soil material in order to be transported by wind must first be loosened from its position on the surface of the land. It may then be lifted, rolled or bounced along the surface of the ground.

These processes are largely the result of wind turbulence, mainly eddies and irregularities of wind movement. Turbulence adds a vertical component to the wind and makes it more erosive. The ability of wind to move and pick up soil particles varies square to cube of the velocity.

The erosion process consists of three distinct phases :

(*i*) Initiation of movement,

(*ii*) Transportation and

(*iii*) Deposition.

(*i*) Initiation of movement. The average forward velocity of wind near the ground increases exponentially with the height above the ground surface which is known as 'velocity gradient'. It is this gradient which determines the shearing force of the wind. At some point, near the surface of the ground, the wind velocity is zero. In rough soils, it is slightly above the average roughness element of the soil surface. Above this level, the velocity first increases rapidly and then reduces as height increases. In this zone, the wind is turbulent which is characterized by eddies movement. The particles entering into that zone of turbulent wind absorb most of the force. If they are large enough they resist the force, otherwise they are lifted up by the force of wind. The particles of the size 0.1 mm in diameter require wind speed of 10 miles per hour, 30 cm above the soil surface. Small particles which exhibit more cohesion and not protrude and hence stronger wind is required for their movement.

(*ii*) Transportation. The transportation of particle take a place by three mechanisms : (*a*) suspension, (*b*) saltation and (*c*) surface creep.,

(a) Suspension. Particles smaller than 0.1 mm may be moved by suspension. The movement of such particles is also initiated by saltation and once they enter the turbulent air, they may be lifted high into the air and may be carried many miles away from where the movement is initiated.

(b) Saltation. This is activated by bouncing or jumping of the particles over the surface. The wind force lifts up the particles almost vertically into air, rotating several hundred revolutions per second and travel 10 to 15 times their height of rise. When the velocity is retarded, they fallout at an angle of 6-12° on the surface. The size of particles for saltation range from 0.1 to 0.5 mm. Saltation is the main process which is responsible for continued movement of soil particles into the air till it is finally deposited. Therefore saltation not only initiates movement but also breaks clods to erodible size. The larger the area, the greater is the number of times individual particle strike the surface. Consequently more number of particles is set in motion. This process is known as saltation (sudden large amount).

(c) Surface creep. It is rolling or sliding of the soil particles along the surface. They are too heavy to be lifted by the wind and are therefore, rolled by the impact of smaller particles in. saltation. The particle size limit in this process varies from 0.5 to 2.0 mm. The rate of soil movement in surface creep in saltation is proportional to the cube of wind velocity.

***(iii)* Deposition.** The moved soil particles ultimately fall at points where wind velocity decreases. The lighter particles fall later than the heavier ones. This deposition may invade fertile agriculture land, homes, roads etc. Since the deposited particles are within the erodible limit and are loose, they are liable to further movement and are a common feature in wind eroded areas. This is known as shifting sand dunes.

Wind erosion takes place normally in arid and semi-arid areas devoid of vegetation, where the wind velocity is high. The soil particles on the land surface are lifted (raise, pick up, haul up) and blown off (puff, carry, thrive, gust, waft) as dust storms. When the velocity of the dust-bearing winds is retarded, coarser soil particles are deposited in the form of dunes (sandbank, hill, mound, and ridge) and thus fertile lands are rendered unfit for cultivation. In other places, fertile soil is blown away by winds and the subsoil is exposed, as a result the productive capacity of the soil is considerably reduced.

Sand drift. The movement of sand is a specialized form of wind erosion whose study will not be complete without studying the mechanics of sand movement. Sand drifts starts either from the marine beeches, unconsolidated sandy river beds or the deserts. Once a bed of sand gets exposed to strong wind, the sand stalls moving, gathering more and more sand from the area it blows over.

Mechanics of Wind Erosion

Wind erosion is mainly a surface phenomenon and is influenced directly by wind velocity in various strata near the ground through which soil particles rise in saltation. Wind structure near the ground the erosion causing wind is always turbulent; that is, its flow is characterised by eddies moving in all directions at variable velocities. Measurements show that zero velocity is somewhere above the roughness elements of the surface.

Wind forces causing soil movement

Moving air exerts three types of pressure on a soil grain resting on the ground. One is a positive pressure against that part of the grain facing into the direction of movement. This pressure results from the impact of air against the grain and is called the impact or velocity pressure. The velocity pressure causing soil movement varies directly as square of the fluid velocity. The second type is a negative pressure on the lee side of the grain, known as viscosity pressure. The third type of pressure is a negative pressure on the top of the grain caused by the Bernoulli Effect. According to Bernoulli law, wherever the fluid velocity is speeded up, as at the top of the soil grain, the pressure is reduced.

Initiation of soil movement

Movement of soil particles in wind erosion is initiated when the pressure by the wind against the surface soil grains overcomes the force of gravity on the grains. The wind forces result from impact or velocity, viscosity and static or external pressure over the surface of the ground. A certain minimum velocity is needed to initiate the movement of soil particles. The velocity at which the movement of most erodible soil particle is initiated is known as the minimum fluid threshold velocity. This minimum fluid threshold velocity depends on the size and weight of soil particles and the friction provided by neighboring particles. This threshold velocity is the lowest for grains of 0.1 to 0.15 mm diameter. Surface winds exceeding about 3 km/hr velocities are turbulent and are responsible for initiating the process of wind erosion. As wind velocity increases beyond this minimum, bigger size particles start moving till the movement of almost all size of particles in a soil containing only erodible fractions is initiated. This critical wind velocity is known as maximum fluid threshold velocity because it also initiates the soil movement by the impact force of moving particles in addition to that by wind pressure. In practice no maximum fluid threshold velocity exists because soil contains both erodible and non-erodible fractions together.

Transportation of soil particles

The lifting of detached soil particles from the surface depends largely upon eddies and cross-air-currents of various strata of air through which soil grain rises. In general, the soil transportation by wind is caused by three distinct types of soil movement *viz*. saltation, suspension and surface creep.

Saltation. Saltation is the first stage of movement of soil particles in series of jumps. The major portion of the soil carried by the wind is moved in a series of short bounces called "saltations". The soil carried in a saltation consists of fine particles ranging from 0.1 to 0.5 mm in diameter (fine sand). Sand sized particles rolling along the surface. Saltation is caused by the direct pressure of wind on soil particles and their collision (clash) with other particles. After being pushed along the ground surface by the wind, the particles leap almost vertically in the first stages of saltation. Some grains rise only a short distance; others leap 30 cm or higher, depending on the velocity of the rise from the ground. Generally 50 to 75 per cent of the weight of soil lost by wind erosion is carried in saltation.

The higher the grain rise, the more the energy they derive from wind. This energy is liberated in bombarding action of the particles on the other particles. Once saltation begins, the erosion is accelerated mainly by the saltation particles except on the windward edge where the direct presence of wind against the ground is the main eroding force.

About 50-75 per cent of particles are moved by saltation and more than 75 per cent of the grains carried by saltation spin rise almost vertically, rotating at a speed of 200-1000 revolutions per second and travel 10-15 times of their height of rise before returning to the surface.

Suspension. Floating of fine dust particles through the air is known as suspension. Very fine soil particles, less than 0.1 mm in diameter, are carried into suspension, being kicked up into the air by the action of particles in saltation. The movement of fine dust in suspension is completely governed by the characteristic movement of the wind. Suspended material is carried long distances from its original location and is thus a complete loss to the eroded area, especially when erosive winds are from different directions. The dust comes down to earth only with rain or when wind velocity is decreased. Generally 3 to 4 per cent of the weight of soil lost by wind erosion is carried in suspension.

About 90 per cent of the total soil movement in wind erosion is below the height of 30 cm, and about 50 per cent of it is within 5 cm of the ground level. The control of wind erosion is mainly based on the reduction or elimination of movement in saltation.

Normally, soils composed of fine dust particles are extremely resistant to erosion by wind because the presence of dust in the soil greatly influences the threshold velocity and the intensity of erosion for a given wind. In saltation, the dust is ejected in the turbulent air-stream in the same manner as dust is kicked up by traveling vehicles, animals, etc. The upward eddies of erosive wind having a velocity more than 3 km/h are capable of lifting silt and very fine sand particles to heights greater than 3-4.5 km. Suspension may move 3 to 36 per cent of soil loss by wind erosion. One can see this kind of movement during dust storms.

Surface creep. Rolling of coarse grains, larger than 0.5 to 3 mm in diameter and too heavy to be lifted, by wind along the surface of the ground is called surface creep. The particles are pushed along the surface of the ground, rolling and not jumping. Generally, 5 to 25 per cent weight of the soil lost by wind erosion is carried in surface creep.

Surface creep is the movement of soil particles due to impact of particles descending and hitting during saltation. The movement of particles by surface creep causes an abrasion of soil surface resulting into breakdown of non-erodible soil aggregates due to impact of moving particles. Quartz grains of about 0.5 to 1.0 mm diameter are too heavy to be moved by saltation but are pushed along the surface by the impact of particles in saltation to force surface creep. Laboratory studies have shown that about 7 to 15 per cent soil may be moved by surface creep.

In general, wind moves the finer and lighter particles faster than the coarser and denser ones despite the fact that the finer particles are less erodible. This results into sorting or separation of particles into the following distinct grades :

(*a*) Residual soil materials containing non-erodible clods and massive rock materials.

(*b*) Lag sands, lag gravels and lag soil aggregates which are semi-erodible grains moved primarily by surface creep.

(*c*) Sand and clay dunes formed by accumulation of highly erodible grains moved primarily in saltation.

(*d*) Loess comprising of dust particles lifted off the ground by saltation, carried in air by suspension and deposited in uniform layers both near and far from dunes.

Forms of Wind Erosion

The form of wind erosion to be countered from a surface, depend not only on the wind direction, but also on the wind force as the function of its velocity. At the velocity, only smaller soil particles are picked up and blown for a shorter distance. The picking and transporting ability of wind get increased, as wind velocity increases.

Abrasion or corrosion, this form is found in cloudy field, with effect of strong winds, clouds are contact and broken-down into small pieces.

Efflation, means to blow out, very fine particles carried away in long distance up to 100 km.

Efflution, this form is found calcareous soil (having very fine and coarse particle), with the effect of strong wind and small particle in carry away in long distance but coarse and heavy particle by rolling or sliding active by wind.

Destruction, these form found where bunds are constructed in cultivated field. The loss of particle slip down upper portion to lower portion.

Extrusion, found in sandy soil where coarse sand particle are dominated the effect of strong storm heavy and big particle transfer from one place to another.

Loss of Soil by Wind Erosion

Wind erosion can be estimated by using equation give by Chepil and Woodruff (1963), which predicts the relationship between annual soil loss by wind erosion from a given field and the five factors influencing wind erosion;

$$E = f(I\ K\ L\ C\ V)$$

where, E = Average soil annual soil loss (t/ha)

I = Soil erodibility index indicated by soil aggregates greater then 0.84 mm in diameter and percentage of land slope

C = Climatic factor (wind velocity and surface soil moisture)

K = Soil surface roughness

L = Unsheltered field widths measured along the direction of the prevailing wind

V = Vegetative cover

WATER EROSION

Removal of soil from one part to another usually down hill, by the action of water is known as water erosion. For such a removal to occur it is necessary that soil particles are detached from the land surface and then transported. Erosive action of water is greatest and most destructive where the protective cover of vegetation has been removed exposing bare land surface to the direct action of rainstorms. The water from rainfall infiltrates into the soil and excess runs off.

The soil transport is greatly caused through this runoff. If the infiltration rate of the soil exceeds the rainfall rate, there will be no runoff and consequently there would be no soil loss. It must, however, be made clear that runoff alone cannot remove soil from the land surface unless soil particles are suspended in the runoff water. The water erosion is, therefore, more due to the dispersive action and transportive power of water, which in turn depend upon amount, intensity and duration of the rainfall, amount and velocity of the surface runoff, nature of the soil, nature of the slope, ground cover and other related factors.

The dispersive action of falling rain drops is due to their beating action on soil aggregates. The aggregates are broken into a state of dispersion and brought into suspension from where they are carried away with the runoff water.

Mechanics of Water Erosion

The process of soil erosion involves three basic phases namely (*i*) detachment of soil particles, (*ii*) transportation of detached soil particles and finally (*iii*) deposition of transported soil particles. A brief discussion of the soil detachment and transportation by water is given below :

(*a*) Soil Detachment. The detachment of soil particles is generally caused due to the impact of raindrop wherein the particles are detached and splashed away. Large quantities of soil are eroded by the simple process of splashing and it is considered to be the first step in erosion process. The soil loss due to splash is considered to be 50 to 90 times greater than the wash off losses. The maximum amount of material in the splash occurs about 2 to 3 minutes after the commencement of the rainfall, when the soil surface is covered with a film of water.

(*b*) **Soil Transportation.** The soil particles detached and dispersed by the impact of raindrops go into suspension and are transported by the surface runoff, either as sheet flow or rill and gully flow. The transportive action of surface runoff is not much on a level land but it is serious on short and steep slopes. The amount of force generated by the surface flow of water is dependent upon the concentration and velocity with which it moves downhill.

The energy of surface flow is a function of mass and velocity of the flowing water. The velocity for any given mass is affected principally by the length of the path of flow for each unit of vertical fall, and the resistance to flow in each unit of slope length. A reduction in either the mass or the velocity will reduce the kinetic energy. An increase in the energy of surface flow will increase its carrying capacity, and generally will cause an increase in the rate of erosion. The impact of raindrops increases the transporting capacity of flowing water as well as soil suspending capacity to standing water. Movement of particles in the runoff water may occur as suspension, saltation and surface creep.

(*c*) **Deposition**

(i) Suspension. Suspended sediments refer to the particles which remain in suspension in the flowing water for a considerable period of time with no contact with the stream bed. Soil particles may be brought in suspension in the moving stream in two ways : (1) due to the impact force of falling raindrops over the sheet of flowing water resulting into splash and turbulence; (2) the flow of water over the soil surface causes lifting of soil particles in the moving stream due to velocity gradients upwards from the surface.

The soil surface being rough offers resistance and tends to reduce the horizontal velocity, while the water just above it will be flowing at a greater velocity. This difference in velocity, sets up a pressure difference between the layers, which undergo change with each pulsation in the upper layers. The changing pressure differences cause vertical currents and eddy to be set up, thereby lifting the soil particles from their moorings and setting them in motion.

(ii) Saltation. In the movement of sediment by saltation, particles skip or bounce along the stream bed. The height of the bounce is directly proportional to the ratio of particle's density to fluid density. In comparison to the total sediment transport, the saltation is considered to be of relatively lesser importance.

(iii) Surface creep or bed load. It is the movement of particles in almost continuous contact with the stream bed. Particles move downhill by the rolling or dragging action of water along the stream bed. Bed load may contribute about 10-50% of the total sediments.

Type of Water Erosion

Removal of soil from land surface by water including runoff from melted snow and ice is termed as water erosion. Water erosion occurs in stages which have been identified as :

(*i*) Rain drop erosion or splash erosion, (*ii*) Sheet erosion (*iii*) Rill erosion (*iv*) Gully erosion

(*v*) Stream bank erosion

Soil erosion by water can occur as splash, sheet, channel, stream, water fall, land slide, and marine erosion. A brief discussion of each type of erosion is given below :

(*i*) Splash erosion

When raindrops strike the ground surface, the soil particles become loose and splashed due to its impact force. Momentary build up of the pressure gradients towards the edges of the drop disintegrates the soil and shoot some particles out. The falling raindrop at an average speed of 75 cm/sec is capable of creating a force of almost 14 times its own weight.

To produce significant erosion, the splashing must throw soil particles into a place where there is a water stream for transportation. The forces that influence splashing are : (*i*) the rain drop mass and velocity; and (*ii*) the soil characteristics (such as roughness, surface slope and aspect), hydraulic conductivity, moisture content, particle size, elasticity, and associated mass of the surface.

In cohesive soils, smaller particles are difficult to detach. On the other hand, to throw out large aggregates, more energy must be transferred from the rain drop. Coarse grained, dry soil will reduce the momentary build up of pressure in the rain drop because of surface roughness and faster energy dissipation caused by flow into the soil. The saturation of soil will weaken the cohesive forces, reduce seepage and enable stronger splashing. However, a thick enough water layer will protect the soil. Raindrop action can be cumulative, initially breaking aggregates and later throwing them out. We know from the laws of kinetic energy that a falling body has Kinetic energy = 1/2 × mass × velocity^2 :: 1/2 mv^2. The mass of rain drop depends on its size.

It is now established that collision of rain drops on bare soil and resulting splash is the major cause of soil erosion by water. About 95 per cent of soil is splashed by falling rain drops and runoff water erodes less than 5 per cent of the soil.

(*ii*) Sheet Erosion

It is the uniform removal of soil in thin layers from sloping land caused by sheet or overland flow of water. The breaking action of rain drop combined with surface flow is the major cause of sheet erosion. Areas where loose, shallow top soil overlies compact soil are most susceptible to sheet erosion. The eroding and transporting power of sheet flow are functions of depth and velocity of runoff for a given size, shape and quantity of soil particles or aggregates. In the initial stages of soil erosion, rain drops churn (mix, roil, agitate, shake, stir, toss) the top soil and along with runoff (excess, overflow) the muddy water moves away from the field. It is uniform removal of top soil in thin layer from the field. It is least conspicuous (apparent, obvious, noticeable, evident) and is the first stage of erosion.

Sheet erosion is a most serious problem in red soils covering 72 million ha in India. The depths of soils vary from 20 to 100 cm and rainfall intensity is very high though the total annual rainfall may not be high. Similarly, the laterite soils, suffer from severe rill erosion because of fairly high rainfall. The black soils, occupying nearly 88 million ha, when fallow during the monsoon, are subject to severe sheet erosion hazards. The annual loss of top soil may range from 11 to 43 tonnes/ha along with 10 to 30% of runoff loss.

(*iii*) Rill erosion

Rill erosion is the removal of soil by runoff water with the formation of shallow channels that can be smoothed out completely by normal cultivation. Rills develop as a result of concentration of runoff water where the silt laden runoff water starts flowing along the slopes through small finger-like channels. The soil eroded from upland areas comes from these small channels, called rills, and from inter-rill areas between them. The primary mechanism for soil detachment and transport from inter-rill areas is the energy resulting from raindrop impact while the primary mechanism for soil detachment and transport for rill erosion is the distributed shear force on the rill channel boundary due to concentrated flow of runoff water.

During a rainfall event flow is quickly concentrated in micro-rills, which in turn flows into larger rills and eventually discharge to an existing channel system. The concentration of flow in rills increases the erosive power of the flow resulting in increased soil detachment from the rill channel boundary. In general, rill erosion is incipient gully erosion. If rill erosion continues only for a short while, tillage operations may smoothen out the surface completely, so that the resulting soil profile is identical to one that is damaged by sheet erosion.

(*iv*) Gully erosion

As the volume of concentrated water increases and attains more velocity on slopes, it enlarges the rills into gullies. Here rills become so deep that the ground cannot be smoothed out by ordinary tillage tools. Gully can also originate from any depression such as cart tracks and cattle trails and indicates neglect of land over a long period of time. An advanced stage of gully results into ravine which is sometimes more than 16 to 33 m deep.

The rate of gully erosion depends primarily on the runoff producing characteristics of the watershed, soil characteristics, alignment, size and shape of the gully and the slope in the channel. Loose, open, well drained sloping soils gully rather easily when water is concentrated on them. A heavy or compacted soil often checks the rate at which gullying takes place. Gullies are sometimes as deep as 6 to 12 m. Gully erosion is most spectacular in 4 Mha land in India.

Four stages of gully development are recognised

Stage 1. ***Formation stage***—In this stage, the rill erosion Scour of the top soil in the direction of general slope as the runoff water concentrates. This stage normally proceeds slowly where the top soil is fairly resistant to erosion.

Stale 2. ***Development stage***—In this stage, there occurs up stream movement of the gully head and enlargement of the gully in width and depth. The gully cuts to the C-horizon. and the parent material is also removed rapidly as water flows.

Stage 3. ***Healing stage***—In this stage, vegetation starts growing in the gully.

Stage 4. ***Stabilisation stage***—In this stage, gully reaches a stable gradient, gully walls attain a stable slope, sufficient vegetation cover develops over the gully surface to anchor the soil and permit development of new top soil.

Classification of gullies

(*a*) On the basis of depth, width and side slop;

Character	Very shallow (G1)	Shallow (G2)	Medium (G3)	Deep and narrow (G4)
Deep	Up to 3 m	Up to 3 m	3-9 m	> 9 m
Width	Not > 18 m	> 18 m	Not < 18 m	Vary
Wide shape	Vary	8-15%	8-15%	Mostly steep

(*b*) On the basis of shapes, the gullies can be classified into two categories;

(*i*) U-shaped gully and

(*ii*) V-shaped gully.

U-shaped gullies are generally found in alluvial valleys where both the surface and sub-surface soils are easily eroded. V-shaped gullies are generally found in areas where subsoil is resistant to erosion. In latter stages when gully cuts through the resistant layers, it changes to 'U' shape.

(*c*) On the basis of state of gully;

(*i*) Active gully

(*ii*) Inactive gully

Active gullies the dimension are enlarging with time but inactive gully is constant with the time. Active gully generally found in plain areas while inactive gully occur in rocky areas.

(*v*) Stream erosion

Stream erosion is the scouring of soil material from the stream bed and cutting of the stream banks by the force of running water. Stream bank erosion is often increased by the removal of vegetation, overgrazing or tillage near the banks. Scouring is influenced by the velocity and direction of the flow, depth and width of the stream, soil texture and alignment of the stream. Rivers and streams often meander and change their course by cutting one bank and depositing sand and silt loads on the other. The damage is manifolds during flash floods.

Other type water erosion

(*i*) Channel erosion. In contrast to sheet erosion, channel erosion occurs where surface water has concentrated and a large mass of water supplies the energy, both for detaching and transporting the soil. Channel erosion exists as rill erosion, gully erosion and stream erosion. However, there are no distinct boundaries between rill and gully erosion, and between gully and stream erosion, except that in all the cases the detachment is caused by the energy of flowing water and not by the impact of raindrops.

(*ii*) Water fall erosion. Water causing sheet and channel erosion in flowing down over a sloppy land may cut a hole on an unprotected spot. Such a hole often becomes a small waterfall. As the water goes over the face of the fall it tends to undercut at its base and the top soil falls in. Thus, in time, the waterfall leads to a gully unless the waterfall is controlled in the early stages.

(*iii*) Marine erosion. The Rivers in spate discharge their silt laden muddy water into the sea. This usually results in silting up of the harbours and ports which consequently need dredging operations. The tidal waters of sea cause considerable soil erosion along the coast. The roaring waves rush and dash on the coast swallowing every time bits of coastal lands. In this way, the coastal lands are not only washed off, they are turned into vast strips of Khar lands due to creeping of sea water into the low lying better shore lands.

***(iv)* Landslide or slip erosion.** Sliding down of large chunk (piece, hunk, mass, lump, portion) of soil due to steep (sharp, sudden, abrupt) slopes is called landslides. Landslides occur in mountain slopes when the slope exceeds 20 per cent and width 6 m. A landslide is defined as an outward and downward movement of the slope forming material, composed of natural rocks, soil; artificial fills, etc. The fundamental causes of landslides are topography of the region and geological structure, the kinds of rocks and their physical characteristics. The immediate cause of a slide may be an earthquake, or a heavy rainfall, which unduly saturates the ground or a part of a road. However, these are accidents rather than fundamental causes.

***(v)* Ravines.** These are manifestation of a prolonged process of gully erosion, typically found in the large expanses (area) of deep alluvial soils. They are deep and wide gullies and their formation indicates very advanced stage of gully erosion.

***(vi)* Water fall erosion.** It has been seen that gully formation takes place due to the flow of concentrated runoff on sloping land in fixed channels. The water fall action both scours the soil where it lands and also it splashes and swirls against the face of the water fall. The bottom of the face is eroded away leaving the top over hanging. The overhang breaks away to give a vertical face; then the cycle repeats again. The result is that head of gully works up stream and the height of waterfall increases. This over fall is usually the most actively eroding part of gully and helps the gully to extend upwards into the table land.

***(vii)* Pot-hole erosion.** Where the gully passes through an area with great difference in levels, water finds pockets which are more easily erodible than the rest of the place. It swirls round in these places and scours the soil leaving depression in the shape of pot holes.

***(viii)* Stream bank erosion.** Small streams, rivulets, torrents (hill streams) are subjected to stream-bank erosion due to obstruction to their flow. Vegetation sprouts when the streams dry up and obstructs the flow causing cutting of bank or changing of the flow course. Tollents with flashy flows and swift currents bring boulders or uprooted plants and are deposited in the downstream side causing overflowing arid stream-bank erosion.

Stream banks are eroded by water either flowing over the sides of a stream or scouring at the base. The erosion of the bank is due to surface flow and thereby scouring and under cutting the soil below the water surface. Stream bank erosion is aggravated by removal of vegetation, over grazing or by taking the cultivation field near to the stream banks.

***(ix)* Wave erosion.** Erosion caused by the combined action of wind and water is called wave erosion. Wave erosion mainly occurs in canal and river banks. It can be controlled by lining canals.

FACTORS AFFECTING SOIL EROSION

The major variables affecting soil erosion, *viz*., climate, soil properties, topography, vegetation and other related factors, are briefly described below:

1. Climate

Climatic variables affecting erosion are precipitation, wind velocity, temperature, humidity and radiation receipts.

The effect of climate on natural vegetation and on soil development shows that soil and vegetation boundaries coincide in a general way with climatic boundaries. Consequently, climate affects the erosion conditions of an area directly as well as through the vegetation that occurs. In arid climates, wind erosion is mote severe than in humid ones. Lack of organic matter in soils of arid and semi-arid regions makes them more susceptible to erosion by water as well as by wind.

In terms of temperature, the climate is defined as tropical, sub-tropical, temperate, cold temperate, arctic and sub-arctic. Generally, rainfall intensity increases near the equator because of the ability of warm air to absorb more water. Therefore, erosion by water is quite serious in tropical and sub-tropical countries. The amount of annual precipitation is affected by the prevailing wind, the distance from the sea, the topography and the temperature. The cooler the climate, the more likely it is for rainfall to be gentle. In arctic regions, water erosion would be of little consequence even if there were extensive agriculture, because there is little rainfall. Similarly, strong winds mainly in arid and semi-arid areas cause considerable soil loss through saltation, suspension and surface creep. Soil particles are picked up from one location and are blown to another, often hundreds of kilometers away. Wind erosion causes dust storms, forms sand dunes, buries localities with deposition and creates drier conditions.

The climatic factors influencing wind erosion are wind velocity in addition to temperature and rainfall. Wind velocity of 8 to 10 m/s can carry 490 million tonnes of soil/ha on a 100 m front. On a loose soil, wind velocity is the primary agent of wind erosion. Temperature and rainfall influence wind erosion through their effect on soil moisture. Soil moisture decreases wind erosion.

2. Soil Properties

Soil erodibility is largely dependent upon texture, structure, organic matter, nature of clay and the amounts and kinds of salts present. Generally, fine textured and alkali soils are more erodible. On the other hand, soils with low silica/sesquioxide ratio, common in humid tropics, *e.g.*, latosals and other lateritic soils, are reported to be less erodible. Soils with greater absorptive and retentive capacities reduce runoff and are, therefore, less erodible.

Coarser textured soils containing a greater proportion of sand are more susceptible to wind erosion. This applies to all sand fractions less than about 1 mm in diameter. In addition, low silt, clay and organic matter content in such soils deters clod formation, and even if some clods are formed they are far less stable. In general, any process which reduces consolidation usually increases erodibility.

Soil factors influencing wind erosion are texture, structure, cohesiveness, bulk density, organic matter, moisture content and surface roughness. Sands erode easily because they contain a great proportion of particles of saltation size, but little binding material. High sand percentages are also not conducive to clod formation and generally undergo high erodibility. Soils, high in clay and silt, are rather stable because they are coherent (clay acting as binding agent) and easily form a protective crust at the surface. Clods formed by clay and sand are harder and less subject to abrasion by wind borne sand than those formed by silt and sand. Although silt fraction encourages greater clod formation, but the clods are softer and more readily abraded than those formed from clay and sand. Soil containing 20 to 30% clay, 40 to 50% silt and 20 to 40% sand produced a greater proportion of non-erodible and mechanically stable clods.

3. Topography

Slope accelerates erosion as it increases the velocity of the flowing water. The four time increase in the degree of slope doubles the velocity of flowing water which can increase its erosive power four times and the silt-carrying capacity 32 times. Unidirectional general slope of the field results into sheet erosion while an undulating field with local slopes in more than one direction results into rill or gully erosion in addition to imperceptible sheet erosion. Lateritic soils, associated with rolling topography in high rainfall areas, also suffer from sheet and rill erosion. Different characteristics of slope such as steepness of slope, length of slope, configuration, variation in steepness, micro-topography and aspect of slope, all affect the soil erosion.

Level land is generally more liable to wind erosion than rolling land, because the wind encounters less resistance. Nevertheless, some of the greatest erosion hazards exist on knolls, ridges and in the lee of pockets, because the wind presses against such areas instead of flowing parallel to the surface. Small depressions catch saltating particles, thus protecting soil from wind erosion. Hummocks formed by deposits of saltating particles erode easily, as they stick out from the general ground level and are, therefore, exposed to stronger winds.

4. Biological Factors

Biological factors attributing to soil erosion include vegetation, residue mulch, animals and shifting cultivation practiced by tribal in hilly areas. Heavy destruction of natural protective cover like trees and grasses accelerates erosion in hilly areas. Shifting cultivation, particularly on steep slopes without any protective measures and animal traffic destroys natural vegetation and exposes soil surface to direct action of raindrops and runoff water.

The presence of vegetation acts as an erosion retarding factor. Forests and grasses provide better cover than the cultivated crops. Vegetation intercepts the beating action of falling raindrops, retards the amount and velocity of surface runoff, permits more water flow into the soil, and checks the abrasive power of wind. It also reduces runoff as part of the intercepted rainfall is evaporated directly from the plant surface. Lack of vegetation creates erosion-permitting conditions. Plant roots and other residues of vegetation help to improve soil aggregation and porosity and hereby enhance infiltration and reduce runoff.

Many times, animal traffic severely affects soil erosion. Action of animal hooves, especially the small cloven type of sheep and goats, is extremely adverse to the surface soil in destroying vegetation cover by treading upon the soil. Their mechanical pulverization often greatly increases erodibility, and where heavy grazing denudes the land of vegetation or vegetative residue, serious wind blowing or water erosion Results.

Man and beast accelerate erosion by extractive farming and excessive grazing. Practices like cultivation on steep slopes, cultivation along the slope, cutting and burning the forests lead to heavy erosion. Excessive grazing destroys all vegetation, leaving the land bare for ravages of erosion.

Loss of soil by water erosion

Soil erosion is estimated to be taking place at 16.35 t/ha annually in India which is more than the permissible value of 11 t/ha. About 29 per cent of the total eroded soil is lost permanently to the sea and 10 per cent is deposited in reservoirs. Loss of plant nutrients from the top soil due to erosion is an economic loss to the farmer. The soluble forms of these nutrients are lost along with runoff water, whereas exchangeable and fixed forms are lost with sediment. The major amount of loss is in the sediment compared to soluble form. The loss of nutrients are depends 0n rainfall, soil fertility, amount of fertilizers applied and crops grown. The loss of nutrients from a watershed grown continuously with cotton was 49.7 and 19.7 kg N and P ha/year respectively. About 38 and 7 per cent of the total (soluble + sediment) N and P were transported in solution and the remainder transported in the sediment.

Universal soil loss equation (USLE)

The equation is given by A = RKLSCP

A = Average annual soil loss (tones/ha)
R = Rainfall factor (erositivity index)
K = Soil erodibility factor
L = Length of slope factor
S = Steepness of slope factor
C = Crop management factor
P = Conservation practice factor (Terracing, strip cropping and contouring)

Rainfall erosivity (R) is the product of kinetic energy and 30 minute maximum rainfall intensity. It is a numerical value.

Soil erodibility factor (K) is expressed as tones of soil loss per hectare per unit rainfall erosivity index from a unit standard erosion plot.

Factor (LS) is also called a topographic factor

Crop management factor (C). Ratio of soil loss from cropped land to that of continuous fallow land provided the soil type, slope and rainfall condition are identical.

Conservation practices factor (P). It is the ratio of soil loss for a given conservation practice to that of from an up and down the slope practice.

Erosivity and Erodibility

"The potential ability of rain to cause the erosion is called erosivity"

It is dependent upon the physical characteristics of rainfall, which include;

- raindrop size
- drop size distribution
- kinetic energy
- terminal velocity etc.

"Susceptibility of soil to get soil erosion is called erodibility" Bouyoucous (1935) suggested that, the soil erodibility depends on mechanical composition of soil, such as sand, silt and clay it is presented in the ratio, given as :

$$\text{Erodibility E} = \frac{\%\text{sand} + \%\text{slit}}{\%\text{clay}}$$

SOIL AND WATER CONSERVATION MEASURES

(A) Mechanical and Engineering Measures

Since mechanical protection is expensive and time consuming, they deserve careful thought and planning. Firstly, because mechanical works are expensive and secondly man-made earth works are generally subject to constant wear and tear and their effectiveness would be short lived unless they are adequately repaired and maintained. Therefore, only high valued arable land would justify these costly mechanical measures. Mechanical measures, however,

1. Terracing

Terracing is a method of erosion Control accomplished by constructing broad channels across the slope of the rolling land. A horizontal strip of length, either raised or more or less level, usually constructed on or nearly on a Contour is playa very vital role in controlling and preventing soil erosion on agricultural lands. They are adopted to supplement the agricultural practices (biological methods). The mechanical measures include diversions, terraces, budding, sub-soiling, basin listing, and water ways.

Terraces are classified roughly into two principal types such as broad base terraces and bench terraces. A brief description of these is given below :

(a) **Broad base terraces.** A terrace is a combination of ridge and channel built across the slope on a controlled grade. These terraces have wide base and low height of ridge and usually formed with machinery. Excess rain water is led at non-erosive velocity into grassed waterways. A broad base terrace is a broad surface channel or embankment constructed across the slope of the rolling land. Broad base terraces are useful for reducing runoff erosion and for moisture conservation.

(i) Grade (channel type) terraces. This type of terrace is meant to remove excess water in such a way as to minimize erosion. These types of terraces are also known as drainage terrace because erosion losses are reduced by decreasing the slope lengths and removing the runoff water to a safe outlet at a non- erosive velocity. These terraces are constructed on areas where the slope is between 3-10% and the soil permeability is slow.

(ii) Level (ridge type) terraces. This terrace is primarily meant for moisture conservation. Therefore, it is also known as absorption terrace.

(b) **Bench terracing.** On steeply sloping and undulated land, intensive farming is possible only with bench terracing. It is usually practiced on slopes ranging from 16 to 33 per cent. Bench terracing consists of principally transforming relatively steep land into a series of level strips or platforms across the slope of the land. It reduces the slope length and consequently erosion. The field is made into a series of benches by excavating the soil from upper part of the terrace and filling in the lower part. A good soil depth is required to avoid exposure of unproductive soil during leveling. The vertical drop may vary from 60 to 180 cm, depending on the slope and soil conditions and width required for easy cultural operations. Depending on the soil and rainfall conditions, different types of terraces are adopted.

(c) **Zing Terracing.** Zing terracing is adopted in lands with 3 to 10 per cent slopes and; bench terracing is recommended on steeper slopes. Zing terraces are constructed in medium to

deep soils in moderate to high rainfall areas. The length of the field is divided into donor area and receiving area in the ratio of 2 : 1 to 5 : 1, but usually 2 : 1. The donor area is not leveled whereas lower receiving area is leveled and provided with a bund of cross-sections area 0.3 to 1.5 m^2. Zing terracing is adopted to cut

2. Bunding

The problem of loss of rain water by surface runoff is most important in low as well as high rainfall areas. In high rainfall areas the water should not be allowed to attain an erosive velocity. On the other hand, part of the rain water can be saved and made available in dry areas for profitable production of crops. The most obvious remedy to control runoff of rain water and the soil erosion is to place an embankment or a bund across the slope made by using a part of the soil surface itself.

The following types of bunds are common in one or other areas :

Peripheral bund is the one which is constructed to encircle the boundaries of the area.

Marginal bund is the one which is constructed at the lowest part of the catchments without any reference to contour.

Lateral bund is constructed at an interval of about 100 ft along the contour bund slope of the land and at right angle to the contour bund to prevent flow of water towards and accumulation in a depression.

Side bund is the one which is constructed along the slope usually at right angle to the contour bund.

Contour budding. Contour bund is the most common for soil and water conservation. It is constructed in regions having less than 75 cm of annual rainfall; soil depth more than 20 cm; land slope less than 7% and good infiltration capacity. Contour bonding is the construction of small bound across the slope of the land on a contour so that the long slope is cut into a series of small and each contour bund acts as a barrier to the flow of water, thus making the water to walk rather than run, at the same time impounding a greater part of it against it for increasing soil moisture. Contour bunds divide the length of the slope, reduce the volume of runoff water, and thus preventing or minimising the soil erosion.

Graded bunding. In situations where the rain water is not readily absorbed either due to high rainfall or low in the soil, graded bunding is recommended. Graded bunds are spaced at the same intervals as contour bunds. The spoil from the excavation of the channel is formed into a bund on the downstream to guide the water into a grassed waterway.

Silt retention dam

The silt retention dams are constructed below the watershed which have small percentage of row crops and protected by terrace or other suitable means of erosion control. The failure of siltation dams may be due to either or a combination of the following:

(1) Large siltation than expected in the dam, (2) Inadequate provision of spillways, (3) Organic matter in the filled, (4) Inadequate storage capacity, (5) Insufficient compaction of fill materials, (6) Inadequate drainage area, (7) Seepage, (8) Side slope too steep and (9) Inadequate fencing.

(B) Agronomical Measures

Tillage. Tillage alters the soil physical characters like porosity, bulk density, surface roughness and hardness of pans. Different types of tillage implements influence these physical characteristics in their own way and thus affect erosion. Tillage can be distinguished into conventional tillage and conservation tillage. Conventional tillage includes ploughing twice or thrice, followed by harrowing and planking. Conservation tillage is disturbing the soil to the minimum extent necessary and leaving crop residues on the soil. Conservation tillage systems (minimum and zero tillage) can reduce soil loss. In most cases, conservation tillage reduces soil loss by 50 per cent over conventional tillage.

Mulching. The value of mulch in erosion control is well recognised and is of special value for the periods when the crop itself does not adequately protect the soil. Mulches are more effective on land capability classes II, III and IV. Covering soil surface with crop residue can reduce soil loss by 50% or more depending upon the amount of rainfall and mulch, soil type and other characteristics. Various types of material used for mulches are straw, stubble, stover, saw-dust, woodchips and shaving paper. It dissipates the force of falling rain drops and reduces splash erosion, reduces surface sealing and gives water a better chance to be soaked into the soil. The dead residues are absorptive and help to hold considerable water at soil surface. Furthermore, the mulches tend to retard the soil surface flow which permits more time for water to infiltrate the soil. Mulches increase soil moisture because they improve infiltration of rainfall and slow down evaporation from soil surface. It helps to improve yield, if moisture becomes limiting in dry years or dry farming areas.

Crop rotation. The crops in a rotation may be cereals, legumes, a grass or legume or grass- legume mixture. The benefits of rotations in soil conservation include :

(*i*) Crop rotation provides high degree of protection to the soil thereby reducing soil erosion. (*ii*) Legumes include in the rotation leave behind crop residues which add organic matter and nitrogen and improve soil structure.

A system of crop rotations is commonly used on dry land subject to soil blowing. In areas, where moisture is available, legumes and grasses should also be included in the rotations. Crop rotations especially those that include legumes and grasses often improve soil tilth and productivity, but their major function is to provide year round cover that prevent soil blowing.

Contour cultivation. The term contouring, also referred to as contour farming, applies to the tillage practices or applying all treatments on the contour in agriculture pasture or range land. Contour cultivation includes contour ploughing, contour sowing and other intercultural operations. By ploughing and sowing across the slope, each ridge of plough furrow and each row of the crop act as an obstruction to runoff, providing more opportune time for water to enter into the soil and reduce soil loss. Contour cultivation is a very simple practice and can easily be practiced. In unbunded areas, cultural operations can be done across the general slope. This practice reduces runoff and soil loss.

Strip cropping. Strip cropping is a system of crop production in which long and narrow strips of erosion resistant crops (close growing crops) are alternated with strips of erosion permitting crops (erect growing crops). The strips are laid across the slope. Strips of close growing crops reduce the transporting and eroding power of water by forming obstruction to runoff and filter out the soil from the runoff and retains it in the field. Some of the erosion resistant crops are groundnut, moth bean, horse gram and erosion permitting crops are sorghum, maize and millet.

It is generally true that wind with a wide, unbroken sweep carries more drifting material than it does over narrow strip, and, therefore, its sand-blast action is greater on unstripped land. This seems to be at least one reason why strip-crop farming assists in control in most of the localities. In clay soils, drifting frequently piles the soil in the stubble at the edges of each strip to as great an extent as on the edge of a large field. Strip cropping on this type of soil, there-fore, has definite limitations.

Strip cropping aids in the control of soil blowing by shortening the distance that loose soil can move. Strips laid out on contour lines also conserve moisture which in turn helps to prevent blowing. To control wind erosion, crop strips are, run straight and at right angles to the prevailing winds. To control water erosion, crop strips follow the contour of the land whenever possible, the relative severity of the two types of erosion determine which way to place the strips. In controlling soil blowing, however, even contour strip cropping is better than planting large areas of a single crop.

Cover Crops

A cover crop is any crop planted solely to control erosion. Wheat, rye, oats, sorghums and peas have been used successfully as cover crops. Cover crops are more suited to humid areas because in drier areas they compete for moisture. In drier areas, the cover crops are used only for control on erosion-susceptible knolls, on land without protective cover, or on cultivated land. In the first two cases, pasturing should be avoided or extremely limited because the aim is to produce vegetative cover for the land. In the third case, overgrazing must be avoided to retain enough residues to protect the land.

Planting beans or sorghum in summer can provide a protective cover for the critical wind period in field where former crops have not left adequate residue and severe soil blowing in imminent.

Deep ploughing. Deep ploughing provides wind erosion control on sandy soils if adequate amounts of clod forming clay sub-soil can be brought to the surface. This is done with large moldboard or disc ploughs to a depth of about 40 to 120 cm. Generally, the increased cloddiness and roughness that results from deep ploughing of sandy soils is only temporary. Therefore, the practice must be supplemented with other wind erosion control measures.

Alternate Land Use Systems for important agro-ecological Regions

In order to provide stability to farm income and also utilize the marginal lands for production of fodder, fuel wood and fibre, a number of alternate land use systems evolved based on location specific experimentation and cafeteria studies. The general recommendations for alternate land use systems based on annual rainfall and land capability. These systems are now being studied on-farm to balance land capability with the farmer's priorities, requirements and resources.

(*i*) **Agri-silviculture.** This system is recommended for soils in land capability Class with annual rainfall up to 750 mm. A number of tree-crop combinations, particularly of nitrogen fixing trees (NFTs) with sorghum, groundnut, castor, and pulses were evaluated in Alfisols and Vertisols. Though the NFTs improve the soil fertility, the excessive competition for moisture between the tree component and arable crops did not make this system popular with the farmers.

(*ii*) **Silvi-pasture.** The system is recommended for marginal soils (LCC V and higher). It involves integrating a tree component with a perennial legume or grass species as pasture. *Cenchrus ciliaris* and *Stylosanthes hamata* were extensively evaluated in different soil types and rainfall zones. In marginal lands the grass forage system is recommended along with the locally important tree component. On the other hand, *Stylosanthes hamata* can be independently established as a sole pasture on degraded marginal lands. This system has been widely adopted by hundreds of farmers in Rayalaseema area of Andhra Pradresh, North Karnataka, and Marathwada.

(*iii*) **Agri-horticulture.** In medium deep soil areas (LCC II to IV) receiving annual rainfall of more than 750 mm, agri-horticultural systems consisting of a fruit tree intercropped with annual arable crop is recommended. Ber with clusterbean, cowpea, horsegram or other grain legumes has been widely adopted in the dry tracts of Andhra Pradesh, Maharashtra and Karnataka.

(*iv*) **Alley cropping.** Trees or bushes grown in alleys act as live bunds and control runoff. Width of the alley and management of the tree crops are the key to success with this system. Long duration crops, however, suffer from yield loss due to competition. Therefore, the system could not become popular with farmers. Permanent alleys provide fodder during drought.

Agroforestry

Agroforestry combines agriculture and forestry technologies to create more integrated, diverse, productive, profitable, healthy and sustainable land use systems. National Agroforestry Center (NAC). The World Agroforestry Centre (ICRAF) made this definition in 1993: "Agroforestry is a collective name for land use systems and practices in which woody prennials are deliberately integrated with crops and/or animals on the same land management units.

Knowledge, careful selection of species and good management of trees and crops are needed to maximize the production and positive effects of trees and to minimize negative competitive effects on crops.

Agroforestry is defined by some as a dynamic, ecologically-based natural farm management system that along with agriculture and the integration of trees on farms has many environmental benefits. Put simply, agroforestry is using trees on farms. Trees can provide many products such as timber, fodder, fuel wood, medicines, and oils. It also helps to conserve soil, enhance soil fertility and provide shelter belts for crops and fruit trees.

❑❑❑

CHAPTER 27

Soil Survey and Land Use Planning

Soil survey is the systematic examination, description, classification and mapping of soils in an area. Soil surveys are classified according to the kind and intensity of field examination.

The aims and objectives of soil survey

(1) To determine the morphology of soils.
(2) To classify them according to their characteristics.
(3) To show their distribution on maps.
(4) To describe their characteristics particularly with reference to the growth of economic crops, grasses and trees.

Use of soil survey

(1) Soil survey bulletins and maps are useful as a basis for other scientific work.
(2) It helps in planning and conduct of research.
(3) Land evaluation and sociological investigations are made from soil survey.
(4) It is used for tax assessment.
(5) Engineers and hydrologist also use soil survey information in practical way.
(6) It provides general education on natural resources.

Type of soil survey

Three principal types of soil surveys are recognized *viz*.

(*i*) Reconnaissance
(*ii*) Detailed
(*iii*) Detailed-Reconnaissance.

Remote Sensing Application in Soil Study

Remote sensing is the science and art of acquiring information about objects from measurements made at a distance without any physical contact. Infect, when we see an object and understand what it is, our eye is sensing that object, remotely. Similarly, the term remote sensing is generally used form observing out earth surface from space using satellites or from the air using aircraft after suitable modification.

TABLE 27.1. Relationship of scale of soil map and frequency of field observations

Kind of survey	*Scale of base map*	*Distance between field observations*	*Mapping unit*	*Soil boundaries*
Reconnaissance	1 : 250,000 1 : 100,000	2.5 km 1.0 km	Phases of association of soil families	Soils are identified by traversing sample strips; boundaries are plotted mostly by interpretation of remotely-sensed data and verified with observations (at random).
Detail-reconnaissance (Semi-detailed)	1 : 50,000	500 m	Phases of soil series/ association of soil series	Boundaries in each delineation of the sample areas are identified by actual traversing: others are generally plotted by interpretations of remotely sensed data and verified with at random, and grid observations and sampling.
Detailed Low intensity	1 : 10,000	100 m	Phases of soil series	Almost all boundaries are checked through the course of traversing: remotely sensed data is used as an aid in boundary delineation.
High intensity	1 : 5,000	50 m	Phase of soil series	All boundaries are checked through the course of traversing: remotely sensed data is used as an aid in boundary delineation.

TABLE 27.2. Land Capability Classification System

Land

Land Use Suitability (broad grouping)

- Land suitable for cultivation
- Land not suitable for cultivation

Land Capability Class

- Class I Very good land (with no limitation)
- Class II Good land (with minor limitation)
- Class III Moderately good land (with major limitation)
- Class IV Fairly good land (with major limitation)
- Suitable for pasture, grazingand forestry
  - Class V (with no limitation)
  - Class VI (with minor limitation)
  - Class VII (with major limitation)
- Class VIII (Suitable for wild life and watershed)

Land Capability Sub-class

[Grouped according to kind of limitation in each subclass *viz.,* erosion (e), climate (c), excess of wetness (w), soil limitations (s)]

Land Capability Units

(Land management groups based on physical characteristics-land that is suited for essentially the same kind of management and same kind of soil and water conservation treatment)

Examples. IIe, IIw mean good land with problem of erosion, climate condition, wetness and soil limitations, respectively.

TABLE 27.3. Specifications for Land and Soil Irrigability Classes

Land Characteristics	*Irrigable Land Class*				*Class 5 Temporarily Non-irrigable (Unclassified)*	*Class 6 not suitable for irrigation.*
	Class 1	Class 2	Class 3	Class 4		
	SOILS					
Soil Irrigability Class	A	A to B	A to C	A to D		
	TOPOGRAPHY					
1. Slope 2. Surface grading	Less than 1% No restriction.	1-3% Moderate restrictions	3-5% Moderately Severe restrictions	5-10% Severe Restrictions	Further investigations needed	Includes lands which do not meet the minimum requirements for the other land classes and are not suitable for irrigation or small isolated tracts (specifying size or distance from canal) not susceptible to delivery of irrigation water.
	DRAINAGE					
1. Outlets	Available	Available	Available	Not Available	Further investigations needed	
2. Subsurface	No subsurface drainage needed	No subsurface drainage needed	Subsurface drainage needed	No natural drainage outlets available; pump required		
3. Depth of water table	More than 5 meters	3.0-5 meters	1.5-3 meters and below	1.5 meters		

With regard to items under Topography (2) and Drainage (2) and (3) the criteria will have to be worked out for each project on the basis of local conditions.

Remote Sensing (RS), also called tele-detection or earth observation, refers in a general sense to the instrumentation, techniques and methods used to observe (Sense) the surface of the earth usually by the formation of an image (portrait) in a position stationary or mobile at a distance remote from that surface.

Use and potentialities of remote sensing in agriculture and forestry:

(*i*) Identification and area measurements of various major agricultural crop types.
(*ii*) Mapping of soil and water temperatures.
(*iii*) Mapping of surface water, including snow-pack.
(*iv*) Mapping of disease and insect invasion.
(*v*) Mapping of gross forest types.
(*vi*) Mapping of forest-fire boundaries.
(*vii*) Assessment of crop and timber-stand vigour.
(*viii*) Determination of soil characteristics and soil moisture condition.
(*ix*) Delineation of rangeland productivity.
(*x*) Mapping of areas of potential forest-fire hazard.
(*xi*) Mapping of major soil boundaries.

In the field of soil studies, the remote sensing techniques have been employed in obtaining land-use inventories, soil surveys, detection of salinity, and detection of moisture stress, soil mapping and measuring thermal properties of soils.

TABLE 27.4. Possible Use of Remote Sensing Techniques in Assessment and Monitoring of Land, Water and Crop Resources

A. Soil and Land resources	• Soil characteristics, soil survey and land use planning.
	• Watershed characterization and management.
	• Waste land mapping and monitoring.
B. Soil salinity & water logging	• Extent of saline and effect of reclamation measures.
	• Seasonal water logging, extent of wetland areas.
C. Soil erosion & Soil conservation	• Fluvial erosion, extent and depth of gullies.
	• Eolian erosion, sand dune movement, shifting cultivation.
D. Agricultural disasters	• Desertification arid land forms and change in vegetative cover.
	• Agricultural draught management.
	• Extent and damage due to floods.
E. Water resources	• Surface water bodies, ground water targeting.
	• Soil moisture status and soil moisture mapping.
	• Irrigation scheduling, evapotranspiration estimation.
F. Crop resource estimation	• Crop identification, discrimination & acreage estimation.
	• Crop yield modeling and crop production forecasting.
	• Crop condition assessment, crop stress detection (water, nutrient and diseases).

Remote sensing in soil survey

Use of remote sensing techniques for soil survey has been advanced to a great extent from aerial photo-interpretation to visual interpretation of aerospace multispectral data and digital analysis. Introduction of microwave remote sensing for soil moisture studies has been of high value for soil mapping.

Aerial photographs have been used since sixties and often soil scientists have found it very useful tool for preparation of small and medium scale soil maps. Large scale aerial photographs have been used for detailed soil survey with intensive and judicious field checks.

Aerial photography in soil survey. Aerial photographs are the pictures taken by an aerial camera fitted into a plane flying under certain specific conditions of flight. Aerial photographs are of two types (1) oblique and (2) vertical.

Importance

Aerial photographs are only pictures of earth's surface, but not of the soil which is a three dimensional piece of land shape having specific morphological, physical, chemical and biological characteristics. This information of soil profile is required for soil classification and mapping.

In normal soil survey about 80 per cent of the observations are made in the field are needed for locating the soil boundaries and the other 20 per cent are used to describe the soils. So aerial photographs reduce the time spent for locating the soil boundaries.

Methods of image interpretation

Visual Interpretation. For visual interpretation, imagery of visible and infrared bands i.e., standard False Color Composites (FCCs) are used in identifying the various elements for soil survey. The steps involved are summarized below :

- Procurement of satellite imagery and toposheet of scale 1 : 250,000 or 1 : 50,000.
- Construction of tentative legends.
- Monoscopic visual interpretation of the imagery for physiography, based on differences in tone and texture or a combination of these two elements to prepare pre field physiographic map.
- Transfer of physiographic delineation into a topo-base of scale of satellite imagery.
- Selection of sample areas/sample strips for detailed study.
- Procurement of aerial photographs of the sample areas.
- Transfer of broad land types from satellite imagery to aerial photograph.
- Detailed photo-interpretation of the aerial photographs.
- Selection of sample area on aerial photographs.
- Ground observations in sample areas of photo/imagery to correlate land type (physiographic unit) and soil relation-ship.
- A minimum of five to seven soil observations are done within each physiographic delineation.
- Compilation of the legend from sample strips and construction of final legend.
- The soil map of the sample area is prepared.

The above information is transferred over a base map. Once the soil composition of each land unit is established, the interpretation of the imagery can be done for the entire area by extrapolation. Thus a physiographic-soil map is prepared.

GEOGRAPHIC INFORMATION SYSTEM (GIS)

With the advancement of computer technology digital image processing techniques are also being used for soil mapping. Wherever there is close relationship between physiographic and land use, digital analysis proves to be useful. Thus digital soil mapping requires incorporation of landforms, topography (slope/aspect) and vegetation (land use/land cover) information to improve the accuracy while classifying remotely sensed data. GIS has been emerged as a powerful tool to integrate this information's to improve the classification. Ancillary data are of any type of spatial and non-spatial information that may be value in the image classification process; including elevation, slope aspect, geology, and hydrology and vegetation maps.

What is GIS ?

A geographic information system (GIS) is a computer-based tool for mapping and analyzing things that exist and events that happen on Earth. The system which provides for the entry, storing, manipulation, analysis, retrieval and display of spatially orients data, through digital techniques. The major components are:

- Data input
- Editing and manipulation
- Data analysis
- Output generation and presentation
- Data encoding (topology creation)
- Data conversion
- Data base management

Fundamental concepts of GIS

Any data that can be mapped has both location and possess an attribute, attribute can be both qualitative (*e.g.* land use, geology, etc.) or quantitative (*e.g.* elevation, dip, population, etc.) and it may sometime very with time (*e.g.* temperature, land use, population etc.) These three components *viz*., location, attributed and time represent the content of most GIS. The real value of any information, derived from any source, depends on whether or not it can be interrelated with other spatially distributed (cartographic) information. This is possible only when the varied information is stored in GIS format.

Potential areas of GIS for Agriculture

GIS is a useful tool for database management analysis and presenting of all types of spatial data with the textual information. By integrating the crop simulation models with the research information generated at various location across variable natural resources environment, optimum by plans at farm, regional and national level can be derived. GIS could be of immense use in the following areas of agriculture.

- Land suitability assessment
- Irrigation scheduling
- Farm management
- Fisheries management
- Wasteland development
- Agriculture production marketing
- Crop condition monitoring
- Soil and water management
- Wet land management
- Disaster management

❑❑❑

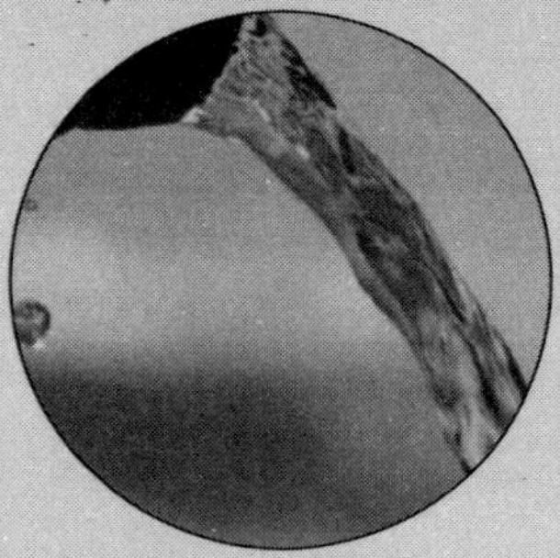

CHAPTER 28

Water Management

IRRIGATION

India with 2.4% of the world's total area has 16% of the world's population; but has only 4% of the total available fresh water. This clearly indicates the need for water resource development, conservation, and optimum use.

Importance of Irrigation Water Management

The importance of irrigation in the world is well stated by N.D. Gulhati of India : "Irrigation in many countries including India is an age old art as old as civilization but for the whole world, it is a modern science of survival".

The pressure of survival and the need for additional food supplies are necessitating a rapid expansion of irrigation throughout the world including India. Production and productivity of agricultural lands is primarily dependent upon the availability of irrigation water to crops. Expansion of irrigation has paid rich dividends in India. After independence, production registered nearly 4.52 times increase from around 50.8 million tons in 1950-51 to about 230 million tons in 2007-08. This has been mainly attributed to three factors *viz*., high yielding cereals, expansion of area under irrigation and fertilizer use. Irrigation may be considered as the major factor of modern intensive agriculture as it aids in efficient use of costly fertilizers and other inputs besides meeting crop water needs. On the other hand, improper irrigation causes wastage of large amounts of water, leaches mineral nutrients from the root zone into the deeper layers contaminating groundwater, and impairs the productivity of soil, or yield losses may occur if insufficient water applied. Excessive application of water causes waterlogging and increase high water tables or seepage spots to develop which may be corrected only by the construction of expensive drainage systems. In addition, salts accumulate and an alkali soil may develop. Water for irrigation and other uses is becoming more and more valuable due to increasing cost of irrigation projects and a limited supply of good quality water.

Definition

It is generally defined as "application of water to soil for the purpose of supplying the moisture essential for normal plant growth and development". In other words it is the human manipulation of hydrological cycle to improve crop production and quality and to decrease the economic effects of drought. However, a broader and more meaningful definition is that irrigation is the application of water to the soil for the following purposes :

- To add water to the soil for supplying moisture essential for normal plant growth and development.
- To provide crop insurance against short duration droughts.
- To leach or dilute excessive salts in the crop root zone, thereby providing a favorable environment in the soil profile for absorption of water and nutrients.
- To soften tillage pans.
- To cool the soil and atmosphere, thereby making more favorable microenvironment for plant growth.

Objectives of Irrigation

The broad objectives of irrigation are as follows :

(*a*) To increase crop production on sustainable basis where water is a limitation
- To increase national income/national cash-flow
- To increase labour employment
- To increase standard of living

(*b*) Modification of soil & climatic environment
- For leaching of salts
- For reclamation of sodic soils
- For frost protection

(*c*) To mitigate *i.e.*, lessen the risk of catastrophes caused by drought
- To overcome food shortages
- To protect high value crops/trees

(*d*) To increase population of arid and sparsely populated areas
- For national defense
- For population re-distribution

(*e*) National security *i.e.*, self sufficiency in food grain production.

Water Resources and Irrigation Development in India

Surface Water Resources. India is blessed with an average annual rainfall of about 1194 mm. However, the bounty is not evenly spread both in time and space with the result flood-drought-flood syndrome still persists. As much as 85-90% of the rainfall is received only in the southwest monsoon season of June to October. It is that during the four rainy months of June to September the Arabian Sea branch of the monsoon carries moisture amounting to about 770 million ha meters and the Bay of Bengal branch about 340 million ha meters of water of the monsoon moisture, about 25-30% precipitates in the form of rainfall. There are an average 130 rainy days in a year in the country.

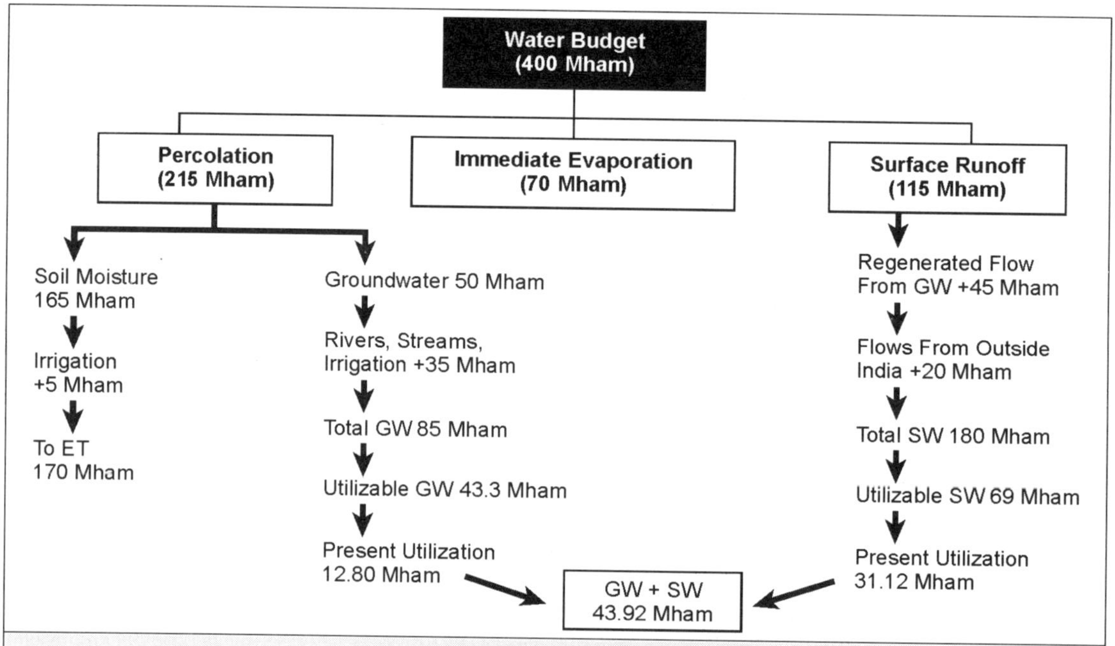

Fig. 28.1. Water resources of India

The rainfall when considered over the geographical area of 329 million ha amounts to 392.8 million ha meters. This may be rounded off to 400 million ha meters including snowfall whose potential is not yet fully recorded (Fig. 28.1).

Out of the estimated 400 million ha meters precipitation, about 70 million ha meters is lost to atmosphere as evaporation, about 115 million ha meters flows as surface run-off and the remaining 215 million ha meters infiltrates into the ground. The total surface water resources of India after considering the above have been assessed at 180 million ha meters, which is of the same magnitude as is available to United States of America annually, though India's geographical area is only about 40% of that of the United States. This 180 million ha meters includes about 20 million ha meters brought in by streams and rivers from catchments lying outside the country and about 45 million ha meters pertains to regenerated flow from groundwater as assessed from river flows during non-rainy months. The remaining 115 million ha meters constitutes direct contribution by precipitation, of which about 10 million ha meters is received as snowfall. Of the 180 million ha meters, due to limitations imposed by topography, climate, soil conditions etc., only about 69 million ha meters are considered utilizable. The present utilization of the surface water is estimated to be about 31.12 million ha meters, of which about 95% is used for irrigation with the remaining being put to other uses.

Irrigation Development in India

There was a great spurt in irrigated area which increased from 22.6 million ha in Pre-plan period to 87.23 million ha by the end of the 10th Five Year Plan (34.42 million ha under major and medium irrigation projects and 52.81 minor irrigation schemes) (Fig. 28.2). With an average irrigation intensity of 140%, the actual net irrigated area is likely to be around 62.31 million ha, which is only 43% of the net sown area of the country (142 million ha).

According to latest estimates, it has been assessed that the gross cropped area that can ultimately be irrigated would be 139.89 million ha without inter-basin sharing of water and 175 million ha with inter-basin sharing of water. Even after achieving the ultimate irrigation potential of 139.89 million ha and considering the average irrigation intensity of 140%, the ultimate irrigated area in the country would be only 70% of the net sown area.

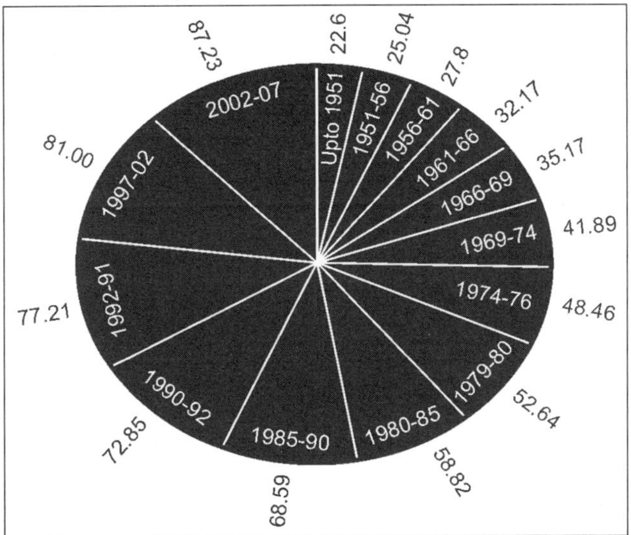

Fig. 28.2. Progressive irrigation development in India

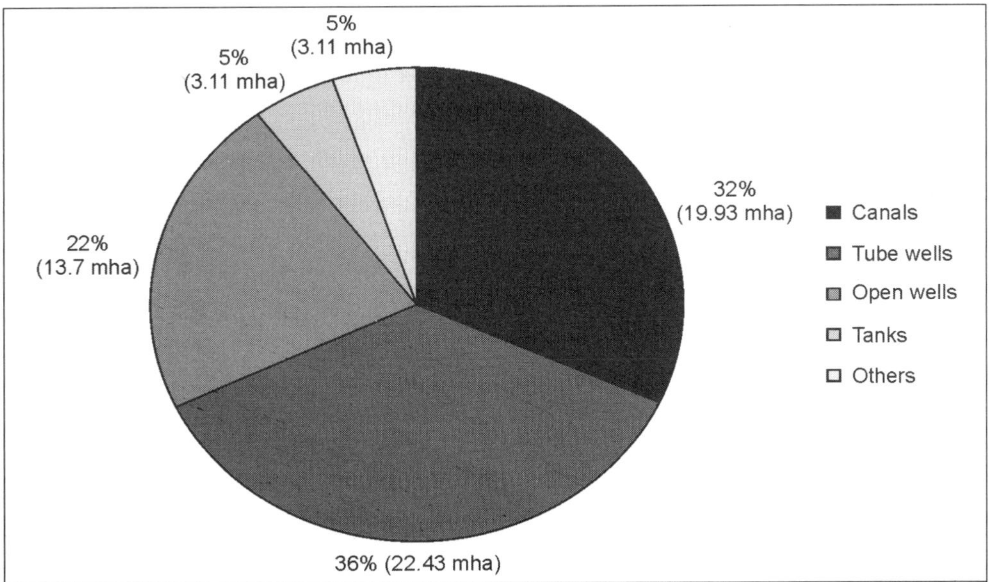

Fig. 28.3. Sourcewise irrigated area in India

According FAO estimates of 2009, out of the total 1628 million ha of cultivated area in the world, only 17.0% (277 million ha) is under irrigation (Fig. 28.3). The largest irrigated area in the world is in India (62.3 million ha) followed by China (56 million ha) and USA (28 million ha).

Effective Rainfall

Defined effective rainfall as "that portion of the total annual or seasonal rainfall which is useful directly and/or indirectly for meeting the crop water needs in crop production at the site where it falls but without pumping".

Scheduling of Irrigation to Crops–Soil Water Regime Approach

Scientific irrigation scheduling is a technique providing knowledge on correct time and optimum quantity of water application at each irrigation to optimize crop yields with maximum water use efficiency and at the same time ensuring minimum damage to the soil properties.

Criteria for scheduling irrigation

With the advancement of knowledge in the field of soil-plant-atmospheric system several criteria for scheduling irrigations are now available and are being used by investigators and farmers. All the available criteria can be broadly classified into the following three categories :

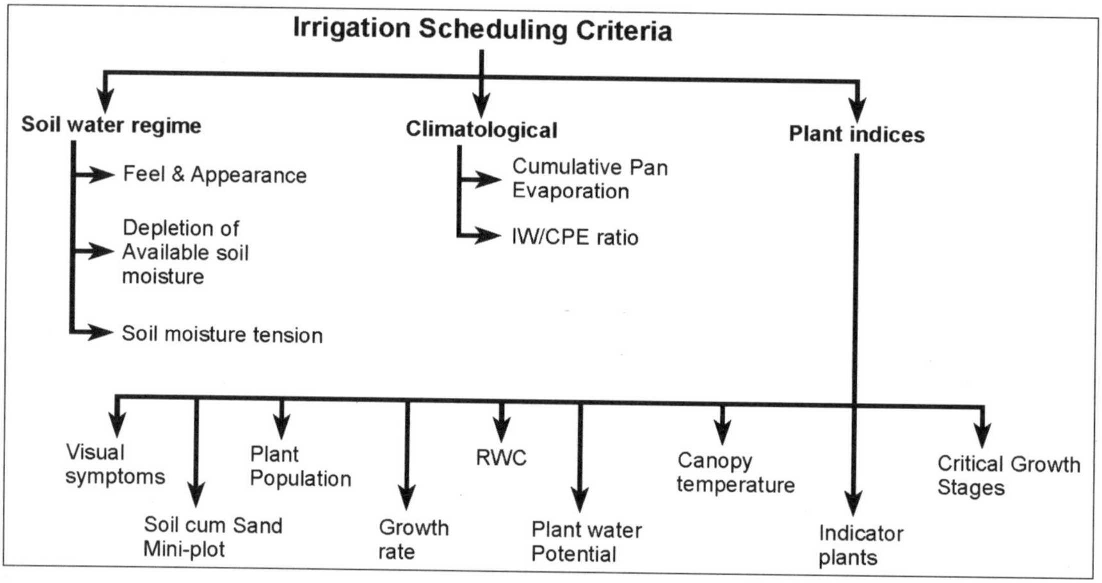

Advantages of Irrigation Scheduling

Irrigation scheduling offers several advantages :

(*a*) It enables the farmer to schedule water rotation among the various fields to minimize crop water stress and maximize yields.

(*b*) It reduces the farmer's cost of water and labour through fewer irrigations, thereby making maximum use of soil moisture storage.

(*c*) It lowers fertilizer costs by holding surface runoff and deep percolation (leaching) to a minimum.

(*d*) It increases net returns by increasing crop yields and crop quality.

(*e*) It minimizes water-logging problems by reducing the drainage requirements.

(*f*) It assists in controlling root zone salinity problems through controlled leaching.

(*g*) It results in additional returns by using the "saved" water to irrigate non-cash crops that otherwise would not be irrigated during water-short periods.

Type of irrigation

1. Surface Methods of Irrigation
2. Sprinkler Method of Irrigation
3. Drip Method of Irrigation

1. Surface Methods of Irrigation

Surface irrigation method refers to the manner or plan of water application by gravity flow to the cultivated land wetting either the entire field (uncontrolled flooding) or part of the field (furrows, basins, border strips).

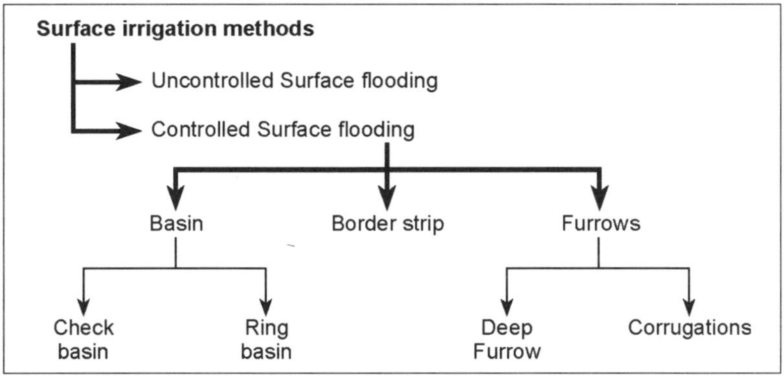

Uncontrolled Flooding

It consists of applying water to the field without any bunds to guide the flow of water wetting the soil surface completely. Generally it is practiced only when irrigation water is abundant and where land leveling is not followed. Sometimes it is also adopted in the initial stages of land development. This method is most commonly used for irrigation of crops sown by broadcasting method *viz*., rice, low value pastures, lawns and millets etc.

Advantages

1. No land leveling and land shaping.
2. Low labour and land preparation costs.
3. Less skill required by irrigator.

Disadvantages

1. Applied water is lost by deep percolation and surface runoff.
2. Low irrigation application efficiency.

CONTROLLED FLOODING

1. Check basin method

In this method the field is divided into square or rectangular plots of 4 to 4000 m^2 guided by bunds on all the sides. This method is usually practiced in nearly leveled lands, thus no run-off of soil or water takes place and wetting depth is more uniform. However, it is particularly useful on fine textured soils with low permeability rate where it is necessary to hold the water on the surface to secure adequate penetration. The field channels supply water to each basin, during which the basins are filled to desired depth and water is retained until it infiltrates into the soil. This method is most commonly used for irrigating crops like groundnut, finger millet, sorghum, vegetable crops etc. Check basins are also used for leaching salts below the crop root zone depth by percolating water in the reclamation of saline soils.

Advantages

1. Water can be applied uniformly.
2. Even small streams can be used for irrigation of crops efficiently.
3. Simple and cheap when equipment is used for constructing bunds.

Disadvantages

1. Unless the land is leveled, distribution of water in plot is uneven.
2. Considerable area is lost under field channels and bunds *i.e.* nearly 30% of area.
3. Bunds interfere in working of inter-cultivation equipment.
4. More labour is required for field layout and irrigation.

2. Ring basin method

This method is a modification of check basin method and is suitable for sparsely grown orchard crops and cucurbits, in this method a circular bund is constructed around each tree/plant or group of plants/trees to create a basin for irrigation. These basins are suitably connected to irrigation conveyance channels in such a way that either each basin is irrigated separately or group of basins by flowing water from one basin to another through inter-connections.

Advantages

1. High irrigation application efficiency can be achieved with properly designed system.
2. Unskilled labour can be used, as there is no danger of erosion.

Disadvantages

1. High labour requirement.
2. Bunds restrict use of modern machinery in the field.
3. Limited to relatively uniform lands.

3. Border strip method

The cultivated field to be irrigated is divided into a number of long parallel strips, generally 5 to 15 m in width and 75 to 300 m in length separated by small border ridges or low dykes of about 15 cm high, laid out in the direction of the slope The objective is to advance a sheet of water down the narrow strip of land, allowing it to enter the soil as the sheet advances. Irrigation water is released into each strip connected directly to irrigation channel situated at the upstream end of the border strip. After sufficient water has been applied to one strip, the irrigation stream is turned into another strip. A specific requirement in border irrigation is that the longitudinal slope must be uniform, and the transverse slope must be zero or negligible (< 0.03%). This method is suitable for irrigating a wide variety of close growing crops such as wheat, barley, groundnut, bajra and berseem.

Advantages

1. Large water streams can be used safely.
2. Provides uniform wetting of soil profile.
3. Low labour requirement.

Disadvantages

1. Requires relatively large water streams for quick advance of water to minimize deep percolation losses at the upper end of the border strip.
2. Wastage of water by deep percolation in coarse textured soils.

4. Deep furrow methods

In furrow method of irrigation, the flat bed surface is converted into a series of ridges and furrows running down the slope. The spacing of the furrow is ordinarily determined by the spacing of row crop. The length of the furrow and slope depends on several factors *viz.*, texture, intake rate etc. Depending on the soil, crop spacing, farm equipment used etc spacing between furrows varies from 60 to 120 cm. Depending on the soil texture furrow length ranges from 20 to 300 m or even more. To avoid overtopping and scouring problems furrow inflow rates are normally limited to 2 to 15 m^3/hr/furrow. This method can be used either with small or large streams of irrigation water because it can be diverted into any number of furrows. Slope along the furrows may range from 0.2 to 2%. Where the land is too slopy (> 5%), the furrows must be constructed on contours. Among the various surface irrigation methods, there is a relative saving of water in furrow method; hence efficient use of water is possible. In case of limited water, alternate furrows may be irrigated without much adverse effect on the crop yield. This method is commonly used for irrigating crops like potato, sugarcane, maize, cotton, melons, sugarbeets and vegetables like lettuce. When furrow irrigation is practiced under saline and alkaline conditions, the lateral movement of soil moisture coupled with evaporation causes salt to accumulate in the ridges between furrows. If the salt accumulation reaches harmful levels, planting is advocated on the relatively salt free bottom of the furrows following pre-plant irrigation.

Advantages

1. Fairly high irrigation application efficiency among surface irrigation methods.
2. Furrows serve as field drains in areas of heavy rainfall.
3. Low evaporation losses.

Disadvantages

1. Not suitable in coarse textured soils with high infiltration rates
2. Possibility of intra-furrow soil erosion.
3. Labour intensive.

5. Corrugations

This is a special method of furrow irrigation. Corrugations or rills are shallow furrows running down the slope from head ditches or laterals, which are sometimes very close to each other. Water moves down through several corrugations simultaneously and soaks laterally through the soil, wetting the area between the corrugations. This method is used for irrigating close growing crops, which do not require interculture operations and may also be used in conjunction with border irrigation. Corrugations are often used in fine textured soils that take water slowly and in soils, which tend to seal over and crust when flooded. The spacing and size of the corrugations vary with soil type, but in general, the more porous the soil, the more closely spaced the corrugations to permit rapid wetting between them without excessive deep percolation losses. The length of the corrugations should be such that upper end of the field has not been over irrigated by the time the lower end has received sufficient water.

Sprinkler Method of Irrigation

Sprinkler irrigation is a method of applying irrigation water which is similar to natural rainfall. Water is conveyed under desired pressure (2 to 5 kg/cm^2) developed by a pump through a network of pipes, called mainlines and submains to one or more laterals and is sprayed into the air through sprinkler nozzles or perforations so that it breaks up in to small water drops (0.5 to 4 mm in size) which fall over the land or crop surface in an uniform pattern at a rate (0.06-5000 LPH) less than the infiltrability of soil. The pump supply system, sprinklers and operating conditions must be designed to enable a uniform application of water.

Advantages

- Elimination of field channels and their maintenance, which increase the production area.
- Harmful ditch weeds, which have allelopethic effects, do not appear with sprinkler irrigation.
- No water losses in conveyance, which amounts to 35% in surface irrigation methods.
- Close control over water application *i.e.*, no runoff losses because water is applied below or equal to infiltration rate.
- Convenient for giving light and frequent irrigations.
- Higher application efficiency over surface methods of irrigation.
- Sprinklers give a gentle rain that does not clog or compact the soil ensuring better and quicker germination of seeds resulting in more plants per unit area
- Suitable in undulated lands, soils with shallow depth and areas located at higher elevation than the water source.
- Feasibility of frequent, short water applications for germination, cooling and frost protection to plants, etc.
- Higher yield and water saving over surface irrigation methods.

Disadvantage

- Uneven distribution of water due to high wind velocities particularly during summer season.

- Higher evaporation losses when operating under high temperatures.
- Mechanical difficulties such as sprinklers fail to rotate, nozzles may clog, couplers may leak or engine may require repair.
- Initial investment and recurrent operating costs are much higher than in surface irrigation methods.
- Moving the portable lines, when the soil is wet results in the destruction of soil structure
- Use of saline water for irrigation is not possible since it will be harmful to crops.
- Higher water pressure required hence extra energy cost.

Drip Method of Irrigation

Irrigation advancements within the last 2 decades have been astounding. Drip or trickle irrigation is one of the latest innovations for applying water, and represents a definite advancement in irrigation technology. Drip irrigation is defined as the precise, slow and frequent application of small quantities of water to the soil in the form of discrete drops, continuous drops, and tiny streams through emitters located at selected points along a water delivery lateral line. It differs from sprinkler irrigation by the fact that only part of the soil surface is wetted. Based on the observation that a large tree near a leaking faucet exhibited a more vigorous growth than other trees in the area, he developed the first patented drip irrigation system. From Israel, the concept spread to Australia, North America and South Africa by the late 1960s, and eventually throughout the world. The availability of low cost plastic pipe for water delivery lateral lines helped to speed up the field use of drip irrigation system. At present the largest area is in the USA and Spain (1.5 million ha each) followed by India (1.43 million ha). Total coverage in the world has increased from 4000 ha in 1972 to over 8 million ha in 2008.

Advantages. Many reports have listed and summarized potential advantages of drip irrigation as compared to other irrigation methods.

- Enhanced plant growth, crop yield and premium quality produce.
- Water saving due to increased beneficial use of available water and higher water application efficiency.
- Precise and uniform delivery of water to crops due to controlled water application.
- Maintenance of higher soil water potential in the root zone.
- Compact and efficient root system.
- Combined water and fertilizer (fertigation) application minimizes nutrient losses and improves fertilizer use efficiency and contributes to fertilizer saving in some crops.
- Reduced salinity hazards to crop plants when low quality saline water is used for irrigation.
- Suitable for irrigating high-value crops raised in greenhouses, plastic tunnels, potted plants and under plastic mulches.
- Lower operating pressures means reduced pumping energy costs.
- Limited weed growth because only a fraction of the soil surface is irrigated.

- Reduced operational and labour costs due to improved weed control and simultaneous application of water, fertilizers, herbicide, insecticide, fungicide and other additives through the drip irrigation system.
- Feasible to irrigate crops raised in small & irregularly shaped narrow lawns, and on undulated land terrains.
- Maintenance of dry foliage means improved disease and pest management.
- Suitable to highly permeable & low water holding sandy and desert soils, saline and slowly permeable alkaline soils, wastelands, slopy lands and rocky hills, road embankments, abandoned mine areas etc.
- Improved and continuous cultural operations such as spraying, weeding, thinning and harvesting of tree and row crops is possible without interrupting the drip irrigation cycle for any prolonged period of time.
- Environmental protection and ecological security.

Limitations. Despite observed successes, some important possible limitations of drip irrigation as compared to other irrigation methods have been encountered for some soils, water quality and environmental conditions, which include :

- Sensitivity to emitter clogging.
- Salt accumulation in soil.
- Mechanical damage to system components.
- Lack of microclimate control such as frost protection and evaporative cooling.
- Operational constraints such as high technical skills, stringent filtration and operating pressures etc.

WATERSHED

"A geographical unit draining at a common point by a system of streams, is called watershed."

All land everywhere is part of some watershed. Thus essentially a watershed is all the land and water area which contributes run off to a common point.

It is a land area that captures rainfall and conveys the overland flow and run off to an outlet in the main flow channel.

Extent and Size of Watershed

A small watershed of few hectares draining into a small stream may form part of larger watershed, which in turn may form larger watershed, which in turn may form part of a still larger watershed. All combined watershed may become a major river basin draining millions of square kilometers of land.

The sizes of watersheds are those where the overland flows are not affected by the channel characteristics. On the large watersheds, the channel flows are highly pronounced and peak flows are influenced by the channels characteristics. The area to be managed for soil and water conservation programme is also important is categorized a watershed. Thus, these are sub-divided into different levels called as sub-, milli-, micro- and mini-watersheds managing the area of 10000-50000 ha, 1000-10000 ha, 100-1000 and 10-100 ha, respectively.

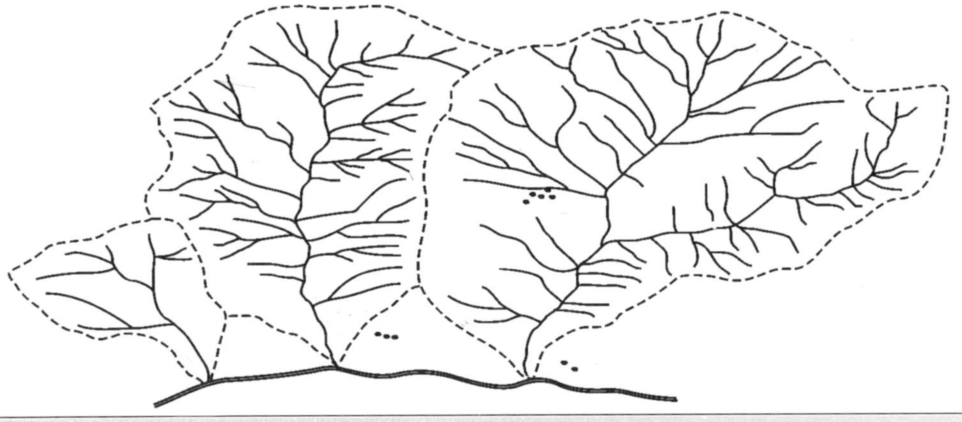

Fig. 28.4. Watershed in a catchment area

The people and animals inhabiting in the watershed are part of the watershed community. The size of the watershed may vary from a few square kilometeres to thousands of square kilometers. The size becomes important if we consider the objective of the watershed management. For some area near major stream does not fall in any of the lower order watersheds.

Effect of Watershed on the Community

A Watershed has a wide ranging effects on the lives of people at large as soil, water and vegetation are the most vital natural resources and Watershed effects them all. The sustained productivity of food, fuel, fodder, forage, fiber, fruit and small timber can be ensured by judicious and effective management of soil water and vegetation.

(i) **Soil.** The rate and magnitude of soil erosion and sedimentation are vital for watershed community *i.e.* people and animal. Accelerated erosion,

- results in a loss of land mass as a natural resource,
- adversely effects the productivity and production on agricultural horticultural, forest lands and grasslands; (at higher elevation),
- results in higher production due to transportation of silt and sediments into the rivers and reservoirs and then on agricultural land but also results into the reduction of life and benefits of the reservoir, (in plains),
- results in situation of streams and rivers which causes flash floods,
- results in severe drought due to low soil infiltration, excessive runoff etc.,
- results in converting useful economic assets into useless commodities by formation of ravines etc and results in damage to property.

(ii) **Water.** Water quality, quantity and regime are influenced by watershed conditions. Runoff,

- results into loss if water from the watershed which could have been utilized by the community for drinking, domestic use, irrigation, industry etc.,
- results in sheet grill, gully or ravenous erosion of soil from the watershed,

- leads to decline in ground water table and effects recharge adversely, and
- results in damage to property and life.

***(iii)* Vegetation.** Vegetation is a very crucial factor that affects erosion, runoff and climatic factors of the area. It provides food, fruit, fuel, fodder, forage, small timber NWFPs etc. to the community which is vital for the survival of humanity. For *e.g.* in Jhabua (MP) Rajiv Gandhi Mission on Watershed Development (REMWD) has been managed with following objectives.

1. To augment and conserve soil and water (surface/ground) resources as a means of providing sustainable livelihood and reducing vulnerability to droughts.
2. To develop and easily accessible repository of scientific and technological inputs for planning & implementation.
3. To maximize people's participation for sustainable resource management.
4. To improve the environmental resource base.

Watershed Characteristics

Physiographic

(*a*) ***Size.*** The size or area of a watershed is an important parameter in determining the peak rate of runoff. The rate and volume of runoff increase with size of the watershed area.

(*b*) ***Shape.*** Long and narrow watersheds are likely to have longer time of concentration resulting in lower runoff rates than square shaped watershed of the same size. The longer it takes water to leave the watershed, the move the opportunity or the water to infiltrate in the soil.

(*c*) ***Land Slope.*** The speed and extent of runoff depends on his shape of the land. The velocity of flow if the runoff increases with increase in land slope. The erosive capacity of the runoff is directly proportional to the slope of land on which the runoff occurs. Thus soil erosion also increases with increase in slope. The land use is also determined by the slope.

(*d*) ***Drainage density and pattern.*** High drainage density watershed drains runoff water rapidly Drainage pattern is influenced by the slope, lithology, structure, distribution of rock systems etc. The coarser the drainage texture, the higher the conductivity.

(*e*) ***Land use.*** The land in a watershed has to be used for numerous purposes like cultivation forestry, livestock production, housing water harvesting etc. The land use affects rate of runoff, infiltration and types and quality of vegetation. Suitable land use minimizes the soil erosion and reduces the runoff.

Vegetative cover

The type, quantity and quality of vegetative cover in watershed influences runoff, erosion and sediment production, rate of evaporation and infiltration rate. The first effect of vegetation is to intercept a portion of the rain through the process of wetting the leaves, branches and stem. In dense vegetation with three tiers of trees, shrubs and grasses, this intercepted moisture may be substantial.

Following the end of precipitation a portion of this moisture falls to the ground due to wind. This delayed precipitation prolongs the period of rainfall at the ground surface and tends to increase infiltration into the ground. The second influence of vegetation is to protect and shade the soil. Vegetation protects the soil against the impact if direct rainfall through its leaves (which reduces the rain drop velocity) and roots (which anchor soil particles).

Vegetation has a large effect on infiltration by shielding the surface from impact, by roots opening channels in the soil for transmission of water by falling leaves becoming a mulch on the soil surface (an important ingredient for soil building process) and through the process of transpiration creating moisture deficiency or storage potential. A good cover of vegetation, thus, reduces soil erosion and runoff.

Rainfall

The amount, frequency and intensity of rainfall determine the behaviors of watershed. Evenly dispersed rainfall is less damaging the soil and water than sudden, sharp showers.

Socio-economic factors:

(*a*) ***Demographic profile.*** Total population of the area, sex-age-ethnic group stratification, location and occupation of the population, migration, future demon graphic trends decide the behavioral characteristics of watershed.

(*b*) ***Sociological stratification.*** Caste, lineage, families, lines of authority, heterogeneity, political organization, groupings, social status and political role individual, members, relations between members, spatial distribution of the community and CPR (Common Property Resources) modify the watershed characteristics.

(*c*) ***Farm Structure.*** Area of farm, number of farm workers, division of labour on farm, collective/individual farming, traditional clopping area, agricultural techniques, land management systems are important factors affecting a watershed.

(*d*) ***Attitude and behavior.*** Attitudes, aptitude and behavioral patterns, value systems may also play and important role in the performance of the watershed.

(*e*) ***Land tenure systems.*** Land holding sizes, dominant classes, landholding classes and castes, methods of land acquisition, alienation of land rights, relationship between land rights and social, political or religious systems, land leasing, share cropping, marketing system of agricultural Forestry produce affect watershed functioning area.

Causes of Watershed Deterioration

Uncontrolled, unplanned, unscientific land use and interventions lead to deterioration of the watershed area. Some of the activities detrimental to watershed all.

(1) Agricultural land. Cultivation on sloping land without adequate peculations, cultivation without agronomic measures to conserve soil and water, cultivation along susceptible nalla banks, cultivation of erosion—permitting crops, over cropping without soil fertility replenishment, frailty agricultural techniques etc.

(2) Grass land. Excessive and uncontrolled grazing, growth of weeds development of cattle tracks causing damage and compaction of soil resulting in lower infiltration rates, fires, theft etc.

(3) Forest. Excessive and uncontrolled grazing which inhibits regeneration from seed or coppice stock, clear felling on steep slopes, destruction of forest land by fires and thefts, biotic pressure for fuel, fodder, NTFP and small timber, drastic thinning of plantation along slopes etc.

(4) Shifting cultivation. Shifting cultivation or Jhum kheti practiced in certain areas of counties (like North East India etc.) has proved to be very damaging to protective and productive vegetation. This practice results in damage to the topsoil and inhabits the growth of grasses, shrubs and trees.

(5) Unscientific mining and construction activities. These activities damage the vegetation and the landscape. The natural drainage lines are often blocked by debris.

(6) Fire. Intentional/accidental fires result in loss of vegetation, organic matter and micro-organisms.

(7) Non-cooperation of the community. Non-cooperation of the community in conserving, protecting and enriching then ecosystem and CPR has also resulted in most of the ills.

Principles of Watershed Management

Watershed management may be defined as the process of formulating and carrying out a course of action involving manipulation of natural, agricultural and human resources of a watershed to provide resources that are desired by and suitable to the watershed community, but under the condition that soil and water resources are not adversely affected.

Watershed management must consider the social, economic and institutional factors operating within and outside the watershed management practices are there changes in land use vegetative cover and other non-structural and structural actions that are taken on a watershed to achieve watershed development objections. Watershed management is an integrated and interdisciplinary approach. It generally requires land use adjustment measures which contribute to the reduction in soil erosion rates *vis-a-vis* increased agricultural production generation of neutral employment and balanced growth of national economy.

Watershed management usually involves the use, by the people of the watershed are a of the watershed natural resources, especially the land, water and vegetation, with the active participation of their institutions and organizations and in harmony with eco-system.

Objectives

The objectives of each watershed development project should be :

(1) To promote the economic development of the village community which is directly or indirectly dependent on the watershed through;

   (*a*) Optimum utilization of the watershed's natural resources like land water vegetation etc. that will mitigate the adverse effects of drought and prevent further ecological degradation, and

   (*b*) Employment generation and development of the human and other economic resources of the village in order to promote savings and other income generation activities.

(2) To encourage restoration of ecological balance in the village through;

(*a*) Sustained community action for the operation and maintenance of assets created and further development of the potential of the natural resources in the watershed.

(*b*) Simple easy and affordable technological solutions and institutional arrangements that make use of and build upon, local technical knowledge and available materials.

(3) Special emphasis to improve the economic and social conditions of the resource poor and the disadvantaged sections of the "Watershed C`ommunity" such as asset less and the women through:

(*a*) More equitable distribution of benefits of land and water resources development and the consequent biomass production; and

(*b*) Greater access to income generating opportunities and focus on human resource development.

(4) All the members of Watershed Development Committee, staff and volunteers have been given orientation training to improve their knowledge and upgrade technical/managerial and community organizational skills on with drawl of watershed development team from the project.

Why Watershed Development ?

The need of the hour is to shift towards regeneration oriented development. It is difficult to regenerate resources without conserving them.

The process of conservation begins with better and efficient management of primary resources. Land (Soil) and water conservation are insuperable and their interaction influences the quality of life or living standards. The only option to manage this interaction of primary resources is to work within a hydrologically defined unit *i.e.* watershed.

All the processes within the limits of a watershed influence one another. The sustainability of any process this depends upon understanding there.

Constraints in Watershed Development

There are many natural and man-made limiting factors that tend to inhibit normal pace of watershed development;

(*i*) Lack of awareness

(*ii*) Lack of people's participation especially women folk

(*iii*) Lack of accessibility due to difficult topography and poor infrastructural facilities

(*iv*) Sensitive environment

(*v*) Lack of technical know how and required manpower

(*vi*) Access to information (Data collection)

(*vii*) Financial constructs

(*viii*) Corruption at implementation stage.

Selection of Watersheds

In each selected village a watershed of approximately 500 ha. Should be identified in consultation with village panchayat/community but if it is not possible to find watershed of this size, area can be increased or decreased, keeping in view that Project Implementation Agency (PIA) handles a total area of 5000 to 6000 ha. Following criteria should be used in selecting a watershed.

(*a*) Watershed which has acute water shortage.

(*b*) Watershed which has a large population of socially and economically backward and poor sections of society dependent on if.

(*c*) Watershed which has a preponderance of common lands.

(*d*) Watershed having preponderance of waste lands.

(*e*) Watersheds where actual wages are significantly lower than the legal minimum wages.

(*f*) Watershed which is continuous to another watershed which has already been developed is selected for development.

(*g*) Watersheds which have previously been taken up for comprehensive development/ treatment works under any of the programmes like DDAP/DDP/NWDPRA/WDP shall not be taken up again.

(*h*) 500 ha. is the usual norm but if on actual ground survey a watershed is found to vane slightly less or more area, it may shall be taken up for treatment. Even small contiguous watersheds with an approximates total area if 500 ha may also be taken up.

(*i*) Though a watershed should normally fall within the village boundaries, but if a small part of the watershed falls outside the village boundary, it may still be taken up for development with the consent of the neighboring village/panchayats.

Components of Watershed Treatment Plan

1. Agronomic measures in agricultural land (*e.g.* strip cropping, crop canopy, residue management, land management etc.)
2. Mechanical measures in agricultural land (*e.g.* contour and graded bunds, bench terracing, contour cultivation etc.)
3. Erosion control measures for non-agricultural land (*e.g.* Contour trances, gully control measures, nalla bunds check dams etc.)
4. Water conservation and harvesting structures (*e.g.* farm ponds, earthen embankments, weirs etc.)
5. Groundwater recharge and management (*e.g.* percolation tanks, sub-surface dykes etc).
6. Nursery raising and community plantation of fuel, fodder, fruit and small timber species in combination of NWFPs like medicinal plants, floriculture etc.
7. Grassland development on recharge, transition and discharge zones.

8. Agroforestry
9. Animal husbandry, horticulture, apiculture and allied activities development for income generation.
10. Protection, conservation and enrichment of degraded forest land in watersheds through JFM.

DRAINAGE

Definition

Agricultural drainage is the artificial removal and safe disposal of excess water either from the land surface or soil profile, more specifically, the removal and safe disposal of excess gravitational water from the crop root zone to create favourable conditions for crop growth to enhance agricultural production.

Benefits of drainage

(*a*) It provides better soil environment for plant growth by creating favourable soil aeration conditions.

(*b*) It improves the soil structure and increases the soil infiltration.

(*c*) High infiltration capacity reduces soil erosion.

(*d*) It hastens the warming of the soils and maintains desirable soil temperature, which accelerates plant growth and bacterial activity.

(*e*) It promotes increased leaching of salts and prevents accumulation of salts in the crop root zone.

(*f*) In well drained soils, less time and less labour are required for tillage operations.

Types of Drainage

Broadly drainage systems are of two types-Surface and Sub-surface.

1. Surface Drainage Systems

Safe removal and disposal of excess water primarily from land surface or cropped area by a network of surface drains or constructed channels and through proper land shaping is known as surface drainage. There are four general types of surface drainage systems used in flat areas having a slope of < 2% *viz*.,

(*a*) Random drain system
(*b*) Parallel field drain system
(*c*) Parallel open ditch system and
(*d*) Bedding system

(*a*) Random drain system. This system is usually adopted in areas where the ground surface is characterized by a series and depression (undulating land surface) and where small depressions are to be drained off. Depending upon the possibility the field drains are designed in such a way to connect one depression to another and water is safely on eyed to lateral drains. These lateral drains ultimately guide the water to main outlet drain. The field drains sides occupying the land area are likely to interfere with farm operations.

(*b*) Parallel field drain system. The parallel field ditch system is used in places where the surface is uniform and has few noticeable ridges or depressions. In this system the surface of individual fields is graded in such a way so that the runoff water drains into field drains, which in turn discharge water into field laterals bordering the field and finally the laterals in turn lead water into the main outlet ditch through protected over falls. Laterals and mains should be deeper than field drains to provide free out-fall. Maximum spacing of parallel field drains is about 200 m for sandy soils and about 100 m for clay soils. It is the most desirable surface drainage method and is well suited both for irrigated and rainfed areas.

(*c*) **Parallel open ditch system.** The parallel open ditch system is similar to parallel field drain system in all respects except that the drains are replaced by open ditches which are comparatively deeper and have steeper side slopes than the field drains. Maximum length of grade draining to ditch should not be > 180 m. The spacing of the ditches depends upon the soil and water table conditions and may vary from 60-200m. This system is applicable in soils, which require both surface and sub-surface drainage.

(*d*) **Bedding system.** This system is usually adopted in fields with very little slope, usually 0.5% or less and slowly permeable soils. It is essentially a tillage operation wherein the land is ploughed into a series of parallel beds separated by dead furrows, which run in the direction of greatest slope lateral drains are located perpendicular to slope. The ploughing operations are to be carried out parallel to the furrows. The bed width and length varies between 8 to 30 m and 10 to 300m respectively depending upon field conditions i.e., land use, slope, soil permeability and farming operations.

2. Sub-Surface Drainage Systems

The removal and safe disposal of excess water that has already entered the soil profile is considered sub-surface drainage. Though several sub-surface systems are available, the most commonly used and effective ones are Tile drainage and Mole drainage systems.

Tile drainage systems. Tile drains removes excess water from the soil through a continuous line of tiles (pipes) laid at specified depth and grade. The pipes are made of either concrete or burnt clay. Free water enters through the tile joints and flows out by gravity, so that the water table is lowered below the root zone of the plants. The common tile drainage system layout followed is: Random or natural system, Parallel lines system and cut off or intercepting system.

(*a*) **Random system.** The random system is used in areas that have scattered wet areas somewhat isolated from each other. Tile lines are laid more or less at random to drain the wet patches.

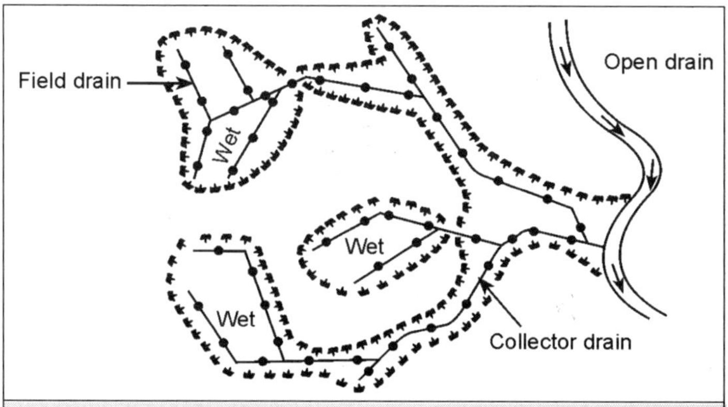

Fig. 28.5. Random tile drain system

(*b*) **Herringbone system.** The system is applicable in places where the main or sub-main is located in a narrow depression *i.e.*, in areas that have a concave surface or a narrow depression with the land sloping to it from both directions. The parallel laterals enter the sub-main from both sides. It is less economical, because considerable double drainage occurs where the laterals and mains join.

(*c*) Gridiron and parallel systems. The gridiron and parallel systems are similar to that of herringbone system except that the laterals enter the main or sub-main from only one side. It is the most economical arrangement than herringbone system because one main or sub-main serves as many laterals as possible.

(*d*) Double main system. The double main system is a modification of the gridiron system. It may be used where the sub-main is in a broad, flat depression, which frequently is a natural watercourse and sometimes may be wet because of small amounts of seepage water from nearby slopes.

(*e*) Intercepting system. This system involves the interception of seepage water that flows over the surface of an impervious sub-soil. The tile line is placed approximately at the impervious layer along which the seepage water travels, so that water will be intercepted and wet condition is relieved. The tile line should be located in such a way that there is at least 60 cm of soil cover over the top of the tile.

Mole drainage system

Mole drainage is a semi-permanent method of sub-surface drainage, similar to tile drain in layout and operation. Instead of permanent tiles a continuous circular mole drain (channel) is prepared below the ground surface in the soil profile at desired depth and spacing using a special implement known as mole plough. The depth of the mole drain varies from 4.5 cm to 120 cm depending on the moling equipment and water table. Diameter of the mole varies from 7.5 to 15 cm. The life the mole drain is 10-15 years. It is adapted to a particular type of soil because the soil stability is more important in this type of sub-surface drainage.

Drainage Coefficient

It is defined as the depth of water (cm) to be removed in 24 hours period from the entire drainage area. It ranges from 0.6 to 2.5 cm/day and in extreme cases 10 cm/day.

❑ ❑ ❑

CHAPTER 29

Soil Management

1. CALCAREOUS SOIL MANAGEMENT

Calcareous soil contains sufficient calcium carbonate and there is visible effervescence when treated with hydrochloric acid.

Classification of Calcareous Soil

Calcareous soil divided into following 4 classes :

Group	*Calcium Carbonate (%)*
(*i*) Slight calcareous	0-5
(*ii*) Moderate calcareous	5-10
(*iii*) Strong calcareous	10-20
(*iv*) Very strong calcareous	20-30

Formation of Calcareous Soil

Calcareous soil is formed in arid as well as humid regions. It is more common in arid areas. In dry regions, calcareous soil is formed in situ whereas, it has secondary origin in water-logged areas.

(A) Formation of Calcareous Soil *in-situ* by Weathering of Parent Rock Materials. There is formation of calcium carbonate ($CaCO_3$) due to weathering of rocks. The low rainfall in arid and semi-arid regions is not sufficient to leach out the soluble products of weathering to ground water. In dry weather, the salt moves up with the water by capillary movement to the surface where they are deposited.

(B) Development of Calcareous Soil by Secondary Origin. Calcareous soil of secondary origin is developed in lowlying areas or in basin shaped areas. Generally, drainage is impeded in these lowlying areas. During the rainy season, soluble calcium bicarbonate of nearby areas accumulates in the lowlying areas. During dry season, calcium bicarbonate converted into calcium carbonate and deposited on the soil surface by capillary movement.

Characteristics of Calcareous Soil

(*i*) Calcareous soil mainly contains calcium carbonate in free form and magnesium carbonate may remain present in small quantity.

(*ii*) There is effervescence when calcareous soils come in contact with the acid.

(*iii*) Soil colloids contain about 90 per cent calcium and magnesium carbonate as adsorbed bases.

(*iv*) Such soils usually having about pH 8.0 but pH may range from 7.0 to 8.3.

Effect of Calcareous Soil

(A) Physical Properties of Soil

(*i*) Calcareous soils remain in a flocculated condition (granulated). Soil is permeable to water and air due to large number of pore spaces.

(*ii*) Flocculation in heavy (clay) soil increases pore spaces and consequently drainage but in light (sandy) soil it decreases water holding capacity.

(B) Availability of Nutrients

(*i*) ***Phosphorus.*** In calcareous soil, the solubility of phosphorus is depressed which result in the decrease of P availability.

(*ii*) ***Potassium.*** Availability of potassium is decreased due to presence of excess calcium carbonate.

(*iii*) ***Zinc.*** Availability of zinc is reduced.

(C) Activity of Microorganism. Moisture is essential for microorganism activity. Microorganism activity in wet calcareous soil is normal but it is affected in dry calcareous soil.

Management

Management and reclamation of calcareous soil are not difficult because pH in such soil is not very high. Generally, there is no need of chemical amendment for reclamation of calcareous soil. The calcareous soil can be managed in the following ways.

(*i*) ***Tillage Operation.*** Light (sandy) calcareous soil develops large number of pore spaces due to flocculation. These types of soils have poor water-holding capacity. Therefore, such type of soil needs compaction by plank or roller to increases the water-holding capacity.

(*ii*) ***Application of Organic Manure.*** When sufficient amount of farm yard manure, compost and green manure are added, the amount of carbon dioxide and acid increases and as a result pH of soil decrease.

(*iii*) ***Use of Chemical Fertilizer.*** Availability of phosphorus is low in calcareous soil. To increase the availability of P, the phosphatic fertilizers should be used in the following manner :

(*a*) Phosphatic fertilizers should be used near the roots of plant.

(*b*) Use of phosphatic fertilizers in ball form also increases its availability.

(*c*) May be used in split dose.

(*iv*) *Use of Micronutrients*. Addition of micronutrients like zinc, copper, iron would be helpful in increasing yield.

Occurrences of Calcareous Soil

The calcareous soils in India are located in eastern U.P. and North Bihar. In Bihar, calcareous soils are found in Muzaffarpur, Darbhanga, Saran, Champaran and Munger district of North Bihar.

2. CLAYEY SOIL MANAGEMENT

The black soils posses high water storage capacity and very favorable water release characteristics over a wide soil suction range. These two properties of the soils are very important in an agricultural system, where rains are unreliable. Despite the fact that the black soils are potentially productive to cropping through the year, there are certain soil related constraints to the agricultural potential, which limit the productivity of various crops.

Physical constraints and their management

(1) Low infiltration and poor internal drainage. The high clay content and dominance of montmorillnite impart poor infiltration in majority of black soils crops grown on such soils are subjects to water logging and possible oxygen stress. Since the poor intrinsic permeability of black soils limits the internal drainage the solution to the problem must lie in land and water management practices which concourage surface drainage and recharge of the soil profile with rain water without accelerarating soil erosion. The useful land treatments are as follow :

(1) broad-bed furrow system

(2) graded furrow system

(3) raised and sunken bed system

(2) Narrow workable soil water range. The problems of narrow workable soil water range and consequently that of difficulties of cultivation in rainy season has been greatly overcome through appropriate land treatments designed to improve surface drainage. Use of broad bed and furrows, ridges, graded slopes and raised and sunken beds appear to be suitable management treatments. Timeliness of field operations, of course, has no substitute.

(3) Poor crop stand. Establishment of a good crop stand in black soil is often difficult due to water logging associated with poor drainage of the seed zone in the rainy season and to poor seed-soil contact manifested by warse tilth and water stress in post rainy season. Black soil regions with annual rainfall greater than 750 mm are usually worst affected. Sub-optimal oxygen diffusion rates (ODR) of the soil encountered during rainy season not only reduce seedling emergence of upland crops but also interfere with normal root activity of an established crop. Maize, black gram, green gram, and pigeon pea are highly sensitive to poor soil aeration, where as soybean and sorghum, once established, and is affected to a lesser extent. Since major area under black soils in the country receives scanty rainfall and crops are rainfed, prevalence of soil water stress and relatively poor seed-soil contact during seeding of post-rainy season crops invariably cause poor crop stand, better *in situ* conservation of rain through broad bed and furrows, raised and sunken beds, deeper seed placement, use of metered seeding implement with a packing device tend to improve seedling emergence and crop stand of post-rainy crops. Use of plastic mulch to conserve seed zone soil moisture during the dry period preceding planting of wheat in deep black soils improved crop stand, yield and water use.

(4) Evaporation from soil surface and shrinkage cracks. The sustenance of unirrigated post-rainy season crops depends mainly on the profile stored water. As the water from the upper soil layers is depleted through evapotranspiration, the soil develops shrinkage cracks. The water loss through evaporation from cracks may be as high 55 per cent of that evaporated at the surface.

The evaporation losses through shrinkage cracks are effectively controlled through shallow cultivation with a blade harrow in between crop rows. Besides covering the cracks, the loose soil thus crated acts as effective mulch. Tilling of surface soil (3-5 cm) and use of 1.5 to 2 cm thick layer of wheat straw mulch on a wet black soil has been observed to reduce evaporation by 30 per cent. Sorghum stubble mulch 27.5 t/ha has also been reported to substantially reduce development of shrinkage cracks and therefore evaporation.

(5) Runoff and soil erosion. Runoff measurement studies have shown that 21 to 53% of the total rainfall is available as runoff from medium black soils. An annual runoff to the extent of 10 to 20 per cent of the rainfall commonly occurs in black soils and this may carry away 6 to 43 t/ha of fertile top soils per annum depending upon location.

Soil erosion can be effectively controlled through adoption of carefully selected land treatments and water disposal systems. Broad beds and furrow, broad based bunds, diversion bunds lease boulders structure, graded furrow, and bench terracing are the commonly recommended land treatments.

3. SANDY SOIL MANAGEMENT

Sandy soils have a low content of clay and silt fractions and large preponderance of sand in their mechanical composition. It is to be conceded that some marginal sandy loams may still be found problematic, where those loamy sands dominated by very fine sand fraction may, in fact, be quite productive, without an extraordinary management.

(A) Physical constraints

(1) Low water retention capacity. Arising from the large preponderance of macropores, the sandy soils are able to retain only a small amount of water the sand and loamy sand soils of fluvio-aeolian plains due to appreciable proportion of very fine sand fraction appear to hold more available water than the Aeolian plain soils. The very fine sand fraction (0.02-0.1 mm) is able to retain three to four times more water than the coarser sand fractions in field capacity moisture range. Water retained by sandy soils is only half to one third of that retained by non-sandy soils, which makes the sandy soils droughty and prone to large deep percolation losses of water received during occasional heavy rainfall or irrigation.

(2) Low unsaturated state hydraulic conductivity. The sandy soils possess high infiltration (95 to 20 cm/ha) as well as a high saturated hydraulic conductivity. These properties permit a rapid soaking in of rain and a negligible runoff though it does create a problem of uneven distribution of water under irrigated management. However, under unsaturated condition, the behavior of sandy soils is just the reverse. The hydraulic conductivity of sandy soils in field moisture range decrease far more rapidly with increasing tension.

The law unsaturated hydraulic conductivity in coarse textures soils has significant implications. Highly restricted water movement permits full utilization of the stored available moisture only if the plant roots are able to reach the sites where it is actually hold. Since, nutrient uptake by plants through mass flow or infiltration is with water as a medium, the low water conductivity retracts the utilization of native or applied nutrients.

(3) Poor structure and high credibility. Depending upon clay content, loose to very weak structure is developed in sandy soils. They suffer from intensive erosion under the prevailing wind regime of the desert region.

(4) Mechanical resistance. Lack of cohesiveness enables the sandy soils to be worked at almost any water content. However this also makes these soils prone to high compaction and development of plough pan where heavy machinery is used in farm operations. The soils under compaction can develop bulk densities of 1.8 to 2.0 mg m^{-3} as against 1.5 to 1.6 mg m^{-3} in normal uncompacted situation. The penetration strength of sandy soils is high when moist as compared to other soils which have lesser interparticals friction due to lubricating effect of clay.

Behavioral Aspects of Sandy Soils

***(i)* Exacting fertility maintenance requirements.** Since the pool of available and potentially available nutrients in coarse textured soils is small fertility maintenance poses special problems, particularly under intensive cropping. Under intensive cropping system, multiple nutrient deficiencies are observed in sandy soils, therefore, a far more vigorous and comprehensive fertilization programmed is required to be followed. However, under rainfed conditions, the situation is different. Like all other soils of region, the sandy soils show marked response to application of H. Among the micronutrients, a marked response to application of zinc was reported in case of pearl millet.

***(ii)* Low productivity and water application efficiency.** In order to minimize water losses in arid zone the farmers adopt pond-silt lining of water courses and a check basin system with plot sizes of 2m × 3 m or 3 m × 4 m.

Excessive loss of irrigation water in deep percolation is another major limitation in sandy soils. Under farmer's conditions, the water application efficiency in wheat crop in sandy soils ranged between 47 and 56 per cent, whereas in loamy very fine sand and fine sandy loam soils, it was 68 to 84 per cent. While emphasizing the importance of very fine sand fraction in improving water application efficiency, it was shown that nearly half of the applied water in sandy soils was lost in deep percolation.

***(iii)* Dry land productivity potential.** But for their erodibility sandy soils are fairly well situated to production of biomass in an aridic environment. Through potentially does exists to upgrade production two to three fold from the current level.

Techniques for Improved Management

(1) Compaction. The philosophy of compaction is to create a layer of high bulk density and allow permeability in highly previous soils in order to reduce excessive mobility of water and nutrients. In order to realize maximum bulk density, specific soil moisture is optimum, which is found by using Proctors test. Even if surface soil was dry, the sub-soil could still experience compaction provided soil water content was at optimum level. The saving of 22 to 36 per cent of irrigation water was observed due to compaction.

Crop growth was 7 to 25 per cent higher in treatments having soil compaction. This advantage seems attributable to reduction in leaching losses of nutrients. Surface compaction resulted in retention of more nitrate in surface compaction resulted in retention of more nitrate in surface 30 cm soil compared to uncompacted soil. Leaching of nitrate was reducing from 56 to 26 per cent due to compaction.

(2) Deep Tillage. Though sandy soils are porous and friable, poor structure makes them prone to formation of dense layer or plough sole which can hinder proliferation and penetration of root system. Deep tillage caused some reduction in bulk density (1.6 to 1.51 Mg m).

(3) Use of Amendments. Amendment of soil by the addition of fine textured materials is an age-old practice on irrigated holdings in the region. Application of pond sediments @ 152 to ha^{-1} had increased field capacity from 8.6 (control) to 11.5 per cent. Yield of pearl millet from 10.3 to 17.5 q ha^{-1} and reduced infiltration rate from 15.0 to 10.8 cm h^{-1} in a normal rainfall year.

(4) Sub-surface Barrier. This is one more technique to reduce deep percolation losses. Formation of a barrier with bentonite clay resulted in water storage increase in the sandy soil by about 40 per cent. Superimposition of runoff concentration brought about further improvement in the system and enabled successful raising of vegetable crops. Placement of 3 mm thick asphalt barrier at 60 cm depth increase water retention in soil from 80 to 176 mm and reduced deep percolation from 120 to 24 mm.

(5) Soil Mulching. Mulches are effective means to conserve soil water and moderate surface soil temperature. Improved physical environment due to mulches leads to better utilization of native and applied nutrients in surface soil greater seeding emergence, reduced weed growth and ultimate higher yields and water was efficiency.

There are three types of mulches

(1) Soil mulches

(2) Straw mulch

(3) Plastic mulch

Another effective treatment is solarization. It is a technique that involves trapping of solar energy by covering the soil with transparent polythene sheet during hot summer to increase soil temp. Primarily it has been used for control of soil bear pathogens', but also reduces weeds and improves in mineralization.

(6) Methods of irrigation. With low stream sizes as available from wells and tube wells, the farmers in the area of sandy soils follow a check-basin system. Lining of channels with a paste of FYN and pond silt is done to reduce conveyance losses. As an improvement sprinkles system of irrigation has been tried and the method has gained widespread popularity assist serves irrigation water depending upon type of crop and soil. Drip irrigation is also a good management practice to save water in arid and semi arid areas with limited and inferior quality of waters.

(7) Management of Applied Nutrients. The first irrigation of 5.5 and 9.5 cm leached, respectively, 50 and 81 per cent of nitrate nitrogen from top loam soil and 29 and 52 per cent from 105 cm depth. The trend was maintained with increasing number of irrigation.

Reduced leaching with light irrigation was marked by increased nitrogen uptake and significantly higher yields. Three spilts of fertilizer maintained higher NO_3 status in top 60 cm soil and produced 30, 14 and 9 per cent higher yield of wheat then that from 1, 2 or 4 splits.

EFFICIENT RESOURCE MANAGEMENT SYSTEM FOR DRY LANDS OF INDIA

India is a vast country with different agro-climatic regions. About 70 per cent of the 143.5 mha of arable land depends entirely on natural precipitation for crop production. Much of this land is best described as dry land. It is important to distinguish between dry land agriculture in particular and rain-fed agriculture in general. Clearly, they both exclude irrigation. The emphasis for rain-fed yields, high levels of fertilizer inputs, and water erosion constraints. In dry agriculture, emphasis is on water conservation, sustainable crop yields, limited inputs of fertilizer, and both wind and water erosion constraints. Dry land generally receives less than 750 mm of rainfall annually and are arid to semiarid. However, an absolute value cannot be stated because seasonal rainfall distribution and temperature affect crop water requirements and thus the kinds of soil and water management practices. Thus a region with annual rainfall of 750 mm with good monthly distribution in a cool climate might utilize rain-fed agriculture-type managements systems, whereas in a hot climate a region with poorly distributed rainfall of less than 750 mm per year might appropriately require dry land farming techniques. Both dry land agriculture and rain-fed agriculture are considered in this review, but attention is focused on dry lands.

I. Soil of Dry lands in India

India has large variety of soils and crops. Broadly speaking, the soils can be grouped as :

1. Sierozemic soils (Aridisols).
2. Submontane soils (Mollisols, Inceptisols, and Entisols).
3. Alluviums (Inceptisols, Alfisols, and Entisols).
4. Red soils (Alfisols).
5. Black soils (Vertisols).

Important soil characteristics in relation to crop production are discussed in the following paragraphs. The profile analysis and nomenclature were obtained from Murthy *et al*. (1981) and Soil Survey staff (1978).

A. Sierozems (Aridisols). Camborthids and solorthids are the major groups in Aridisols. These soils are extremely light-sandy, loamy sand, or sandy loams. Calcium carbonate occurs at various depths influencing the effective depth of the soil. Crusting is a serious problem in these soils. Soil erosion by wind is even more serious. The thickness of the solum varies from 70 to 100cm.

Because the soils are very sandy, they hold only low amount of water and nutrients. They are universally poor in nitrogen and sometimes inadequate even in phosphorus. Subsoil salinity is not uncommon due to extreme aridity. The predominant clay minerals are smectite, mica, and kaolinite.

The texture largely determines the soil water storage capacity. In deep sandy loams, either a rainy or postrainy crop can be produced. But in loamy sands or sand, only rainy season cropping is possible.

The major characteristics of typical Camborthid profile from Jodhpur. These soils (Chirai series) were developed on old alluvium modified by aeolian material and occur in Jodhpur and Bikaner districts of Rajsthan. Usually the cambic horizon is encountered below 10-25 cm and extends upward to the zone of calcium accumulation. The above profile is from a Typic Camborthid of Jodhpur.

B. Submontane Soils (Mollisols, Inceptisols, and Entisols). Hapludolls (Mollisols), Haplaquepts (Inceptisols), and Udorthents (Entisols) are more common in the region occuring on level to gently sloping lands, lower elements of slopes, respectively. These soils are generally deep, the texture being silty loam to loam and hold as much as 300 mm of water per meter of profile. Land slides and soil erosion are common.

They respond well to nitrogen. Phosphorus becomes limiting only at high production levels. In lower reaches (Haplaquepts), water stagnation is possible, which calls for special efforts in nutrient management, particularly of nitrogen. The predominant clay minerals are illite, smectite, and chlorite/smectite.

C. Alluviums (Incepticols, Alfisols, and Entisols). The more common groups are Ustocherpts (Incepticols), Ochraqualfs (Alfisols), loams, depth not being a constraint. With low clay content, they hold less water (0.1-0.2 kg. of water per kg of dry soil). The nutrient holding capacity is also less. They are neutral to alkaline in reaction. Water intake is high. Crusting could be serious due to either a beating rain or high temperatures. This might accelerate the problem of runoff with subsequent rains. The slopes are mostly incipient.

The productivity of these soils is high, but they require liberal applications of nitrogen for high yields. Phosphorus is needed only for very high yields. Potassium is adequate. The predominant clay minerals are illite, smectilte, kaolinite, and chlorite.

The lower reaches of the catena develop alkalinity. As the soils become heaver in texture, the waterholding capacity increase, and leading to scope for taking two crops in a year.

D. Red soils (Alfisols). The most prominent groups are Haplustalfs, Rhodustalfs, and Patelustalfs. They are usually encountered on mild slopes of interfluves and higher terraces. These are more weathered soils. They are generally low in clay content and the predominant clays are kaolinite and illite. Most of them are sandy loams with an illuvial of higher clay below the plough layer. Due to illuviation, the subsoil is more compact, interspersed with saprolite. These soils tend to crust after a being rain or with high temperatures. Crusting leads to higher runoff.

These soils are universally deficient in nitrogen and often in phosphorus as well. Potassium may be limiting with high production systems. Sometimes calcium can be deficient, more so when the soils are monocropped with high calcium demand crops like peanuts.

The alfisols developed on granites are generally moderately deep, while the depth tends to increase with those developed on chernoklites, limestone, quartzite and sandstone. Incidentally, it has been observed that as the rainfall increases, the solum thickness also tends to increase.

E. Black soils (Vertisols). The important groups are chromusterts and pellusterts. Vertisols are more productive than Alfisols. As the soil organic matter is low in Indian vertisoils, the productivity is largely dependent on the quality of clay. These soils vary both in depth (15-240 cm) and clay content (30-70%). They are rich in bases. The predominant clay minerals are semectite, montmorillonite, nontronite,and beidellite. They hold more water than other predominant soils and are alkaline in reaction. With semiarid conditions, subsoil salinity is common. Boron toxicity can also be a problem.

Due to the high clay content, these soils tend to crack on drying. In low rainfall area, cracking occurs in late December when the conventional long-duration crops are at flowering stage. This leads to increased loss of soil moisture. Consequently, the long-duration crop suffer.

These soils have a tendency for sheet erosion. The runoff varies from 10% to 40% increasing with increase in rainfall. Many deep soils are calcareous. Heavy structure and water logging make it difficult for early management of these soils. To cope with hard pans and or increased weed infestation, these soils are commonly deep ploughed once in 3 years.

II. Untapped yield potential in drylands of India

The low yields in the existing systems of farming in drylands of India are primarily due to:

1. Use of conventional verities of crops that have low yield potential.
2. Less adequate attention on timely operations like sowing and weeding.
3. Lack of response to fertilizer by the local verities.
4. Improved land management systems.

The local varieties are long in duration and undergo any stress and strain that occurs in the rainy season due to improper distribution of rainfall. In the post-rainy season, the verities are too long to mature on the stored soil moisture, particularly in the vertisols of the deccan. The local varieties are shallow rooted and are surface feeders. They are also bred to perform as individual plants, which mean they perform well only at low plant population per unit area.

1. bunding with bund former to conserve soil and water
2. deep plowing once in 3 years for better intake and storage of rainfall
3. use of farm yard manure (FYM) to supply plant nutrients
4. use of low seed rate
5. intercultivation of crops for efficient utilization of the limited soil water

With the improved practices, there as greater hope of increasing the productivity even to eight times the existing yields, particularly in optimal resource situations.

The improved practices included;

1. Proper tillage
2. Early sowing
3. Choice of suitable crops and varieties
4. Optimum plant population
5. Timely weeding and pest control
6. Moderate use of fertilizers.

The Indian farmers most often have resources, and particularly so in the dry lands. More than 70% of the farming community is of this nature. A crop production technology can not be a package that costs two or three times more than the traditional system of farming. So a tier system of crop production is needed. In other words, the contribution of individual components in crop production must be evaluated.

1. Efficient management, which is possible at the farm level, per se contributed up to 22% increase in yield of crops.
2. Seed and fertilizer each contribute as much as 40% and 50% increase in yield respectively.
3. Even more important is the synergism when seed and fertilizer plus management lead to 16.4% increase in yields.

Simply stated, there is no substitute for efficient management in dry land crop production. And this should form the basic first step in improved crop production in dry lands. This can be followed by improved seed and moderate levels of fertilizers.

III. Cropping systems

The drylands are usually monocropped. That is the cropping intensity is 100. But with a careful analysis of the environment (soils and rainfall), it has now become possible to suggest different cropping intensities in different locations.

***(a)* Soils.** The soils hold water and nutrients for use by plants. The conventional available water capacity (AWC) is defined as the difference in volumetric water content between-0.33 bar and-15 bar of soil matric potential. A rooting depth may be assumed or measured to provide an estimate of total AWC in the profile.

***(b)* Rainfall.** Rain constitute the only source of water to dryland crops. So the total rain, their distribution, and potential evapotranspiration are important to determine the period of dependable water availability in a given region. The water requirement of dryland crops is met when the ratio of rainfall to potential evapotranspiration is at least 0.33. The ratio is also called moisture availability index (MAI) when the dependable amount of rainfall is considered as the criterion. In this context, the dependable rainfall is one where the rainfall occurs with a probability of more than 75 per cent.

***(c)* Water Balance Approach.** For planning proper agricultural strategies, a combination of the rainfall data with the water-holding capacities of soils would be useful. They help in identifying the growing season with assured moisture availability. It varies from monocrop in shallow soil to double cropping in deep soils.

IV. Tillage

The proper tillage is needed for (1) early seed bed preparation for timely sowing, and (2) enabling precipitation to enter the soil. Primary tillage is essentially done by wooden country plough prior to sowing of crops. It is generally a shallow tillage (15-22.5 cm) through opening of furrows on a criss-cross pattern. This is then followed by Blanding with harrows. Besides opening the soil surface, it also helps in minimizing weed problems.

***(a)* Light Cultivation.** In light textured soils, shallow preparatory tillage was found to be beneficial. In the alfisols of semiarid Telengana, off season plowing followed by Blanding was found useful in increasing the yield of crops. The effect of such tillage is more pronounced in subnormal rainfall years, such a system permits early sowing, which is a very important requirement in drylands, particularly when crops are grown during the rainy season.

(*b*) Deep Tillage. Deep tillage is needed at least in three distinct situations. They are :

(1) Areas with hard pans (*e.g.* Inceptisol of gangetic plains, which tend to develop hard pans due to consistent cultivation with a country plow).

(2) Areas with persistent weeds (*e.g.* cyperus and cynadon).

(3) Areas with textural profiles (Alfisols and related red soils)

V. Mulching

Mulching aims at slowing the movement of moisture from soil into the atmosphere. It has been a subject of mulch interest and has been studied intensively concerning the theory and mechanisms.

The shallow tillage and application of organic mulches at the surface are beneficial to conserve water, particularly in the upper layers of the profile in loamy sand. It was 0.07 kg per kg of dry soil more with mulching, varying from 0.03 to 0.27 kg per kg depending on the rainfall of the various mulches studied, soil mulch and organic mulch are of importance in the Indian context where crops are grown, both with the monsoon rains as well as during post monsoon period. And studied on mulching were carried out for both situation.

Vertical mulching; the effect of mulching, by and large, is beneficial to post rainy crops in India. This also enables the farmers to use most of the mulch back as a feed as it does not tend to decompose faster in the post rainy period. And this is so important since most of the organic residues are also used as feed in India where there is a great need because of bovines.

VI. Fertilizer Use

Drylands are sometimes more hungry than thirsty. The soils in India are universally deficient in nitrogen. Phosphorus is low in 43.9% of soils. It is found to be limiting at high production levels. Potash is adequate in many areas except in light textured soils or at continued high levels of crop production.

If fertilizer use is to be effective, improved management systems must be introduced. The cardinal principles in fertilizer use are :

(1) Law of diminishing returns

(2) Law of Minimum

A perusal brings out

(1) The response to the first increment is always higher irrespective of the rainfall received during the growing season.

(2) As the vertisols have more carry-over moisture, there is stability in production. Yields up to 5.0 mg/ha were achieved even in low moisture retentive alfisols where the clay was varying from 15 to 30% depth being moderate.

Response to highly deficient nitrogen can be low if other nutrients are limiting. More frequently, phosphorus is limiting the response to applied nitrogen in the semiarid alfisols as well as vertisols

The fertilizer use efficiency can be increased by placement of a basal dose of nutrients and by spilt application of nitrogen to monsoon crops. The fertilizer for post rainy crops must be deep placed in the moist zone for increasing its use efficiency in the recent past; two areas of fertilizer use research have received attention.

1. Edaphic factors in fertilizer use
2. Organic recycling as a means to incorporate or improve fertilizer use efficiency.

1. Edaphic factors. The productivity of different soils varies. Largely, the clay type and content determine the productivity in the Indian soils as the soil organic matter is generally low. The other important factor is the rainfall. As rainfall increases, there is less variability, and also the possible drought periods during the growing season become less. There is stability in production over years in high rainfall areas.

However the productivity of the post rainy crops varies significantly with the soil depth and/or texture. In vertisols, it is the depth that determines the plant available water, while in entisols and inceptisols; it is the texture that is most important.

2. Organic recycling. The use of farmyard manure to dryland crops is a common practice in India. However, it is largely practiced only near villages. This is primarily because of two factors. One is that most of the farmers have some parcels of land near villages that can be guarded and cared for. The other is the logistics. It is difficult to carry FYM long distances. Generally speaking, the better lands are nearer to the villages and the richer communities also possess most of these lands. As a corollary then, the poorer communities use less of the available FYM and their lands are also of poorer endowments. Hence, there has been a conscientious effort to identify measures of on farm residue management.

1. *Residue incorporation.* Organic matter with a low C : N ratio (less than 75) decomposes very fast, and has a rapid and positive effect on aggregation. On the other hand, organic matter with a high C : N ratio (greater than 150) decomposes too slowly to be effective. The most suitable C : N ratio has been found to be 75-150. Most of the crop residues fall in this range. If not, inorganic nitrogen can be added to hasten the process of decomposition. Such potentialities exist in several parts of India.

2. *Improving soil productivity through cropping systems.* India is a vast country with a large variety of crops and agro-climatic situations. Intercropping and double-cropping is possible. Food legumes and fodder legumes can be find a place in these systems. The nitrogen economy can be improved with such an approach. Even when a legume is rotated with a cereal, there is a definite improvement in the yield of cereal. In fact that there is increased fertilizer nitrogen use efficiency with a legume being a part of the crop rotation.

- Legume in crop rotation
- Legume in intercropping
- Legume in double cropping

VII. On–Farm Rain Water Management

Rain fall is the only source of water to crop plants grown in dryland areas. The precipitation enters the soil through the surface of the land. If it is not receptive, more of the rainwater moves off the field as runoff. For instance, even though the light soils (loamy sands and sandy loams) have high infiltration, if they form a crust on the surface, more of the rainwater moves off the fields as runoff. Similarly, the deep black solid are characterized by low infiltration. On these lands, the soil surface has to be kept more receptive. There are several measures. Among others, they included

(1) Terracing
(2) Interterrace treatment
(3) Chemical amendments
(4) Crop residue management

(*a*) Terracing. The structures are not meant only for moisture conservation, but also to minimize loss of fertile surface soil by erosion. The net benefit accruing out of this programme is not beyond 15% additional yield over a base yield of 200-400 kg /ha, which is not significant enough to warrant adoption by farmers.

(*b*) Interterrace treatment. The aims of these treatments are :

1. To have uniform and on farm rainwater recharge in the profile
2. To minimize movement of soil within the terraces.
3. To increase moisture retention for extended times to either delay drought affects due to short dry spells or to help in establishing a second crop in high rainfall situation

(*c*) Chemical amendments. The ill effects of sodium on soil productivity are well established. On wetting the sodic soils disperse and they shrink heavily on drying. The hydraulic conductivity is adversely affected with increase in exchangeable sodium percentage (ESP).

(*d*) Residue management. In India, the stalks or haulms are often times used as fodder or fuel. The estimated yield of residue is 185.3 mt per annum from the important arable they contribute about 1.24 Mt of nitrogen, 0.16 Mt of phosphorus, and 2.0 Mt of potassium. One third would be available for incorporation as residues in arable lands.

Incorporation of organic matter in any form not only adds nutrients but also improves soil physical conditions. But certain basic principles are important. In the tropics, the rate of decomposition of added organics is so rapid that nearly 90% of what is added is decomposed within 1 year. The approach needs to be one of the turn over of organics in small quantities , rather than application of large quantities at one time aiming at a build up at one time. Of all the possibilities, the most attractive one is raising good crops with proper fertilizer use where there would be adequate residues partly for fodder/fuel and also incorporation.

VIII. Runoff Collection and Recycling

Runoff is inevitable in tropics and subtropics. Some that aspects received attention in India included.

1. Identification of critical periods of crops when the effects of moisture stress would be maximum.
2. Sealing the ponds to prevent the percolation losses.
3. Efficient use of harvested runoff water.

(*a*) Critical periods. Critical stages are namely crown root initiation, tillering/branching, flowering and seed setting/boll bursting were critical in reducing yield of different crops.

(*b*) Sealing of ponds. While the problem of percolation losses is less with deep vertisols, it is serious in light-textured Alfisols, Inceptisols and Aridisols. Some efforts have been made in identifying sealants for effectively arresting the percolation losses.

(c) Coefficient use. The harvested water should never be considered for use as a normal irrigation source. It must be used for (1) critical stages of crop growth (2) in most efficient way flooding versus furrow irrigation was tested in different centers and it was found that furrow-alternate furrow method would be more effective.

Lifting and conveyance device have not yet received full attention in runoff recycling. Furthermore, these methods of water harvesting have not, so far, been fully tested on real farm situations.

IX. Stability in Crop Production in Dry Lands

Broadly speaking, the rain fall determines the cropping pattern. Based on the rainfall patterns, the more efficient crops have been identified by the National Commission on Agriculture (1976). The stability in production also varies over different climatic conditions.

1. The coefficient of variation in productivity increases with decrease in rainfall.
2. In low-rainfall areas such variation is more with traditional practices.
3. The productivity remains higher with improved management practices.

X. Agro-Technology Transfer

The basic assumptions made were

(1) That the soils in the same category have similar management problems.

(2) The soil family provides the link between soil classification and land capability.

Bhattacharyaji and land identified minimum data sets needed for agro-technology transfer. They included :

1. Soil depth.
2. Effective depth of root ramification zone.
3. Particle size distribution, particularly of fine clay fraction.
4. Cation exchange capacity (CEC) and saturating cations.
5. Bulk density and coefficient of linear extensibility (COLE).
6. Soil temperatures at different moisture tensions.
7. Saturated hydraulic conductivity and depth of water table.
8. Available moisture receptivity.
9. Level of available nutrients.
10. Weekly data of climatic components infusing crop production.
11. Socioeconomic status of the farmer.

The agro technology transfer is possible only at a higher level of management, which constitutes about 30% in their sample study. Even for end aver, the taxonomic characteristics that are the inherent properties of the soils become important. To sum up, agro-technology transfer based on soil classification and land capability is a new area of research and is gaining popularity in India.

❑❑❑

CHAPTER 30

Problematic Soils in Different Ecosystems

Land, agriculture and ecology are intrinsically related and govern our agricultural systems holistically. Climatic factors such as temperature, rainfall, humidity, sunshine and wind are the primary determinants of climate of any region. And climate and soil interactions provide suitable environment for agricultural production, and also affect physical processes of land degradation. To conserve natural resources for sustainable food production, an inclusive approach is needed to create relatively homogeneous regions in terms of soil, climate and physiography, termed as agro-ecological regions. Delineation of such regions will help understanding of agricultural potentialities of the regions for different land uses and also for conservation of their physical environment.

Agroclimatic region is the land unit in terms of major climate, superimposed on length of growing period (moisture availability period), and an agro-ecological zone is the land unit carved out of the agroclimatic region, superimposed on the landform, which acts as a modifier to climate and length of growing period (Sehgal and Abrol, 1994).

To understand implications and role of climatic and edaphic resources in agricultural and allied sectors, the NBSS&LUP prepared an agro-ecological map, based on the physiography, soils, bioclimate and length of growing period (GP), and refined it through several approximations. The data from 474 meteorological stations were used for preparing water balances (Thornthwaite and Mather, 1955). Length of growing period (LGP) was calculated using FAO (1983) model, adopted after Higgins and Kassam (1981). The GP as per the model starts when precipitation (P) exceeds 0.5 potential evapotranspiration (PET) and ends with utilization of 100 mm of stored soil moisture once P falls below PET. Growing period values for 474 observation sites were plotted and isolines were drawn at 30 days intervals. It has been observed that arid regions generally correspond with growing period of less than 90 days and semi-arid region with 90–150 days. Subhumid zone has GP more or less between 150 and 210 days. Humid and per- humid zones correspond with GP of 210 to 270 days and more than 270 days per year.

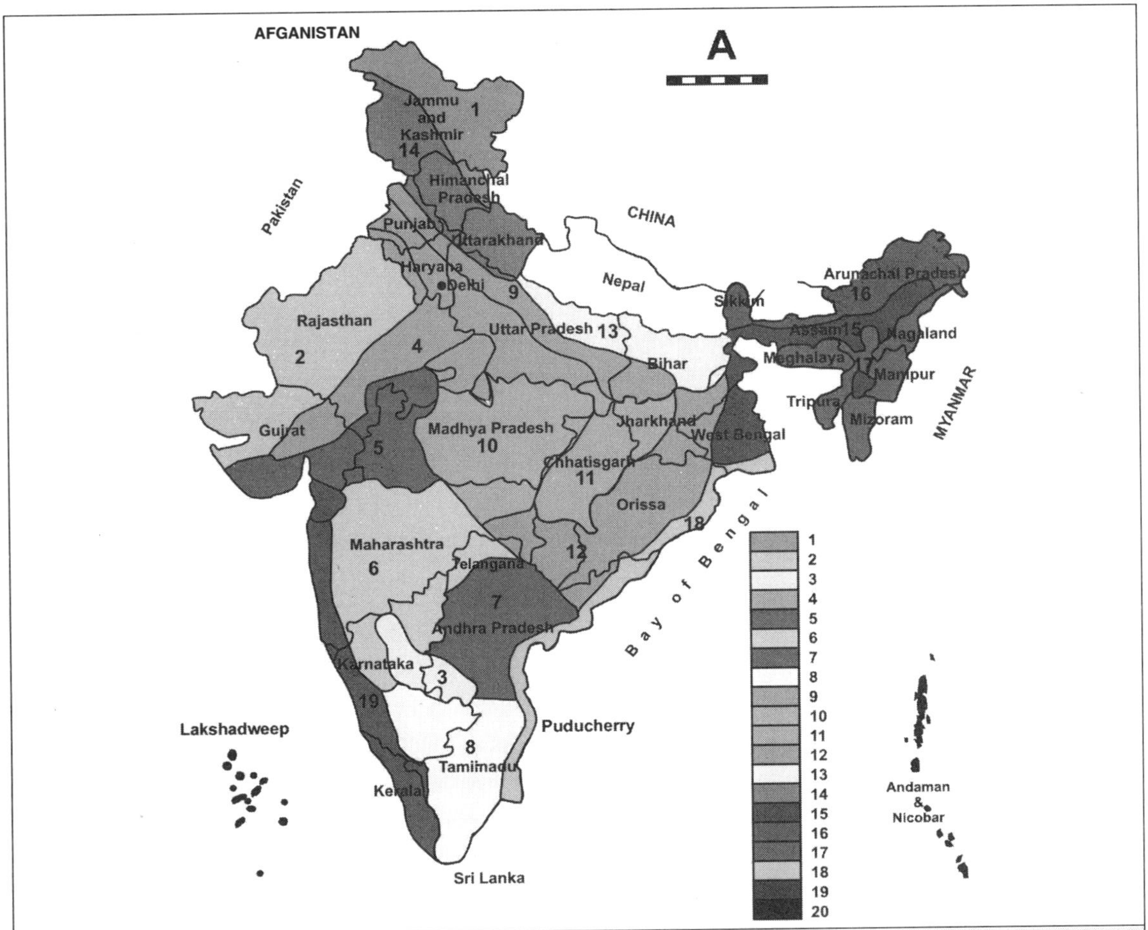

Fig. 30.1 Agro Ecological Regions in India

Fig. 30.1: Agro-ecological regions (AERs) of India; **1.** Western Himalayas cold arid ecoregion, with shallow skeletal soils and length of growing period (GP) <90 days; **2.** Western plain, Kachchh and part of Kathiawar peninsula, hot arid ecoregion, with desert and saline soils and GP <90 days; **3.** Deccan plateau, hot arid ecoregion, with red and black soils and GP <90 days; **4.** Northern plain and central highlands including Aravallis, hot semi-arid ecoregion, with alluvium derived soils and GP 90–150 days; **5.** Central (Malwa) highlands, Gujarat plains and Kathiawar peninsula, hot semi-arid ecoregion, with medium and deep black soils and GP 90–150 days; **6.** Deccan plateau, hot semi-arid ecoregion, with shallow and medium (with inclusion of deep) black soils and GP 90–150 days; **7.** Deccan (Telangana) plateau and Eastern Ghats, hot semi-arid ecoregion, with red and black soils and GP 90–150 days; **8.** Eastern Ghats, Tamil Nadu uplands and Deccan (Karnataka) plateau, hot semi-arid ecoregion, with red loamy soils and GP 90–150 days; **9.** Northern plain, hot sub-humid (dry) ecoregion, with alluvium derived soils and GP 90–150 days; **10.** Central Highlands (Malwa, Bundelkhand and Eastern Satpura), hot sub-humid ecoregion, with black and red soils and GP 150–180 (to 210) days; **11.** Eastern plateau (Chhattisgarh), hot subhumid ecoregion, with red and yellow soils and GP 150–180 days; **12.** Eastern (Chhotanagpur) plateau and Eastern Ghats, hot subhumid ecoregion, with red and lateritic soils, and GP 150–180 (to 210) days; **13.** Eastern plain, hot subhumid (moist) ecoregion, with alluvium derived soils and GP 180–210 days; **14.** Western Himalayas, warm subhumid (to humid with inclusion per-humid) ecoregion, with brown forest and podzolic soils and GP 180–210+ days; **15.** Bengal and Asom plain, hot subhumid (moist) to humid (inclusion of per-humid) ecoregion, with alluvium derived soils and GP 210+ days; **16.** Eastern Himalayas, warm per-humid ecoregion, with brown and red hill soils and GP 210+ days; **17.** North-Eastern Hills (Purvanchal), warm perhumid ecoregion, with red and lateritic soils and GP 210+ days; **18.** Eastern Coastal plain, hot subhumid to semi-arid ecoregion, with coastal alluvium derived soils and GP 90–210+ days; **19.** Western Ghats and Coastal plain, hot humid–per-humid ecoregion, with red, lateritic and alluvium derived soils and GP 210+ days; **20.** Islands of Andaman-Nicobar and Lakshadweep, hot humid and perhumid island ecoregion, with red loamy and sandy soils and GP 210+ days.

Distribution of soils in different Agro ecological and Sub-Agro ecological zones

1. **Western Himalayas, cold arid eco-region**
   1.1. Eastern aspect of Ladakh Plateau, cold, hyper-arid eco-subregion (ESR) with shallow skeletal soils, very low AWC and LGP <60 days.
   1.2. Western Aspect of Ladakh Plateau and north Kashmir Himalayas, cold to cool, typic-arid ESR with shallow, loamy-skeletal soils, low AWC and LGP 60-90 days.
2. **Western Plain, Kachchh and part of Kathiawar Peninsula, hot arid eco-region**
   2.1. Marusthali hot, hyper arid ESR with shallow and deep sandy desert soils very low AWC and LGP < 60 days.
   2.2. Kachchh Peninsula (Great Rann of Kutch as inclusion), hot hyper-arid ESR with deep loamy saline and alkali soils, low AWC and LGP <60 days.
   2.3. Rajasthan Bagar, North Gujarat Plain and South-Western Punjab Plain, hot typic- arid ESR with deep, loamy desert soils (inclusion of saline phase), low AWC and LGP 60-90 days.
   2.4. South Kachchh and North Kathiawar Peninsula, hot arid ESR with deep loamy saline and alkali soils, low AWC and LGP 60-90 days.
3. **Deccan plateau, hot arid ecosubregion (K6E2)**
   3.0. Karnataka Plateau (Rayalseema as inclusion), hot arid ESR with deep loamy and clayey mixed Red and Black soils, low to medium AWC and LGP 60-90 days.
4. **Northern Plain (and Central Highlands) including Aravallis, hot semi-arid ecoregion (N8D2)**
   4.1. North Punjab Plain, Ganga-Yamuna Doab and Rajasthan Upland, hot semi-arid ESR with deep loamy alluvium-derived soils (occasional saline and sodic phases), medium AWC and LGP 90-120 days.
   4.2. North Gujarat Plain (inclusion of Aravalli range and east Rajasthan Uplands), hot dry semiarid ESR with deep loamy Gray Brown and alluvium-derived soils, medium AWC and LGP 90-120 days.
   4.3. Ganga Yamuna Doab, Rohilkhand and Avadah Plain, hot moist semi-arid ESR with deep, loamy alluvium-derived soils (sodic phase inclusion), medium to high AWC and LGP 120-150 days.
   4.4. Madhya Bharat Plateau and Bundelkhand Uplands, hot, moist semi-arid ESR with Deep loamy and clayey mixed Red and Black soils, medium to high AWC and LGP 90-120 days (N6Dm4).
5. **Central (Malwa) Highlands, Gujarat plains and Kathiawar Peninsula Ecoregion**
   5.1. Central Kathiawar Peninsula, hot, dry semiarid ESR with shallow and medium loamy to clayey black soils (deep black soils as inclusion) medium AWC and LGP 120-150 days.

5.2. Madhya Bharat Plateau, Western Malwa Plateau, Eastern Gujarat Plain, Vindhyan and Satpura range and Narmada Valley, hot moist semi-arid ESR with medium and deep, clayey Black soils (shallow black soils as inclusions), medium to high AWC and LGP 120-150 days.

5.3. Coastal Kathiawar Peninsula, hot moist semi-arid ESR with deep loamy coastal alluvium-derived soils (saline/phases inclusion), low to medium AWC and LGP 120-150 days.

6. Deccan Plateau, hot semi-arid eco-region

6.1. South Western Maharashtra and North Karnataka Plateau, hot dry semi-arid ESR with shallow and medium loamy Black soils (deep clayey Black soils as inclusion), medium to high AWC and LGP 90-120 days.

6.2. Central and Western Maharashtra Plateau and North Karnataka Plateau and North Western Telangana Plateau, hot moist semi-arid ESR with shallow and medium loamy to clayey Black soils (medium land deep clayey Black soils as inclusion), medium to high AWC and LGP 120-150 days.

6.3. Eastern Maharashtra Plateau, hot moist semi-arid ESR with medium land deep clayey Black soils (shallow loamy to clayey Black soils as inclusion), medium to high AWC and LGP 120-150 days .

6.4. North Sahyadris and Western Karnataka Plateau, hot dry subhumid ESR.

7. Deccan Plateau (Telangana) and Eastern Ghats, hot semi-arid ecoregion

7.1. South Telangana Plateau (Rayalseema) and Eastern Ghat, hot dry semi-arid ESR with deep loamy to clayey mixed Red and Black soils, medium AWC and LGP 90-120 days.

7.2. North Telangana Plateau, hot moist semi-arid ESR with deep loamy and clayey mixed Red and Black soils, medium to very high AWC and LGP 120-150 days.

7.3. Eastern Ghat (South), hot moist semi-arid/dry subhumid ESR with medium to deep, loamy to clayey mixed Red and Black soils, medium AWC and LGP 150-180 days.

8. Eastern Ghats and Tamil Nadu Uplands and Deccan (Karnataka) Plateau, hot semiarid eco-region

8.1. Tamil Nadu Uplands and Leeward Flanks of South Sahyadris, hot dry semi-arid ESR with moderately deep to deep, loamy to clayey, mixed Red and Black soils, medium AWC and LGP 90-120 days.

8.2. Central Karnataka Plateau, hot moist semi-arid ESR with medium to deep Red loamy soils, low AWC and LGP 120-150 days.

8.3. Tamil Nadu Uplands and Plains, hot moist semi-arid ESR with deep red loamy soils, low AWC and LGP 120-150 days.

9. Northern Plain, hot subhumid (dry) eco-region

9.1. Punjab and Rohilkhand Plains, hot dry/moist subhumid transitional ESR with deep, loamy to clayey alluvium-derived (inclusion of saline and sodic phases) soils, medium AWC and LGP 120-150 days.

9.2. Rohilkhand, Avadh and south Bihar Plains, hot dry subhumid ESR with deep loamy alluvium-derived soils, medium to high AWC and LGP 150-180 days .

10. Central Highlands (Malwa and Bundelkhand), hot subhumid (dry) eco-region

10.1. Malwa Plateau, Vindhyan Scarpland and Narmada Valley, hot dry subhumid ESR with medium and deep clayey Black soils (shallow loamy Black soils as inclusion), high AWC and LGP 150-180 days.

10.2. Satpura and Eastern Maharashtra Plateau, hot dry subhumid ESR with shallow and medium loamy to clayey Black soils (deep clayey Black soils as inclusion), medium to high AWC and LGP 150-180 days.

10.3. Vindhyan Scarpland and Bundelkhand Plateau, hot dry subhumid ESR with deep loamy to clayey mixed Red and Black soils, medium to high AWC and LGP 150-180 days.

10.4. Satpura range and Wainganga Valley, hot moist subhumid ESR with shallow to deep loamy to clayey mixed Red and Black soils, low to medium AWC and LGP 180-210 days.

11. Chhattisgarh/Mahanadi Basin Agro-eco-region

11.0. Moderately to gently sloping Chattisgarh/Mahanadi Basin, hot moist/dry subhumid transitional ESR with deep loamy lto clayey Red and Yellow soils, medium AWC and LGP 150-180 days.

12. Eastern Plateau (Chhotanagpur) and Eastern Ghats, hot subhumid eco-region

12.1. Garjat Hills, Dandakaranya and Eastern Ghats, hot moist subhumid ESR with deep loamy Red and Lateritic soils, low to medium AWC and LGP 180-210 days.

12.2. Eastern Ghats, hot moist subhumid ESR with medium to deep loamy Red and Lateritic soils, medium AWC and LGP 180-210 days.

12.3. Chhotanagpur Plateau and Garjat Hills, hot, dry subhumid ESR with moderately deep to deep loamy to clayey Red and Lateritic soils, medium AWC and LGP of 150-180 days.

13. Eastern Plain, hot subhumid (moist) ecoregion

13.1. North Bihar and Avadh Plains, hot dry to moist subhumid transitional ESR with deep, loamy alluvium-derived soils, low to medium AWC and LGP 180-210 days.

13.2. Foothills of Central Himalayas, warm to hot moist subhumid ESR with deep loamy to clayey Tarai soils, high AWC and LGP 180-210 days.

14. Western Himalayas, warm subhumid (to humid with inclusion of perhumid) ecoregion

14.1. South Kashmir and Punjab Himalayas, cold and warm by dry semi-arid/dry subhumid ESR with shallow to medium deep loamy Brown Forest and Podzolic soils, low to medium AWC and LGP 90-120 days.

14.2. South Kashmir and Kumaun Himalayas, warm moist to dry subhumid transitional ESR with medium to deep loamy to clayey Brown Forest and Podzolic soils, medium AWC and LGP 150-210 days.

14.3. Punjab Himalayas, warm humid to perhumid transitional ESR with shallow to medium deep loamy brown forest and podzolic soils, low to medium AWC and LGP 270-300+ days.

14.4. Kumaun Himalayas, warm humid to perhumid transitional ESR with shallow to medium deep loamy Red and Yellow soils, low AWC and LGP 270-300+ days.

14.5. Foothills of Kumaun Himalayas (Subdued), warm moist subhumid ESR with medium to deep, loamy arai soils, medium AWC and LGP 270-300 days.

15. Assam and Bengal Plain, hot subhumid to humid (inclusion of perhumid) eco-region

15.1. Bengal basin and North Bihar Plain, hot moist subhumid ESR with deep loamy to clayey alluvium-derived soils, medium to high AWC and LGP 210-240 days.

15.2. Middle Brahmaputra Plain, hot humid ESR with deep, loamy to clayey alluvium-derived soils, medium AWC and LGP 240-270 days.

15.3. Teesta, lower Brahmaputra Plain and Barak Valley, hot moist humid to perhumid ESR with deep, loamy to clayey alluvium-derived soils, medium AWC and LGP 270-300 days.

15.4. Upper Brahmaputra Plain, warm to hot perhumid ESR with moderately deep to deep loamy, alluvium-derived soils, medium AWC and LGP 300 days.

16. Eastern Himalayas, warm perhumid eco-region

16.1. Foot-hills of Eastern Himalayas (Bhutan foot-hills), warm to hot perhumid ESR with shallow to medium, loamy-skeletal to loamy Tarai soils, low to medium AWC and LGP 270-300 days.

16.2. Darjeeling and Sikkim Himalayas, warm perhumid ESR with shallow to medium deep loamy Brown and Red Hill soils, low to medium AWC and LGP 300 days.

16.3. Arunachal Pradesh (Subdued Eastern Himalayas), warm to hot perhumid ESR with deep, loamy to clayey Red Loamy soils, low to medium AWC and LGP 300 days.

17. North-eastern Hills (Purvanchal), warm perhumid eco-region

17.1. Meghalaya Plateau land Nagaland Hill, warm to hot moist humid to perhumid ESR with medium to deep loamy to clayey Red and Lateritic soils, medium AWC and LGP 270-300+ days.

17.2. Purvachal (Eastern Range), warm to hot perhumid ESR with medium to deep loamy Red and Yellow soils, low to medium AWC and LGP 300 days.

18. Eastern Coastal Plain, hot subhumid to semiarid ecoregion

18.1. South Tamil Nadu Plains (Coastal), hot dry semi-arid ESR with deep, loamy to clayey, alkaline Coastal and deltaic alluvium-derived soils, medium AWC and LGP 90-120 days.

18.2. North Tamil Nadu Plains (Coastal), hot moist semi-arid ESR with deep, clayey and cracking Coastal land Deltaic alluvium-derived soils, high AWC and LGP 120-150 days.

18.3. Andhra Plain, hot dry subhumid ESR with deep, clayey Coastal and Deltaic alluvium-derived soils, low to medium AWC and LGP 150-180 days.

18.4. Utkal Plain and East Godavari Delta, hot dry subhumid ESR with deep, loamy to clayey Coastal and deltaic alluvium-derived soils, medium AWC and LGP 180-210 days.

18.5. Gangetic Delta, hot moist subhumid to humid ESR with deep, loamy to clayey Coastal and deltaic alluvium-derived soils, medium AWC and LGP 240-270 days.

19. Western Ghats and Coastal Plain, hot humid-perhumid eco-region

19.1. North Sahyadris and Konkan Coast, hot humid ESR with medium to deep loamy to clayey mixed Red and Black soils, medium to high AWC and LGP 210-240 days.

19.2. Central and South Sahyadris, hot moist subhumid to humid transitional ESR with deep, loamy to clayey Red and Lateritic soils, low to medium AWC and LGP 210-270 days.

19.3. Konkan, Karnataka and Kerala Coastal plain, hot humid to per humid transitional ESR with deep, clayey to loamy acidic coastal alluvium-derived soils, low AWC and LGP 240-270 days.

20. Islands of Andaman-Nicobar and Lakshadweep, hot humid to perhumid island ecoregion

20.1. Andaman and Nicobar group of Islands, hot perhumid ESR with shallow to medium deep, loamy to clayey Red and Yellow and Red Loamy soils, low to medium AWC and LGP 300 days.

20.2. Level Lakshadweep and group of Island, hot humid ESR with shallow to medium deep loamy to sandy Black, sandy and Littoral soils, low to medium AWC and LGP 240-270 days.

*LGP= Length of Growing Period; AWC= Available Water Capacity

*<90 days : Feasible for single short duration crop

90-150 days : Suitable for one medium duration crop or single short duration crop plus relay crop

>210 days : Feasible for double cropping

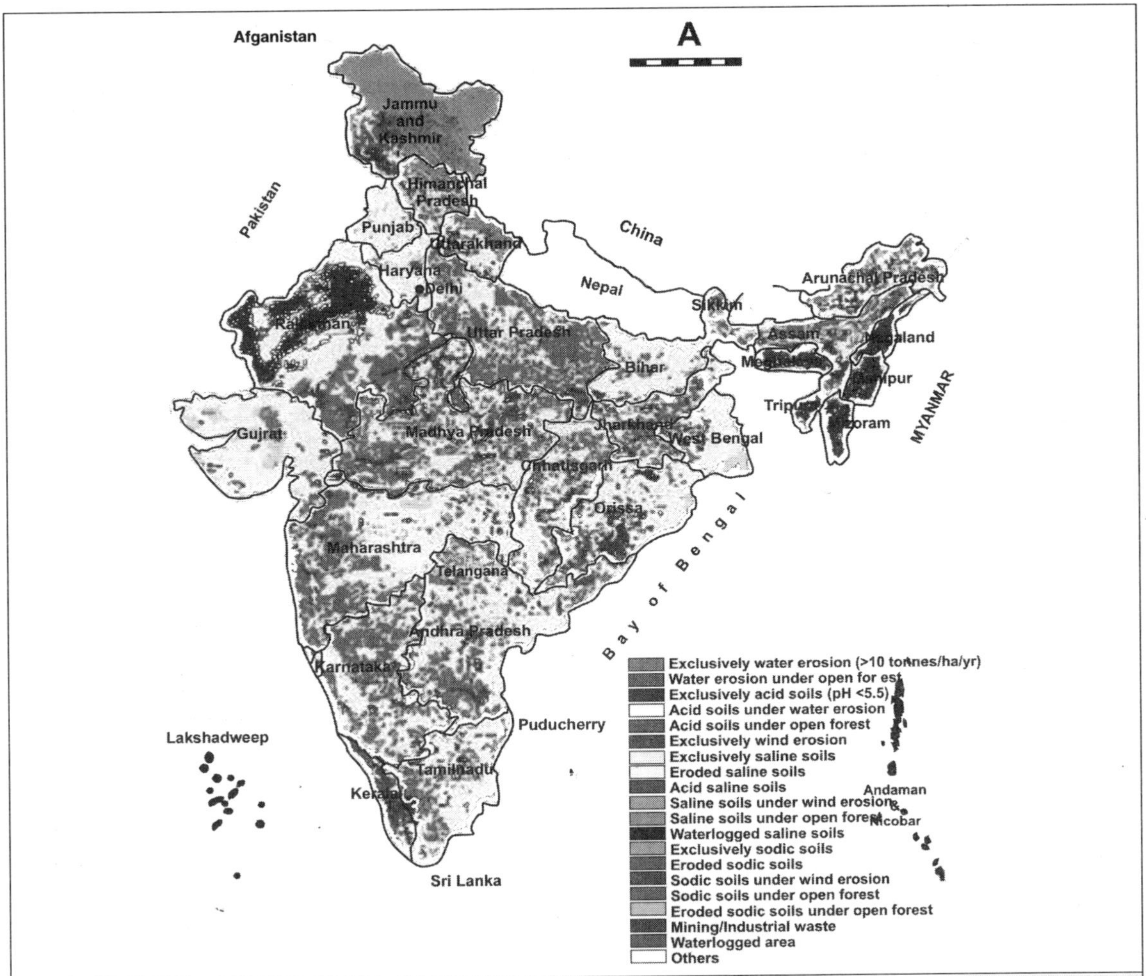

Fig. 30.2: Degraded and wastelands in the Agro-ecological regions of India, *Source:* NBSS&LUP

Agro-ecological regions map was prepared by superimposing bioclimatic- cum-growing period map over the base soil-scape map (soil + physiography) on 1:4 m scale. Derived homogeneous units were delineated, adjusting boundaries with the district boundaries to arrive at the agro-ecological regions map. On the basis of the procedure followed, the country has been broadly grouped into 20 agro-ecological regions (Sehgal *et al.*, 1992) (Fig. 1; see Annexure 1).

To understand the distribution of degraded and wastelands in different agro- ecoregions, the agro-ecoregion map was superimposed on the degraded and wastelands map (Fig. 10), and areal statistics was worked out.

The area estimates of the degraded and wastelands in different AERs (Table 30.1) reveal that region 4 is highly degraded with area coverage of 14,960 thousand ha. The other AERs having appreciably high area coverage are AER-2 (13,913 thousand ha), AER-5 (11,270 thousand ha), AER-10 (8,288 thousand ha), AER-12 (8,193 thousand ha), and AER-17 (7,519 thousand ha). Though all the AERs are affected but the least affected are AER-1 and AER-20.

TABLE 30.1. Area under degraded and wastelands of India under different AERs

AERs	Degraded and wastelands classes*('000 ha)																		
	1	2	3	4	5	6	7	8	9	10	11	12	13	14	15	16	17	18	19	Total degraded area
1	19	0	0	0	0	0	0	0	0	0	0	0	0	0	0	0	0	0	0	19
2	638	123	0	0	0	11,419	1,106	6	0	110	60	0	405	1	30	0	0	8	7	13,913
3	2,341	76	0	0	0	0	1	0	0	0	0	0	75	47	0	0	0	20	0	2,560
4	12,109	1,024	0	1	0	6	367	7	0	0	0	0	929	423	0	1	11	14	68	14,960
5	6,455	983	3	22	0	0	184	2	0	0	0	0	25	15	0	0	5	6	0	7,700
6	10,374	257	0	0	0	0	171	6	0	0	0	0	269	175	0	0	1	17	0	11,270
7	4,376	465	12	7	0	0	0	0	0	0	0	0	79	15	0	0	1	31	0	4,986
8	4,412	391	272	151	60	0	3	1	0	0	0	0	287	36	0	17	2	48	5	5,685
9	3,122	378	3	3	0	0	2	3	0	0	0	0	368	293	0	2	0	9	89	4,272
10	6,934	822	119	308	28	0	0	0	0	0	0	0	35	20	0	1	0	21	0	8,288
11	3,843	514	653	726	159	0	0	0	0	0	0	0	11	3	0	0	0	16	0	5,925
12	4,917	1,512	469	1,089	142	0	2	0	0	0	0	0	0	0	0	0	0	38	24	8,193
13	3,803	48	41	41	0	0	40	9	0	0	0	5	2	24	0	0	0	1	163	4,177
14	4,009	1,025	75	289	222	0	0	0	0	0	0	0	10	0	0	0	0	4	61	5,695
15	2,011	213	647	1,229	328	0	64	0	0	0	0	0	0	0	0	0	0	1	242	4,735
16	576	229	275	651	782	0	0	0	0	0	0	0	0	0	0	0	0	0	10	2,523
17	210	992	439	516	5,330	0	0	0	0	0	0	0	0	0	0	0	0	1	31	7,519
18	928	48	43	12	3	0	574	4	0	0	0	25	115	6	0	0	0	10	83	1,851
19	2,944	187	2,029	674	76	0	40	1	20	0	0	0	0	0	0	0	0	15	76	6,062
20	0	0	0	0	0	0	77	0	0	0	0	0	0	0	0	0	0	0	0	77
Total	74,021	9,287	5,080	5,719	7,130	11,425	2,631	39	20	110	60	30	2,610	1,058	30	21	20	260	859	120,410

Note: Classes*: 1. Exclusively water erosion (>10 tonnes/ha/yr); Water erosion under open forest, 2. Forest; 3. Exclusively acid soils (*p*H <5.5); 4. Acid soils under water erosion; 5. Acid soils under open forest; 6. Exclusively wind erosion; 7. Exclusively saline soils; 8. Eroded saline soils; 9. Acid saline soils; 10. Saline soils under wind erosion; 11. Saline soils under open forest; 12. Water logged saline soils; 13. Exclusively sodic soils; 14. Eroded sodic soils; 15. Sodic soils under wind erosion; 16. Sodic soils under open forest; 17. Eroded sodic soils under open forest; 18. Mining / Industrial waste; 19. Waterlogged area (Permanent)

Source: NBSS&LUP

Water erosion (classes 1, 2) has affected almost all AERs and AERs with large affected areas are: AER-4 (13,133 thousand ha), AER-6 (10,631 thousand ha), AER- 5 (7,438 thousand ha), AER-12 (6,429 thousand ha), AER-14 (5,034 thousand ha), AER-7 (4,841 thousand ha) and AER-8 (4,803 thousand ha). Least affected AERs are AER-20, AER-1 and AER-17. Soil acidity (classes 3,4,5) has been observed in all AERs, excepting AER-1, AER-2, AER-3 and AER-20. Very little land areas are affected in AER-4 and AER-6. Highly affected AERs are AER-17 (6,285 thousand ha), AER-19 (2,779 thousand ha), AER-15 (2,204 thousand ha), AER-12 (1,700 thousand ha) and AER-11 (1,538 thousand ha).

Salinity affected (classes 7, 8, 9, 10, 11, 12) agro-ecological regions are located in the semi-arid and sub-humid climatic zones of the country. Highest area coverage with salinity is in AER-2 (1,282 thousand ha), followed by AER-18 and AER-4 with 603 and 374 thousand ha, respectively.

Sodicity and salinity are observed in combination in some of the AERs. Notable among them are AER-2, AER-4, AER-6 and AER-18. Agroclimatic conditions coupled with management practices (including irrigation) are the main reasons for the development of soil sodicity. Highest sodicity (classes 13,14,15,16,17) is observed in AER-4 (1,364 thousand ha), followed by AER-9 (663 thousand ha), AER-6 (445 thousand ha), AER-2 (436 thousand ha), AER-8 (342 thousand ha), and it is not a problem in AER-1, AER-11, AER-12, AER-15, AER-16, AER-17, AER-19 and AER-20.

Wind erosion (class 6) is predominant in AER-2 and has a little affected area in AER-4.

Degraded and wastelands status in different areas

For planning, reclamation/conservation and ameliorative measures for the restoration of the degraded and wastelands, it is necessary to have their spatial extent at the state and district levels. Keeping this in view, the national degraded wasteland map has been utilized to generate area statistics of various states and their districts. A brief description of the states, their geographical setting and land degradational statistics is presented in state wise as per different region under different state here.

- North-eastern region
- Eastern region
- Western region
- Northern region
- Central region
- Southern region

Now, we discussed problematic soils found in ecosystem of Uttar Pradesh under Northern regions as blow:

NORTHERN REGION

The northern region comprises Delhi, Haryana, Himachal Pradesh, Jammu and Kashmir, Punjab, Uttar Pradesh and Uttarakhand.

UTTAR PRADESH

Location

Uttar Pradesh is located between 23°52'to 31°28'N latitudes and 77°06'to 84°37'E longitudes with an area of 23.8 M ha (238,566 km^2). It is the fourth largest state in India and is a land locked state bounded by China and Nepal in the north, Himachal Pradesh in the north-west, Haryana and Delhi in the west, Rajasthan in the south-west, Madhya Pradesh and Chhattisgarh in the south, Jharkhand in the south-east and Bihar in the east.

Physiography

The state has three distinct physiographic divisions: the Himalayas, the Gangetic plains; the southern highlands, plateaux and scarplands.

The Gangetic plains lie between Himalayas on the north side and highlands, plateaux and scarplands on the south side. The Great Ganga plain covers almost 70% area of the state. Piedmonts and tarai are the most significant and complex part of the Gangetic plains in the submontane belt running along the foot of Siwaliks from west to east. Alluvial plain is a riverine plain and is featureless. Its monotony is broken by red-stone hillocks of Aravalli hills on the western part of Mathura district, and on the micro-level by the river bluffs, levees and dead arms of river channels. The Aravalli plain constitutes a discontinuous central hilly sub-surface tract of the Aravallis. The southern highlands, plateaux and scarplands comprise eastern Rajasthan uplands, Bundelkhand uplands, Vindhyan scarplands and Eastern Plateau. Eastern Rajasthan uplands are formed by the riverine action of the Banas and Mahi rivers. These originate from Aravalli ranges. Bundelkhand uplands and Vindhyan scarplands are located in the south of Gangetic plains; the region forms a part of the foreland of the Deccan Peninsula. The western part of this tract is known as Bundelkhand and eastern part forms natural division known as Vindhyas. The Eastern plateau is peneplained surface with a rugged topography. It includes rounded hills with rolling dissected plateaux.

Geology

The Gangetic plains are characterized by an almost imperceptible change in elevation and uniform river-line material. The pre-tertiary river-borne material from the peninsula has later been supplemented rather more vigorously by the upper and post-tertiary Himalayan materials.

The south-western region of the state is largely composed of crystalline igneous and metamorphic rocks. The typical rock of this region is popularly termed as 'Bundelkhand gneiss'. In fact granite and gneiss both are conspicuous in which former predominates. The Vindhyan scarplands in the south-eastern part comprise Vindhyan and Kaimur sandstone, shales and mixed conglomerates. However, the plain within the region is formed by the alluvium deposited by the rivers of the central highlands.

Climate

It is, in general, subtropical, continental, monsoonic, with mild and dry winters and hot uncomfortable summers. Rainfall is orographic in nature, and is caused by the obstruction of the high mountain wall in the north to the monsoon. June to September is the rainy season during which 88% of the total annual rainfall is received. Northern districts adjacent to foothills of Himalayas constitute area of maximum rainfall (>1,400 mm), and the districts adjacent to east Rajasthan receive minimum rainfall (<600 mm).

April, May and June are the summer months when hot winds (the loo) blow from the west. May is the hottest month with mean maximum temperature of 41°C in the Gangetic plains. However, Plateau region and elevated places, in general, record 2° to 5°C lower temparature. January is coldest with mean minimum temperature ranging from 6.5° to 10°C. The north-western districts experience extreme cold during winters. Hailstorms in February and March are not uncommon.

Natural Vegetation

Lower regions have several species interspersed with bamboos, climbers, and evergreen shrubs. The dominant species of the state are sal, gular, jhingal, pipal, shisham. Widely scattered thorny trees, mainly, thorny legumes, euphorbias and dwarf grass species are found extensively. The trees are generally stunted, forming open dry forest. Important trees of the region are phulai, khair, kokke, dhaman.

Soils

Soils of Glacio-Fluvial Valleys are moderately shallow, excessively drained, coarse-loamy, slightly acidic, and are moderately stony. Typic Udorthents arefound in association with rock outcrops. The lower valley slopes are occupied with moderately shallow, well-drained, sandy-skeletal/coarse-loamy, slightly acidic, slightly eroded and strongly stony soils with low water-holding capacity. These are classified as Typic Udorthents.

Soils of Piedmont plain are deep, well-drained, neutral to slightly alkaline, coarse-loamy/fine-loamy (calcareous/non-calcareous), Udic Haplustepts that occur in association with deep, well-drained, neutral to slightly acidic coarse- loamy over fragmental and fine-loamy over sandy, Udifluventic Haplustepts. At places, soils are deep and excessively drained Typic Udipsamments, and fine- silty, Udic Haplustolls have also been noticed.

Soils of tarai are dominantly very deep, well-drained, slightly alkaline, coarse-loamy/fine-loamy, Udic Haplustepts. The other soils are mapped as coarse-loamy (calcareous), Udic Haplustolls and fine-loamy over sandy-skeletal, Udifluventic Haplustepts. These soils are rich in organic matter, plant nutrients and have fairly good water-holding capacity.

Soils of sandstone landscape are shallow to moderately shallow, somewhat excessively drained, loamy-skeletal, Lithic/Typic Ustorthents.

The intervening basin on the other hand is occupied with deep, moderately well-drained, fine (montmorillonitic), Vertic Haplustepts and Entic Haplusterts. The other soils mapped are moderately shallow to deep, well to moderately well-drained, fine-loamy (calcareous/non-calcareous), Typic Haplustepts.

The soils of the state belong to 5 orders, 11 suborders, 21 great groups and 41 subgroups. Nearly 70% of area is under Inceptisols, followed by Entisols (19%), Alfisols (5%), Vertisols (2%) and Mollisols (<1%). The total area under mapping units is 99%, and the rest (1%) is under miscellaneous soils (Singh et al., 2003).

Land Use

The changes in the land use pattern over passage of time have revealed that of the total geographic area of 24 M ha, the cultivated area is about 18,600 thousand ha (62%). It comprises 17,500 thousand ha as net sown area that is irrigated area also, and about 1,000 thousand ha as the current fallows. The net sown area increased from 16,200 in 1950–51 to 17,500 thousand ha in 1971; and since then till 1997–98 showed no further increase. That increase was largely due to the extension of cultivation on the marginal lands including culturable wastes and lands under miscellaneous trees and groves. About 1,800 thousand ha (6%) of the area is under fallow, which is either due to the lack of irrigation facilities or related problems of waterlogging, salinity/sodicity.

Although unculturable and culturable wastelands have declined significantly over the time, yet they accounted nearly 10% in 1997–98, indicating that nearly 6% of the land in the state is not being put to productive use. Due to uncontrolled and unplanned urbanization and industrialization, area under non- agricultural uses has increased continuously from 1,800 thousand ha (6.3%) in 1951–52 to 2,500 thousand ha (8.5%) in 1997–98, indicating conversion of prime agricultural lands for non-agricultural purposes.

Degraded and Wastelands

The soils are highly susceptible to degradation by water erosion, covering 12,884 thousand ha (54% of TGA of the state). Almost all districts are affected barring Gautam Buddhanagar and Bareilly. The highly affected districts are: Lakhimpur Kheri (468 thousand ha), Sondhara (437 thousand ha), Jhansi (426 thousand ha), Lalitpur (416 thousand ha), Baharaich (406 thousand ha) and Allahabad (381 thousand ha). Banda, Agra, Bijnor, Hamirpur, Mirzapur, Sultanpur and Saharanpur each has more than 300 thousand ha area affected by water erosion (Fig. 30.3; Table 30.2).

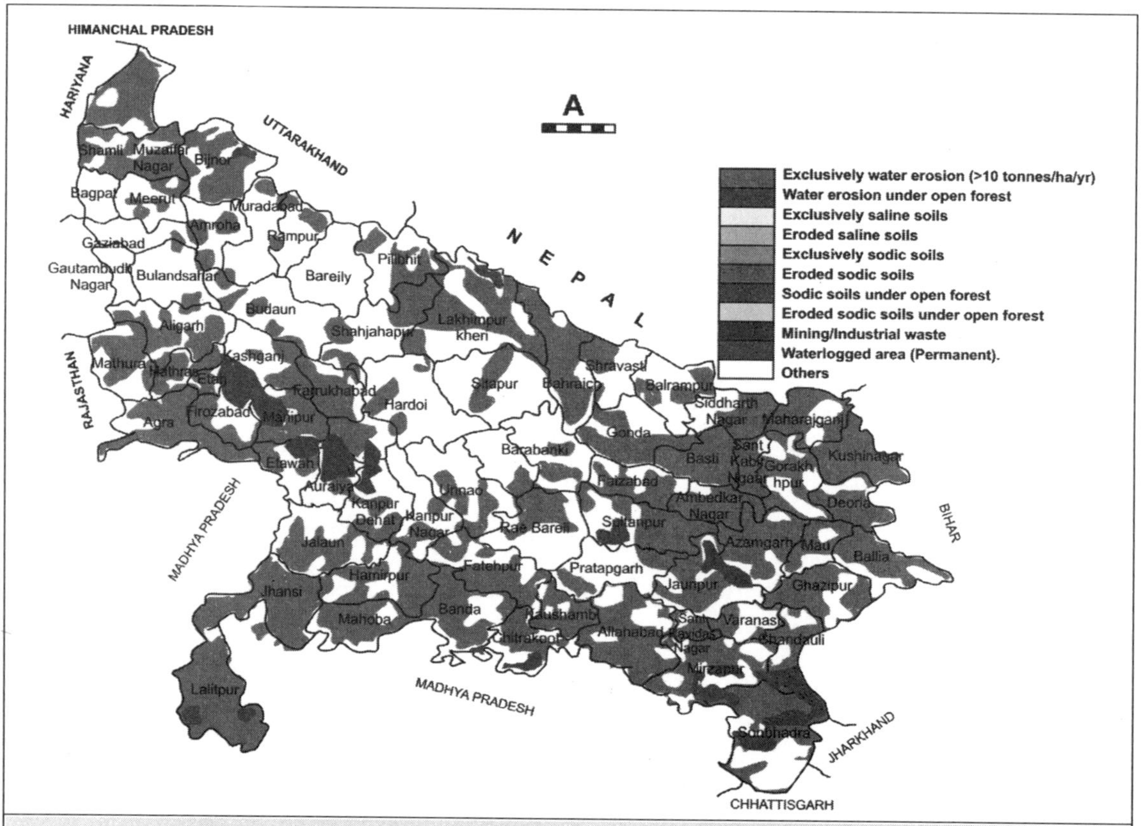

Fig. 30.3: Degraded and wastelands of Uttar Pradesh, *Source:* NBSS&LUP

TABLE 30.2: Degraded and wastelands statistics of Uttar Pradesh (Area in '000 ha)

Districts (70)	Degraded and wastelands classes*										Total of classes	Other**	Total
	1	2	7	8	13	14	16	17	18	19			
Agra	333	0	0	0	2	1	0	0	0	0	336	63	399
Aligarh	206	0	0	0	4	12	0	0	0	4	226	145	371
Prayagraj	381	0	0	0	19	16	0	0	0	8	424	115	539
Ambedkar Nagar	194	0	0	0	0	24	0	0	0	3	221	14	235
Auraiya	17	0	0	0	37	18	0	0	0	0	72	132	204
Azamgarh	244	0	0	1	32	68	0	0	0	11	356	64	420
Baghpat	23	0	0	0	0	0	0	0	0	0	23	113	136
Baharaich	406	0	0	0	0	0	0	0	0	10	416	153	569
Ballia	236	0	0	6	5	6	0	0	0	3	256	40	296
Balrampur	109	1	0	0	0	0	0	0	0	1	111	178	289
Banda	346	3	0	0	0	0	0	0	0	0	349	89	438
Bara Banki	111	0	0	0	6	2	0	0	0	5	124	253	377
Bareilly	2	0	0	0	0	0	0	0	0	2	4	401	405
Basti	291	0	0	0	0	1	0	0	0	3	295	7	302
Bijnor	308	13	0	0	0	0	0	0	0	0	321	130	451
Badaun	134	0	0	0	2	0	0	0	0	1	137	373	510
Bulandshahar	73	0	0	0	0	0	0	0	0	0	73	293	366
Chandauli	130	66	0	0	7	13	0	0	0	2	218	36	254
Chitrakut	173	68	0	0	0	0	0	0	0	1	242	75	317
Deoria	208	0	0	1	0	1	0	0	0	1	211	42	253
Etah	146	0	0	0	55	24	0	0	0	8	233	208	441
Etawah	73	0	0	0	30	18	0	0	0	0	121	105	226
Faizabad	190	0	0	0	2	5	0	0	0	3	200	74	274
Farrukhabad	153	0	0	0	0	14	0	0	0	0	167	58	225
Fatehpur	282	0	0	0	0	1	0	0	0	3	286	125	411
Firozabad	99	0	0	0	36	7	0	0	0	0	142	92	234
Gautam Buddha Nagar	2	0	0	0	0	0	0	0	0	1	3	122	125
Ghaziabad	30	0	0	0	0	0	0	0	0	3	33	160	193
Ghazipur	201	0	0	0	21	44	0	0	0	6	272	64	336
Gonda	276	0	0	0	0	0	0	0	0	3	279	159	438
Gorakhpur	210	6	0	0	2	10	0	0	0	1	229	100	329
Hamirpur	326	0	0	0	1	0	0	0	0	0	327	101	428
Hardoi	94	0	0	0	0	0	0	0	0	10	104	485	589
Hatras	126	0	0	0	6	13	0	0	0	1	146	29	175
Jalaun	272	0	0	0	0	0	0	0	0	0	272	180	452
Jaunpur	160	0	0	0	56	69	0	0	0	9	294	108	402

Jhansi	426	0	0	0	0	0	0	0	0	0	426	72	498
Jyotiba Phule Nagar	92	0	0	0	1	1	0	0	0	0	94	135	229
Kabirnagar	131	0	0	0	0	2	0	0	0	2	135	8	143
Kannauj	74	0	0	0	36	17	0	0	0	0	127	71	198
Kanpur Dehat	94	0	0	0	31	2	0	0	0	0	127	184	311
Kanpur Nagar	74	0	0	0	10	1	0	0	0	0	85	214	299
Kaushambi	150	0	0	0	0	0	0	0	0	0	150	32	182
Kushinagar	264	1	0	0	0	0	0	0	0	1	266	23	289
Lakhimpur Kheri	432	36	0	0	0	0	0	0	0	23	491	269	760
Lalitpur	367	49	0	0	0	0	0	0	1	0	417	84	501
Lucknow	66	14	5	0	17	20	2	0	0	1	125	126	251
Maharajganj	229	0	0	0	0	0	0	0	0	1	230	63	293
Mainpuri	105	0	0	0	57	63	0	0	0	0	225	49	274
Mathura	201	0	0	0	6	12	0	0	0	3	222	108	330
Mau	110	0	0	4	7	7	0	0	0	6	134	37	171
Meerut	89	0	0	0	0	0	0	0	0	0	89	160	249
Mirzapur	245	69	0	0	1	1	0	0	0	1	317	131	448
Mohoba	244	0	0	0	0	0	0	0	0	0	244	38	282
Moradabad	73	0	0	0	0	0	0	0	1	0	74	285	359
Muzaffarnagar	277	0	0	0	0	0	0	0	0	0	277	121	398
Partapgarh	116	0	0	0	34	60	0	0	0	3	213	154	367
Pilibhit	148	0	0	0	0	0	0	0	0	1	149	196	345
Rai Bareli	154	0	0	0	32	39	0	0	0	2	227	226	453
Rampur	63	0	0	0	0	0	0	0	0	1	64	170	234
Saharanpur	306	3	0	0	0	0	0	0	0	0	309	57	366
Sant Ravidas	51	0	0	0	7	10	0	0	0	0	68	26	94
Shahjahanpur	214	0	0	0	0	0	0	0	0	4	218	234	452
Shrawasti	46	0	0	0	0	0	0	0	0	0	46	65	111
Siddharthnagar	1	0	0	0	0	0	0	0	2	163	110	273	160
Sitapur	142	0	0	0	20	9	0	0	0	7	178	388	566
Sondhara	253	184	0	0	0	0	0	0	1	0	438	235	673
Sultanpur	217	0	0	0	26	59	0	0	0	10	312	128	440
Unnao	135	0	4	1	6	11	0	0	0	1	158	292	450
Varanasi	57	0	0	0	12	11	0	0	0	4	84	72	156
Total	12,370	514	9	13	626	692	2	0	3	176	14,405	9,449	23,854

Notes: Classes*:1 .Exclusively water erosion (>10 tonnes/ha/yr); 2. Water erosion under open forest; 7 Exclusively saline soils; 8 Eroded saline soils; 13 Exclusively sodic soils; 14 Eroded sodic soils; 16 Sodic soils under open forest; 17 Eroded sodic soils under open forest; 18 Mining/Industrial waste; 19 Waterlogged area (Permanent).

Others**: Normal agricultural lands, water-bodies, rivers, lakes and habitats etc. (based on the limited reconnaisance survey), Source: NBSS&LUP

Saline soils cover 22 thousand ha, affecting Balia (6 thousand ha), Unnao (5 thousand ha) and Lucknow (5 thousand ha), and about 1,320 thousand ha (about 6% of TGA) is covered by sodic soils.

Jaunpur (125 thousand ha), Mainpuri (120 thousand ha), Azamgarh (100 thousand ha), Pratapgarh (94 thousand ha) and Sultanpur (85 thousand ha) are affected by sodicity. Other districts where sodicity is encountered are Etah, Gazipur, Auraiya and Kannauj.

Area affected due to mining accounts for 176 thousand ha. Districts having mining wastes are Lakhimpur Kheri, Sultanpur, Hardoi, Azamgarh and Etah.

Severe land degradation of different states

Among the 19 identified classes of land degradation, water erosion, acid soils, salinity and sodicity are the predominant ones, and occupy larger areas in different states. To plan conservation/ameliorative measures through different agencies, statewise and districtwise statistics of the areas affected by the prominent degradation classes is a prerequisite. This statistics will also be useful for sanctioning grants to various centrally sponsored schemes by the Government, and will be a guide to donor agencies. Statewise area statistics under four prominent degradation classes has been presented in this Chapter. The rankings are based on the percentage area of the TGA of the affected state.

Water erosion is the most predominant degradation class affecting large number of states. Uttar Pradesh is the worst affected state, covering 54% of the TGA, followed by Madhya Pradesh, Karnataka, Jharkhand, Arunachal Pradesh and Meghalaya, covering 44%, 41%, 40%, 32% and 31% of the TGA. Asom, with 30% affected area ranks seventh and Maharashtra with 29% ranks eighth.

The second major degradation class is soil acidity, particularly in soils having pH <5.5. Though soils with pH 5.5–6.5 qualify for acid soils, their affect on crop productivity is not so severe to rank them as problematic. Many crops grow successfully in this pH range. Moreover, soils of the North-Eastern Region within this pH range support a luxuriant forest vegetation. Nagaland with 91% of TGA, ranks first among states affected with soil acidity, followed by Manipur (72%). The other states following in order are Tripura, Kerala, Mizoram, Meghalaya, Goa, Asom, Arunachal Pradesh and Chhattisgarh. Jharkhand where research on acid soils has received countrywide recognition, ranks tenth (Table 30.1). It may be suggested that ameliorative amendments like liming materials need to be supplied on a priority basis to these states.

And soil salinity is another major degradation class affecting mainly coastal states. Salinity is highest in Andaman and Nicobar islands, covering 9% of TGA followed by Gujarat (8%) and West Bengal (5%). Orissa, Rajasthan, Maharashtra and Haryana each has 1% affected area.

Soil sodicity has been found to affect physical and nutritional characteristics of the lands and ultimately rendering them partially or fully non-productive. Sodicity problem is very intensive in Uttar Pradesh, affecting 6% of the TGA, (Table 30.1), followed by Haryana (4%) and Punjab, Gujarat and Tamil Nadu (3% each). The need for amendments or reclaiming sodic soils is to be prioritized accordingly. Other states of the country are not affected by sodicity.

❑❑❑

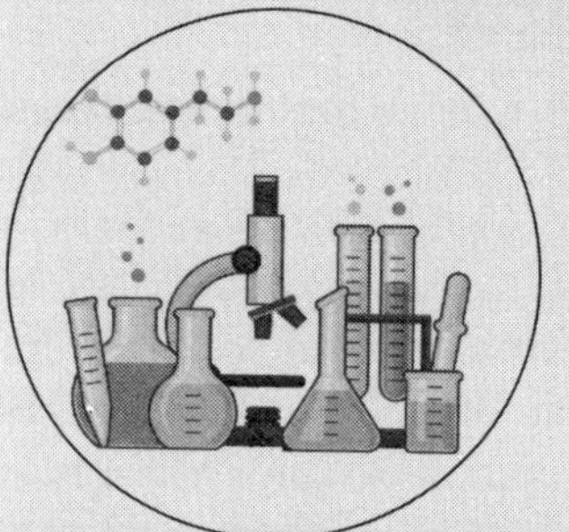

CHAPTER 31

Practical's and Analytical Chemistry

DEFINITIONS

Atom. It is the unit cell of the element, which contains mostly electron, proton and neutron. The simplest portion of element that can take part in a chemical reaction.

Element. It is simplest form of the substance. It has definite properties and cannot be changed in other minute form. *e.g.* gold, carbon, iron, mercury etc.

Molecules. When two or more atoms combine togather, they form molecule.

$$O + O = O_2, Cl + Cl = Cl_2, Na + Cl = NaCl.$$

Compound. When two or more elements combining togather in a definite proportion, form third substance, the product is called compound.

$$C + O_2 = CO_2, Fe + S = FeS.$$

Mixture. When two or more substances are mixed togather and they can be detected easily the product is known as mixture.

Solid + Solid = Sand, wheat grain
Solid + Liquid = Milk
Solid + Gas = Smoke

Atomic. Weight of proton and neutron togather is known as atomic weight.

Weight. The number of times an atom is heavier than that of one part of Hydrogen atom. When atomic weight is expressed in gram called as grain atomic weight.

Molecular. How many times the weight of one molecules of any element.

Weight. compound is more than that of the atomic weight of hydrogen. The atomic weight of hydrogen is known as 1. If it is written in gram, it is called as gram molecular weight.

Molecular weight of Na + Cl = 23 + 35.5 = 58.5
HCl = 1 + 35.5 = 36.5

$$H_2SO_4 = 2 + 32 + 64 = 98$$
$$CaCO_3 = 40 + 12 = 48 = 100$$

Equivalent weight. Equivalent weight of any element of compounds that combines or displaces by weight of one parts of Hydrogen (or 8 parts of oxygen or 35.5 parts of chloride)

When it is expressed in gram, it is known as gram equivalent weight.

The gram equivalent weight of a substance is the weight of substance in gram which in its reaction corresponds to one g. atom of H, one g. Mole of OH, one half gram of O, or one gram atom of monovalent ion, one half gram atom of develop ion or equivalent weight of concerned substance or ion.

Mill equivalent weight. It is the equivalent weight in milligram or one thousand part of g. *e.g.* weight.

$$\text{eq. wt.} = \frac{\text{Atomic/molecular weight}}{\text{Valency}}$$

(*i*)	Eq. wt. of acid	=	Molecular weight/Number of replaceable H^+ atoms
	Eq. wt of HCl	=	Mole. weight/1 = 1 + 35.5 = 36.5
	Eq. wt of H_2SO_4	=	Mole. weight/2 = 2 + 32 + 64 = 98/2 = 49.
	Eq. wt. of H_3PO_4	=	Mole. weight/3 = 3 + 31 + 64 = 98/3 = 32.68
(*ii*)	Eq. wt. of base	=	Molecular weight/Number of replaceable OH ions Eq. wt. of
	NaOH	=	Molecular weight = 23 + 16 +1 = 40
	$Ca(OH)_2$	=	mole. weight/2 = 40 + 32 + 2 = 74/2 = 37.00
	$Al(OH)_3$	=	mole. weight/3 = 27 + 48 + 3 = 78/3 = 26.00
(*iii*)	Eq. wt. of salt	=	Mole. Weight/Valency Eq.wt. of
	NaCl	=	23 + 35.5 = 58.5
	$NaHCO_3$	=	23 + 12 +48 = 84
	$CaCO_3$	=	40 + 12 + 48 = 100/2 = 50
	$CaCl_2$	=	40 + 71 = 111/2 = 55.50

(*iv*) Eq. wt. of oxidizing agent

= Atomic weight or mole wt./Change in the oxidation number

= Eq. wt. of $KMnO_4$ (in acid medium).

= $2KMnO_4 + 3H_2SO_4 = 2MnSO_4 + K_2SO_4 + 3H_2O + 5(O)$

K	Mn	O_4	Mn	S	O_4
1	7	–8	+2	+6	–8

The change in the oxidation number of Mn is from +7 to +2 of by 5 units. Hence, the Eq. wt. of $KMnO_4$ = Mol. wt./5, = 39 + 55 + 64 = 158/5 = 31.6

Solution. It is a perfectly homogenous mixture of a solute in a solvent.

Solute. It is the substance which is being dissolved in solvent.

Solvent. It is the liquid or other phase in which the solute is being dissolved.

Standard solution. (1) A known amount of solute is dissolved in a known volume of solvent.

(2) Solution of which strength or concentration is knows.

Strength. %, ppm, Normality, Morality, Molality.

Percent %. is the g (mg% is the mg) of solute present in 100 g. solution (w/w) or 100 ml solution (w/v) (or 100 g substance (w/w).

ppm. Ppm is the parts of unit weight present in one million (1000 × 1000) unit weight or volume.

Normal solution. When gram equivalent weight of the substance is dissolved in water and volume is made one litre, the solution is known as Normal solution (N or 1N). (When one tenth of gram of wt. is dissolved in water and volume is made on litre, the solution is called deci normal (0.1 N or N/10, likewise N/20 (0.05 N), N/30 (0.033) N/50 (0.02 N) etc.).

Normality (N). Is the number of gram eq. wt. of the solute contained in one litre of the solution. g. wt. (solute) per litre solution/eq. wt.

Molar solution (M). Which contains one mole or a gram molecular weight of the substance dissolved in a litre of the solution ?

Morality (M). It is the number of molecules of the solute contained in one litre of the solution. g weight (Solution) per litre solution/mole weight.

Molal solution (m). This contains a gram mole weight of the substances dissolved in 1000 grams of the solvent (water) (The final volume of the solution is generally greater than one litter).

Molality (m). It is the number of molecules of the solute per kilogram of solvent contained in the solution.

ANALYTICAL CHEMISTRY

The Science involving the determination of composition of the constituents in terms of elements and compounds is called "Analytical chemistry" which has of late, made tremendous progress with the introduction of instrumental methods of analysis. Although analytical chemistry is moving rapidly towards more sophisticated methods, yet the latest model and costly instruments are not available in most of the Agricultural and commercial laboratories.

1. Principles of different methods of soil analysis,
2. Total and available nutrients in soil,
3. Cation exchange capacity,
4. Exchangeable bases,
5. Lime content and secondary nutrient,
6. Analysis of irrigation water,
7. Interpretation of results.

The nutrient status of a soil may be evaluated in several ways, among these are:

- Crop symptoms
- Rapid tissue or sap analysis
- Plant analysis
- Field plot fertilizer trials
- Green house/pot experiments

- Biological test *i.e.* growing micro organisms on the soil to detect a nutrient deficiency or toxicity
- Rapid chemical analysis.

Each of above has certain limitation when applied to individual farmer fields or on a general service basis.

Deficiency symptoms indicate only the very severe deficiency or toxicity condition and usually appear too late in a growing season for a farmer to intimate remedial actions for at that we are helpless to prevent loss.

Rapid tissue test or sap analysis and plant analysis are as like post mortem which help to explain what was wrong that year on that soil but don't qualitatively predict fertilizer needs.

Field plot fertilizer trials practically can't be conducted on every farmer field and the research result is not easily transferred from one field to another.

Green house fertilizer trials are costly, time consuming and highly restrictive in the number of soils that can be handled and it can be handled and it can't be quantitatively extra plotted to the field.

Biological test can determine the nutrient status of soil when properly conducted but are costly and time consuming.

In contrast, soil testing or chemical analysis of soil can be rapid, less expensive and accurate and serve as the transfer agent of field, green house and laboratory research into reliable predication of fertilizer or gypsum needs before crops are seeded (growing).

Soil Test

- It is a chemical method for estimating the nutrient supplying power of soil.
- Measure availability of nutrients to crops.
- Measure a part of the total nutrient present in soil that supply to plant.

Objective of the soil test

- To know status of particular element in given soil.
- To build and/or maintain fertility status of a given field.
- To provide the probability of obtaining a profitable response to fertilizer.
- To provide a basis for recommendation of fertilizer. How much fertilizer should be apply to particular crops.

To evaluate the fertility status of soils on the country soil area or statewise basis by the use of soil test summary.

Soil testing programme

It is divided in to four phases :

I. Collection of the soil sample.
II. Extracting and determining the available nutrients.
III. Interpreting the analytical results.
IV. Making the fertilizer recommendations.

One should, therefore, say that success of soil testing programme depends as much as on good individual judgments as it does on accurate chemical analysis.

The criteria for essentiality of element (Arnon. 1954)

I. The plant must be unable to grow normally or complete its life cycle in the absence of the element.

II. The element is specific and can't be replaced by another.

III. The element should play a direct role in metabolism.

Available nutrient (Bray, 1948)

I. The available amount of the nutrient in the soil is that portion, whose variation is mainly responsible for the variation in the yield and the response to the added fertilizer.

The first condition. Content of the available nutrient in a soil is high, it should not be respond to fertilizer application.

The second condition. Available nutrient content is low it should be response to the applied fertilizer.

II. Fraction of the total content, which is susceptible to absorption by plants during its growth.

Selection of Methods

Bray (1948) proposed that a good soil test should meet the following three criteria.

1. The extractant used should extract all or a proportionate part of the available form or forms of a nutrient from soils with variable properties.
2. The amount of nutrient extracted should be measured with reasonable accuracy and speed.
3. The amount extracted should be correlated with the growth and response of each crop to that nutrient under various conditions.

Collection and Processing of Soil for Analysis

Soil sampling is perhaps the most vital step for any soil analysis. As a very small fraction of the huge soil mass is used for analysis, it becomes extremely important to get a truly representative soil sample of the field. A wrong sample is not only wasting of time and money but also leads to the erroneous conclusions and recommendations, which will prove costly to the farmers.

Objectives of soil sampling

1. To evaluate soil fertility status for making fertilizer recommendations.
2. To predict the probable crop response to applied nutrients.
3. To classify soil into different types of soil groups, fertility groups for preparing soil maps and soil fertility maps.
4. To identify the types and degree of soil related problems like salinity, alkalinity and acidity etc. and to suggest appropriate reclamation/amelioration measures.

5. To find out suitability for growing crops and orchard.
6. To find out suitability for irrigation.
7. To study the soil genesis.

1. Sample each field separately

When area within a field differs in crop growth in the appearance of soil in elevation or is known to have been cropped or manure differently, divide the field accordingly and sample each area separately.

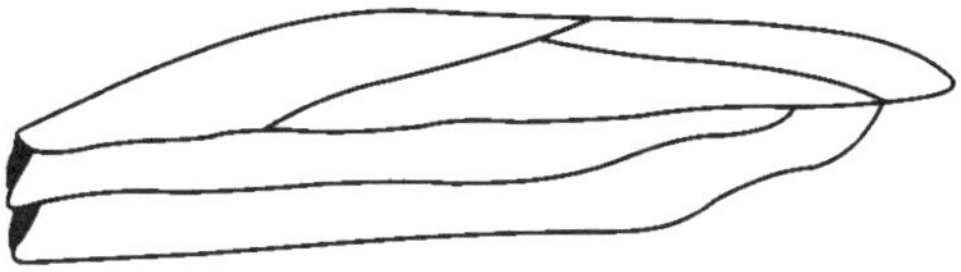

2. Take a composite sample

Take a composite sample from each area, scrape away surface little then draw a sample from surface to plough depth (or 0-15 cm) in 15 to 20 spots. Collect these in a clean cloth bag. If you use a khurpi or a kassi, first dig a 'V' shaped hole and take one thin slice (2 to 2.5 cm).

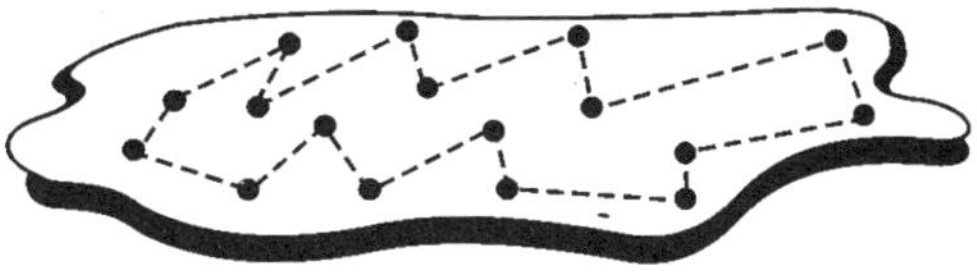

3. Sample between lines in planted crops

When crops have been planted in rows, sample in between lines do not sample unusual area avoid recently fertilized area, old bunds, marshy spots, near trees or compost piles or other non representative locations.

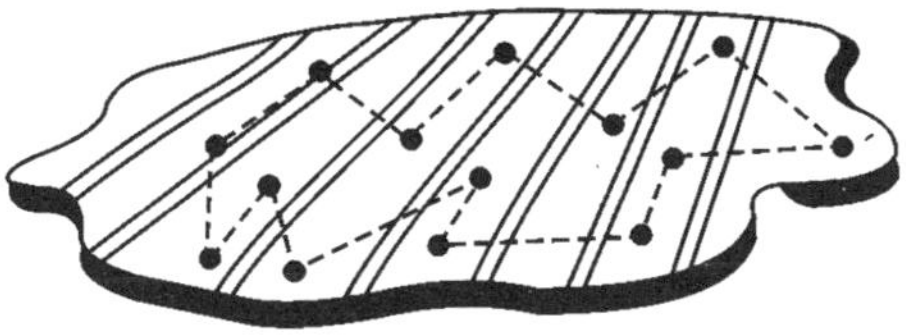

4. Use proper sample tools

Use proper sampling tools. Sample can be taken quite satisfactorily with a soil tube, an auger, a kassi or a kurpi. Soil tube and auger are more suited for drawing samples from lower depths.

4. Use proper sample tools

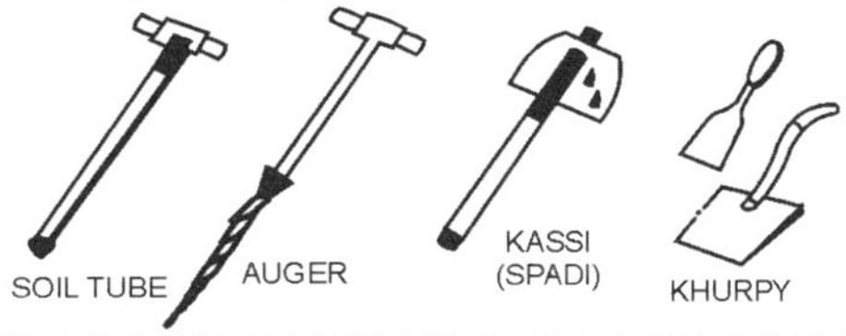

5. Mix sample thoroughly

Mix the sample well by stirring with hands on a clean piece or cloth, paper or polythene sheet, Discard all but 0.5kg of soil by the process of quartering ensures a representative final sample dry in shade and fill in cloth or polythene bag

5. Mix sample thoroughly

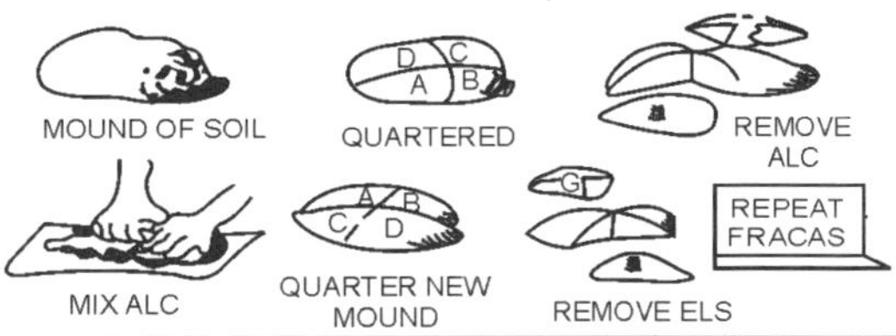

6. Packing and marking

Place a durable label inside and a tag outside. The bag giving details of the location, depth of sampling number the soil sample bags. Tie the bag properly for sending to soil testing laboratory

For collecting a representative soil sample, following points must be taken into considerations

1. The sample must truly represent the field it belongs to.

2. A field can be treated as a single sampling unit and it is appreciably uniform. Generally, an area not exceeding 0.5 ha is taken as one sampling unit.
3. Variations in slope, colour, texture, crop growth and management practices are the important factors that should be taken into account for sampling. Separate samples are required from areas differing in these characteristics.
4. Sampling from recently fertilized plots, bunds, channels, marshy tracts and areas near trees, wells, compost piles or other non-representative locations must be carefully avoided.

Precautions in collection and storing of samples

1. Don't take sample from unusual spots, such as area recently fertilized, old bunds, marshy spots, compost pit or other representative locations and near building, gates, field margins and highway.
2. Care in handling the soil samples against contamination is extremely important. Any possibility of contact with chemicals, fertilizer, or manure's must be avoided. Cotton, jute or plastic bag which are previously been containing fertilizer, salt or lime should not be used at any stage. Special precautions should be taken if the samples are to be tested for micronutrient elements. i.e. plastic sieve wooden mortar and pestle should be used.

Laboratory Apparatus and Reagent

In science, the most important thing that has happened is the advance in instrumental designs. We are dependent on all manner of physical instruments for the chemical analysis of soils.

ANALYTICAL PROCEDURE

Type of reaction in titration

(1) Acid base reaction (Neutralization reaction)

All titration in which an acid and an alkali react are classified under this head. NaOH, H_2SO_4.

Acidimetry. Is the determination of the strength of an acid by titrating it against a standard solution of a base.

Alkalimetry. is the determination of the strength of an alkali by titrating it against a standard solution of an acid.

(2) Precipitation reaction

The titrant forms an insoluble product with analyze. *e.g.* The titration of chloride ion with

$$AgNO_3.BaCl_2 + H_2SO_4 \longrightarrow BaSO_4 + 2HCl.$$

$$AgNO_3 + NaCl \longrightarrow \underset{\text{ppt}}{AgCl} + NaNO_3$$

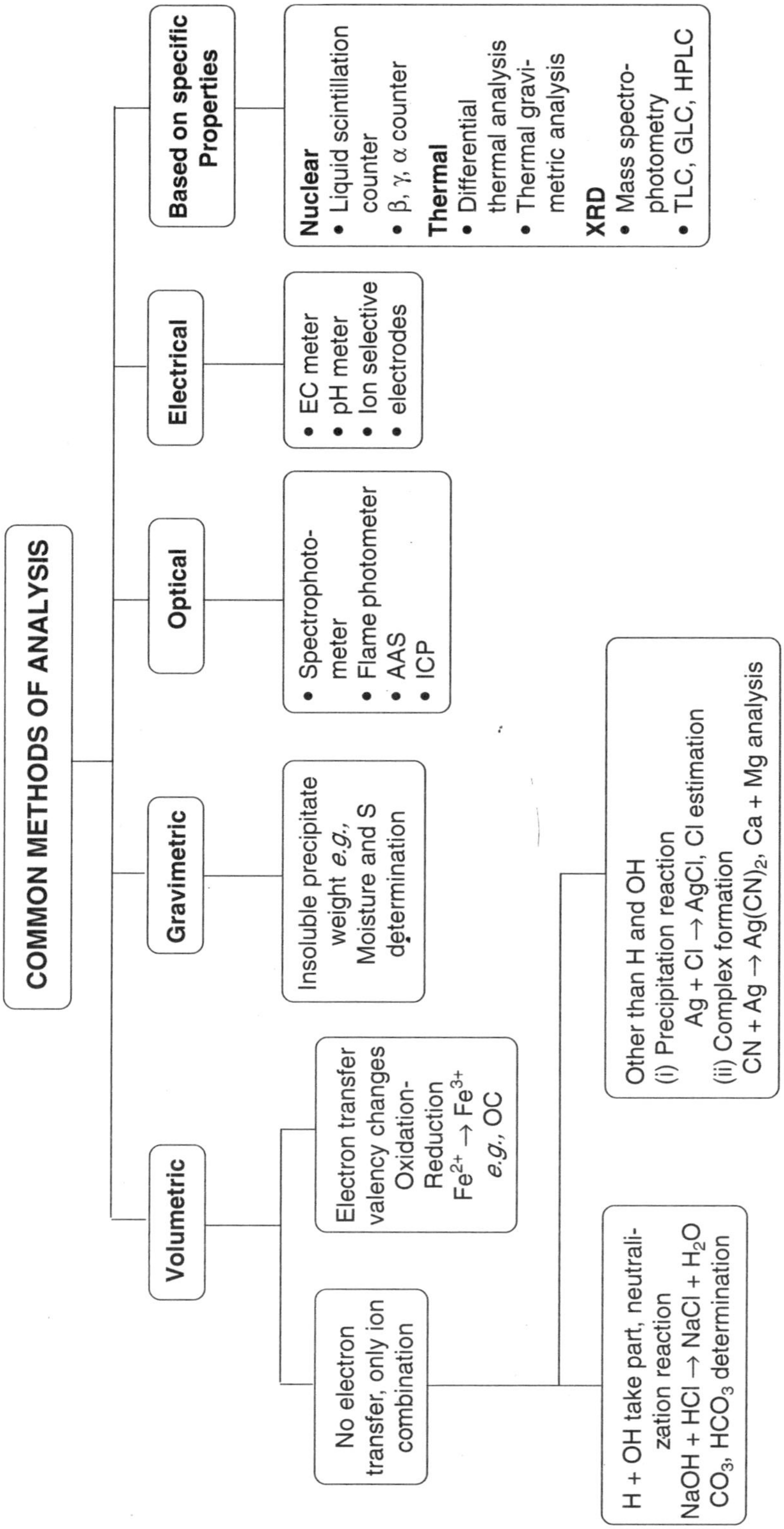
COMMON METHODS OF ANALYSIS
Volumetric
Gravimetric
Optical
Electrical
Based on specific Properties
No electron transfer, only ion combination
Electron transfer valency changes Oxidation-Reduction $Fe^{2+} \rightarrow Fe^{3+}$ e.g., OC
H + OH take part, neutralization reaction NaOH + HCl → NaCl + H_2O CO_3, HCO_3 determination
Other than H and OH
(i) Precipitation reaction Ag + Cl → AgCl, Cl estimation
(ii) Complex formation CN + Ag → $Ag(CN)_2$, Ca + Mg analysis
Insoluble precipitate weight e.g., Moisture and S determination
• Spectrophotometer
• Flame photometer
• AAS
• ICP
• EC meter
• pH meter
• Ion selective
• electrodes
Nuclear
• Liquid scintillation counter
• β, γ, α counter
Thermal
• Differential thermal analysis
• Thermal gravimetric analysis
XRD
• Mass spectrophotometry
• TLC, GLC, HPLC

The titration reaction in which one of the reagents is silver nitrate ($AgNO_3$) is known an Argentometry.

(1) **Complexometry titration.** Process in which ions form stable complex (chelate) with versanate. *i.e.* Ca, mg → EDTA. Fe, Mn, Zn, Cu → DTPA.

(2) **Oxidation reduction or redox reaction.** The chemical processes in which the transfer of electrons between the reacting substances taken place are known as oxidation reduction or redox reaction *i.e.* use of $FeSO_4$, $KMnO_4$.

(*i*) $2FeSO_4 + H_2SO_4 + O \longrightarrow Fe_2(SO_4)_3 + H_2O$.

(*ii*) $2KMnO_4 + 3H_2SO_4 \longrightarrow K_2SO_4 + 2MnSO_4 + 3H_2O + 5(O)$.

(3) **Iodometry titration.** Volumetric analysis in which standard solution of iodine is used to estimate the concentration of the substance present in solution is termed as iodometry.

(4) **Iodometry titration.** Volumetric analysis in which iodine is determined which is liberated during the chemical reaction from a substance.

(5) **Potentiometer or conductometric titrations.** Most often, the end point of a titration is found in a visual way with the aid of a suitable indicator. However, in many cases, this method is not applicable potentiometer or conductometric titration are used in such cases *i.e.*

(*i*) Colour change at the end point may be too much ranging.

(*ii*) Some times solution is self-coloured, so that colour change detection is difficult.

The case in which the ordinary method fail to give useful result, one may often resort to a physico-chemical determinations of the end point which are based in change in some physico-chemical property of solution when the end point is reached or passed. Two of these potentiometer and conductometric methods are the most important.

Standard Solution

Solution of which strength or concentration or normally is know. All titrimetric methods depend upon standard solutions, which contain exact known amounts of the reagents in unit volume of the solution. It is prepared by weighing out a known amount of the pure solid reagent, dissolving it in water and making the solution up to a known volume in a graduated flask. It is not always possible, however, to obtain the desired reagent in a pure form. In such cases a solution is prepared which will have approximately the desired concentration and thus solution is then standardized by titrating it with another substance, which can be obtained in highly purified form. Such a substance is called a primary standard.

Primary Standard

The substances, which are available in highly pure form and used to prepare primary standard solutions, are known as primary standard.

Primary standard substances must have the following properties.

- It must be available in pure form or in a state of know purity.
- It must be non hygroscopic.

- It must react in one way only under the condition of titration and there must be no side reaction.
- It is desirable that equivalent weight of primary standard substances must be as large as possible to reduce the effect of error in weighing.
- An acid or base should preferably strong so that they have a high dissociation constant.

Some substances are not used as primary standards due to the reasons given below :

- NaOH and KOH are hygroscopic so they absorb water from atmosphere. Further they also combine with CO_2 of atmosphere and form layer of carbonate on their surface. $2NaOH + CO_2 \rightarrow Na_2CO_3 + H_2O$.

Care to be taken for preservation of Std. Solution

- The bottle must be kept tightly stopped to prevent evaporation of solvent; otherwise it would cause an increase in solute concentration.
- Some of the std. solutions must be protected from atmospheric gases *e.g.* solution of NaOH and KOH absorb CO_2 from atmosphere and converted in to sodium and potassium carbonate.
- Solution of $AgNO_3$ must be preserved in dark coloured (amber) glass bottle to prevent the effect of light.
- The inside of bottle, containing concentrated solution of NaOH and KOH must be coated with wax to protect the glass from the action of alkali.
- The container should be shaken before with drawl of a portion of solution to ensure uniform composition of the solution.

	M. wt.	*Eq. wt.*
Primary Standards		
Acid (Alkalimetry)		
1. Potassium hydrogen phthalate $C_6H_4 \begin{matrix} COOH \\ \vert \\ COOH \end{matrix}$	204.2	204.2
Bases (Acidimetry)		
2. Sodium carbonate Na_2CO_3	106	53
Oxidizing agent		
3. Potassium dichromate, $K_2Cr_2O_7$	296.20	49.04
Reducing agent		
4. Anhydrous oxalic acid $(COOH)_2$	90	45
Oxalic acid $(COOH)_2\,2H_2O$	126	63
5. Argentometry		
Sodium chloride NaCl	58.45	58.45
Secondary Standards (not used as primary std.)		
Acid		
1. Hydrochloric acid HCl	36.5	36.5
2. Sulphuric acid H_2SO_4	98	49

Bases		
3. Sodium hydroxide NaOH	40	40
4. Potassium hydroxide KOH	56	56
5. Calcium hydroxide $Ca(OH)_2$	74	37
Oxidizing agent:		
6. Pot. permanaganate $KMnO_4$	158	31.6
7. Copper sulphate $(CaSO_45H_2O)$	.7	249.7
Reducing agent		
8. Ferrous sulphate $FeSO_47H_2O$	278	278
9. Ferrous ammo. sulphate $FeSO_4(NH_4)_2SO_4.6H_2O$	392	392
Argenatometry		
10. Silver nitrate $AgNO_3$	169.90	169.90

Acid

Any hydrogen containing substances (a mole, or ion) that can release a proton to any other substances.

An acid is any species, which can accept a share in an electron pair. An acid is proton donor.

Three types of acids

Molecular = $HCl \rightarrow H^+ + Cl^-$

Cationic = $Al\,(H_2O)_6 \rightarrow H^+ + Al\,(H_2O)_5\,OH^{2+}$

Anionic = $HCO_3 \rightarrow H^+ + CO_3{}^{2-}$

Base

Any substance (Mole or ion) that can accept a proton from any other substance. A base is any species, which can share an electron pair with an acid. A base is a proton acceptor.

Three types of Bases.

Molecular = $Py + H^+ \rightarrow PyH^+$

Cationic = $Al\,(H_2O)_5\,OH^{2+} + H^+ - Al\,(H_2O)_6{}^3$

Anionic = $HCO_3 + H^+ \rightarrow H_2CO_3$

Oxidation

A process in which a substance (atom, ion or molecule) looses one or more electrons. Previously, it was called as chemical reaction in which oxygen was added to or hydrogen removed from an element or a compound.

$$Na = Na^+ + e^- \text{ (oxidation)}$$

$$Cl + e^- = Cl^- \text{ (Reduction)}$$

$$Na + Cl = Na^+Cl^- \text{ (Redox)}$$

(*i*) $C + O_2 = CO_2$ – (Addition of oxygen)

(*ii*) $Fe + 2\,HCl = FeCl_2 + H_2$ (Removal of H)

(*iii*) $2FeCl_2 + Cl_2 = 2\ FeCl_3$ (Electric negative ions or non metal ions increases)

(*iv*) $2K_4$ (Fe (CN) + Cl_2 = 2 KCl $2K_3$ (Fe $(CN)_6$
(electric positive ions or molar ions decrease)

Oxidation-four type

(*i*) Gain of Molecular oxygen

(*ii*) Removal of hydrogen (Hydrogenation)

(*iii*) Change in valency

(*iv*) Hydration followed by dehydrogenation

Reduction

A process in which electrons are gained by a substance, previously it was called as chemical reaction involving the removal of oxygen or addition of hydrogen.

$$Cl + e^- = Cl \text{ (Reduction)}$$

(*i*) $H_2 + S = H_2S$ combination of hydrogen

(*ii*) $2Fe_2O_3 \rightarrow 4FeO + O_2$ Removal of oxygen

(*iii*) $2FeCl_3 + H_2S \rightarrow 2FeCl_2 + 2HCl + S$ (Negative ions or non metal ions decreased)

(*iv*) $CaCO_3 + 2HCl \rightarrow CaCl_2 + H_2O + CO_2$ (Position ions or metal ions increase).

Redox reaction

The chemical process in which the transfer of electrons between the reacting substances taken place are known as oxidation-reduction reaction or Redox reaction. In any oxidation-reduction reaction the number of electrons lost by the one spices is equal to the number gain by other. Oxidation involves the loss of electrons by a substances and reduction is the process where in electron are gained. For example, when a piece of metallic zinc is immersed in solution of cupric sulphate.

The overall reaction

$$Zn + Cu^{+2} > Zn^{+2} + Cu$$

Two half reaction.

1. Oxidation of zinc – $Zn > Zn^{+2} + 2e$
2. Reduction of cupric ions – $Cu^{+2} + 2 > Cu$

There are some substances which possessing a strong affinity for electrons causes other substances to be oxidized by extracting electrons from them. Reagents that function in this manner is called oxidizing agent and consequently reagents are themselves reduced. In this case, cupric in l^3 oxidizing agent and itself (cupric) reduced to metallic copper.

Example

$2KMnO_4 + 3H_2SO_4 \rightarrow K_2SO_4 + 2MnSO_4 + 3H_2O + 5(O)$.

Oxidizing agent – $Mn^{+7} \rightarrow 5e - Mn^{+2}$ – reduction – gain or electron.

$K_2Cr_2O_7 + 4H_2SO_4 - Cr_2\ (SO_7)_3 + 4H_2O + K_2O$.

Oxidizing agent

$Cr_2O_7 - Cr^{+6} = 3e - Cr^{3+}$.

Reducing agent

Substances, which readily give up electrons thereby causing some other species to be reduced. In this process, the reducing agent is itself oxidized.

1. $2FeSO_4 + H_2SO_4 + O \rightarrow Fe_2(SO_4)_3 + H_2O$.
   Reducing agent $Fe^{+2} - e \rightarrow Fe^{+3}$.
2. $SnCl_2 \rightarrow SnCl_4 = Sn^{+2} - 2e \rightarrow Sn^{+4}$.

In our discussion, extractable P will be a term preferred to available because the available means certain quantity of element is present in a soil and can be absorbed by plant. This is not the case, because the quantity of element utilized by plants growing on a soil may be more or less than that of the extractable element.

Soil testing procedure can provide an accurate 'relative index' of the quantity of element that plants may utilize from a soil, but rarely can they provide an absolute measure of it. That is why we should speak of extractable rather than available soil P.

For movement of element from soil (Solid) – solution plant.

Three parameters are important

1. **Intensity factor.** Concentration of element in solution at a time.
2. **Capacity factor.** Buffering characteristics reflect the ability of a soil to maintain this concentration by buffering against the withdrawal of element from solution by roots.
3. **Kinetic (Rate).** Rate of release.

Generally intensity factor most directly and simply reflected in extraction with water or a very dilute acid.

For capacity factor stronger extractant are used and categorized as under :

(*i*) Solution of strong mineral acid
(*ii*) Buffered solution of weak acid
(*iii*) Buffered solution of base
(*iv*) Solution of neutral salt
(*v*) Water or other dilutes salts or acid.

(A) ANALYTICAL PROCEDURE OF SOIL CHEMICAL PROPERTIES

Available Nutrients	*Method and Technique*
(*a*) **Chemical properties**	
1. pH	Soil suspension made using 1 part of soil with 2.5 parts of distilled water. The pH of the soil suspension is measured by a pH meter.
2. EC	Soil suspension made using1 part of soil with 2.5 parts of distilled water. The EC of the soil suspension is measured by Electrical conductivity meter.

(*b*) Available Major Nutrients	
3. Organic Carbon	Oxidation of organic matter by 1 N $K_2Cr_2O_7$ and conc. H_2SO_4 and back titration of ferrous ammonium sulphate as per Walkley and Black.
4. Available Nitrogen	Alkaline potassium permanganate (0.32% $KMnO_4$ + 2.5% NaOH). Subbiah and Asija (1956).
5. Available Phosphorus	Olsen's extractants (0.5 M $NaHCO_3$, pH 8.5). P from the extract is determined by a colorimeter.
6. Available Potash	1 N NH_4OAC extractants, K from the extract is determined by a flame photometer.
(*c*) Available Secondary Nutrients	
7. Available S	Heat soluble By turbidimetric method (Chaudhary and Cornfield, 1966)
8. Calcium and Magnesium	Versenate method (Cheng and Bray, 1951)
(*d*) Available Micronutrients	
9. Zn, Fe, Mn, Cu	DTPA (diethylene triamine penta acetic acid, 0.005 M DTPA) extractants. The micronutrient cations from the extract are determined by an atomic absorption spectrophotometer (AAS).
10. B	Hot water soluble. B from the extract is determined by a colorimeter.
11. Mo	Ammonium oxalate (pH 3.3). Mo from the extract is determined by a colorimeter.

ESTIMATION OF ORGANIC CARBON CONTENT IN SOIL

Principle

A suitable quantity of the soil is digested with chromic and sulphuric acids, making use of the heat of dilution of sulphuric acid. The excess of chromic acid left over unreduced by the organic matter of the soil is determined by a titration with standard ferrous sulphate or ferrous ammonium solution using diphenylamine as an internal indicator.

Apparatus

(1) 500 ml beaker (2) Pipette (3) Burette (4) Analytical balance (5) Glass rod.

Reagents

1. **Potassium dichromate solution.** 1 N. Dissolve 49.04 g pure crystals of potassium dichromate in water and dilute to 1 litre.
2. **Ferrous sulphate solution.** 0.5 N. dissolve 139 g $FeSO_4.7H_2O$ in water and add 15 ml conc. H_2SO_4 and dilute to 1 litre. Ferrous ammonium sulphate $Fe(NH_4SO_4)_2 \cdot 6H_2O$ can also be used and if that is to be used dissolve 785 g of the salt in 4 litres of water containing 100 ml conc. H_2SO_4.

3. **Phosphoric acid (H_3PO_4).** 95%.
4. **Diphenylamine.** Dissolve 0.5 g diphenylamine in a mixture of 100 ml conc. H_2SO_4 and 20 ml water.
5. **Sulphuric acid.** Not less than 96% purity.

Procedure

1. Weigh 1.0 g soil sample in a 500 ml beaker.
2. Add 10 ml 1N $K_2Cr_2O_7$ by means of a pipette and 20 ml concentrated H_2SO_4 by measuring cylinder.
3. Mix thoroughly and allow the reaction to proceed for 30 minutes on asbestos sheet.
4. Dilute the reaction mixture with 200 ml of water and 10 ml H_3PO_4 by measuring cylinder and add 7-8 drops of diphenylamine indicator.
5. Titrate the solution with std. 0.5 N $Fe(NH_4)_2(SO_4)_2$ to a brilliant green colour.
6. A blank without soil should be run simultaneously.
7. Calculate the organic carbon content of a given soil sample.

On the basis of organic carbon content soil is classified as follows:

Low	—	< 0.5%
Medium	—	0.5-0.75%
High	—	> 0.75%

NITROGEN

Plant growth is limited by N more than by any other element. The interpretation of N is more misunderstanding than with after elements for the form and content of nitrogen in soil is profoundly affected by climate.

Form of N in Soils

In most soils, nitrogen occur mainly in

(*i*) Organic forms

(*ii*) Inorganic forms NO_3^-, NO_2^-, NH_4^+ (very minute quantity).

The principal source of plant available N is the organic nitrogen which is micro biologically converted via NH_4 and NO_2 into NO_3 (nitrate). These above particular forms could not clear the picture of availability to plant so that available N should be measured.

Total Nitrogen

A general approximation of total soil N content can be made from:

1. Total N% = O.M. × 0.05

2. Total N% = (Ignition loss at 400°C.)

= loss × 0.022 to 0.03

These approximate factors are subject to change widely in different soils.

Determination of Soil Total N

Two methods

1. Dumas method : Dry oxidation (combustion) technique.
2. Kjeldahl method : Wet oxidation procedure.

Dumas method is a time consuming and complicated process and hence kjeldahl method is widely used for determination of total N.

Kjeldahl method–wet oxidation procedure

In this method, the N in the sample is converted to ammonium (NH_4) by digestion with concentrated H_2SO_4 containing substance which promote this conversion and then the ammonium is determined from the amount of NH_3 liberated by distillation of the digest with alkali substances used:

1. K_2SO_4 or Na_2SO_4. increase the temperature of digestion.
2. Hg, Cu, or Se. Increase the rate of oxidation of organic matter by H_2SO_4

Hg,	Cu,	or	Se.
1	2		3
Mercury	Copper		Selenium

This method is quite satisfactory for total N of most of the nitrogenous compounds occur in soil and plant analysis. However, it does not give accurate results with compounds containing N-N and N-O linkage and also inorganic N in the form of nitrate or nitrite which contain N-O linkage and it could not recovered by this method. Generally, this method includes only both organic and ammonium (NH_4) forms. Some modification in Kjeldahl method or pretreatment is given for including above other forms (NO_3 and NO_2).

Kjeldahl method involves two steps

(*i*) Digestion of the sample to convert the N to ammonium.

(*ii*) Determination of the ammonium of the digest by distillation.

1. Digestion

1. Pretreatment of water should be given (especially for clayey soil).

(*a*) Soil containing some material which cemented the soil particles together which protected organic matter inside the particle from the action of H_2SO_4 and that this cementing material was not readily soluble in concentrated H_2SO_4 but was easily dissolved by dilute H_2SO_4.

(*b*) Soil crumbs can't disperse in the acid only.

(*c*) Considerable portion of N in soils (particularly sub soil) is in the form of ammonium trapped in the lattice of clay minerals.

Water treatment permit expansion of lattice during treatment with H_2SO_4 unless it could not included. If water treatment is omitted, very much coarser and darker residue from digestion is obtained.

2. The soil should be more finely ground in order to assure complete oxidation of the organic matter within the small aggregates especially in the case of heavy clay soil.

3. Most important consideration is
   (*i*) Selection of catalyst and its concentration
   (*ii*) Digestion temperature
   (*iii*) Time of digestion

N.B. H_2SO_4 is used during digestion for

(*a*) Oxidation of organic matter : should be used maximum
(*b*) Reaction with soil mineral :
(*c*) Lost by volatilization : This should be minimize otherwise salt concentration will be increased.

The catalyst most frequently employed for Kjeldahl digestion are those containing Se, Hg and Cu. Efficiency is in the order of Se > Hg > Cu.

Se is safe and effective catalyst when properly used and loss of N only occur when it is used in excessive quality or with large amount of K_2SO_4 or Na_2SO_4 and digestion is fairly prolonged.

Hg is the most effective single catalyst of course. It has practical difficulty encountered in the determination of ammonium from digests containing Hg. When digest containing Hg^{2+} is treated with alkali, some of the ammonium in the digest reacts with the mercuric oxide precipitated by the alkali to form a mercury ammonium complex and ammonium in this complex is not readily liberated by distillation with alkali.

To avoid this low determination, it is necessary to add sodium sulphide or sodium trio sulphate to precipitate HgS as HgS or Zn dust to reduce the Hg to metallic mercury.

2. Temperature

- Temperature should be 360-410°C.
- Below 360°C release of N is slow or incomplete.
- High than 410°C. Some loss of NH_3 from mixture and acid may volatile.

Temperature is controlled by amount of catalyst (K_2SO_4 or Na_2SO_4). Optimum K_2SO_4 is 0.7 to 0.8 gm/ml of H_2SO_4 High concentration have some defect like (*i*) Solidity on cooling (*ii*) considerable forting.

3. Time

An hour of digestion may be necessary after the digest turn (clear) to release of all the nitrogen.

Determination of NH_4^+ (ammonium)—Distillation

The NH_4 evolved in digestion is estimated by distillation of the digest with strong alkali. In distillation, NH_3 liberated is collected in an accurately measured amount of standard mineral acid (usually H_2SO_4) and determined by titration of the excess acid with std. alkali (usually NaOH) using appropriate indicator.

This method gives excellent result. Winkler (1913) modified this method in which the NH_3 is distilled into H_3BO_3 and titrated with standard H_2SO_4.

Kjeldahl method—Three type

(*i*) Macro Kjeldahl method
(*ii*) Semi micro Kjedahl method
(*iii*) Micro Kjeldahl method.

When a limited amount of sample is available for analysis. In this method, sample should be finely ground to control sampling error.

Modification of the Kjeldahl method to include soil NO_3 and NO_2 analysis

(*i*) The alicylic acid modification : Object is to reduce
(*ii*) The alkali reduction modification : NO_3 and NO_2 in to NH_4
(*iii*) The permanganate reduced iron modification

Available nitrogen

In soil, 97 to 99% of the N is present in very complex organic compounds that are not available to plants (through macrobial decompositiaion of organic matter and conversion into available inorganic form).

The problem of developing test for available soil N is further complicated by the fact that

(*i*) The rate at which macro organisms decompose soil organic matter is dependent on temperature, moisture, duration, type of organic matter, pH and some other factors.
(*ii*) The main form of available N, nitrate nitrogen (NO_3–N), is subject to leaching, denitrification and immobilization by micro organisms.

Nitrogen availability index tests

Nitrogen availability indexes are a measure of the potential of a soil to supply N to plants.

A. Biological test or indexes. Biological indexes for N availability are considered most reliable because living organisms are used. The most disadvantages is longer time is needed.

B. Chemical method. This method is attractive, more rapid and convenient and generally more precise. Alkaline permangent method (Richard *et al.*, 1960) is used.

The test consists of measuring the amount of ammonia (NH_3) liberated when a soil sample is boiled in a solution containing pot. permanganate ($KMnO_4$) and sodium carbonate (Na_2CO_3).

In order to include nitrate N which forms 14-40% of available N in the soil test add 1.5 g Deverda's alloy to the distillation flash in addition to alkaline permanganate. The modification include distillation as in standard method until 50 ml distillate is collected, then addition of Deverda's alloy followed by further distillation until another 25 ml is collected. Two stage distillation was recommended because the action of Deverda's alloy appeared to interfere with oxidation of organic N by alkaline $KMnO_4$.

Two measure, which have received considerable attention to assess available N (soil) profit nitrate level and mineral N (NH_4-N) released under anaerobic condition.

Following are some suggestions to be kept in mind while determining available N

Prepare 2.5% NaOH solution fresh as NaOH absorb CO_2 and the strength of alkali comes down. Avoid blockade of mouth of the reagent bottle by using rubber stopper in place of glass stopper.

- Check leakages in the distillation unit before use.
- Steam the apparatus with distilled water before use.
- In the original method, it is recommended to collect 30 ml distillate in 30 minutes.
- It is preferable to specify the time and amount of distillate collected as the amount of estimated would increase with time.

The Estimation of Available Phosphorus in Soil

The available phosphorus in a soil represents a fraction of the total phosphorus which is susceptible to absorb by plant during its growth.

Phosphorus exists in soil mainly in two forms.

(*i*) **Organic fraction :** Low quantity due to low o.m. content in soil.

(*ii*) **Inorganic fraction :** This fraction is in a dynamic equilibrium with water soluble P.

As general phosphorus present in soil as

(*i*) Water soluble P (*ii*) Ca-P

(*iii*) Al-P (*iv*) Fe-P

(*v*) Reductant soluble-P (coated with Fe oxide)

(*vi*) Organic-P

Plants take up phosphorus as soluble form (H_2PO_4, HPO_4) but the water soluble phosphorus at any time is very small, unavailable forms of phosphorus is converted in water soluble form during crop growth. For the movement of phosphorus from soil solid solution plant, three parameters are important.

(*i*) Intensity factor. Concentration of P in soil solution at a time. Most directly measured and simply reflected immediate available to plant. Extracted with water or very dilute acid.

(*ii*) Capacity factor (Buffering characteristics). Reflect the ability of a soil to maintain the concentration by buffering against the withdrawal of phosphorus from solution by plant roots.

(*iii*) Kinetics (Rate). Rate of release. For estimation of availability of phosphorus to plants, capacity factor is important.

Generally, estimation is classified in two steps

(*i*) Extraction

(*ii*) Determination.

1. Extraction

A number of extraction have been proposed for measuring available P content in soil that could be correlated with field response of crops. The degree of correlation values according to the nature of soil. Extractant, which are used for P determination, are categorized as under:

(1) Water or other dilute salts or acids.

(*a*) Carbonated water H_2CO_3

(2) Solution of neutral salts ($CaCl_2$ or KCl (Mettison)

(3) Solution of strong mineral acid.

(*a*) 25% HCl

(*b*) 0.2 N H_2SO_4

(4) Weak organic acid.

(*a*) 1% citric acid (Dyer's-1894).

(*b*) 2.5 % Acetic acid (Williams-1943).

(5) Mixture of different chemicals.

(*a*) 0.03 N NH_4 F + 0.025 N HCl-Bray & Kurtz-I.

(*b*) 0.03 N NH_4 + 0.1 N HCl-Bray & Kurtz-II.

(6) Buffered solution of acid.

(*a*) Sodium acetate and acetic acid pH 4-8 (Morgen 1950)

(*b*) 0.02 N H_2SO_4 pH 3.00 (Troug-1930)

(7) Buffered solution of base.

0.5 M $NaHCO_3$ pH 8.5 (Olsen *et al.*, 1954).

As a general, term extractable phosphorus will be more prepared to available P because, the available, means, certain quantity of P present in a soil that can be absorbed by plants. This is not the case, because the quantity of P utilized by plants growing on a soil may be more or less than that of the extractable phosphorus.

Soil testing procedures can provide an accurate relative index of the quantity of P that plants may utilize from a soil, but rarely can they provide an absolute measure of it. That is why we should speak of extractable rather than available P.

Methods for Phosphorus determination:

In past, less sensitive and more laborious precipitation, gravimetric and titrimetric methods have long been employed. Now, after development of sensitive colorimetric method, the Olson's method has been extensively adopted.

Four Olson's modifications are as under

1. Chlorostannous reduced molybdo phosphoric blue colour method in a sulphuric acid system.
2. Chlorstannous reduced molybdo phosphoric blue colour method, in a hydro chloric acid system.
3. Molybdenum reduced molybdophosphoric blue colour method, in a sulphuric acid system.
4. 1-2-4 ananonaphtosulphonic reduced molybdo phosphoric blue colour method, in a perchloric or sulphuric acid system, and this also include method v_1 unreduced vanadomolybdo phosphoric yellow colour method in nitric acid system.

Each of above methods offers its respective advantages like.

(*i*) Sensitivity

(*ii*) Tolerance to various levels of interfering sub (element)
(*iii*) Speed
(*iv*) Stability of colour.

Choice of method

Sensitivity and freedom from interfering ions are the most important factors for the choice of method.

Method : Suitability

1. Greatest sensitivity, most satisfactory for P extract from in fertile soil.
2. Suitable for systems high in chloride (2000 ppm).
3. Relative sensitive, eliminates the effect of arsenic.
4. Less sensitive, eliminates the effect of arsenate and Fe^{+3}/colour stability, Freedom from the reduction step.
   - Greater freedom from interfering ions and contamination from glass ware.
   - Adaptability to HNO_3, HCl, H_2SO_4, $HClO_4$ system.

Optimum concentration of reagents

The optimum concentration of acid, molybdate and reluctant is that which will give the maximum of colour per unit of P present and the minimum of fading.

The rang of acidity over which the colour is not affected by the acid concentration may be termed the Acid stability plateau.

This plateau narrow as the P concentration increase and widens as it decrease.

Colorimetric estimation of phosphorus by ascorbic acid method

When $SnCl_2$ is used as reducing agent, blue colour is stable for 15-20 minutes and measurement should be done within these times. Instead of $SnCl_2$, ascorbic acid has become favourable as reducing agent owing to the fact that the blue colour of the reduced complex is stable for a long time, enabling reduced solution to be kept overnight if necessary before measurement.

This method is based on reduction of the ammonium molybdophosphate complex by ascorbic acid in the presence of antimony.

DETERMINATION OF SOIL pH

Principle

pH meter works on the principle as mentioned in Nerst equation.

It consists of two electrodes :

(*i*) Glass electrode or indicator electrode and
(*ii*) Calomel electrode or reference electrode.

When the two electrodes are dipped into aqueous solution under test, the potential is develops in the solution. The difference in potential between both the electrodes is measured by pH meter.

Apparatus

- Glass electrode
- pH meter
- 50 ml beaker
- volumetric cylinder and glass rod

Preparation of buffer solution (pH 7.0, 9.2, 4.0)

The buffer tablets of standard pH are available. Particular tablet is to be dissolved in freshly double distilled water and made upto 100 ml. It is necessary to prepare a fresh buffer after every few days as the solution do not keep for long. It should be stored in polythelene or pyrex glass container.

Procedure

Take 10 g soil in 50 ml beakers. Add 20 ml of distilled water and stir intermittently with glass rod for 30 minutes.

Determine pH of the soil suspension with the pH meter as per directions with the instrument. Stir the suspension in each beaker with a glass rod again just before taking the pH reading. Wash the electrodes with distilled water after each determination.

Express pH to the nearest tenth of pH unit.

Precautions in the Use of Glass Electrodes

The glass electrode if fragile and subject to excessively rapid deteriorated if not properly care for.

(*i*) The electrode is not allowed to remain in the test saturation or suspension longer than necessary, especially if pH is more alkaline (more than 9.0).

(*ii*) Immediately after testing, the electrode should be washed off with a strong stream of distilled water from a wash bottle. If the system was alkaline the electrode should be dipped for a few seconds in the dilute HCl solution to remove the film of $CaCO_3$ that sometimes forms.

(*iii*) For storage, after cleaning the electrode should be suspended in distilled water and the system is protected from evaporation. Drying out of the electrode should be avoided.

(*iv*) Failure of the glass electrode pH meter is indicated when after standardization it gives slow response to larger pH change. At this condition the glass electrode is immersed in an alkaline buffer then in the original acid standard buffer.

Classification

pH	*Category*
6.6-7.3	Neutral
7.4-7.8	Mildly alkaline
7.9-8.4	Moderately alkaline
8.5-9.0	Strongly alkaline
> 9.0	Very strongly alkaline

Readings:

Sl. No.	pH of saturation extract	pH of 1 : 2 soil : water suspension	pH of 1 : 2.5 soil : water suspension
1	8.3	8.2	8.3
2	9.1	9.0	9.1
3	8.8	8.8	8.8
4	8.6	8.6	8.6

DETERMINATION OF ELECTRICAL CONDUCTIVITY OF SOIL

Principle

The solution offers some resistance to the passage of electrical current through them depending upon the concentration and the type of ions present. Higher the salt content, lesser the resistance to the flow of current. The resistance (R) is defined by Ohm's law as the ratio of electrical potential in volts (E) and strength of current in ampere (I).

$$E/I = \frac{\text{Volts}}{\text{Current}} = R \text{ in Ohm}$$

Electrical conductivity or conductance is the reverse of resistance.

$C = 1/R = 1/\text{Ohm} = \text{Ohm}^{-1}$ = mho (reverse of Ohm)

Apparatus

- Conductivity meter and a conductivity cell with known cell constant,
- Beaker 50 ml,
- Volumetric cylinder,
- Glass rod, etc.

Reagents

(1) Saturated solution of calcium sulphate (reagent quality)

(2) 0.01 N KCl solution : Dissolve 0.7456 g of potassium chloride in distilled water and dilute to 1 litre.

Procedure

(1) Calibrate instrument at 0 and 100 or as per directions supplied with the instrument.

(2) Check the instrument with the saturated calcium sulphate (EC = 2.2 mhos/cm) or 0.01 N KCl solution (EC = 1.41 dSm^{-1}) before proceeding with the samples.

(3) The same soil suspension prepared for determination of pH is also used for salinity determination, after recording the soil pH. Allow the soil suspension in the beaker to settle (or take 10 g soil in 50 ml beaker and add 20 ml of distilled water and stir with glass rod intermittently for 30 minutes). Pour the supernatant liquid into the conductivity tube after rinsing it with the same supernatant solution.

(4) Dip the conductivity cell and read on direct conductivity meter.

(5) Express conductivity in dSm^{-1} (mmhos/cm) at 25°C to the nearest first decimal.

Classification

EC (dSm^{-1})	*Nature of soil*
< 0.8	Normal
0.8 – 1.6	Critical for salt sensitive crops
1.6 – 2.5	Critical for salt tolerant crops
> 2.5	Injurious to all crops

Readings

Sample No.	1 : 2 volume ratio	EC (mmhos/cm) 1 : 2.5 weight ratio	Saturation extract
1	3.40	2.20	1.2
2	0.60	0.50	1.4
3	1.30	1.10	4.0
4	0.55	0.36	1.0

GYPSUM REQUIREMENT OF ALKALI SOIL (Schoonover method)

Principle

Reclamation of Na-affected soil usually involves replacement of exchangeable Na with Ca. This Ca may originally from the saturation of Ca containing mineral in the soil. Such amendment is gypsum and $CaCl_2$.

Reclamation of sodic soil or alkali soil of which pH in water suspension 8.5 require removal of part of the most of exchangeable Na and its replacement by Ca. The required amount of soluble Ca can be added by using amendment like gypsum which containing about 70 to 80 % $CaSO_4$. The amount of gypsum requires to replace Na ion from exchange complex is called gypsum requirement.

Na [Exchange complex] + $CaSO_4$ → Ca [Exchange complex] + Na_2SO_4/ leached

Na_2SO_4 is leached out by flooding. GR determine by adding known excess of saturated gypsum solution to the soil and estimating its unread amount by EDTA or versenate titration.

Apparatus

- Mechanical shaker
- 50 ml beaker
- 100 ml pipette

Reagents

1. **Saturated gypsum solution :** Shake 5 g $CaSO_4$ with 1 litre of distilled water for 10 minutes on mechanical shaker and filtered (28 to 30 me Ca/l).
2. **Buffer solution for 10 pH :** Dissolve 67.5 g NH_4Cl in 570 ml NH_4OH and dilute to 1 litre.
3. **Erichrome Black-T (EBT) :** Dissolve 0.5 g EBT and 4.5 g hydroxylamine hydrochloride in 100 ml of 95% ethanol.

4. **Standard $CaCl_2$ solution 0.01 N :** Dissolve 0.5 g pure $CaCO_3$ in 10 ml of 3 N HCl and dilute to 1 litre.
5. **EDTA solution 0.01 N :** Dissolve 2 g EDTA and 0.05 g $MgCl_2$ in 900 ml water and standardize with 0.01 N $CaCl_2$ solution.

Procedure

Take 5 g air dried soil into 250 ml conical flask and add 100 ml saturated gypsum solution with volumetric pipette.

Shake for 5 minutes on mechanical shaker or 30 minutes on rotary shaker and filter it. Pipette out 5 ml of soil extract into 100 ml conical flask and dilute to 25 ml distilled water. Add 0.5 ml buffer solution, 3-4 drops of EBT indicator and titrate with 0.01 N standard EDTA solution until the colour change from wine red to blue.

Titrate similarly 5 ml of saturated gypsum solution.

In the modified method of GR, Abrol *et al*. (1975) suggested washing with alcohol before adding gypsum saturation solution. Remaining procedure is same.

Observations and Calculation:

Sample No.	GR as per Schoonover method		GR as per modified Schoonover method	
	Reading	Difference	Reading	Difference
Blank	14.65	—	14.65	—
1	14.05	0.60	13.60	1.05
2	14.00	0.65	13.70	0.95
3	11.65	3.00	11.45	3.20
4	14.30	0.35	14.35	0.30

1N 1 litre EDTA = 86 g $CaSO_4.2H_2O$ (gypsum)

0.01N 1 ml EDTA = 0.01 me = 0.86 mg gypsum

% GR = Difference × (0.86/1000) × (100/5) × (100/5)

ppm GR = Difference × (0.86/1000) × (100/5) × (100/5) × 10,000

kg/ha GR = Difference × (0.86/1000) × (100/5) × (100/5) × 10,000 × 2.24

t/ha GR = Difference × 7.7

GR meq/100 g = (Ca conc. of added gypsum solution in meq/l – Ca + Mg conc. of filtrate in meq/l) × 2

DETERMINATION OF CO_3^{2-}, HCO_3^- AND Cl^-

(1) Carbonate and Bicarbonate Ions

Principle

The estimation is based on simple acidimetric titration using different indicators. The CO_3^{2-} and HCO_3^- ions in water sample can be determined by titrating the water sample against standard H_2SO_4 using phenophthalin and methyl orange indicators, respectively.

First titration indicates half of the neutralization of carbonate, colour change from pink to colourless (indicator : phenophthalin). Half CO_3^{2-} is converted into HCO_3^-.

At this stage, methyl orange indicator is added which give yellow colour and the titration is continued, when colour change from yellow to pinkish red (orange), it indicates the end point for the complete neutralization of half carbonate (converted to HCO_3^-) and whole of HCO_3^- ions.

Chemical Reaction

First titration in the presence of phenophthalin :

$$2Na_2CO_3 + H_2SO_4 \leftrightarrow 2NaHCO_3 + Na_2SO_4$$

Half of carbonate is neutralized and half is converted into HCO_3^-.

Second titration in the presence of methyl orange; bicarbonate obtained by conversion of carbonate and also originally present in the solution are total neutralized.

$$2NaHCO_3 + H_2SO_4 \leftrightarrow Na_2SO_4 + 2H_2O + 2CO_2$$

The above equations shows that the amount of acid required to convert data and carbonate to $H_2O + CO_2$ are equal. Hence, double the titrate volume in the presence of phenophthalin will be total amount of acid required for neutralizing total carbonates, likewise titrate value in the presence of methyl orange minus value in the presence of phenophthalin will give total bicarbonates (actually).

Reagents

1. 0.1 N H_2SO_4. Dissolve 2.85 ml concentrated H_2SO_4 in distilled water and make volume to 1 litre.
2. Phenophthalin (indicator). Dissolve 0.5 g phenophthalin powder in 100 ml ethanol.
3. Methyl orange (indicator). Dissolve 100 mg methyl orange powder in 100 ml distilled water.

Apparatus

- 50 ml burette
- 25 ml conical flask
- 250 ml wash bottle
- 25 ml pipette
- 150 ml beakers
- Indicator bottle, etc.

Procedure

The entire technique of titration is divided into two steps :

1st Step

1. Take accurately 25 ml of the irrigation water into a clean conical flask by the pipette and add 2-3 drops of phenophthalin indicator which would give the pink colour solution.
2. Titrate it with 0.1 N standard H_2SO_4 solution drop by drop (finally at 5 second interval) until the pink colour solution is converted into colourless and note down the burette reading (**X**).

2nd Step

1. Add 2-3 drops of methyl orange in the same conical flask which would give the yellow colour solution.
2. Titrate it again with the same standard H_2SO_4 solution drop by drop until the yellow colour solution is converted into pinkish (rose) red colour. Note down the burette reading (**Y**).

(2) Chloride Ion

Principle

Chlorides in the irrigation water can be determined by titration with standard solution of $AgNO_3$ using K_2CrO_4 as an indicator.

Initially chloride is precipitated as silver chloride as white precipitation after complete neutralization of Cl, Ag would be reacted with CrO_4 ions and chocolate red colour precipitates of Ag_2CrO_4 are formed which indicates end point.

Chemical Reaction

$$2NaCl + AgNO_3 \leftrightarrow \underset{\text{white precipitation}}{AgCl_2 + 2NaNO_3}$$

$$2AgNO_3 + K_2CrO_4 \leftrightarrow \underset{\text{chocolate red precipitation}}{Ag_2CrO_4 + 2KNO_3}$$

Note. Silver chromate is not precipitates along with the silver chloride due to following reasons :

1. The concentration of chromate ions is extremely low as compared to chloride ions. Hence, precipitations of AgCl occur first.
2. The solubility products of AgCl and Ag_2CrO_4 salts indicate that AgCl is less soluble.

$$AgCl = 1.2 \times 10^{-10}, Ag_2CrO_4 = 1.7 \times 10^{-12}.$$

The concentration of Ag^+ ions increase Cl^- ions decreases with the progress of the titration and at critical concentration of Ag^+ (3×10^{-5} moles) all the Cl^- is completely precipitated as AgCl, further addition of a fraction of a drop of the $AgNO_3$ increases the concentration of Ag^+ ions beyond the critical point giving a red precipitation of Ag_2CrO_4 showing end point.

Potassium chromate can't be used in alkaline solution because of AgOH is likely to be precipitated which is again converted into silver oxide.

$$AgNO_3 + KOH \rightarrow AgOH + KNO_3$$

So that aliquot of CO_3^{2-}, HCO_3^- is used because it have neutralized or when fresh aliquot taken, it should be made acidic.

Apparatus

- 50 ml burette
- 25 ml pipette
- 150 ml conical flask
- beakers, indicator bottle, etc.

Reagents

1. 0.1 N $AgNO_3$. Dissolve 17 g $AgNO_3$ in distilled water and make 1 litre volume. Standardize it with 0.1 N NaCl solution. Dilute it at 10 times to 0.01 N $AgNO_3$.
2. Potassium chromate (K_2CrO_4) 5%. Dissolve 5 g of K_2CrO_4 in approximately 75 ml of bottle add 1 N or saturated solution of $AgNO_3$ until the slight permanent red precipitate is produced in let the solution settle in the dark for 24 hours. Then filter it to remove the Ag_2CrO_4 and make to 100 ml.

Procedure

1. Take the sample preserved from the carbonate, bicarbonate determination add 8-10 drops of K_2CrO_4 as an indicator, which will give the yellow colour solution.
2. Titrate it with 0.01 N standard $AgNO_3$ solution drop wise until the yellow colour solution is converted into chocolate red colour. Note down the burette reading.

Observations and Calculation

(A) For CO_3^{2-} and HCO_3^-

Sr. No.	Aliquot taken by pipette	0.1 N H_2SO_4 in Burette							
		CO_3^{2-} (phenophthalin)				HCO_3^- (methyl orange)			
		I	F	D	M	I	F	D	M
1	25	00	6.3	6.3		6.3	18.6	12.3	
2	25	18.6	25.6	6.0	6.2	25.6	37.4	11.8	12.3
3	25	37.4	43.8	6.4		00	12.6	12.6	

Color change

Phenophthalin : CO_3^{2-} : Pink to colourless

Methyl orange: HCO_3^- : Yellow to orange

(B) For Cl^-

Sr. No.	Aliquot taken	0.01 N $AgNO_3$ in Burette			
		I	F	D	M
1	25	0.0	11.2	11.2	
2	25	0.0	11.0	11.0	11.0
3	25	0.0	10.8	10.8	

Where, I = Initial, F = Final, D = Difference, M = Mean

Calculation

1. Volume of acid used to neutralize CO_3^{2-} present in solution (aliquot) = 2**X** ml

   = **Y** – **X** ml
2. Volume of $AgNO_3$ used to neutralize total Cl^- present in solution (aliquot) = **X** ml

For CO_3^{2-} = me/l = (2**X** × N × 1000)/aliquot (ml)
For HCO_3^- = me/l = [(**Y**–**X**) × N × 1000]/aliquot (ml)
For Cl^- = me/l = (**X** × N × 1000)/ aliquot (ml)

DETERMINATION OF Ca AND Mg IONS (Versenate EDTA method)

Principle

The method is based on the fact that Ca^{++}, Mg^{++} and number of other ions from suitable complexes with a versenate at different pH. The Sn, Fe, Zn and Mn interfere in the determination of Ca^{++} and Mg^{++} present in appreciable amounts. Their interference is checked by the use of 2% NaCN or KCN solution or carbonate crystals.

Ca^{++}

A known volume of solution is titrated with 0.01 N EDTA solution using ammonium perpurate (murexide) indicator in the presence of NaOH solution. The end point is the change of colour from orange red to purple at pH 12.0 when the whole of calcium forms a complex with EDTA.

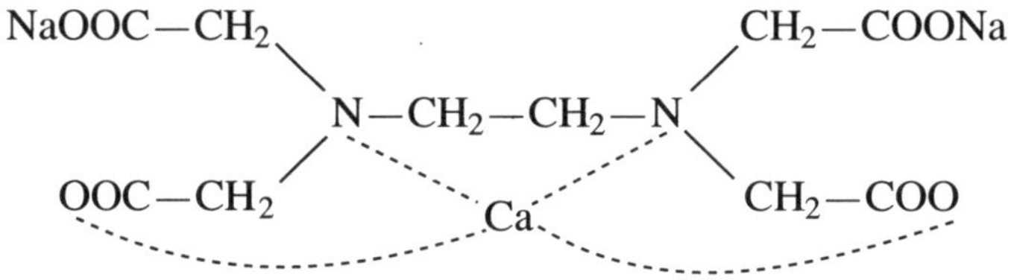

Apparatus

- 50 ml burette
- 150 ml conical flask
- 150 ml beakers

Reagents

1. Standard 0.01 N calcium solution. Take accurately 0.5 g pure AR grade $CaCO_3$ and dissolve in a minimum volume of 0.2 N HCl. Boil to expel CO_2 and then make volume to 1 litre with distilled water.
2. EDTA solution 0.01 N. Take 2 g EDTA and 0.025 g $MgCl_2$ and dissolve it in water and make the final volume of 1 litre.

   Titrate it with 0.01 N calcium solution as per procedure given below and make necessary dilution so that its normality may be exactly equal to 0.01 N.

   Keep in polythene container or in glass because titration may be change.
3. Murexide indicator powder. Take 0.2 g ammonium perpurate and mix it with 40 g powdered potassium sulphate (K_2SO_4).

   This indicator is not stored in the form of solution as it gets oxidized.
4. NaOH 4 N or 16%. Take 160 g pure NaOH and dissolve it in distilled water and make volume 1 litre.

Procedure

1. Take a suitable aliquot 5 to 25 ml which containing not more than 0.1 meq of Ca^{++} into porcelain dish (8 cm diameter). Dilute to a volume of approximately 25 ml.
2. Add 5 ml of 16% NaOH and 0.1 g murexide powder which will give the orange red colour solution.
3. Titrate it with 0.01 N standard solution of EDTA drop wise until the orange red colour is converted into reddish violet (purple).

It is advised to add a drop of EDTA at every 5 or 10 seconds as the change of colour is not instaneous. End point of blank is very distinguished so that end point must be compared with a blank reading. If solution is over titrated, it should be back titrated with standard calcium solution and exact volume used is thus found. Note down the burette reading and calculate the strength of Ca^{++} from a given solution.

Note. Any metal whose versenate complex is less dissociated than that of Ca (whose equilibrium constant is high) will be preferentially complexed before a Ca and thus it will be included in the Ca titration.

Interfering ions are Hg, Sn, Co, Zn, Fe, Mn. If Mn is present more than 0.5 mg it makes the end point less distilled. The Mn can be removed as :

(1) Carbonate

(2) MnO_2 by the addition of Na_2S to the solution and filter prior to titration

(3) MnO_2 by $KMnO_4$

The murexide indicator is best as the powder since it is extremely susceptible to oxidation when as a titration.

Destruction of NH_4^+ Salt

1. To facilitate the rising of solution pH upto 12.
2. The sharpness of the end point is greatly reduced by large concentration of salts which may be avoided.

Murexide ammonium perpurate forms an orange red complex with Ca at pH 12.0 which is converted to a red violet when the Ca ions are completely complexed by versenate.

Ca^{++} + Mg^{++} (Versenate method)

Principle

Mg solution can be treated with 0.01 N EDTA solution using Erichrome Black-T as indicator at pH 10.0 in the presence of ammonium chloride and ammonium hydroxide buffer.

The end point is the change of colour from wine red to blue or green. If Ca is also present this titration will estimate Ca and Mg beyond pH 10 is not bound strongly Erichrome black-T to give a distinct end point.

Reagents

(*i*) EDTA solution 0.01 N.

(*ii*) Ammonium chloride-Ammonium hydroxide buffer : Dissolve 67.5 g ammonium chloride in 570 ml of concentrated ammonia and make volume 1 litre.

(*iii*) Sodium hydroxide 4 N : Prepare 16% soda solution by dissolving 160 g pure NaOH in water and make volume to 1 litre.

(*iv*) Erichrome Black-T indicator (EBT) : Dissolve 0.5 g Erichrome black-T and 4.5 g hydroxylamine hydrochloride in 100 ml of 95% ethanol. Hydroxylamine hydrochloride removes the interference of manganese.

(*v*) KCN 1% or NaCN 2% solution or sodium diethyl diethio carbamate crystal : This is used to remove the interference of Cu, Co and Ni.

Procedure

1. Pipette out 10 ml (5 to 25 ml) aliquot containing not more than 0.1 meq of Ca + Mg of solution into 150 ml Erlenmeyer flask.
2. Dilute to a volume of approximately 25 ml.
3. Add 2-3 carbamate crystals and add 3 drops of EBT indicator and 5 ml (10 drops) of NH_4Cl-NH_4OH buffer.
4. Titrate it against 0.01 N EDTA solution. The end point will be clear by the change of colour from wine red to blue or bluish green.

   At the end point, number of the red colour should be removed.

Note. The Erichrome black-T dye gives a wine red colour complex with Mg but change to blue green when all the Mg ions have been removed by the versenate. The formation of Mg complex is optimum at pH 10 in the presence of NH_4Cl and NH_4OH.

The Ca is complexed by versenate before the Mg and therefore the titration value gives total Ca + Mg.

Ions which would interfere Co, Cu, Ni which formed complex with the indicator (not decomposed by the versenate titration) which precipitates the dye and if the latter is added before the solution is made alkaline and observe the end point if presence in large amounts.

Mn which is present as MnO_2 cause flooding of the dye and an indistinct end point.

Precaution

Removal of interfering ions Cu, Co, Ni complexed by NaCN. Fe, Mn, Cu removed by the carbamate.

The hydroxylamine keeps any traces of Mn in divalent form means inhibit oxidation of Mn.

Calculation

Ca^{++} :

$$\text{Ca meq/l} = \frac{\text{ml of versenate solution used} \times \text{Normality (EDTA)} \times 1000}{\text{ml of aliquot taken}}$$

$$= N \times R \times 1000/\text{Aliquot}$$

$$= 0.02 \times R \times 1000/10$$

$$= R \times 2$$

$$\text{Ca meq/100 g} = N \times R \times (250/100) \times (100/10)$$
$$= 0.02 \times R \times 250/100 \times 100/10$$
$$= R \times 0.5$$

$Ca^{++} + Mg^{++}$:

$$\text{Ca+Mg meq/l} = \frac{\text{ml of versenate solution used} \times \text{Normality (EDTA)} \times 1000}{\text{ml of aliquot taken}}$$
$$= N \times R \times 1000/\text{Aliquot}$$
$$= 0.02 \times R \times 1000/10$$
$$= R \times 2$$
$$\text{Ca+Mg} = N \times R \times (250/100) \times (100/10)$$
$$\text{meq/100 g} = 0.02 \times R \times 250/100 \times 100/10$$
$$= R \times 0.5$$
$$\text{Mg meq/l} = (\text{Ca + Mg meq/l})\text{-Ca meq/l}$$
$$= (\text{Ca + Mg meq/100 g})\text{-Ca meq/100 g}$$

DETERMINATION OF CALCIUM CARBONATE

Principle

A measure amount of standard HCl is added into soil. This acid is utilized for the neutralization of lime. The excess of acid is titrated with standard alkali (NaOH). The amount of acid utilized for the neutralizing the lime (calcium carbonate) is equivalent to the content of lime in the soil.

Apparatus

- 150 ml beaker
- Watch glass
- 25 ml pipette
- 50 ml pipette
- Hot plate or burner
- Indicator bottle, etc.

Reagents

A. HCl 1 N standardized

B. NaOH 0.5 N standardized

C. Phenolphthalin 1% in 60% ethanol

Procedure

One g of sample of dry and ground soil (0.26 mm) is weighed out into 500 ml conical flask. The 25 ml standard 1 N HCl is added. The suspension is swirled to mix thoroughly and then heated nearly to boiling and held on a steam bath for 5 minutes (upto 15 minutes if necessary to complete the reaction). Finally, 100 ml of water is added and the solution is boiled for exactly 1 minute over a small burner and then cooled to room temperature.

Blank titration

Five drops of 1% phenophthalin indicator solution is added and solution is then back titrated with standard 0.5 N NaOH to a pink colour, which persists for 15 seconds as the solution is shaken. This solution is saved if Ca or Mg is to be determined for the proportionally between $CaCO_3$ and $MgCO_3$.

Observations and calculation

- Weight of soil taken = 1 g
- Volume of standard HCl added = 25 ml
- Volume of standard alkali utilized in back titration = **X** ml
- Volume of standard alkali utilized in blank titration = **Y** ml

$$\% \ CaCO_3 = \text{Blank reading - Actual reading} \times 5$$

$$= \frac{(Y - X) \times N \times \text{Molecular weight of } CaCO_3}{2000} \times \frac{100}{S}$$

$$= \frac{(Y - X) \times 0.5 \times 100 \times 100}{2000 \times 1}$$

$$= (Y - X) \times 2.5$$

where, Y = Volume of HCl initially added (blank titration)

X = ml of NaOH utilized in back titration

N = Normality of NaOH

S = Sample weight in g

ESTIMATION OF EXCHANGEABLE CATIONS

(A) Exchangeable Ca and Mg

Exchangeable Ca and Mg are normally determined in ammonium acetate extracts of soils by direct titration with EDTA. The presence of ammonium acetate does not interfere with the titration if this is carried out by the procedure suggested by Hesse (1971). The amount of organic matter dissolved is usually too small to affect the colour change of the indicator.

Reagents

1. Ammonium acetate (NH_4OAC) 1N pH 7.0. To 700 ml distilled water add 57 ml 99.5% glacial acetic acid (CH_3COOH) and then 69 ml of concentrated ammonium hydroxide (NH_4OH). Dilute to a volume of 900 ml and adjust pH to 7.0 by addition of more of 3 N NH_4OH or 3 N CH_3COOH and make up to 1 litre. Store in pyrex or polypropylene bottle.

or

Dissolve 154 g ammonium acetate in water and dilute to 1.8 litres. Mix thoroughly. Adjust pH to 7.0 with dilute NH_4OH or NaOAC as required and make to 2 litres.

2. Other reagents as per estimation of Ca and Mg from saturation extract (water soluble Ca and Mg).

Procedure

(I) Determination of Ca and Mg in the NH_4OAc Extract

1. Place 5 g soil in a 150 ml Erlenmeyer flask (conical flask).
2. Pour in 25 ml of neutral normal ammonium acetate (pH 7.0).

3. Shake on a reciprocating shaker (180 + oscillations/min) for 5 minutes.
4. And immediately filter through Whatman No. 1 filter paper.
5. First few ml of the filtrate may be rejected.

For Ca

1. Pipette an aliquot of the extract containing upto 3 mg Ca into 150 ml tall form beaker and dilute to 10 ml (for soils containing less than 10 me Ca/100 g or solution containing less than 1 mg Ca/10 ml, it is necessary to take larger aliquots in a 250 ml beaker).
2. Add 10 drops each of potassium cyanide, hydroxylamine-hydrochloride and triethanolamine solution.
3. Add 2.5 ml NaOH solution and 1 ml of calcon solution or 0.1 g murexide powder which will gave the orange red colour solution.
4. Titrate with 0.01 N standard EDTA solutions drop by drop until the orange red colour is converted into violet or blue colour.

For Ca + Mg

1. Pipette an aliquot containing upto about 3 mg (Ca + Mg) into a beaker. Dilute to 10 ml.
2. Add 1.5 ml of buffer solution.
3. Then 10 drops each of potassium cyanide, hydroxylamine hydrochloride, potassium hexacyanoferrate (II) and triethanolamine solutions while gently warming the solution on the magnetic stirrer.
4. When all reagents have been added, continue warming for 3 minutes, cool, and
5. Add 10 drops of EBT solution.
6. Titrate with EDTA.

Comments and Suggestions on Ca and Mg

1. Ammonium acetate method is suitable for nearly neutral and non-calcareous soils.
2. Since Ca and Mg carbonates dissolve to a large extent in ammonium acetate at pH 7.0, the contents of these cations are over estimated in calcareous soils.
3. Exchangeable Ca and Mg in saline and calcareous soils can be estimated by lithium chloride acetate method (Yaalon, 1962; Dewis and Freitas, 1984) with extraction at pH 8.2 but can be used on all types of soils by adjusting pH of the saturated and replacing solutions. The use of pH 8.2 solutions can be restricted to soils having pH values (1:5 w/v in water) of 7.8 and above, while pH 7.0 solutions for soils upto pH 7.5.
4. Neutral salt solutions other than ammonium acetate or dilute/weak acids can also be tried equally well.
5. Exchangeable Ca and Mg determination after extraction on Buechner funnel filtration (Knudsen *et al*., 1982) or leaching columns (Hesse, 1971) is recommended only when simultaneously CEC has also to be estimated.

6. Use atomic absorption spectrophotometer to determine Ca and Mg separately, if the instrument is available.
7. Take extreme care in the handling of potassium cyanide. Discard all solutions containing it immediately after one batch of analysis is over and wash all apparatus thoroughly. Flush the drain thoroughly and don't allow acid to come in contact with the cyanide solution (Dewis and Fruitos, 1984).
8. Add hydroxylamine-hydrochloride to reduce iron and manganese interference in the determination of Ca and Mg. Add excess potassium ferrocyanide to precipitate manganese ferrocyanide. Addition of hydroxylamine hydrochloride, potassium cyanide and potassium ferrocyanide may not always be necessary but it advisable to include them as precautionary measure.
9. Murexide powder can be used in place of calcon. Mix 0.2 g murexide with 40 g dry potassium sulphate and store it in a dark bottle, away from light. However, calcon is preferred to murexide.
10. To obtain reproducible values, one reference as well as one block is included in a block of 50 samples, if the analysis is carried out using atomic absorption spectrophoto- meter.
11. Incase of EDTA titration, it is necessary to employ one block as well as one reference in a batch of 20-25 samples.

The precision of the method is not known but the precision of EDTA titration is ± 3% (Hesse, 1971).

SOIL ANALYSIS FOR AVAILABLE MICRONUTRIENTS

Forms of micro nutrients in soils. Soil tests are based on viet's approach which describes the amount of nutrient in definite chemical form *viz.*

Pool A. Water soluble ions : It is usually small or almost non existant for Cu and Zn and small for Fe and Mn in well aerated soils.

Pool B. Cations exchangeable by a weak electrolyte like NH_4 : It is small for Cu and Zn

Pool C. Adsorbed, chelated or complexed ions exchangeable by other cations possessing high affinities for exchange sites OR extractable with stronger chelating agents. It is extractable with chelating agents like EDTA, DTPA, pyrophosphate, carbon tetra chloride, dithizone and chelating compounds which can extract such complexes.

Pool D. Micro nutrient cations in secondary clay minerals and insoluble metal oxides. It depends upon the content of clay and on the amount of its saturation with micronutrients.

Pool E. Cations held in primary minerals : It is determined by the parent material and other geochecmical considerations.

The micro nutrient anions also occurs in pool *i.e.* chloride, because of its negative adsorption, occurs mostly in pool A, it also occurs in pool E, borates occurs in pool E as primary mineral, tourmaline and also in pool C, probably as cheletes with humus, but mostly it occurs in pool A, in solution. Molybdate occurs in all the pools, they can be replaced by oxalates, phosphate and hydroxions. Thus, the availability of Mo is more in alkaline range than in the acid range.

The first three pools are thought to be important in supplying micro nutrients for the plant during a growing season, the available micronutrients, therefore, do not necessarily reflect their total content in soils. The availability of micronutrients in soils is related to their amount in various solid forms which is in equilibrium with that in the soil solution and the rate at which the solution phase is renewed. Soil tests attempt to measure these micronutrient forms which are related to plant availability.

Soil Test Methods for Micro Nutrients

1. Water. An aqueous extract or a saturation extract may represent the potential population of percolating water of course, water does not extract sufficient Cu, Mn, Fe or Mn to represent adequately the labile nutrient available to plant roots.

2. Neutral salts. Reflect readily exchangeable ions extract and used as (*i*) 2 N $MgCl_2$, (*ii*) 0.01 m $CaCl_2$ (*iii*) 0.5 m NH_4 OAC.

3. Weak and strong acids.

(*a*) CO_2 saturated water

(*b*) 0.5 N KCl plus HOAc at pH 3.2

(*c*) 0.1 N HCl

(*d*) 0.05 N HCl + 0.025 N H_2SO_4

(*e*) 0.1 N H_3PO_4

4. Chelating agents. Sometimes, weak solvent or weak acids don't extract enough of the labile solid phase to reflect the soils ability (capacity factor) to replenish nutrients removed by plants from the soil solution. Strong acids, often release to much of the solid phase nutrients. In such cases, chelating agents, if carefully selected, offer one of the promising means of assessing nutrient supplying power of soils especially for micro nutrients cations.

The amount of metal ions that combines the chelating agents is a function of both the activity of the metal ion (intensity factor) and the amount of readily replenishable nutrient (capacity factor). The pH of the extracting media can be carefully selected to avoid many undesirable side reactions.

The chelating agents which are tried.

(*i*) EDTA-0.05 m, 0.02 m—ethylene Diamine Acetic acid

(*ii*) DTPA-0.005 m. Diethyl triamine penta acetic acid.

Remarkable progress has been made in developing soils tests for the micro nutrients cations that measure both the intensity and capacity factor of the soil to supply available nutrients. The chelating agents, EDTA & DTPA, appear most promising as the pH of extraction can be controlled and chemical attack on lime and mineral fractions of the soil minimized. The DTPA soil test appears to give better correlation with uptake of nutrients and fertilizer response in case of four cation micro nutrients (Zn, Fe, Mn, Cu).

Boron

Boron is a non metal compound. It is widely distributed in rocks as allumino silicates such as tourmaline. As a result of weathering a small amount of soluble boron is present in cultivated soil. Plant absorb boron as H_3BO_3.

Extractant method. Hot water (extractant) soluble boron in soils in generally accepted as the best index of availability of boron for plants.

Determination of boron. Quinalizarin, curcumin and carmine methods are available for determination of boron in trace quantities. The first two methods are extremely sensitive but suffer from some limitations. carmine is mostly used.

Measurement of colour. Carmine method Bluish red (violetish blue) colour is measured in colorimeter at 655 mu wave length.

Precautions. Particular attention must be paid to the glassware used. Pyrex and other borosilicate glassware are not satisfactory. Porcelain, silica or signal glassware may be used after cleaning with dilute acid HCl. New glassware is likely to give variable results unless thoroughly weathered in sulphuric acid washed with HCl. Redistilled from all pyrex glass is likely to contain appreciable boron. Distilled (single) water from metal still distillery is satisfactory.

Molybdenum–Mo

In soils, Mo exists in a variety of compounds including primary minerals and reaction products of Molybdate ions with others. Plant may take Mo as MoO_4^{2-}, $HMoO_4$.

The availability of Mo is of interest for two conditions.

(*i*) Deficiency of Mo in soil.

(*ii*) Toxicity to ruminants in soil producing forage. Accurate chemical assessment of the available Mo level of soil is made difficulty by the extremely small amount of the element required for normal crop growth.

Extractant. Variety of extractants have been used to measure available Mo. Tamm's reagent, an acid ammonium oxalate solution of pH 3.3 is widely used.

Mo ion is replaced by oxalate and formed complexed and stabilized in acid medium.

Mo determination. Determination of Mo in soils and plants is based on the thiocyanate orange red (amber) coloured complex, developed through reduction with acetone, ascorbic acid or chloro stannous acid.

This colour is real in a colorimeter with 470 mμ light maxima.

(B) Interpreting the Analytical Results

Analytical results obtained from chemical analyses of soils must be interpreted meaningfully. Therefore, to interpret soil test values, proper correlations of test values with known field responses for the various crops are required. Based on this information, laboratories commonly group the soils into three classes with respect to an available nutrient.

Low. Strong probability of good response-below the critical level

Medium. Maintenance applications desirable-near or slightly above the critical level.

High. Low probability of good response-above the critical level;

Soil critical value refers to that soil test value of available nutrients in soil below which crop response is expected to added fertilizer of the nutrient and above which it is not expected.

The exact soil test values included in each class will vary somewhat from soil to soil and with the anticipated level of production. This information should also be taken into consideration while making a fertilizer recommendation for a given situation.

(C) Fertilizer Recommendation

Fertilizer recommendation for efficient and economic crop production is based on soil testing as one of the essential factors. In Table 31.1 are listed doses of NPK based on soil test values. The ratings seems rather arbitrary and empirical, but are meant to get a reasonable yield. The most pertinent question is the economic return-profitability of fertilizer application. Outputs for different doses of fertilizers are obtained from the response curve. On the basis of costs of inputs and outputs, the following information may be derived:

(1) maximum yield;
(2) maximum profit per hectare;
(3) maximum rate of return per rupee of investment; and
(4) minimum profitable application.

A farmer can make his choice accordingly. Fertilizer recommendation is valid to the extent the soil sample collected for testing represents the soil of the area of operation. In case of doubt or wide soil heterogeneity, a large number of soil samples should be tested.

TABLE 31.1. Rating for classification of soil test values

S. No.	Available Nutrient	Rating			Method Followed
		Low	Medium	High	
1.	Available N (Kg/ha)	Below <250	250-500	Above >500	Alkaline $KMnO_4$ method
2.	Organic Carbon (%)	Below 0.50	0.50-0.75	Above 0.75	Walkley and black method
3.	Available phosphorus	Below 28	28-56	56	Olsen's method (Kg P_2O_5/ha)
4.	Available Potassium (Kg K_2O /ha)	Below 140	140-280	Above 280	Neutral normal NH_4OAC extractant
5.	Available Sulphur (ppm)	Below 10	10-20	Above 20	Heat soluble
6.	Available Iron (ppm)	Below 5.0	5-10	Above 10.0	DTPA (0.005 M) Extractant method
7.	Available Manganese (ppm)	Below 5.0	5-10	Above 10.0	DTPA (0.005 M) Extractant method
8.	Available Zinc (ppm)	Below 0.5	0.5-1.0	Above 1.0	DTPA (0.005 M) Extractant method
9.	Available Copper (ppm)	Below 0.2	0.2-0.4	Above 0.4	DTPA (0.005 M) Extractant method
10.	Available Boron (ppm)	Below 0.1	0.1-0.5	Above 0.5	Hot water soluble
11.	Available Molybdenum (ppm)	Below 0.05	0.05-0.1	Above 0.1	Ammonium oxalate extractant
12.	Soil pH	Below 6.5 Acidic	6.5-7.6 Neutral	Above 7.6 Alkaline	1 : 2.5 soil water ratio
13.	EC mmhos/cm at 25°C	Below 1.0 normal	1.2 Desirable	Above 2.0 Harmful	1:2.5 soil water ratio

TABLE 31.2. Soil test value and fertilizer recommendation*

Organic carbon (%)	*Dose (Kg N/ha)*	*Available Phosphorus (Kg P/ha)*	*Dose (Kg P_2O_5/ha)*	*Available Potassium (Kg K/ha)*	*Dose (Kg K_2O/ha)*
Low					
Below 0.20	160**	Below 10	80	Below100	60
0.21-0.40	140	11-20	60	101-150	50
Medium					
0.41-0.60	120	21-30	45	151-200	40
0.61-0.80	90	31-40	30	101-250	30
High					
0.81-1.00	75	41-55	15	251-300	20
Above 1.00	60	above 55	10	above 300	00

*Fertil. News 19(8) : 25, 1974

**In this case FYM is necessary

+Available Phosphorus by Olsen's method

++ Available Potassium by ammonium acetate method

❑ ❑ ❑

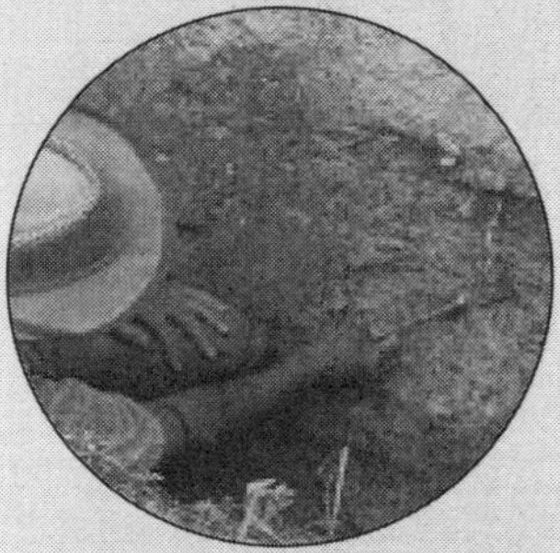

CHAPTER 32

Modern Perspective in Soil Sciences

HYDROPONICS

Hydroponics is a method of growing plant using mineral nutrient solutions, in water without soil. Terrestrial plant may be grown with their roots in the mineral nutrient only or in an inert medium, such as pertile, gravel, or mineral wool.

Some of the reasons why hydroponics is being adopted around the world for food production are the following:

- No soil is needed
- The water stay in system and can be reused lower water cost
- It is possible to control the nutrition in their entirety thus lower nutrition costs
- No nutrition pollution is released into environment because the controlled system
- Stable and high yields
- Pest and diseases are easier to get rid of than in soil because the containers mobility

Today, hydroponics is an established branch of agronomy. Presses has been rapid, and result obtained in varies countries have proved it to be thoroughly practical and to have very definite advantage over conventional method of horticulture. The two chief merits of the soilless cultivation of plants are, first, much higher crop yield, and second, hydroponics can be used in place where in ground agriculture or gardening is not possible.

ARTIFICIAL RAIN

The need to develops and improve rain-making techniques in term of design, operation, monitoring and evaluation by given them a more scientific character is today's need. This includes using computer to study cloud formations and help the rain making operation achieve the goal of the project. The role of weather modification, or rain-makings, is an important in water resource management. The process involved in artificial rain-making involves three easy-to-understand stages. The first stage is agitation that is using chemicals to stimulate the air mass upwind of the target area to rise and from rain clouds. The chemicals used during this stage are calcium chloride, calcium carbide, calcium oxide, a compound of salt of urea, or a urea and ammonium nitrate. These compounds capable of absorbing water vapour from the air mass, thus stimulating the condensation process.

The second stage is called build-up stage. Here the cloud mass is build up using chemicals such as kitchen salt, urea, ammonium nitrate, dry ice, and occasionally also calcium chloride to increase nuclei which also increase the density of clouds. In the third stage of bombardment chemical such as super cool agent : silver iodide and dry ice are used to reach the most unbalanced status which up large beads of water (Nuclei) and makes them fall down as raindrops.

In planning every stage a high degree of expertise and experience is required, in selecting the type and amounts of chemicals to be used, while taking into consideration weather conditions, topographical conditions, wind direction and velocity as well as the location or delineation of the area for chemical seeding. Several other ideas are also involved in rain making. Rockete containing rain making chemical can be fired into the clouds either from aircraft. A jet of rain making chemical is shot from a highly pressurized canister directly into cloud base, so as to coerce clouds which normally hang above maintain tops to cluster up and rain of on the mountain or their slopes. Rain-making chemicals are added to supper-cooled clouds, *i.e.*, those at altitudes above 18,000 meters, to stimulate the formation of ice crystals in the cloud or cloud cluster.

BIOFERTILIZER

Bio-fertilizer is a large population of a specific or a group of beneficial microorganism of enhancing the productivity of soil either by fixing atmospheric nitrogen or by solubilizing soil phosphorus or by stimulating plant growth through synthesis of growth promoting substances.

Bio-fertilizer based on renewable energy source of cost effective supplement to chemical fertilizer, eco-friendly and can help to economics on the high investment needed for chemical fertilizer use as for as nitrogen phosphorus are concerned.

There are varieties of nitrogen fixing microorganism present in the nature. These are broadly divided into three categories, *viz.*,

(*i*) Symbiotic micro-organism *e.g.* Legume-*Rhizobium,* Symbiosis

(*ii*) Asymbiotic of free living *e.g. Azatobactor*, blue green algae

(*iii*) Associative symbiosis, *e.g. Azospirillum*

These micro-organism supplies in addition to nitrogen considerable amount of organic matter enriching structure of soil. Inoculants of these micro-organisms have provided their technical feasibility, economic viability and sociality acceptability. They are therefore called as 'biofertilizer'. Hence the term 'biofertilizer' or microbial inoculants may be defined as preparation containing living or latent cells of efficient strains of nitrogen fixing, phosphorus solubilizing or cellulolytic micro-organism.

VERMICOMPOST

Vermicompost is the product or process of composing utilizing various species of worms, usually red and wiggler, white worms, and earthworms to create a heterogeneous mixture of decomposing vegetable or food waste, bedding materials, and vermicompost. Vermicompost, similarly known as warm castings, worm humus or worm manure, is the end product of back down of organic matter by a species of earthworm. Containing water-soluble nutrients, vermicompost is an excellent, nutrient-rich organic fertilizer and soil conditioner. The process of producing vermicompost is called vermicomposting.

Benefits

- Improve its physical structure.
- Enrich soil with micro-organism (adding enzymes such phosphetase and cellulase).
- Microbial activity in worm casting in 10 to 20 times higher than in the soil and organic matter that the worm ingests.
- Attracts deep-burrowing earthworms already present in the soil.
- Improve water holding capacity.

Plant growth

- Enhance germination, plant growth, and crop yield.
- Improve root growth and structure.
- Enrich the soil micro-organisms (adding plant hormones such as auxins and gibbrelic acid).

Economic

- Bio waste conversion reduces waste flow to landfills.
- Elimination of bio wastes from the waste stream reduces contamination of other recyclables collected in a single bin (a common problem in communities practicing in single-stream recycling).
- Create low-skill jobs at local level.
- Low capital investment and relatively simple technologies make vermicomposting practical for less developed agriculture regions.

Environmental

- Help to close the "metabolic gap" through recycle waste on site.
- Large system often use temperature control and mechanized harvesting, however after equipment is relatively simple and does not wear out quickly.
- Production reduces greenhouse gases emission such as methane and nitric oxide (produced in landfills or incinerators when not composted or through methane harvcst).

As fertilizer

Vermicompost can mix directly into the soil, or sieved in water and made into a worm tea by mixing some vermicompost in water, bubbling in oxygen with a small air pump, and steeping for a number of hours or days. The microbial activity of the compost is greater if it aerated during this period. The resulting liquid is used as a fertilizer or spread on the plants.

The dark brown waste liquid, or leachate, that drains into the bottom of some vermicomposting system as water rich food break down, is best applied back to the bin when added moisture is needed due to the possibility of phototoxic content and organic acids that may be toxic to plants. The pH, nutrient and microbial content of these fertilizers varies upon the inputs fed to the system to raise the pH.

WATER HARVESTING

It means capturing rain where it falls of capturing the runoff in your own village or town, and taking measures to keep that water clean by not allowing polluting activities to take place in the catchment.

Therefore, water harvesting can be undertaken through a variety of ways

- Capturing runoff from rooftops.
- Capturing runoff from local catchments.
- Capturing seasonal flood waters from local streams.
- Conserving water through watershed management.

These techniques can serve the following purposes:

- Provide drinking water.
- Providing irrigation water.
- Increase groundwater recharge.
- Reduce storm water discharges, urban flood and overloading of sewage treatment plants.
- Reduce sewage water and ingress in coastal areas.

WATERSHED MANAGEMENT

Watershed management is the process of creating and implementing plans, programme and project to sustain and enhance watershed function that effect the plant, animal and human communities within watershed boundary. Features of a watershed that agencies seek to manage include water supply, water quality, drainage, storm water runoff, water right and the overall planning and utilization of watersheds. Land owners, land use agencies storm water management experts, environmental specialists, water use surveyors and communities all play an integral part in the management of a watershed.

NO TILLAGE CONCEPT

95 Million hectares under No-tillage World. Since 1987 the technology has experienced a 59 fold increase in Latin America from 70,000 ha to 40.6 million ha in the year 2004 against a 5.6 increase in the USA.

The most important reasons why farmers change to this new farming system are :

- Less work.
- More money.
- Erosion control, environmentally friendly.
- Improvement of the quality of life.

The concept of tillage systems offer numerous benefits that intensive tillage systems cannot match. These advantages have been summarized as fallows :

- Reduced labour requirements.
- Time saving.
- Reduced machinery wear.
- Fuel savings.
- Improved long term productivity.
- Improve surface water quality.
- Reduced soil erosion.
- Greater soil moisture retention.
- Improve water infiltration.
- Decreased soil compaction.
- Improve soil tilth.
- More wildlife.
- Reduced release of carbon gases.
- Reduced air pollution.

MECHANIZED FORMING

Modern farms even sometimes use computers in conjunction with satellite imagery and GPS guidance to increase yields. Mechanized agriculture is the process of using agriculture machinery to massively increase farm output. In modern times, power machinery has replaced many jobs formerly carried out by men or animal such as oxen and horses.

The history of agriculture contains many examples of tool use, but only in recent time has the high rate of machine use at such a level. The first pervasive mechanization of agriculture came with the introduction of the plough, usually powered by animals. It is the use airplanes, helicopter, trucks and tractors, among other vehicles.

GOLDEN RICE

Golden rice is a variety of *Oryza sativa* rice produced through genetic engineering to biosynthesize beta-carotene, a precursor of pro-vitamin A in the edible parts of rice. The scientific details of the rice were first published in 'Science' in 2000. Golden rice was developed as a fortified food to be used in areas where is a shortage of dietary vitamin A, in 2005 a new variety called golden rice 2 was announced which produced up to 23 time more beta-carotene then the original variety of golden rice. Neither variety is currently available for human consumption. Although golden rice was developed as a humanitarian tool, it has met with significant consumption from environment and anti-globalization activists.

GLOBAL WARMING

Global warming is the increase in the average temperature of Earth's near surface air and oceans since the mines-20th century and its projected continuation. Global surface temperature increased 0.74± 0.18°C (1.33 ± 0.32°F) between the start and the end of the 20th century. The Intergovernmental Panel on Climate Change (IPCC) concludes that most be observed temperature increase since the middle of the 20th century was very likely caused by increasing concentrations of greenhouse gases resulting from human activities such as fossil fuel burning and deforestation. The IPCC also concludes that variations in natural phenomena such as solar radiation and volcanic eruptions have a small cooling effect after 1950. These basic conclusions have been endorsed by more than 40 societies and academies of science, including all of the national academies of science of the major industrialized countries.

GREEN HOUSE EFFECT

The green house effect is caused by an atmosphere containing gases that absorb and emit infrared radiation. Greenhouse gases trap heat within the surface-troposphere system, causing heating at the surface of the planet or moon. This mechanism is fundamentally different that of an actual greenhouse, which works by isolating warm air inside the structure so that heat is not lost by convection. The greenhouse effect was discovered by Joseph Fourier in 1824, first reliably experimented on by John Tyndall in 1858, and first reported quantitatively by Sevante Arrhenius in 1896.

The black body temperature of the Earth's is 5.5°C, since the Earth's surface reflects about 28% of incoming sunlight, in the absence of the greenhouse effect the planet's mean temperature would be far lower about –18 or –19°C instead of the much higher current mean temperature, about 14°C.

Global warming, a recent warming of the Earth's surface and lower atmosphere, is believed to be the result of an "enhanced greenhouse effect" mostly due to human referred to as anthropogenic global warming (AGW).

INTEGRATED NUTRIENT MANAGEMENT (FERTILIZER)

The main objective of Integrated Nutrient Management (INM) is to ensure adequate availability of quantity fertilizers to farmers through periodical demand assessment and timely suplly, promoting integrated nutrient management, which is soil test based, judicious and balanced use of chemical fertilizers in conjunction with organic manures and bio-fertilizers, promotion of organic farming and ensuring quality control of fertilizers through implementation of Fertilizer (Control) Order, 1985.

India is the third largest producer and consumer of fertilizers in the world after China and the USA. Against 18.4 million tones of fertilizer nutrient (NPK) consumed during 2004-2005, the nutrient consumption is estimated at 20.2 million tones during 2005-06. The consumption of major fertilizers namely, Urea, DAP, MOP, SSP and Complexes are estimated to be 22.2, 6.8, 2.6, 2.8 and 6.7 million tones respectively during 2005-06. India is, by and large, self sufficient in respect of urea and about 90 per cent in case of DAP. The all India average fertilizer consumption is 94.4 kg ha^{-1} of NPK nutrients through there is wide variation from state to state varying from 197 kg ha^{-1} in Punjab, 164 kg ha^{-1} in Haryana to less than 10 kg ha^{-1} in state like Arunachal Pradesh, Nagaland, Sikkim, etc. Considering the skewed pattern of fertilizer use, Government of India is promoting balanced and integrated use of fertilizer nutrients through various initiatives.

As the results, NPK consumption ratio has now improved to 5.7 : 2.2 : 1 during 2004-05 from 7 : 2.7 : 1 during 2001-02.

INTEGRATED FERTILITY MANAGEMENT

Limited availability of additional land for crop production, along with declining yield growth for major food crops, have heightened concerned about agriculture's ability to feed a world population expected to exceed 7.5 billion by the 2020. Decreasing the soil fertility has also raised concern about the sustainability of agricultural production at current levels. Future strategies for increasing agricultural production at current levels. Future strategies for increasing for agricultural productivity will have to focus on using available nutrient resources more efficiently, and sustainable than in the past. Integrated management of the nutrient of the needed for proper plant growth, together with effective crop, water, soil, and land management, will be critical sustainable agriculture over the long term.

Substantial improvement in the productivity of agricultural systems is required to support growing rural and urban populations in the developing World. Because of strong pressure on land resources, agricultural intensification of existing population system involving increasing cropping intensity and/or increased use of external inputs are often the only way to increase agricultural production. There is however, a broad concern about the sustainability of agricultural production system in many developing countries. Sustainable agriculture, define by FAO, means degrade the environment, and economically viable and socially acceptable. Thus sustainable agriculture manages and uses natural resources to meet people's need both now and in the future.

Much currently cultivated land (estimated at 5 million hectare) is being lost through soil degradation, be it soil erosion, nutrient depletion, desertification, deforestation, Salinization or overgrazing. As agricultural areas become even more crowded, arable land is likely to come under increasing the pressure. Agricultural yields could fall as land becomes more degraded, putting the livehood of millions of subsistence at risk. Integrated soil fertility management (ISFM) is the key in raising productivity levels while maintaining the neutral resources base. ISFM aims to replenish soil nutrient pools, maximize on farm recycling of nutrients, reduced nutrient losses to the environment and improve the efficiency of external inputs.

INTEGRATED WEED MANAGEMENT

A balanced approach to successfully managing resources must include the fallowing processes:

- managing the resource to prevent weeds from invading
- proper identification and knowledge of invasive weed species
- inventory, mapping out and monitoring of weed populations and damage
- making control decisions based on knowledge of potential damage, cost of control method and environmental impact of the weed and control decision
- using control strategies that may include a combination of methods to reduce the weed population to an acceptable level
- evaluation the effectiveness and effects of management decisions

SOIL SOLARIZATION

Soil Solarization is an eco-friendly method of using solar power for controlling disease agents in the soil mulching the soil, usually with transparent polyethylene cover. It may also describe method of decontaminating soil using sunlight or solar power.

Soil disinfestations

Soil Solarization (also referred to as to solar heating of the soil) is relatively new soil disinfestations method, for controlling soil borne pathogens and weeds, mostly as a pre-planting soil treatment. It was achieved by covering (mulching, trapping) the soil with transparent polyethylene during the hot season, thereby heating it and killing the pests.

Soil decontamination

A 2008 study used a solar cell, to generate an electric field for electromagnetic (EK) remediation of cadmium contaminated soil. It was found that a solar cell could be used to drive the electromigration of cadmium in contaminated soil, and removal efficiency achieved by solar cell was comparable with that achieved by conventional power supply.

In Korea in order to evaluate the potential use for *ex situ* remediation, a solar driven, photocatalyzed reactor system was constructed and applied for the treatment of soil slurry and ground water contaminated with benzene using selected advanced oxidation processes (AOP). The remediation method was trilled at a contaminated gas station a site and achieved 98 per cent degradation, and lead to a substantial increase in the removal of benzene.

NUCLEAR AGRICULTURE

The isotopes used in much of the joint FAO/International Atomic Energy Agency programme's work exist in nature- soil, plant, animals and air, and subsequently in the food we eat. Scientist use them in a number of ways in the food and agriculture sector. Combining pest and disease : the sterile insect technique involve mass producing insect past and sterilizing them with gamma radiation emitted by radioisotopes; when the males are released in the target region and mate with wild female of the pest population, then they create no offspring. Gradually, the population is reduced.

GEOGRAPHICAL INFORMATION SYSTEM (GIS)

A Geographical Information System (GIS), is a system that captures, stores, analyzes, manages, and presents data are linked to location. Technically, a GIS is a system that include mapping software and its application to remote sensing, land surveying, areal photography, mathematics, photogrammetry, geography and tools that can be implemented with GIS software. Still, many refer to "Geographical Information System" as "GIS" even through it doesn't cover all tools connected to topography.

In the strictest sense, the term describes any information system that integrates, store edits, analyses, share and displays geographical information. In more generic sense, GIS application are tools the allow users to create interactive queries (user created searches), analyzed spatial information. Geographical information science is the science underlying the geographic concepts, applications and systems, taught in degree and GIS certificate programs at many universities.

In the simplest terms, GIS is the merging of cartography and database technology. Consumer user would likely be familiar with applications for finding driving directions, like a GPS program on their hand-held device. GPS (Global Positioning System) is the real-time location component that uses satellites to show your current position, "where I am now" on your device.

TRICKLE IRRIGATION

Drip irrigation, also known as trickle irrigation or micro irrigation, is an irrigation method which saves water and fertilizer by allowing water to drip slowly to the roots of plants, either onto the soil surface or directly into the root zone, through a network of valves, pipes, tubing and emitters.

Advantages of the drip irrigation

- Minimized fertilizer/nutrient loss due to localized application and reduced leaching.
- High water application efficiency.
- Leveling of the field is not necessary.
- Ability to irrigate irregular shaped field.
- Allows the safe use of recycled water.
- Moisture with in the root zone can be maintained at field capacity.
- Soil type plays less important role in frequency of irrigation.
- Minimize soil erosion.
- Highly uniform distribution of water *i.e.* controlled by out put of each nozzle.
- Lower labour cost.
- Variation in supply can be regulated by regulating the valves and drippers.
- Fertigation can easily be included with minimum waste of fertilizers.
- Foliage remains dry thus reducing the risk of disease.
- Usually operated at lower pressure than other type of pressurized irrigation, reducing energy costs.

Disadvantages of drip irrigation

- Expense, the initial cost can be more than overhead systems.
- Waste, the sun can affect the tubes used for drip irrigation, shortening their unable life. Longevity is variable.
- Clogging, if the water is not properly filtered and the equipment not properly maintained, it can be result in clogging.
- Drip irrigation might be unsatisfactory if herbicides or top dressed fertilizers need sprinkler irrigation for activation.
- Drip tape causes extra cleanup cost after harvest. You'll need to plan for drip tape winding, disposal, recycling or reuse.

DDP WATERSHED DEVELOPMENT PROJECT/HARIYALI SCHEME

The objective of each watershed development project is to promote the economic development of the village community which is directly or indirectly depend on the watershed and encourage restoration of ecological balance in the village. It also includes development of agricultural lands, horticulture, grassland, forest land, soil and water conservation measures, creation of water resources etc. it is a 4/5 year project and during this period amounting to ₹ 30.00 lacs for one watershed development project are allocated for different components (works, training, community, organization, entry point activity etc.) and an area of 1250 Acres (Approx 500 ha.) is covered under this project. Under DDP, there are 4th phase, 6th phase, 7th phase and 8th phase and Hariyali-2nd. Under Hariyali 1st and Hariyali-2nd total 21 watersheds each to be implemented.

AGRI-CLINIC AND AGRI-BUSINESS CENTERS

Agriclinics are envisaged to provide expert service and advice to farmers on cropping practices, technology dissemination, crop production from pests and disease, market trends and prices of various crops in the markets and also clinical services for animal health etc. which would enhance productivity of crops/animals.

Agribusiness Centers : Agribusiness centers are envisaged to provide input supply, farm equipments on hire and other services.

In order to enhance viability of a ventures, Agriculture Graduates may also take up in agriculture and allied areas along with Agriclinics/Agribusiness Centers.

The Ministry of Agriculture, Government of India, in association with NABARD has launched a unique programme to take better methods of farming to each and every farmer across the country.

This programme aims to tap the experience available in the large pool of Agriculture Graduates. Irrespective of whether you are a fresh graduate or not, or whether you are currently employed or not, you can set up your own Agriclinic or Agribusiness Center and offer professional extension services to innumerable farmers.

Combined to this programme, the Government is now also providing start-up training to graduates in Agriculture, or any subject allied to Agriculture like Horticulture, Forestry, Sericulture, Veterinary, Science, Dairy, Poultry Farming and Fisheries, etc. Those completing the training can apply for special start-up loans for venture.

Agribusiness Centers would provide paid services for enhancement of agriculture production and income of farmers. Center would need to advise farmers on crop selection, best farm practices, post harvest value-added options, key agricultural information (including perhaps even Internet-based weather forecast), price trends, market news, risk mitigation and crop insurance, credit and output access, as well as critical sanitary and phyto-sanitary considerations, which the farmers have to keep in mind.

PRECISION FARMING

Precision farming of precision agriculture is an agricultural concept relaying on the existence of in-field variability. It requires the use of new technologies, such as Global Positioning System (GPS), sensor, satellites or areal images, and information management tools to asses of understand variations. Collected information may be used to more precisely evaluate optimum sowing density, estimate fertilizer and other output needs, and more accurately predict crop yields. It seeks to avoid applying inflexible practices local situations of disease or logging.

Satellites allow farmers to easily survey their land. Global Positioning System monitor can find the location of the field to within one meter. It can then present a series of GIS maps that demonstrate which fields are moist or dry, and where there is erosion of soil and other soil factors that stunt plant growth. The data can be used by the farmer to automatically regulate the machine application of fertilizer and pesticide.

In the American Midwest (US) it is associated not with sustainable agriculture but with mainstream farmers who are trying to maximize profits by spending money only in areas that need fertilizer. This practice allows the need identified by GPS guide Grid Sampling. Fertilizer that would have been spread in areas that don't need it can be placed in areas that do, thereby optimize its use.

Precision farming may be used to improve a field or a farm management from several perspectives:

- agronomical perspective: adjustment of cultural practices to take into account the real need of the crop (*e.g.* better fertilization management)
- technical perspective: better time management at the farm level (*e.g.* planning of agricultural activity)
- environmental perspective: reduction of agricultural impacts (better estimation of crop nitrogen needs implying limitation of nitrogen run-off)
- economical perspective: increase of the output and/or reduction of the input, increase of efficiency (*e.g.*, lower cost of nitrogen fertilization practice)

Other benefits for the farmer may be to help him set a history of his/her farm practices and results, to help him in his decision making and traceability requirements (as increasingly required in developed countries)

NANO FERTILIZERS

Agricultural land is decreasing day by day due to erosion, environmental pollution, unconscious irrigation and fertilization. On the other hand, it is necessary to increase agricultural production in order to meet the needs of the developing industry as well as the nutritional needs of the growing population. In the recent years, nano-fertilizers have begun to be produced to obtain the highest amount and quality of production from the unit area. Previous research shows that nano-fertilizers cause an increase in the use efficiency of plant nutrients, reduce soil toxicity, minimize the potential adverse effects of excessive chemical fertilizer use, and reduce fertilizer application frequency. Nano-fertilizers are important in agriculture to increase crop yield and nutrient use efficiency, and to reduce excessive use of chemical fertilizers. The most important properties of these fertilizers are that they contain one or more of macro and micronutrients, they can be applied frequently in small amounts and are environmentally friendly. However, when applied at high doses, they exhibit decreasing effects on plant growth and crop yields, similar to chemical fertilizers. Nano-fertilizers are now being used in specific concentrations, in accordance with the nutritional requirements of the crops, ensuring minimal differential losses.

There are three types of nano-fertilizers: nanoscale fertilizers, nanoscale additive fertilizers, and nanoscale coating fertilizers.

Nanoscale fertilizers are made of nanoparticles that contain nutrients. Nanoscale additive fertilizers are traditional fertilizers with nanoscale additives. Nanoscale coating fertilizers are traditional fertilizers coated or loaded with nanoparticles.

The encapsulation of nutrients most commonly produces nano fertilizers with nanomaterials. Preliminary nanomaterials are produced by using both physical (top-down) and chemical (bottom-up) approaches.

More recently, the targeted nutrients are encapsulated inside nanoporous materials, coated with a thin polymer film particle, or coated with emulsions of nanoscale dimension.

Encapsulation of beneficial microorganisms, such as bacteria or fungi, has shown promise as it can enhance the availability of nitrogen, phosphorus, and potassium in the root zone, thereby improving plant growth.

Nano-fertilizers can also be classified based on their actions: control or slow-release fertilizers; control loss fertilizers; magnetic fertilizers or nanocomposite fertilizers (which use a nanodevice to supply a wide range of macronutrient and micronutrients in desirable concentration).

Porous nanomaterials significantly reduce nitrogen loss by regulating demand-based release, and by enhancing the plant uptake process. Examples of porous nanomaterials include:

- Ammonium charged zeolites, which can enhance the solubility of phosphate minerals, showing an improvement in phosphorus availability and uptake by crops.
- Graphene oxide films, a carbon-based nanomaterial, can prolong potassium nitrate release, extending the time of function and minimizing losses by leaching.
- Nanocalcite ($CaCO_3$-40%) with nano SiO_2 (4%), MgO (1%), and Fe_2O_3 (1%) which not only improve the uptake of calcium, magnesium and iron, but also notably enhance the intake of phosphorous with micronutrients zinc and manganese.

Examples of potential nano-fertilizer designs

Slow release: the nanocapsule slowly releases nutrients over a specified period of time.

Quick release: the nanoparticle shell breaks upon contact with a surface (such as striking a leaf).

Specific release: the shell breaks open when it encounters a specific chemical or enzyme.

Moisture release: the nanoparticle degrades and releases nutrients in the presence of water.

Heat release: the nanoparticle releases nutrients when the temperature exceeds a set point.

pH release: the nanoparticle only degrades in specified acid or alkaline conditions.

Ultrasound release: the nanoparticle is ruptured by an external ultrasound frequency.

Magnetic release: a magnetic nanoparticle ruptures when exposed to a magnetic field.

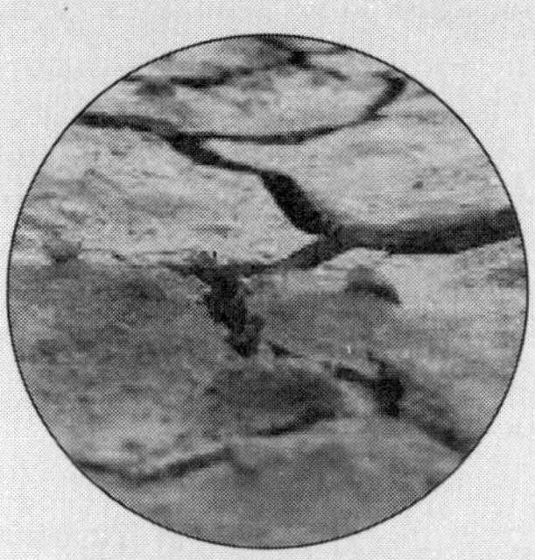

Soil Science Terminology (Lexicon)

Abiotic. Non-living thing. Usually refers to the physical and chemical components of an organism's environment. Also called inorganic.

Abrasion. Physical wearing and grinding of a surface through friction and impact by material carried in air, water, or ice.

Absolute Humidity. Measurement of atmospheric humidity. Absolute humidity is the mass of water vapor in a given volume of air (this measurement is not influenced by the mass of the air). Normally expressed in grams of water vapor per cubic meter of atmosphere at a specific temperature.

Aeolian. Geomorphic process involving wind. Alternative spelling eolian.

Aerial Photography. Form of remote sensing that captures images of objects using photographic cameras and film from platforms in the atmosphere.

Agronomy. Field of science that studies phenomena related to agriculture.

A Horizon. Soil horizon normally found below the O horizon and above the B horizon. This layer is characterized by the following two features.

(1) A layer in which humus and other organic materials are mixed with mineral particles.

(2) A zone of translocation from which eluviation has removed finer particles and soluble substances.

Albedo. Is the reflectivity of a surface.

Alfisols. Soil order (type) of the United States Natural Resources Conservation Service Soil Classification System. Soil associated with forest vegetation. Upper layers of this soil are relatively rich in organic matter. Whitish layer found in the A horizon because of eluviation. Illuvial layer forms in the B horizon.

Alkaline. (1) Having a pH greater than 7.

(2) Substance that releases hydroxyl ions (–OH).

Allophane. Hydrated aluminosilicate substance ordinarily found associated with clay minerals.

Alluvium. Sediment that originates from a stream.

Altitude. Vertical distance above sea-level.

Amino Acid. Organic nitrogen containing acids which are used to construct proteins.

Ammonia. Chemical compound composed of nitrogen and hydrogen. Component of the nitrogen cycle. Immediately released from organic matter upon decomposition.

Ammonium. Chemical compound composed of nitrogen and hydrogen. Component of the nitrogen cycle. Product of organic matter decomposition. Can be fixed to clay minerals and later exchanged.

Andisols. Soil order (type) of the United States Department of Agriculture Comprehensive Soil Classification System. These soils develop from parent materials that are volcanic in origin.

Anion. An ion carrying a negative atomic charge.

Anticyclone. An atmospheric pressure system consisting of an area of high pressure and outward circular surface wind flow. In the Northern Hemisphere winds from an anticyclone blow clockwise, while Southern Hemisphere systems blow counter clockwise.

Aridisols. Soil order (type) of the United States Natural Resources Conservation Service Soil Classification System. Aridisols are commonly found in dry environments that are low in organic matter and rich in deposited salts.

Atom. Smallest unit of an element that still maintains its chemical characteristics.

Autotroph. An organism that produces food molecules inorganically by using light or chemical based sources of external energy. This organism does not require outside sources of organic food energy for survival. Also see chemical autotrophs and photosynthetic autotrophs.

Available Water. Amount of water present in soil that can be readily absorbed by the plant roots. Considering the soil moisture tension, the amount of water held by the soil at a moisture tension between 1/3 atmosphere to 15 atmosphere is known as available water.

Barometer. Instrument that measures atmospheric pressure.

Basalt. A dark colored fine grained igneous rock formed from mafic magma.

Basalt Plateau. Extensive continental deposits of basaltic volcanic rock.

Biodiversity. The diversity of different species (species diversity), genetic variability among individuals within each species (genetic diversity), and variety of ecosystems (ecosystem diversity). Abbreviation of biological diversity.

Biomass. The weight of living tissues usually measured per unit area over a particular time interval. Can include the dead parts of organisms like bark, hair, and nails.

Boulder. Large fragment of rock that has a diameter greater than 256 millimeters (200 millimeters in the United Kingdom).

Brackish. Environment that is influenced by seawater with a salinity less than 35 parts per thousand (usually caused by the presence of an inflow of fresh water).

Breccia. Coarse grained sedimentary rock composed of cemented angular rock fragments.

Calcification. A dry environment soil-forming process that results in the accumulation of calcium carbonate in surface soil layers.

Calcite. Mineral formed from calcium carbonate. Common mineral found in limestone.

Calcium Carbonate. Compound consisting of calcium and carbonate. Calcium carbonate has the following chemical structure $CaCO_3$.

Caliche. An accumulation of calcium carbonate at or near the soil surface.

Quantity of energy. Equals the amount of heat required to raise 1 gram of pure water from 14.5 to 15.5° Celsius at standard atmospheric pressure.

C Horizon. Soil horizon normally found below the B horizon and above the R horizon. This layer is composed of weathered bedrock that has not been yet significantly affected by the pedogenic processes.

Chernozem Soil. (1) Soil order (type) of the Canadian System of Soil Classification. This soil is common on the Canadian Prairies.

(2) Type of soil commonly found in grassland environments. These soils are often black in color and have a well developed A horizon rich in humus.

Chlorofluorocarbons (CFCs). Is an artificially created gas that has become concentrated in the Earth's atmosphere. This very strong greenhouse gas is released from aerosol sprays, refrigerants, and the production of foams. The basic chemical formula for chlorofluorocarbons is CFx Clx.

Clay. Mineral particle with a size less than 0.002 millimeters in diameter. Also see silt and sand.

Cleavage. The tendency of some minerals or rocks to break along planes of weakness. This weakness occurs because of the nature of the bonds between mineral grains.

Contour (Line). Line on a topographic map that connects all points with the same elevation.

Cryosol Soil. Soil order (type) of the Canadian System of Soil Classification. This soil is common to high latitude tundra environments. The main identifying feature of this soil is a layer of permafrost within one meter of the soil surface.

Cyclone. Area of low pressure in the atmosphere that displays circular inward movement of air. In the Northern Hemisphere circulation is counterclockwise, while Southern Hemisphere cyclones have clockwise wind patterns.

Degradation. Readjustment of the stream profile where the stream channel is lowered by the erosion of the stream bed. Usually associated with high discharges.

Delta. Large deposit of alluvial sediment located at the mouth of a stream where it enters a body of standing water.

Desertification. Conversion of marginal rangeland or cropland to a more desert like land type. Desertification can be caused by overgrazing, soil erosion, prolonged drought, or climate change.

Detachment. One of three distinct processes involved in erosion. This process involves the disengagement of a particle from its surroundings.

Detrital Rock. Sedimentary rock that is composed of particles transported to their place of deposition by erosional processes. Examples of such rock include sandstone and shale.

Dew. Condensation of water on the Earth's surface because of atmospheric cooling.

Dew Point. Dew point is the temperature at which water vapor saturates from an air mass into liquid or solid usually forming rain, snow, frost or dew. Dew point normally occurs when a mass of air has a relative humidity of 100%. If the dew point is below freezing, it is referred to as the frost point.

Element. A molecule composed of one type of atom. Chemists have recognized or created 119 different types of elements. Two or more different elements form a compound.

El Niño. Name given to the occasional development of warm ocean surface waters along the coast of Ecuador and Peru. When this warming occurs the tropical Pacific trade winds weaken and the usual upwelling of cold, nutrient rich deep ocean water off the coast of Ecuador and Peru is reduced. The El Niño normally occurs around Christmas and lasts usually for a few weeks to a few months. Sometimes an extremely warm event can develop that lasts for much longer time periods.

Eluviation. Movement of humus, chemical substances, and mineral particles from the upper layers of a soil to lower layers by the downward movement of water through the soil profile. Compare with illuviation.

Entisols. Soil order (type) of the United States Natural Resources Conservation Service Soil Classification System. Soil of recent development with no or poorly developed soil horizons.

Environment. (1) Abiotic and biotic factors that influence the life of an organism.

(2) Abiotic and biotic factors that influence the function of some nonliving natural system.

Eolian. Geomorphic process involving wind. Alternative spelling aeolian.

Erosion. The removal of weathered sediment or rocks by the forces of wind, water, and ice.

Feldspar. A group of common aluminum silicate minerals that contains potassium, sodium, or calcium.

Fermentation. Decomposition and breakdown of organic matter by anaerobic means.

Fertilizer. Substance that adds inorganic or organic nutrients to soil for the purpose of increasing the growth of crops, trees, or other vegetation.

Field Capacity. The water remaining in a soil after the complete draining of the soil's gravitational water.

Flocculation. Chemical processes where salt causes the aggregation of minute clay particles into larger masses that are too heavy to remain suspended water.

Flood. Inundation of a land surface that is not normally submerged by water from quick change in the level of a water body like a lake, stream, or ocean.

Floodplain. Relatively flat area found alongside the stream channel that is prone to flooding and receives alluvium deposits from these inundation events.

Fluvial. Involving running water. Usually pertaining to stream processes.

Food Web. A model describing the organisms found in a food chain. Food webs describe the complex patterns of energy flow in an ecosystem by modeling who consumes who.

Fossil. Geologically preserved remains of an organism that lived in the past.

Freezing. The change in state of matter from liquid to solid that occurs with cooling. Usually used in meteorology when discussing the formation of ice from liquid water.

Frost. Deposition of ice at the Earth's surface because of atmospheric cooling.

Gabbro. An intrusive igneous rock that develops from mafic magma and whose mineral crystals are coarse. Mineralogically this rock is identical to basalt.

Gelisols. Soil order (type) of the United States Natural Resources Conservation Service Soil Classification System. This soil is common to high latitude tundra environments. The main identifying feature of this soil is a layer of permafrost within one meter of the soil surface.

Geographic Information System (GIS). A geographic information system merges information in a computer database with spatial coordinates on a digital map.

Geography. The study natural and human constructed phenomena relative to a spatial dimension.

Geology. The field of knowledge that studies the origin, structure, chemical composition, and history of the Earth and other planets.

Glacier. A large long lasting accumulation of snow and ice that develops on land. Most glaciers flow along topographic gradients because of their weight and gravity.

Gleization. A soil formation process that occurs in poorly drained environments. Results in the development of extensive soil organic layer over a layer of chemically reduced clay that takes on a blue color.

Global Positioning System (GPS). System used to determine latitude, longitude, and elevation anywhere on or above the Earth's surface. This system involves the transmission of radio signals from a number of specialized satellites to a hand held receiving unit. The receiving unit uses triangulation to calculate altitude and spatial position on the Earth's surface.

Global Warming. Warming of the Earth's average global temperature because of an increase in the concentration of greenhouse gases. A greater concentration in greenhouse gases in the atmosphere is believed to result in an enhancement of the greenhouse effect.

Gneiss. A metamorphosed coarse grained igneous rock. In this rock you get the recrystallization of quartz, feldspars, micas and amphiboles into bands.

Gradient. The steepness of a slope as measured in degrees, percentage, or as a distance ratio (rise/run).

Gravitational Water. Water that moves through soil due to gravitational forces. Soil water in excess of hygroscopic water and capillary water.

Gravity. Is the process where any body of mass found in the universe attracts other bodies with a force proportional to the product of their masses and inversely proportional to the distance that separates them. First proposed by Sir Issac Newton in 1686.

Greenhouse Effect. The greenhouse effect causes the atmosphere to trap more heat energy at the Earth's surface and within the atmosphere by absorbing and re-emitting longwave energy. Of the longwave energy emitted back to space, 90% is intercepted and absorbed by greenhouse gases. Without the greenhouse effect the Earth's average global temperature would be-18° Celsius, rather than the present 15° Celsius. In the last few centuries, the activities of humans have directly or indirectly caused the concentration of the major greenhouse gases to increase. Scientists predict that this increase may enhance the greenhouse effect making the planet warmer. Some experts estimate that the Earth's average global temperature has already increased by 0.3 to 0.6° Celsius, since the beginning of this century, because of this enhancement.

Greenhouse Gases. Gases responsible for the greenhouse effect. These gases include water vapor (H_2O), carbon dioxide (CO_2); methane (CH_4); nitrous oxide (N_2O); chlorofluorocarbons (CFxClx); and tropospheric ozone (O_3).

Greenwich Mean Time (GMT). Former standard world time as measured at Greenwich, England (location of the Prime Meridian). Replace in 1928 with Universal Time (UT).

Gypsum. Sedimentary rock created by the chemical precipitation of calcium, sulfur, and oxygen.

Hail. Hail is a solid form of precipitation that has a diameter greater than 5 millimeters. Occasionally, hailstones can be the size of golf balls or larger. Hailstones of this size can be quite destructive. The intense updrafts in mature thunderstorm clouds are a necessary requirement for hail formation.

Half-life. Time required for one half of the nuclei in a radioisotope to emit its radiation. Half-lifes for radioisotopes range from a few millionths of a second to several billion years.

Halite. Sedimentary rock created by the chemical precipitation of sodium and chlorine.

Hazard. Phenomenon which can cause loss of life, injury, disease, economic loss, or environmental damage.

Heat. Heat is defined as energy in the process of being transferred from one object to another because of the temperature difference between them. In the atmosphere, heat is commonly transferred by conduction, convection, advection, and radiation.

Heat Capacity. Is the ratio of the amount of heat energy absorbed by a substance compared to its corresponding temperature rise.

Heat Energy. A form of energy created by the combined internal motion of atoms in a substance.

Histosols. Soil order (type) of the United States Natural Resources Conservation Service Soil Classification System. This soil is composed more than 30% organic matter as a result of saturated environmental conditions.

Horizon. (1) A surface separating two beds in sedimentary rock.

(2) A layer within a soil showing unique pedogenic characteristics. Four major horizons are normally found in a soil profile. A, B, C, and O.

(3) Point at which the visible edge of the Earth's surface meets the sky.

Humidity. A general term used to describe the amount of water vapor found in the atmosphere.

Humus. Dark colored semi-soluble organic substance formed from decomposition of soil organic matter.

Hydration. A form of chemical weathering that involves the rigid attachment of H^+ and OH^- ions to the atoms and molecules of a mineral.

Hydrologic Cycle. Model that describes the movement of water between the hydrosphere, lithosphere, atmosphere, and biosphere.

Hydrology. Field of physical geography that studies the hydrosphere.

Hydrolysis. Chemical weathering process that involves the reaction between mineral ions and the ions of water (OH^- and H^+), and results in the decomposition of the rock surface by forming new compounds, and by increasing the pH of the solution involve through the release of the hydroxide ions.

Hygrometer. An instrument for measuring atmospheric humidity.

Hygroscopic Coefficient. Maximum limit of hygroscopic water around the surface of a soil particle.

Hygroscopic Water. Water held within 0.0002 millimeters of the surface of a soil particle. This water is essentially non-mobile and can only be removed from the soil through heating.

Ideal Gas Law. This law describes the physical relationships that exist between pressure, temperature, volume, and density for gases. Two mathematical equations are commonly used to describe this law. Pressure × Volume = Constant × Temperature and

Pressure = Density × Constant × Temperature

Igneous Rock. Rocks formed by solidification of molten magma either beneath (intrusive igneous rock) or at (extrusive igneous rocks) the Earth's surface.

Illuviation. Deposition of humus, chemical substances, and fine mineral particles in the lower layers of a soil from upper layers because of the downward movement of water through the soil profile. Compare with eluviation.

Inceptisols. Soil order (type) of the United States Natural Resources Conservation Service Soil Classification System. These soils have horizons in the early stages of pedogenesis. Many of these soils are found on glacial drift deposits.

Inorganic. Non-living thing. Usually refers to the physical and chemical components of an organism's environment. Some times called abiotic.

Inosilicate. Subclass of the silicate class of minerals. Inosilicates have two distinct forms. single and double chain silicates.

Isobar. Lines on a map joining points of equal atmospheric pressure.

Isoline. Lines on a map joining points of equal value.

Isotherm. Lines on a map joining points of equal temperature.

Kaolinite. A type of clay that is widespread in tropical and subtropical regions. It is produced from the weathering of granite.

Kelvin Scale. Scale for measuring temperature. In this scale, absolute zero is 0 Kelvins, water boils at 373.15 Kelvins and freezes at 273.15 Kelvins.

Kirchoff's Law. This law suggests that good emitters of radiation are also good absorbers of radiation at specific electromagnetic radiation wavelength bands. It also suggests that poor emitters of radiation are also poor absorbers of radiation at specific wavelength bands.

Köppen Climate Classification. System that uses monthly precipitation and temperature data and total annual precipitation data to classify a location's climate into one of five main categories. Tropical Moist Climates; Dry Climates; Moist Mid-latitude Climates with Mild Winters; Moist Mid-Latitude Climates with Cold Winters; and Polar Climates. These categories are further divided into number of subcategories. First developed in 1918 by German biologist W. Köppen, this system has undergone a number of modifications.

Land Breeze. Local thermal circulation pattern found at the interface between land and water. In this circulation system, surface winds blow from land to water during the night.

Laminar Flow. Movement of water within a stream that occurs as uninterrupted parallel flows. Laminar flow generally occurs in areas where friction is low.

Latent Heat. Is the energy required to change a substance to a higher state of matter (solid > liquid > gas). This same energy is released from the substance when the change of state is reversed (gas > liquid > solid).

Laterite. Hard subsurface deposit of oxides of aluminum and iron found in tropical soils where the water table fluctuates with seasonal changes in precipitation.

Laterization. Soil forming process that creates a laterite layer.

Latitude. Latitude is a north-south measurement of position on the Earth. It is defined by the angle measured from a horizontal plane located at the Earth's center that is perpendicular to the polar axis. A line connecting all places of the same latitude is termed a parallel. Latitude is measured in degrees, minutes, and seconds. Measurements of latitude range from equator 0° to 90° North and South from this point.

Law of the Minimum. This biological law suggests that organisms are normally limited by only one single physical factor that is in shortest supply relative to demand.

Leaching. Process in which water removes and transports soil humus and inorganic nutrients in solution.

Light. A humanly visible form of electromagnetic radiation. This radiation has a wavelength between 0.40 and 0.71 micrometers (μm).

Lignite. Low grade coal. Also called brown coal.

Limestone. Sedimentary rock composed of carbonate minerals, especially calcium carbonate. Limestone can be created by clastic and non-clastic processes. Clastic limestones are formed from the break up and deposition of shells, coral and other marine organisms by wave-action and ocean currents. Non-clastic limestones can be formed either as a precipitate or by the lithification of coral reefs, marine organism shells, or marine organism skeletons.

Lipid. Is an organic compound composed of carbon atoms that have two hydrogen atoms attached. Lipids are commonly known as fats and oils, and belong to the family of molecules known as hydrocarbons.

Liquid. A state of matter where molecules have the ability to flow and the surface of this mass displays the property of surface tension.

Lithosphere. Is the solid inorganic portion of the Earth (composed of rocks, minerals, and elements). It can be regarded as the outer surface and interior of the solid Earth.

Loam. A soil that contains a roughly equal mixture of clay, sand, and silt. Good for growing most crops.

Loess. Deposits of silt laid down by aeolian processes over extensive areas of the mid-latitudes during glacial and postglacial times.

Longitude. Longitude is a west-east measurement of position on the Earth. It is defined by the angle measured from a vertical plane running through the polar axis and the prime meridian. A line connecting all places of the same longitude is termed a meridian. Longitude is measured in degrees, minutes, and seconds. Measurements of longitude range from prime meridian 0° to 180° West and East from this point.

Long Wave. A large wave in the polar jet stream and the westerlies that extends from the middle to the upper troposphere. Often associated with the formation of a mid-latitude cyclone at the ground surface. Contrasts with short waves. Also called Rossby waves.

Lysimeter. Meteorological instrument used to measure potential and actual evapotranspiration.

Macronutrient. Nutritional element required by an organism in relatively large quantities.

Magma. Molten rock originating from the Earth's interior.

Mangrove. Trees wetlands located on the coastlines in warm tropical climates.

Mantle. Layer of the Earth's interior composed of mostly solid rock that extends from the base of crust to a depth of about 2,900 kilometers.

Map. An abstraction of the real world that is used to depict, analyze, store, and communicate spatially organized information about physical and cultural phenomena.

Marble. Metamorphic rock created by the recrystallization of calcite and/or dolomite.

Marine. With reference to ocean environments and processes.

Matric Force. Force that holds soil water from 0.0002 to 0.06 millimeters from the surface of soil particles. This force is due to two processes. Soil particle surface molecular attraction (adhesion and absorption) to water and the cohesion that water molecules have to each other. This force declines in strength with distance from the soil particle. The force becomes nonexistent past 0.06 millimeters.

Mean Sea-Level. The average height of the ocean surface as determined from the mean of all tidal levels recorded at hourly intervals.

Metamorphic Rock. A rock that forms from the recrystallization of igneous, sedimentary or other metamorphic rocks through pressure increase, temperature rise, or chemical alteration.

Meteorology. The scientific study of the atmosphere and its associated phenomena.

Mica. Silicate mineral that exhibits a platy crystal structure and perfect cleavage. Common forms of mica are biotite and muscovite.

Micronutrient. Nutritional element required by an organism in relatively very small quantities.

Microorganism. Extremely small organism that can only be seen using a microscope.

Migration. Movement of organisms in an intentional way between two points in space. Many migrations are seasonal.

Millibar (mb). A unit measurements for quantifying force. Used to measure atmospheric pressure. Equivalent to 1000 dynes per square centimeter.

Mineral. Component of rocks. A naturally occurring inorganic solid with a crystalline structure and a specific chemical composition. Over 2,000 types of minerals have been classified.

Mineralization. Decomposition of organic matter into its inorganic elemental components.

Mitochondria. Organelle in a cell that oxidizes organic (see respiration) energy for use in cellular metabolism.

Molecule. Minute particle that consists of connected atoms of one or many elements.

Mollisols. Soil order (type) of the United States Natural Resources Conservation Service Soil Classification System. A mollisol soil is typically found in semiarid grassland environments. They are rich in organic matter and have an abundance of calcium carbonate nodules within the profile.

Monsoon. A regional scale wind system that predictably change direction with the passing of the seasons. Monsoon winds blow from land to sea in the winter, and from sea to land in the summer. Summer monsoons are often accompanied with precipitation.

Montmorillonite. A type of clay that has a large capacity to shrink and expand with wetting and drying.

Montreal Protocol. Treaty signed in 1987 by 24 nations to cut the emissions of chlorofluorocarbons (CFCs) into the atmosphere. Since 1987 the treaty has been amended to quicken the reduction in CFC production and use.

Moraine. A hill of glacial till deposited directly by a glacier.

Mountain Breeze. Local thermal circulation pattern found in areas of topographic relief. In this circulation system, surface winds blow from areas of higher elevation to valley bottoms during the night.

Mutualism. Interspecific interaction where both species experience and increase in their fitness after interacting with the other species. Mutualistic interactions between species can be of two types : symbiotic or nonsymbiotic.

Mycorrhizae. Mutualistic association of a fungus with the root of higher plant. In this relationship, the fungus helps the plant in extracting certain nutrients from the soil. In exchange, the fungus is provided with a habitat and nutrition in the form of carbohydrates.

Nitrification. The biochemical oxidation of ammonium to nitrite and nitrite to nitrate. This process is carried out by specialized bacteria.

Nitrogen Cycle. Model that describes the movement of nitrogen in its many forms between the hydrosphere, lithosphere, atmosphere and biosphere.

Nitrogen Fixation. Biological or chemical process where gaseous nitrogen is converted into solid forms of nitrogen. Biological fixation of nitrogen is done by specialized organisms like microorganisms like bacteria, actinomycetes, and cyanobacteria. Chemical fixation occurs at high temperatures. One natural process that can produce enough heat to fix atmospheric nitrogen is lightning.

Obsidian. Glassy dark colored volcanic rock usually composed of rhyolite.

'O' Horizon. Topmost layer of most soils. It is composed mainly of plant litter and humus.

Olivine. Common silicate mineral found in rocks formed from mafic magma. Its chemical composition varies between Mg_2SiO_4 and Fe_2SiO_4.

Organic Matter. Mass of matter that contains living organisms or non-living material derived from organisms. Sometime refers to the organic constituents of soil. Also see soil organic matter.

Organism. Any form of life.

Oxidation. (1) Chemical attachment of free oxygen to other elements and compounds. One of the types of chemical weathering.

(2) Loss of an electron during a chemical reaction from one atom to another.

Ozone. Tri-atomic oxygen that exists in the Earth's atmosphere as a gas. Ozone is highest in concentration in the stratosphere (10-50 kilometers above the Earth's surface) where it absorbs the Sun's ultraviolet radiation. Stratospheric ozone is produced naturally and helps to protect life from the harmful effects of solar ultraviolet radiation. Over the last few decades levels of stratospheric ozone have been declining globally, especially in Antarctica. Scientists have determined that chlorine molecules released from the decomposition of chlorofluorocarbons are primarily responsible for ozone destruction in the stratosphere. It is also abundant near the Earth's surface in highly polluted urban centers. In these areas, it forms as a by product of photochemical smog, and is hazardous to human health.

Ozone Hole. Is a sharp seasonal decrease in stratospheric ozone concentration that occurs over Antarctica in the spring. First detected in the late 1970s, the ozone hole continues to appear as a result of complex chemical reaction in the atmosphere that involves CFCs.

Ozone Layer. Atmospheric concentration of ozone found at an altitude of 10 to 50 kilometers above the Earth's surface. This layer is important to life on the Earth because ozone absorbs harmful ultraviolet radiation.

Parts Per Million (ppm). Number of parts of a substance found in one million parts of a particular gas, liquid, or solid.

Parts Per Thousand (ppt). Number of parts of a substance found in one thousand parts of a particular gas, liquid, or solid.

Peat. Partially decomposed remains of plants that once flourished in a waterlogged environment.

Pedogenesis. Process of soil formation.

Pedology. The scientific study of soils.

Pedon. A basic soil sampling unit. Often viewed as a soil profile that goes from the surface to a depth where soil meets bedrock.

Percolation. Vertical movement or infiltration of water from the Earth's surface to its subsurface. Movement usually stops when the flowing water reaches the water table.

Permafrost. Zone of permanently frozen water found in high latitude soils and sediments. Five types of permafrost have been recognized : continuous permafrost, discontinuous permafrost, sporadic permafrost, alpine permafrost, and subsea permafrost.

Permeability. A measure of the ability of soil, sediments, and rock to transport water horizontally and vertically. Permeability is dependent on the porosity of the medium the water is flowing through. Some rocks like granite have very poor permeability, while rocks like shale are actually quite pervious. As for soils, sand is the most pervious, while clay has the lowest permeability. Silt usually is somewhere in the middle.

pH. Scale used to measure the alkalinity or acidity of a substance through the determination of the concentration of hydrogen ions in solution. A pH of 7.0 is neutral. Values below 7.0, to a minimum of 0.0, indicate increasing acidity. Values above 7.0, to a maximum of 14.0, indicate increasing alkalinity.

Podzolization. Soil forming process that produces a strongly leached soil with a distinctive iron hardpan layer in the B horizon. Common in cool, moist forest environments.

Podzol Soil. (1) Soil order (type) of the Canadian System of Soil Classification. This soil type is often found under coniferous forests. Its main identifying traits are a poorly decomposed organic layer, an eluviated A horizon, and a B horizon with illuviated organic matter, aluminum, and iron.

(2) Soil commonly found under coniferous forests.

Pollutant. A substance that has a harmful effect on the health, survival, or activities of humans or other living organisms.

Pollution. Physical, chemical, or biological change in the characteristics of some component of the atmosphere, hydrosphere, lithosphere, or biosphere that adversely influences the health, survival, or activities of humans or other living organisms.

Quartz. Mineral with the chemical formula SiO_2. Quartz is common in continental crust but rare in oceanic crust.

Quartzite. Metamorphic rock rich in quartz created by the recrystallization of sandstone.

Regolith. Loose layer of rocky material overlying bedrock.

Regosol Soil. Soil order (type) of the Canadian System of Soil Classification. This type is any young underdeveloped soil that lacks identifying soil horizons.

Remote Sensing. The gathering of information from an object or surface without direct contact.

Rock. A compact and consolidated mass of mineral matter. Three types of rock are recognized. igneous, sedimentary, and metamorphic.

Salinity. Concentration of dissolved salts found in a sample of water. Measured as the total amount of dissolved salts in parts per thousand. Seawater has an average salinity of about 34 parts per thousand.

Saltation. Transport of sediment initiated by moving air or water where particles move from a resting surface to the transport medium in quick continuous repeated cycles.

Sand. Mineral particle with a size between 0.06 and 2.0 millimeters in diameter. Also see clay and silt.

Sand Dune. A hill or ridge of aeolian sand deposits with a minimum height of less than one meter and a maximum height of about 50 meters. Found in hot deserts and along sandy coastlines.

Scale. A specific relative or proportional size or extent of a phenomena as measured through space and/or time.

Schist. A medium to coarse grained metamorphic rock with well developed bedding planes derived from the foliated recrystrallization of platy like minerals like mica.

Science. Science is a way of acquiring knowledge. To do science, one must follow a specific universal methodology. The central theme in this methodology is the testing of hypotheses and the ability to make predictions. The overall goal of science is to better understand nature and our Universe.

Sediment. Solid material that has been or is being eroded, transported, and deposited. Transport can be due to fluvial, marine, glacial or aeolian agents.

Sedimentary Rock. Rocks formed by the deposition, alteration and/or compression, and lithification of weathered rock debris, chemical precipitates, or organic sediments. Also see clastic vs non-clastic sedimentary rocks.

Silica. Mineral that is composed of silicon dioxide, SiO_2.

Silicate. Group of minerals that have crystal structures based on a silica tetrahedron (SiO_4).

Silt. Mineral particle with a size between 0.004 and 0.06 millimeters in diameter. Also see clay and sand.

Soil. Layer of unconsolidated material found at the Earth's surface that has been influenced by the soil forming factors. climate, relief, parent material, time, and organisms. Soil normally consists of weathered mineral particles, dead and living organic matter, air space, and the soil solution.

Soil Colloids. Very small organic and inorganic particles found in a soil. Inorganic colloids are often clay particles. Soil colloids carry a negative electrical charge and are the primary sites for cation exchange. Soil colloids hold large quantities of elements and compounds which are used by plants for nutrition.

Soil Erosion. Transport of soil mineral particles and organic matter by wind, flowing water, or both. Human activities that disturb the soil surface or remove vegetation can enhance this natural process.

Soil Fertility. The ability of a soil to provide nutrients for plant growth.

Soil Horizon. Layer within a soil profile that differs physically, biologically or chemically from layers above and/or below it.

Soil Permeability. The rate at which water and air move vertically through a soil.

Soil Porosity. The volume of water that can be held in a soil. Also refers to the ratio of the volume of voids to the total volume of the soil.

Soil Profile. Vertical arrangement of layers or horizons in a soil.

Soil Science. The study of soils from an interdisciplinary perspective.

Soil Solution. Aqueous liquid found within a soil. This liquid normally contains ions released from mineral particles, organic matter or plant roots and leaves.

Soil Structure. General term that describes how mineral and particles organic matter of are organized and clumped together in a soil.

Soil Taxonomy. The classification of a soil in a hierarchical system based on its various properties. Grouping goes from general to specific.

Soil Texture. The relative quantities of the different types and sizes of mineral particles in a soil.

Soil Water. The water found occupying the pore spaces between soil particles.

Solum. Part of the soil that is capable of supporting life.

Succession. Directional cumulative change in the types plant species that occupy a given area, through time.

Tetrahedron. Silicon atom joined by four oxygen atoms (SiO_4). The atomic properties of this molecule cause it to develop a unique three dimensional crystal lattice that is pyramid shaped.

Texture. The relative quantities of the different types and sizes of mineral particles in a deposit of sediment.

Turbulent Flow. Movement of water within a stream that occurs as discrete eddies and vortices. Turbulent flow is caused by channel topography and friction.

Ultisols. Soil order (type) of the United States Natural Resources Conservation Service Soil Classification System. Tropical or subtropical soil that is in an advanced state of development. These soils have pronounced eluviation, clay accumulation in a subsurface layer, and are often poor in base cations.

Vertisols. (1) Soil order (type) of the United States Natural Resources Conservation Service Soil Classification System. Tropical or sub-tropical soil that has a high clay and base cation status.

(2) Soil order (type) of the Canadian System of Soil Classification. This soil has a high clay content and exhibits the effects of extreme contraction-expansion due to temporal changes in soil water content.

Viscosity. The amount of the resistance to flow in a fluid due to intermolecular friction.

Volcanic Ash. Small sized particles ejected from explosive volcanoes.

Volatilization. The process where a solid or liquid substance is converted into a gas.

Weathering. Physical, chemical or biological breakdown of rocks and minerals into smaller sized particles.

Wetland. Natural land-use type that is covered by salt water or fresh water for some time period. This land type can be identified by the presence of particular plant species or characteristic conditions.

Xerophytes. Plant that grow in or on extremely dry soils, *e.g.* cacti.

Zero-tillage. Zero tillage is a kind of tillage in which agricultural crop production is possible without any tillage operation.

Multiple Choice Questions

A. Fill in the blanks with appropriate word/term given below:

1. ________ rocks are the most abundant in the earth crust.
   (*a*) Metamorphic (*b*) Igneous
   (*c*) Sedimentary (*d*) Stratified
2. ________ rocks are the most abundant in the earth crust.
   (*a*) Acidic (*b*) Basic
   (*c*) Sub basic (*d*) Sub acidic
3. The Mho's scale hardness of apatite is ________.
   (*a*) 3.0 (*b*) 4.0
   (*c*) 5.0 (*d*) 6.0
4. The chemical composition of hematite is ________.
   (*a*) FeO (*b*) Fe_3O_4
   (*c*) Fe_2O_3 (*d*) FeO_2
5. The horizon A + B are collectively called ________.
   (*a*) Solum (*b*) Profile
   (*c*) Regolith (*d*) Lithosphere
6. The leaching of humus & sesquioxides from upper horizon is known as ________ process.
   (*a*) Gleiazation (*b*) Podzolization
   (*c*) Laterization (*d*) Precipitation
7. The chemical equation of $2 Fe_2O_3 + 3H_2O \rightarrow 2Fe_2O_3 3H_2O$ is ________ type of reaction.
   (*a*) Hydrolysis (*b*) Oxidation
   (*c*) Hydration (*d*) Solution
8. ________ is the active factor of soil formation.
   (*a*) Parent material (*b*) Climate
   (*c*) Time (*d*) Topography

9. The shrinkage and swelling characteristics are observed in ________ order.

(*a*) Entisol (*b*) Mollisol
(*c*) Inceptisol (*d*) Vertisol

10. The latest system of soil classification is ________.

(*a*) Soil genesis (*b*) Soil pedology
(*c*) Soil nomenclature (*d*) Soil taxonomy

11. Parent material deposited by action of glaciers is called ________.

(*a*) Lacustrine (*b*) Marine
(*c*) Moraine (*d*) Colluvial

12. The newly developed soils are placed in ________ order.

(*a*) Entisol (*b*) Inceptisol
(*c*) Oxisol (*d*) Alfisol

13. The scale of mapping of detailed soil survey is ________.

(*a*) 1" = 1 mile (*b*) 1" = 10 mile
(*c*) 8" = 1 mile (*d*) 5" = 1 mile

14. The apatite mineral contains ________ plant nutrient element.

(*a*) Nitrogen (*b*) Phosphorus
(*c*) Potassium (*d*) Sulphur

15. The essential element of ________ is released during weathering of turmaline mineral.

(*a*) Iron (*b*) Boron
(*c*) Zinc (*d*) Manganese

16. The marble is reformed during metamorphism from ________.

(*a*) Sandstone (*b*) Basaltic trap
(*c*) Limestone (*d*) Shale

17. Dolomite is a ________ type mineral.

(*a*) Carbonate (*b*) Oxide
(*c*) Hydroxide (*d*) Bicarbonate

18. ________ is an example of mineral that supply magnesium upon weathering.

(*a*) Turmaline (*b*) Apatite
(*c*) Talc (*d*) Pyrite

19. ________ mineral is the most resistance to chemical weathering.

(*a*) Kaolinite (*b*) Quartz
(*c*) Calcite (*d*) Gypsum

20. There are ________ capability classes in the system of land capability classification.

(*a*) Four (*b*) Five
(*c*) Eight (*d*) Ten

21. Organic mater in the soil ________ with rise in temperature.

(*a*) Increase (*b*) Affected positively
(*c*) Decrease (*d*) Unaffected

22. Water retained by air dried soils, is considered as ________ water.

(*a*) Gravitational (*b*) Capillary
(*c*) Hygroscopic (*d*) Available

23. The most cementing agent organic matter in soil can be removed by treatment of ________.

(*a*) HCl (*b*) H_2O_2
(*c*) C_2H_4 (*d*) H_2O

24. The size of silt partical as per international soil science society is ________

(*a*) 0.02 – 0.002 mm (*b*) less than 0.002 mm
(*c*) 0.2 – 0.02 mm (*d*) 2.0 – 0.2 mm

25. The soil moisture at hygroscopic co-efficient is ________ bar atmosphere.

(*a*) 1.0 (*b*) 0.33
(*c*) 31.0 (*d*) 15.0

26. The amount of air in a soil is generally ________ related to the amount of water in soil.

(*a*) Directly (*b*) Indirectly
(*c*) Not (*d*) Directly

27. Sand, silt and clay particles differ principally in ________.

(*a*) Mineral composition (*b*) Hardness
(*c*) Size (*d*) Density

28. The total surface area of 4 cm cube is ________.

(*a*) 16 cm^2 (*b*) 24 cm^2
(*c*) 64 cm^2 (*d*) 96 cm^2

29. The soil can be rolled into a wire at ________ moisture stage.

(*a*) Lower plastic limit (*b*) Upper plastic limit
(*c*) Wilting point (*d*) Hygroscopic point

30. The most active portion of soil is ________.

(*a*) Clay (*b*) Silt
(*c*) Colloid (*d*) Sand

31. The most important properties of clay minerals are ________.

(*a*) Expanding (*b*) Absorption
(*c*) Desorption (*d*) Contraction

32. The cation exchange capacity (CEC) of vermiculite clay mineral is ________ meq/100 g. soil.

(*a*) 10-20 (*b*) 20-40
(*c*) 40-80 (*d*) 100-200

33. The crystal units of kaolinate are held together by ________ linkages.

(*a*) Oxy – oxy (*b*) Oxy – hydroxy
(*c*) Hydroxy – hydroxy (*d*) Silica – alumina

34. Kaolinite is ________ type of clay mineral.

(*a*) 1:1 (*b*) 2:1
(*c*) 2:2 (*d*) 2:1:1

35. Clay particles are mostly shaped like ________.

(*a*) Sphere (*b*) Egg

(*c*) Flaks (*d*) Cube

36. Sesquioxides is a oxides of ________ cations.

(*a*) Divalent (*b*) Trivalent

(*c*) Tetravalent (*d*) None of these

37. ________ Clay is dominant in vertisol.

(*a*) Kaolinite (*b*) Illite

(*c*) Montmorillonite (*d*) Chlorite

38. The exchangeable cations are generally ________ susceptible to being washed out of soil.

(*a*) Easily (*b*) Equally

(*c*) Much less (*d*) Much more

39. Immobilization of nitrogen takes place at ________ C/N ratio.

(*a*) 10:1 (*b*) 20:1

(*c*) 30:1 (*d*) 60:1

40. CEC values typical of montmorillonite is ________ cmol(+)/kg soil

(*a*) 10 (*b*) 20

(*c*) 40 (*d*) 80

41. The transformation of NH_4 to NO_3 is ________ take place.

(*a*) Aminization (*b*) Amonification

(*c*) Denitrification (*d*) Nitrification

42. Under anaerobic conditions, ________ bacteria can fixed atmospheric nitrogen in soil

(*a*) Azotobacter (*b*) Clostidium

(*c*) Rhizobium (*d*) Psudomonas

43. Most of the nitrogen in soil is in the form of ________.

(*a*) Organic matter (*b*) Soluble ions

(*c*) Exchangeable cation (*d*) Gases

44. Plants generally take up nitrogen from the soil in the form of ________.

(*a*) Humus (*b*) Organic compound

(*c*) Nitrogen gas (*d*) Nitrate ion

45. ________ is the lowest moisture content at which the soil can be readily deformed or mold at without cracking.

(*a*) Plastic limit (*b*) Liquid limit

(*c*) Hygroscopic point (*d*) Saturation point

46. Phosphorus is taken up by plant in the form of ________.

(*a*) Aluminum phosphate (*b*) Iron phosphate

(*c*) Calcium phosphate (*d*) $H_2PO_4^-$ ion

47. In flooded conditions, the best type of nitrogen fertilizer to applied is ________.

(*a*) Urea (*b*) Sodium nitrate

(*c*) Ammonium chloride (*d*) Diammonium phosphate.

48. The most of phosphorus is taken up by plant comes into contact with plant roots by means the process of ________.

(*a*) Mass flow (*b*) Diffusion

(*c*) Root interception (*d*) Hydration

49. ________ is recognized the father of agricultural chemistry.

(*a*) Scofield (*b*) Liebig

(*c*) Arnon (*d*) Gris

50. ________ is known as beneficial elements.

(*a*) Cupper (*b*) Barium

(*c*) Nickel (*d*) Zinc

51. The critical limit of available phosphorus in soil is ________ kg/ha below which plant respond to its application.

(*a*) 10 (*b*) 28

(*c*) 50 (*d*) 140

52. Nematodes are known as ________.

(*a*) Predators (*b*) Parasites

(*c*) Detritivers (*d*) Primary producers

53. Nematode have the shape of ________.

(*a*) Tinymites (*b*) Round worms

(*c*) Branches filaments (*d*) Spirals

54. The most anaerobic organisms in the soil are ________.

(*a*) Bacteria (*b*) Fungi

(*c*) Algae (*d*) Actinomycets

55. Mycorhizae most commonly are significant with regard to increasing plant uptake of ________ nutrients.

(*a*) Nitrogen (*b*) Phosphorus

(*c*) Potassium (*d*) Sulphur

56. When organic matter is added to a soil, the availability of nitrogen may be quickly increased or decreased depending on the ________ of the added material.

(*a*) Acidity (*b*) Freshness

(*c*) C/N ratio (*d*) Moisture content.

57. The well decomposed most of the organic matter has C/N ration of ________

(*a*) 60:1 (*b*) 40:2

(*c*) 20:1 (*d*) 10:1

58. When the C/N ratio reaches to ________ an available nitrogen will begin to appear in the soil.

(*a*) 60:1 (*b*) 40:1

(*c*) 20:1 (*d*) 10:1

59. Released by microorganism of an inorganic plant nutrient in available form from organic matter is called ________.

(*a*) Nitrification (*b*) Mineralization

(*c*) Humification (*d*) Denitrification

60. In composing different soils of various textures, one would expect that the organic matter content would be ________.

(*a*) Smaller in sandy soil
(*b*) Greater in sandy soil
(*c*) Greater in fine textured soils
(*d*) Smaller in fine textured soils

61. Denitrification is carried out principles by ________.

(*a*) Anaerobic heterotrophs
(*b*) Aerobic heterotrophs
(*c*) Anaerobic autotrophs
(*d*) Aerobic cutrotrophs

62. Chlorophyll pigment activates process ________ in plant.

(*a*) Aminisation
(*b*) Oxidation
(*c*) Reductions
(*d*) Photosynthesis

63. ________ hormone can be used for weed control.

(*a*) MH
(*b*) GA_3
(*c*) TBA
(*d*) 2, 4-D

64. ________ occurs in the leaves of tobacco.

(*a*) Cocain
(*b*) Nicotine
(*c*) Colchicine
(*d*) Atropin

65. The ions pass from cell to cell through the ________ protoplasmic connections.

(*a*) Mitochondria
(*b*) Vacuole
(*c*) Plasmodesmeta
(*d*) Nucleae

66. ________ maintains water relations and turger pressure in plants.

(*a*) Calcium
(*b*) Magnesium
(*c*) Potassium
(*d*) Nitrogen

67. ________ nutrient is responsible for the Dieback of citrus.

(*a*) K
(*b*) Mg
(*c*) Cu
(*d*) Zn

68. ________ nutrient element is responsible for resistance to plant diseases.

(*a*) Ca
(*b*) Mg
(*c*) Na
(*d*) K

69. Phosphorus might be considered a potential water pollutant because ________.

(*a*) It is toxic to fish living in ill
(*b*) It is toxic to people who drink
(*c*) It fertilize algae and aquatic weed
(*d*) It acidifies natural waters

70. An excess application of common nitrogen as fertilizer to a farm fields, which modes of pollution would be likely occur ________.

(*a*) Ground water by NH_4
(*b*) Ground water by NO_3
(*c*) Ground water by NO_2
(*d*) Ground water by N_2

71. The RSC of water is ________ for the irrigation water contains 6, 4, 4 and 8 meq/l of Ca^{2+}, Mg^{2+}, CO_3^{2-} and HCO_3^-, respectively.

(*a*) 1.0
(*b*) 2.0
(*c*) 0 (Zero)
(*d*) (-2.0) negative

72. The water having Ca-10 meq/l, Mg-8 meq/l and Na 45 meq/l, its SAR will be ________.

(*a*) 15.0
(*b*) 22.5
(*c*) 34.0
(*d*) 45.0

73. At 0 pH the solution contains H^+ ion concentration of ________.

(*a*) 1 ppm (*b*) 1 mg/l

(*c*) 1 g/l (*d*) 1 percentage

74. The ion concentration in the solution is ________ times more at pH 5.0 as compare to that of at pH 8.0

(*a*) 30 (*b*) 1000

(*c*) 300 (*d*) 3000

75. The concept of pH is suggested by the scientist ________.

(*a*) Lambert (*b*) Hilgard

(*c*) Sorenson (*d*) Beer

76. EC value in dS/m is equal to ________.

(*a*) Micromhos/cm (*b*) Millimhos/cm

(*c*) Mhos/cm (*d*) Desimhos/m

77. To replace 6 cmol/kg exch. Na it required ________ ton gypsum/ha.

(*a*) 1.20 (*b*) 2.00

(*c*) 2.40 (*d*) 5.16

78. Saline soils are dominant in ________ salt.

(*a*) $NaHCO_3$ (*b*) Na_2CO_3

(*c*) NaCl (*d*) $CaSO_4$

79. Sodic soils are dominant in ________ salt.

(*a*) $NaHCO_3$ (*b*) NaCl

(*c*) Na_2SO_4 (*d*) $CaSO_4$

80. Saline alkali soil can be prevents to degradation during leaching with ________.

(*a*) Rain water (*b*) Sweet water

(*c*) Saline water (*d*) Distilled water

81. Soils become hazards when Ca/Mg ration is ________.

(*a*) 0.1 (*b*) 0.0

(*c*) 1.0 (*d*) 2.0

82. The leaching requirement of saline water having conductivity of 3 dS/m is ________ per cent to tolerate field crop at 4 dS/m ECe.

(*a*) 30% (*b*) 40%

(*c*) 60% (*d*) 75%

83. The EC of sea water is ________ dS/m.

(*a*) 48.5 (*b*) 46.0

(*c*) 24.0 (*d*) 58.0

84. Gypsum a soil amendment is very well useful to reclaim ________ soil.

(*a*) Saline (*b*) Acid saline

(*c*) Alkali soil (*d*) Saline alkali

85. One ion of calcium will replace ________ ion of sodium.

(*a*) One (*b*) Two

(*c*) Three (*d*) Four

86. Hazard due to high Na content in irrigation water is expressed by ________.

(*a*) pH (*b*) EC

(*c*) SAR (*d*) ESP

87. The ESP of soil is ________ when the soil having CEC and exch. Na of 20 and 8 cmol/kg, respectively.

(*a*) 10 (*b*) 20

(*c*) 40 (*d*) 48

88. The SAR of water is ________ containing Ca, Mg and Na were 20, 12 and 40 meq/l.

(*a*) 8 (*b*) 10

(*c*) 12 (*d*) 16

89. The salt content in soil at PWP will be ________ than that at the saturation point.

(*a*) Two times higher (*b*) Four times higher

(*c*) One & half times higher (*d*) One fourth times higher

90. The soil having ECe 5 dS/m will create the osmotic pressure ________ in soil solution

(*a*) 1:2 (*b*) 1.5

(*c*) 1.6 (*d*) 1.8

91. The yield of many crop is restricted at soil ECe ________ dS/m.

(*a*) 2-4 (*b*) 4-8

(*c*) 8-16 (*d*) more than 16

92. ________ has suggested RSC concept to evaluate irrigation water.

(*a*) Rechard (*b*) Eaton

(*c*) Scofield (*d*) Hilgard

93. Sodic soils fall in ________ suborder, as per soil taxonomy classification.

(*a*) Salorthid (*b*) Orthid

(*c*) Argid (*d*) Arid

94. In India about ________ million hectare lands is salt affected.

(*a*) 7.0 (*b*) 8.0

(*c*) 10.0 (*d*) 12.0

95. The reserved acidity of soil is measure by ________.

(*a*) pH (*b*) Gypsum requirement

(*c*) Lime requirement (*d*) EC

96. ________ soil have seldom more than 8.5 pH.

(*a*) Saline alkali (*b*) Non saline alkali

(*c*) Black alkali (*d*) Degraded alkali

97. Generally, non-saline alkali soils are developed in ________ climate.

(*a*) Arid (*b*) Semi arid

(*c*) Sub humid (*d*) Humid

98. The soil amendment ________ is the acid former type.

(*a*) Lime (*b*) Gypsum

(*c*) Sulphur (*d*) Dolomite

99. ________ ion on exchange complex is responsible for reserve acidity in soil.

(*a*) Aluminum (*b*) Calcium

(*c*) Potassium (*d*) Magnesium

100. The electrical conductivity of saturated gypsum solution is ________ dS/m.

(*a*) 1.00 (*b*) 1.41

(*c*) 2.20 (*d*) 2.67

101. The titration with EDTA is known as ________ method.

(*a*) Scoonover (*b*) Sorenson

(*c*) Versenate (*d*) Bover

102. The pH of $NH_4OH + NH_4Cl$ buffer solution is ________.

(*a*) 8.2 (*b*) 9.2

(*c*) 9.5 (*d*) 10.2

103. The estimation of gypsum requirement of sodic soil is done by ________ method

(*a*) Versenate (*b*) Scoonover

(*c*) Bover (*d*) Stainberg

104. ppm is equivalent to ________.

(*a*) meq/l (*b*) me/100 g

(*c*) μg/ml (*d*) μg/l

105. During estimation of organic carbon in soil, it will be oxidized with ________ reagent.

(*a*) K_2CrO_4 (*b*) K_2CO_3

(*c*) $K_2Cr_2O_7$ (*d*) $KHCO_3$

106. ________ reagent is used to extract available phosphorus in soil.

(*a*) $NaSO_4$ (*b*) NaCl

(*c*) Na_2CO_3 (*d*) $NaHCO_3$

107. During phosphorus determination, a blue colour is developed with ________ reagent.

(*a*) $BaCl_2$ (*b*) K_2CrO_4

(*c*) NaCl (*d*) $SnCl_2$

108. Copper wires carry electric current faster than ________ wire.

(*a*) Aluminum (*b*) Silver

(*c*) Gold (*d*) Platinum

109. A^0 (angstron) is equal to ________.

(*a*) 10^{-8} cm (*b*) 10^{-8} mm

(*c*) 10^{-10} cm (*d*) 10^{-9} mm

110. Iodides are act as ________ agent.

(*a*) Oxidizing agent (*b*) Reducing

(*c*) Strong oxidizing (*d*) Weak oxidizing

111. ________ is used as desiccating agent.

(*a*) $CaCO_3$ (*b*) $CaSO_4$

(*c*) $CaCl_2$ (*d*) $CaHCO_3$

112. The intensity of blue colour is measured using ________ filter in photoelectric colourimeter.

(*a*) Red coloured
(*b*) Yellow coloured
(*c*) Green coloured
(*d*) Blue coloured

113. ________ in aqueous solution gives acidic reaction.

(*a*) Na_2SO_4
(*b*) NaCl
(*c*) $CaCl_2$
(*d*) $CaCO_3$

114. The pH range of colour change for phenolphthalein indicator is ________.

(*a*) 7.00 – 7.8
(*b*) 7.8 – 8.2
(*c*) 8.3 – 10.0
(*d*) 9.0 – 10.6

115. ________ is used as primary standard in most of the chemical laboratories.

(*a*) Potassium hydroxide
(*b*) Potassium hydrogen phthalate
(*c*) Potassium permanganate
(*d*) Potassium chromate

116. ________ is used in ion chromatography.

(*a*) Resine
(*b*) Silica gel
(*c*) Plaster of paris
(*d*) Kaoline

117. The flamephotometric is used for the determination of ________ ions.

(*a*) Nitrogen
(*b*) Phosphorus
(*c*) Potassium
(*d*) Sulphur

118. ________ Method is used widely in the soil testing laboratory for evaluation available P status.

(*a*) Subbiah and Bajaj
(*b*) Ramamoorthy
(*c*) Olsen
(*d*) Bray

119. ________ method has become the most widely accepted procedure for measuring the exchangeable K.

(*a*) 1N ammonium acetate
(*b*) Alkaline permanganate
(*c*) Versenate
(*d*) Morgan

120. The Soil critical value of nutrient below, which plant responds to nutrient, is fixed by the method described by ________.

(*a*) Cate and Nelson
(*b*) Waugh and Fitts
(*c*) Schmehl and Humbert
(*d*) Krishnamoorthy

121. Nitrate can also be toxic to mammals if present in ground water at concentration more than ________ ppm.

(*a*) 10
(*b*) 15
(*c*) 30
(*d*) 45

ANSWERS

1.	b	2.	c	3.	c	4.	c	5.	a	6.	a	7.	b	8.	c	9.	b	10.	d
11.	c	12.	a	13.	c	14.	d	15.	b	16.	c	17.	a	18.	c	19.	a	20.	c
21.	c	22.	c	23.	b	24.	a	25.	c	26.	d	27.	c	28.	d	29.	a	30.	c

31.	d	32.	d	33.	b	34.	a	35.	c	36.	c	37.	c	38.	c	39.	d	40.	d
41.	d	42.	a	43.	a	44.	d	45.	a	46.	d	47.	c	48.	d	49.	b	50.	c
51.	b	52.	d	53.	b	54.	a	55.	b	56.	c	57.	d	58.	d	59.	b	60.	c
61.	b	62.	d	63.	d	64.	d	65.	c	66.	c	67.	c	68.	d	69.	c	70.	a
71.	b	72.	a	73.	c	74.	b	75.	c	76.	b	77.	d	78.	c	79.	a	80.	c
81.	a	82.	d	83.	d	84.	c	85.	b	86.	c	87.	c	88.	b	89.	b	90.	a
91.	b	92.	b	93.	c	94.	a	95.	c	96.	d	97.	c	98.	c	99.	a	100.	c
101.	c	102.	d	103.	d	104.	c	105.	c	106.	d	107.	d	108.	a	109.	a	110.	b
111.	c	112.	b	113.	c	114.	c	115.	b	116.	a	117.	c	118.	c	119.	a	120.	a
121.	b																		

(*b*) Select the most suitable alternative given below for the following statements

1. **Which of the following rock has an acidic nature.**
   (*a*) Gabro (*b*) Basaltic trap
   (*c*) Diorite (*d*) Granite
2. **Which of the following minerals is softer than fingernail?**
   (*a*) Quartz (*b*) Gypsum
   (*c*) Calcite (*d*) Corundum
3. **Which of the following mineral has the chemical composition $Fe_2O_3\ 3H_2O$.**
   (*a*) Limonite (*b*) Haematite
   (*c*) Mangesite (*d*) Magnesite
4. **Micashist is one of the following types of metamorphic rock?**
   (*a*) Hydro metamorphic (*b*) Dynemo metamorphic
   (*c*) Thermo metamorphic (*d*) Conglomarate type rock
5. **Which of the following mineral contains potassium element?**
   (*a*) Gibsite (*b*) Calcite
   (*c*) Biotite mica (*d*) Falsite
6. **How much oxygen present in the earth crust.**
   (*a*) 25% (*b*) 32%
   (*c*) 46% (*d*) 52%
7. **Which of the following soil is formal recently?**
   (*a*) Vertisol (*b*) Alfisol
   (*c*) Histisol (*d*) Entisol
8. **Which of the following is a secondary mineral?**
   (*a*) Feldspare (*b*) Biotite
   (*c*) Kaolinite (*d*) Hornblend

9. Which of the following soils has pH more than 9.0 ?

(*a*) Saline (*b*) Saline alkali
(*c*) Non saline alkali (*d*) White alkali

10. Which of the following is least resistant to weathering mineral?

(*a*) Gypsum (*b*) Kaolinite
(*c*) Musco white mica (*d*) Quartz

11. Which of the following mineral is element form?

(*a*) Graphite (*b*) Apatite
(*c*) Talc (*d*) Calcite

12. From which of the following slate is reformed metamorphically.

(*a*) Sand stone (*b*) Shale
(*c*) Lime stone (*d*) Silicate clay

13. Which of the following is oldest of rock?

(*a*) Basaltic trap (*b*) Granite
(*c*) Sand stone (*d*) Lime stone

14. Soils derived from trap are generally.

(*a*) Poor in fertility (*b*) Fertile
(*c*) Acidic in nature (*d*) Sandy in texture

15. Which of the following type soil is generally easiest to manage for crops?

(*a*) Loamy sand (*b*) Clay loam
(*c*) Silty loam (*d*) Sandy loam

16. Which of the following has prismatic structure with round shape?

(*a*) Columnar (*b*) Laminar
(*c*) Angular blocky (*d*) Sub angular blocky

17. The extent of damage due to a crop by a period of waterlogged condition will damage on the following.

(*a*) Plant species (*b*) Stage of growth
(*c*) Organic nature (*d*) None of them

18. Which of the following is most sticky and plastic when wet.

(*a*) Vermiculite (*b*) Kaolinite
(*c*) Illite (*d*) Smectite

19. Which of the following has very low net negative charge of approximately 2-3 cmol/kg?

(*a*) Allophane (*b*) Vermiculite
(*c*) Smectite (*d*) Illite

20. One of the following is an example of non-expanding silicate clay.

(*a*) Kaolinite (*b*) Fine grind mica (Illite)
(*c*) Smactite (*d*) Motmorillonite

21. Which of the following mineral is called ferromagnesium ?

(*a*) Limonite (*b*) Muscovite
(*c*) Feldspare (*d*) Olivine

22. Which of the following is non silicate mineral ?

(*a*) Apatite (*b*) Mica
(*c*) Badeline (*d*) Chlorite

23. Which of the following mineral is common in sulphur containing mineral?

(*a*) Dolomite (*b*) Apatite
(*c*) Pyrite (*d*) Calcite

24. Clay particles are mostly shaped.

(*a*) Prism (*b*) Egg
(*c*) Cube (*d*) Flakes

25. The distance between adjacent crystal layer is narrowest in.

(*a*) Illite (*b*) Kaolinite
(*c*) Vermiculite (*d*) Smectite

26. Give the name of one of the weathering process from the following match with the equation $4\ FeO + O_2 \rightarrow 2\ Fe_2O_3$

(*a*) Carbonation (*b*) Oxidation
(*c*) Hydrolysis (*d*) Hydration

27. The process of washing out is term.

(*a*) Illuviation (*b*) Eluvial
(*c*) Eluviations (*d*) Illuvial

28. Which of the following is generally taken up by plant in the greatest amount?

(*a*) N (*b*) P
(*c*) K (*d*) Ca

29. Which of the following is less essential for plant growth than next to N.

(*a*) P (*b*) K
(*c*) S (*d*) Zn

30. Which of the following is most closely associate with physiological functions of protein synthesis?

(*a*) Ca (*b*) Zn
(*c*) K (*d*) N

31. Which of the following type structure tends to impede drainage?

(*a*) Blocky (*b*) Prismatic
(*c*) Platy (*d*) Columnar

32. The mechanical separations of soil particles are based on one of the following law.

(*a*) Boyle's (*b*) Darcy's
(*c*) Charl's (*d*) Stokes

33. Term loam refers to soil.

(*a*) With equal percentage of sand, silt and clay
(*b*) Equally influenced by sand, silt and clay
(*c*) With well developed granular structure
(*d*) In good tilth

34. Which of the factors listed below would tend to promote warmer soil temperature in spring?

(*a*) Organic mulch
(*b*) Sandy texture
(*c*) High moisture content
(*d*) Sowing at N-W direction

35. Which of the following texture is more susceptible to water caused erosion?

(*a*) Sandy
(*b*) Silty
(*c*) Loamy
(*d*) Clayey

36. Which one of the following soil has highest bulk density?

(*a*) Sandy loam
(*b*) Sandy
(*c*) Loamy sand
(*d*) Sandy clay loam

37. Which of the following water is utilized by plant from the soil?

(*a*) Gravitational water
(*b*) Capillary water
(*c*) Capillary water
(*d*) Hygroscopic water

38. Higher the valency of ion has replacing power.

(*a*) Lower
(*b*) Medium
(*c*) Greater
(*d*) Nothing

39. Colloidal partical are generally less than.

(*a*) 1 micrometer
(*b*) 2 micrometer
(*c*) 10 micrometer
(*d*) 100 micrometer

40. If the following values are for soil moisture potential, which soil is the driest?

(*a*) 5 bar
(*b*) 3 atms
(*c*) 500 cm H_2O
(*d*) 1 Mpa

41. Pascal is a unit of.

(*a*) Force
(*b*) Energy
(*c*) Pressure
(*d*) Area

42. Which ODR indicate the better soil aeration?

(*a*) 15×10^{-8} g cm^{-1} min^{-1}
(*b*) 30×10^{-8} g cm^{-1} min^{-1}
(*c*) 60×10^{-8} g cm^{-1} min^{-1}
(*d*) 45×10^{-8} g cm^{-1} min^{-1}

43. Which of the listed below specific heats is typical of a dry soil ?

(*a*) 0.1 cal g^{-1} °C^{-1}
(*b*) 0.2 cal g^{-1} °C^{-1}
(*c*) 1.0 cal g^{-1} °C^{-1}
(*d*) 2.0 cal g^{-1} °C^{-1}

44. Which group of organisms is generally the most numerous in soil ?

(*a*) Fungi
(*b*) Algae
(*c*) Bacteria
(*d*) Earthworms

45. The following organism is generally dominant in fresh plant residues.

(*a*) Fungi
(*b*) Bacteria
(*c*) Algae
(*d*) Actinomycetes

46. Which of the following organism is generally credited with producing the sweet aroma of freshly ploughed soil ?

(*a*) Fungi
(*b*) Bacteria
(*c*) Algae
(*d*) Actinomycetes

47. The rapid decomposition of organic matter supporting a large number of heterotrophs in soil.

(*a*) Destroys the soil granular structure
(*b*) Release extra oxygen in soil
(*c*) Suppresses the incidence at root disease
(*d*) Uses up soil moisture before plant can get it

48. The 'ash' is a small but important fraction of the organic matter because it contains.

(*a*) Carbon (*b*) Carbon dioxide
(*c*) Mineral elements (*d*) Nitrogen

49. In what form is carbon commonly lost from a soil in the drainage water.

(*a*) CO_2 (*b*) C_2H_4
(*c*) HCO_3 (*d*) CO

50. A hetrotrophs bacteria has which one of the following characteristics.

(*a*) Can live at a wide range of pH
(*b*) Can photosynthesis in light
(*c*) Get it carbon from CO_2
(*d*) Needs energy rich organic substances for food

51. Under which of the following conditions would it be most important to mix soybean seed with rhizobia inoculums at sowing.

(*a*) The field had been cropped to soybean in a monoculture
(*b*) The field had been cropped to corn-soybean rotation with less fertilization
(*c*) No soybean had been grown in the field previously
(*d*) The field had been limed recently

52. Which of the following compound is not ionized or not an electrolyte substance.

(*a*) Muriate of potash (*b*) Diammonium phosphate
(*c*) Ammonium sulphate (*d*) Urea

53. Origin of negative charge in kaolinite is due to.

(*a*) Isomorphus replacement (*b*) Dissociation of OH- ion
(*c*) pH dependent (*d*) Broken edge

54. The transformation of NH_4^+ to NO_3^- is due to.

(*a*) Aminization (*b*) Amonification
(*c*) Denitrification (*d*) Nitrification

55. Available phosphorus in soil is governed by.

(*a*) C/N ratio (*b*) Sesquioxide/silica ratio
(*c*) Ca/Mg ratio (*d*) Na/K ratio

56. Which of the following type of clay can most readily fix NH_4^+ ion ?

(*a*) Chlorite (*b*) Kaolinite
(*c*) Vermiculite (*d*) All phase

57. Farmers often speak of 'light' or 'heavy' soils. These terms reflect to.

(*a*) Particle density (*b*) Bulk density
(*c*) Soil texture (*d*) Soil porosity

58. What is the Q of a soil with bulk density D_b = 1.4 Mg/m^3 and water content w = 45% ?

(*a*) 14% (*b*) 45%
(*c*) 63% (*d*) 72%

59. Which of the following soil contains the greatest volume of water at 15 bar pressure?

(*a*) Sandy loam (*b*) Clayey
(*c*) Silty loam (*d*) Clay loam

60. At what pH range P generally most available for plant.

(*a*) 5.5 – 6.5 (*b*) 6.5 – 7.5
(*c*) 7.5 – 8.5 (*d*) 8.5 – 9.5

61. Which of the following element is most commonly involved with "Luxury consumption"?

(*a*) Sulphur (*b*) Potassium
(*c*) Phosphorus (*d*) Nitrogen

62. Luxury consumption is detrimental because.

(*a*) It is wasteful (*b*) It is cause K toxicity
(*c*) It cause low yield (*d*) More uptake by plant

63. The proportion of the total soil K that is available form is usually.

(*a*) About 50 % (*b*) About 25 %
(*c*) Very large proportion (*d*) Very small proportion

64. Plant root generally take up sulphur in the form of.

(*a*) SO_4^{2-} (*b*) H_2S
(*c*) S^{2-} (*d*) SO_2

65. Which of the following micronutrient element is found in plant in the greatest quantity ?

(*a*) Zn (*b*) Fe
(*c*) Cu (*d*) Mo

66. Which of the following condition would be most increase the availability of Fe ?

(*a*) Well aerated dry soil with low pH (*b*) Well aerated dry soil with high pH
(*c*) Wet soil with low pH (*d*) Wet soil with high pH

67. Which of the following constituent of chlorophyll and is located at its center?

(*a*) Ca (*b*) Mg
(*c*) K (*d*) Na

68. The translocation of sugars in plant is governed by.

(*a*) Mo (*b*) S
(*c*) N (*d*) B

69. Which of the following element is require for fixation of atmospheric nitrogen in soil ?

(*a*) B (*b*) Mo
(*c*) S (*d*) P

70. Which of the following yellowing symptoms of plant is observed for nitrogen deficiency?

(*a*) Upper leaves (*b*) Middle leaves
(*c*) Lower leaves (*d*) Small spots on leaves

71. Which of the following nutrient is responsible for the gummosis in citrus ?

(*a*) Cu (*b*) Zn
(*c*) B (*d*) Mo

72. An abnormal mitosis in plant takes place due to.

(*a*) Ca deficiency (*b*) P deficiency
(*c*) B deficiency (*d*) Mn deficiency

73. Which of the following is responsible for the little leaf of cotton?

(*a*) Cu (*b*) Fe
(*c*) Zn (*d*) P

74. A hollow stem of cauliflower is caused by.

(*a*) Mo (*b*) B
(*c*) Cu (*d*) Zn

75. Which of the following element is responsible for energy transfer process in plant?

(*a*) Sulphur (*b*) Phosphorus
(*c*) Boron (*d*) Iron

76. The reduction of NO_3 to NO_2 is due to.

(*a*) B (*b*) Co
(*c*) Mo (*d*) S

77. Which of the following nutrient encourage vegetative growth?

(*a*) Mg (*b*) N
(*c*) S (*d*) K

78. Root growth is particularly affected by.

(*a*) Copper (*b*) Phosphorus
(*c*) Zinc (*d*) Magnesium

79. Almost 95 % of Indian soils are low or medium in.

(*a*) Zinc (*b*) Phosphorus
(*c*) Potassium (*d*) Sulphur

80. A straight fertilizer is one which.

(*a*) Comes straight from the factory (*b*) Dissolves quickly
(*c*) Has one major nutrient (*d*) In liquid form

81. Which of the following fertilizer create the acidity in soil with continuous application?

(*a*) DAP (*b*) MOP
(*c*) SSP (*d*) Nitrate

82. The optimum fertilizer dose is one which maximizes.

(*a*) Soil fertility (*b*) Yield
(*c*) Profits (*d*) Water use

83. The most important source of sulphur for the Indian soils is.

(*a*) Gypsum (*b*) SSP
(*c*) Pyrite (*d*) AS

84. The state using most fertilizer per hectare.

(*a*) Tamilnadu (*b*) Punjab
(*c*) West Bengal (*d*) Kerala

85. The central fertilizer quality control institute is located at.

(*a*) Hyderabad (*b*) Krishi Bhavan
(*c*) Faridabad (*d*) Pune

86. Cereal straw is particularly rich source of.

(*a*) Calcium (*b*) Potassium
(*c*) Ferrous iron (*d*) Zinc

87. Indian depends completely on import for its need of.

(*a*) Rock phosphorus (*b*) Potash
(*c*) Gas (*d*) Zinc ash

88. Most commonly soil type found in India is.

(*a*) Black (*b*) Red
(*c*) Alkali (*d*) Laterite

89. A soil having pH 8.8 is called.

(*a*) Normal (*b*) Alkaline
(*c*) Alkali (*d*) White alkali

90. Which of the following method of irrigation the salt are accumulates the maximum at surface?

(*a*) Flood irrigation (*b*) Sprinkler irrigation
(*c*) Drip Irrigation (*d*) Ridge and furrow irrigation

91. The Na hazard in irrigation water can best be expressed by.

(*a*) pH (*b*) SAR
(*c*) EC (*d*) ESP

92. The soil having pH 7.8, ECe 2.4 and ESP 24 is classified as.

(*a*) Saline alkali (*b*) Non saline alkali
(*c*) White alkali (*d*) Normal one

93. What will be SAR of water containing Ca^{+2}, Mg^{+2} and Na^{+} ions 20, 12 and 40 mg/l, respectively?

(*a*) 4.0 (*b*) 5.0
(*c*) 10.0 (*d*) 20.0

94. Which of the following state rank first in per cent of salt affected soil that of net cultivated area of the state?

(*a*) UP (*b*) Haryana
(*c*) Gujarat (*d*) Rajasthan

95. Phosphorus might be considered a potential waters pollutant because.

(*a*) It is toxic to fish living in water (*b*) It is toxic to reapply who drink
(*c*) It fertilize algae and aquatic weed (*d*) It acidify natural waters

96. Which of the gases listed below is most severally toxic to plant growth?

(*a*) CO_2 (*b*) N_2
(*c*) C_2H_4 (*d*) Argon

97. Which form of nitrogen is comparatively more toxic?

(*a*) NO_2^- (*b*) NO_3^-
(*c*) NH_4^+ (*d*) $CO(NH_2)_2$

98. **According to National Academy of Science, the toxic limit of fluride in water is.**
(*a*) 1.0 mg/l (*b*) 2.0 mg/l
(*c*) 3.0 mg/l (*d*) 5.0 mg/l

99. **Which of the following salts comparatively more toxic for the plant growth.**
(*a*) $MgSO_4$ (*b*) Na_2SO_4
(*c*) Na_2CO_3 (*d*) $CaSO_4$

100. **Following one is the lower toxic limit of boron content in irrigation water.**
(*a*) 0.33 ppm (*b*) 0.67 ppm
(*c*) 0.1 ppm (*d*) 1.0 ppm

101. **Most energy required to detach the particle size.**
(*a*) 0.1 mm diameter (*b*) 0.01 mm diameter
(*c*) 0.001 mm diameter (*d*) 0.0001 mm diameter

102. **Which of the following type of particle is most susceptible to wind erosion?**
(*a*) Coarse sand (*b*) Fine sand
(*c*) Silt (*d*) Clay

103. **Properties of the silicon deficient Asian soils include–**
(*a*) High base saturation (*b*) High total silicon
(*c*) High pH (*d*) High total aluminium content

104. **It is generally accepted that the Gramineae members contain ________ times the silicon concentration normally found in legumes and other dicotyledonous plants.**
(*a*) 10-20 (*b*) 20-30
(*c*) 05-10 (*d*) 05-10

105. **Nitrogen fertilizer use efficiency in rice can be increased by using–**
(*a*) Sulphur coated urea (*b*) Neem coated urea
(*c*) Urea super granules (*d*) All of the above

106. **Which one of the following nutrients plays the most effective role in controlling the rate of transpiration?**
(*a*) Phosphorus (*b*) Zinc
(*c*) Potassium (*d*) Phosphorus

107. **Crops during any season are generally able to recover only________ of the added fertilizer phosphorus–**
(*a*) Less than 30% (*b*) Less than 25%
(*c*) Less than 35% (*d*) None of these

108. **Potassium salts are–**
(*a*) Less mobile than phosphorus (*b*) Less mobile than nitrates
(*c*) More mobile than nitrates (*d*) None of these

109. **Broadcast potassium is ________than banded–**
(*a*) More efficient (*b*) Less efficient than
(*c*) As efficient as (*d*) None of these

110. **Winter application of phosphorus is followed by ________.**
(*a*) Warm areas (*b*) Cool areas
(*c*) Both of these (*d*) None of these

111. Potassium is utilized more efficiently if applied ________.

(a) Before/at planning (b) Side dressed
(c) Top dressed (d) None of these

112. Tillage of the soil ________ rate of disappearance of organic matter.

(a) Increases (b) Maintains
(c) Reduces (d) Has no effect.

113. Amongst micronutrients application of which one of the following has become necessary in paddy crop in north India–

(a) Iron (b) Zinc
(c) Boron (d) Copper

114. Availability o phosphorus to crop plants is most effected by–

(a) Soil pH (b) Temperature
(c) Biological factors (d) Soil moisture stress

115. Nitrogen in DAP is–

(a) 36% (b) 9%
(c) 18% (d) 46%

116. In mustard crop gypsum is applied to supply–

(a) Sulphur (b) Calcium
(c) Nitrogen (d) Zinc

117. Among oil cakes the highest nitrogen content is in–

(a) Neem cake (b) Castor cake
(c) Coconut cake (d) Groundnut cake

118. In saline soil major problem is due to–

(a) High exchangeable sodium. (b) Low soil pH
(c) High pH (d) High content of soluble salts.

119. Symptoms of iron deficiency in plants are–

(a) Yellowing of whole plant (b) Drying of lower leaves
(c) Yellowing of lower leaves (d) Yellowing of young growing leaves.

120. Opening of stomata is related with–

(a) Potassium (b) Iron
(c) Calcium (d) Magnesium

121. Which of the following adsorbed cations are largely responsible for soil acidity?

(a) Hydrogen (b) Sodium
(c) Calcium (d) Aluminium

122. Which of the following soils have electrical conductivity less than 4 dS/m.

(a) Acid (b) Saline
(c) Saline-sodic (d) Sodic

123. Which of the following are salt sensitive crops ?

(a) Barley (b) Onion
(c) Potato (d) Sugarbeet

124. Which of the following are metamorphic rocks?

(*a*) Schist (*b*) Slate

(*c*) Dolomite (*d*) Shales

125. Per cent pore space can not be calculated correctly by–

(*a*) % Pore space = (BD/PD) × 100 (*b*) % pore space = 100% solid

(*c*) % Pore space = (PD/BD) × 100 (*d*) % Pore space = (BD/2.65 g/cc.) X 100

126. The earth worm casts care definitely higher in ________ than the soil.

(*a*) Bacteria (*b*) Organic matter

(*c*) Available nutrients (*d*) All of these

127. Development of acid soils in humid areas is largely associated with–

(*a*) Intense weathering (*b*) Leaching out of basic cations

(*c*) Oxidation of pyrite (*d*) Use of poor quality irrigation water

128. Use of phospho-gypsum has been found to be useful in the amelioration of–

(*a*) Sub-soil acidity (*b*) Alkali soils

(*c*) Saline soils (*d*) Acid sulphate soils

129. Silica-sesquioxide ratio is useful in the evaluation of sol in respect of–

(*a*) Silicon content (*b*) Nutrient availability

(*c*) Its age (*d*) Iron & aluminium content

130. Consider the following statements cation exchange of soil colloidal clay is due to–

(*a*) Silicon tetrahedrallayer (*b*) Hydration of clays

(*c*) Broken edges of clay lattices (*d*) Isorphious substitution

131. Non-essential but useful nutrients for plants would include–

(*a*) Vanadium and Sodium (*b*) Vanadium and Chlorine

(*c*) Carbon and Vanadium (*d*) Sodium and Chlorine

132. Which of the following are the criteria for determining the essentiality of nutrients elements–

1. A deficiency of the particular element makes it impossible for the plant to grow normally or complete its life cycle.

2. The nutrient is abundantly present in the soil for rapid plant absorption.

3. The element is directly involved in the plant metabolism

4. The deficiency symptoms can be corrected only by supplying the nutrients in question.

Select the correct answer using the codes given–

(*a*) 1, 3 & 4 (*b*) 1, 2, 3 & 4

(*c*) 2, 3 &4 (*d*) 1, 2 & 4

133. Which one of the following nitrogen factors would bring down wide C : N ratio material of 100 : 1 to the desirable C : N ratio of 40 : 1 for compost making ?

(*a*) 1.5 (*b*) 2.5

(*c*) 2.0 (*d*) 1.0

134. Which of the following elements is part of the chlorophyll?

(*a*) Iron (*b*) Magnesium

(*c*) Zinc (*d*) Manganese

135. Which of the following mineral elements is essential for nitrogen metabolism in green plants?

(*a*) P (*b*) Zn
(*c*) Mo (*d*) K

136. Which element is immobile in the plants?

(*a*) Potassium (*b*) Nitrogen
(*c*) Calcium (*d*) Phosphorus

137. The chemical characteristics feature of non saline alkali soil: EC, pH and ESP respectively.

(*a*) $< 4, > 15, > 8.5$ (*b*) $< 4, < 15, > 8.5$
(*c*) $< 4, > 15, < 8.5$ (*d*) $> 4, > 15, > 8.5$

138. What is the upper crops tolerable limit of Biuret in urea?

(*a*) 1.5% (*b*) 1.5%
(*c*) 1.0% (*d*) 3.0%

139. The crop plants transpire more when there is

(*a*) High temperature and low humidity (*b*) High humidity and high wind velocity.
(*c*) High temperature and high humidity (*d*) Low temperature and low humidity.

140. An organism which converts nitrite to nitrate is–

(*a*) Azotobactor (*b*) Nitrobacter
(*c*) Nitrosomonas (*d*) Nitrogenase

141. The efficiency of field irrigation would be more in–

(*a*) Sandy loam (*b*) Loam
(*c*) Clay loam (*d*) Heavy loam

142. Which one of the following occupies the highest volume percent in a fine sandy loam surface soil in good condition, for plant growth?

(*a*) Organic matter
(*b*) Mineral matter
(*c*) Pore space which includes air and/or water
(*d*) Others including macro and micro flora and fauna

143. Pedology considers soil as a:

(*a*) Natural body (*b*) Medium for plant growth.
(*c*) Powdered rock mass of the earth's crust (*d*) Purely a synthesized one.

144. The fundamental role of root hairs in plants is

(*a*) To absorb water and mineral salts from the Soil
(*b*) To bind soil particles to the root for firm fixation o the plant
(*c*) To product the young root from damage by coarse soil particles
(*d*) To protect he root from soil microbes

145. Water and mineral salts are Translocated in plants in the–

(*a*) Xylem (*b*) Pholem
(*c*) Collenchyma (*d*) Porenchyma1, 2 & 4

146. The layers in soil are referred to as–

(*a*) Hard pans (*b*) Horizons
(*c*) Profile (*d*) Pedocals

147. Chlorites are basically silicates of–

(*a*) Aluminium with some magnesium and luminium
(*b*) Iron and Aluinium
(*c*) Magnesium with some iron and aluminium
(*d*) Iron with some magnesium and aluminium.

148. The cation exchange capacity of a mineral soil containing predominately kolinitic clay minerals generally ranges between–

(*a*) 80-100 me e per 10 gm, Soil (*b*) More hen 100 m.e. per 100gm soil
(*c*) 3.15 m.e. per 100g soil (*d*) 15-40 m.e. per 100 gm soil

149. In soil science micelle stands for–

(*a*) Negatively charged silt particles with high CEC
(*b*) Negatively charged sand particles with high CEC
(*c*) Micropores in between textural particles
(*d*) Colloidalparticle carrying negative change

150. Soils high in swelling clays which crack widely upon drying resulting in shrinking, shearing and soil mass movement are characteristics of–

(*a*) Podzols (*b*) Entisols
(*c*) Ultisols (*d*) Vertisols

151. Which one of the following micro-organisms is responsible for maximum nutrient cycling in the soil?

(*a*) Fungi (*b*) Actinomycetes
(*c*) Bacteria (*d*) Algae

152. Which state is devoid of arid zone?

(*a*) Madhya Pradesh (*b*) Andhra Pradesh
(*c*) Punjab (*d*) Maharashtra

153. Indian Institute of Soil Science is located at–

(*a*) Ludhiana (*b*) Hisar
(*c*) New Delhi (*d*) Bhopal

154. The layer in the soil profile where material removed from the two overlying horizons is deposited is called–

(*a*) A-Horizon (*b*) D-horizons
(*c*) C-horizon (*d*) B-horizon

155. The layer in the soil profile where material removed from the two overlying horizons is wasing out is called–

(*a*) A-Horizon (*b*) D-horizons
(*c*) C-horizon (*d*) B-horizon

156. The diameter of very fine sand particles is–

(*a*) Below 0.001 mm (*b*) Below 0.002 mm
(*c*) Below 0.005 mm (*d*) 0.01-0.05 mm

157. The mineral weathering and clay formation are rapid where the climate is–

(*a*) Warm and moist (*b*) Warm and dry

(*c*) Cold and dry (*d*) Cold and moist

158. When organic matter with wide C : N ratio (70 : 1) is added to the soil, the net effect is the disappearance of mineral nitrogen due to–

(*a*) Mineralization (*b*) Nitrogen reduction

(*c*) Immobilization (*d*) Nitrogen transformation

159. The addition of excess soluble phosphatic fertilizers to soil may affect plant growth by–

(*a*) Inhibiting the growth of icroorganisms

(*b*) Reducing the availability of zinc

(*c*) Reducing the availability, the concentration of plant nutrients

(*d*) Precipitating iron and aluminium

160. In order to assess the immediate fertility level of a given soil for potassium, which one of the following forms of potassium present in soil would one test for?

(*a*) Exchangeable K (*b*) K held in the silt

(*c*) Water soluble K (*d*) Total K

161. What culture should be given priority on groundnut cultivation–

(*a*) Azospirilla (*b*) Rhizobia

(*c*) Mycorrhiza (*d*) Frankia

162. Which one of the following concentrated organic manures has maximum phosphorus content?

(*a*) Fish meal (*b*) Guano

(*c*) Steral meal (*d*) Poultary manual

163. Alkali soils are treated with gypsum to correct the deficiency of–

(*a*) Sulphur (*b*) Calcium

(*c*) Zinc (*d*) Magnesium

164. Which micronutrient is most deficient in Indo-Gangatic alluvium soils?

(*a*) Copper (*b*) Zinc

(*c*) Iron (*d*) Manganese

165. Which fertilizer is most beneficial for alkali soils?

(*a*) Urea (*b*) Ammonium nitrate

(*c*) Ammonium sulphate (*d*) Calcium ammonium nitrate

166. The most productive normal soils have pH–

(*a*) 5-7 (*b*) 7-9

(*c*) 4-6 (*d*) 6-8

167. Which is the most harmful salt in salt affected soils?

(*a*) Sodium carbonate (*b*) Sodium sulphate

(*c*) Sodium chloride (*d*) Sodium bicarbonate

168. Which element in not phytotoxic?

(*a*) Selenium (*b*) Lethium

(*c*) Flourine (*d*) Boron

169. What happens when a saline-alkali soil is leached with water?

(*a*) pH and EC both decrease (*b*) pH increase and EC decrease

(*c*) pH and EC both increase (*d*) pH and EC both decrease

170. Which fraction of humus is soluble both in alkali and alcohol?

(*a*) Fluric acid (*b*) Humic acid

(*c*) Hymaomelanic acid (*d*) Humin

171. Which crop has the maximum nitrogen fixing potential–

(*a*) Pigeon pea (*b*) Soybean

(*c*) Guar (*d*) Groundnut

172. Rhizobium inoculation is effective only when an active and efficient strain is used under optimum–

(*a*) EC (*b*) N

(*c*) pH (*d*) Zn

173. Which fruit free is sensitive to acidity and salinity–

(*a*) Plum (*b*) Guava

(*c*) Phalsa (*d*) Aonla

174. If the nitrogen content of a soil is 0.56% the organic matter (%)–

(*a*) 5.6 (*b*) 0.95

(*c*) 9.5 (*d*) 1.72

175. Which one of the following actinomycetes is responsible for N-fixation–

(*a*) Anabaena (*b*) Frankia

(*c*) Clostridum (*d*) Azolla

176. The nitrogenous fertilizer manufactured in India which occupies the first place in production today is–

(*a*) Urea (*b*) Ammonium phosphate

(*c*) Ammonium sulpahte (*d*) Calcium ammonium nitrate

177. Which one of the following fertilizers is least hygroscopic

(*a*) Ammonium sulpahte (*b*) Calcium ammonium nitrate

(*c*) Ammonium phosphate (*d*) Urea

178. Which one of the following fertilizers is least hygroscopic

(*a*) Ammonium sulpahte (*b*) Diammonium phosphate

(*c*) Calcium ammonium nitrate (*d*) Urea

179. Diammonium phosphate requirement for supplying 45 kg N and 115 kg P_2O_4 to one hectare peanut crop is–

(*a*) 150 kg (*b*) 250kg

(*c*) 200 kg (*d*) 100 kg

180. Fruit formation is suppressed due to deficiency of–

(*a*) Boron (*b*) Magnesium

(*c*) Sulphur (*d*) Calcium

181. In photosyntheis oxygen is liberated due to–

(*a*) Breakdown (*b*) Reduction of CO_2

(*c*) Oxidation of H_2O (*d*) Breakdown of chlorophyll

182. The plants which manufacture their own food in presence of light are known as–

(*a*) Photoautotroph (*b*) Phototropic
(*c*) Autotropic (*d*) Photophytic

183. Photosynthesis does not take place in fungi due to absence of–

(*a*) Chlorophyll (*b*) Potassium
(*c*) Nitrogen (*d*) Phosphorus

184. Zinc, Iron, Copper, Manganese and molybdenum are called micronutrients because they are–

(*a*) Nutrients which produce microscopic effects
(*b*) Essential nutrients but are required in minute quantities
(*c*) Nutrients required by micro-organisms
(*d*) Nutrients of microscopic significance

185. The waterlogged saline soils can be reclaimed through–

(*a*) Chemical amendment (*b*) Fertilizers
(*c*) Biodrainage (*d*) Farmyard manure

186. Total dissolved solids in water having EC of 5dS/m will be about–

(*a*) 3200 ppm (*b*) 4400 ppm
(*c*) 4000 ppm (*d*) 3600 ppm

187. The Sodium Absorption Ratio (SAR) of the soil containing Na, Mg and Ca ions as 100, 30 and 20 meq/L, respectively, will be–

(*a*) 10 (*b*) 15
(*c*) 20 (*d*) 5

188. The Residual Sodium Carbonate of water containing 35, 20 , 10 and 20 meq/l, CO_3, HCO_3, Ca and Mg respectively, will be–

(*a*) 0 meq/l (*b*) 5 meq/l
(*c*) 10 meq/l (*d*) 20 meq/l

189. According to modern concepts, the major function of inter row tillage is–

(*a*) Moisture conservation through soil mulching
(*b*) Improved soil aeration
(*c*) Moisture conservation through weed destruction
(*d*) Improved soil granulation

190. Sodic soils generally exhibit soil structure of the type

(*a*) Platy (*b*) Granuated
(*c*) Subangular (*d*) Prismatic/columnar

191. Soil water content (%) at field capacity is maximum/highest with–

(*a*) Loam (*b*) Silt loam
(*c*) Clayey soils (*d*) Clay loam

192. Carryover fertilizer effects are more pronounced in the case of–

(*a*) Urea (*b*) Calcium ammonium nitrate
(*c*) Ammonium nitrate (*d*) Single super phosphate

193. Symbiotic nitrogen fixation in *Cajanus cajan* (tur/arhar) madiated by–

(*a*) Rhizobium spp (cowpea miscellany group)

(*b*) Rhizobium phaseli

(*c*) Rhizobium lupine

(*d*) Rhizobium leguminosarum

194. The ionic form of phosphorus is determined by pH of the solution. At pH 4.0 the predominated ionic forms of phosphorus, present are–

(*a*) H_2PO_4 (*b*) $H_2PO_4^{-1}$ and PO_4^{-1}

(*c*) HPO_4 (*d*) $H_2PO_4^{-1}$ and HPO_4^{-1}

195. Journal of soil science is published from–

(*a*) India (*b*) Canada

(*c*) Australia (*d*) None of the above countries.

196. X-ray different technique (s) is used to study–

(*a*) Tracer studies (*b*) Photosynthesis

(*c*) Clay mineralogy (*d*) None of these

197. Alkali soils can be reclaimed by the addition of–

(*a*) Pyrites (*b*) Basic slag

(*c*) Lime (*d*) Calcite

198. The available water pre ent in soil for better plant growth is between–

(*a*) Field capacity and w ting percentage

(*b*) Field capacity ar r dry soil

(*c*) Wilting percenta and Hydroscopic coefficient

(*d*) None of the abov

199. At 1 × 10^{-9} H^+ conce tration, what will be the pH value?

(*a*) 6 (*b*) 10

(*c*) 5 (*d*) 9

200. Anion exchange capacity is found minimum in the case of–

(*a*) Motmorillonite (*b*) Kaolinite

(*c*) Illite (*d*) None of these

201. Cation exchange capacity is found minimum in the case of–

(*a*) Motmorillonite (*b*) Humus

(*c*) Illite (*d*) Kaolinite

202. Chemical weathering is governs mostly by the process–

(*a*) Hydrogen (*b*) Nitrogen

(*c*) Carbonation (*d*) None of these

203. The systematic examination, description, classification and mapping of soil of an area is known as–

(*a*) Soil survey (*b*) Soil classification

(*c*) Soil mapping (*d*) All of the above

204. All India Soil Survey and Land Use Organization was established in–

(*a*) 1962 (*b*) 1958

(*c*) 1956 (*d*) 1960

205. The head office of All India Soil Survey and Land Use Organization is at–

(*a*) Chennai (*b*) Mumbai
(*c*) Nagpur (*d*) New Delhi

206. Which acts also as a nitrification inhibitor over and above a manure–

(*a*) Groundnut (*b*) Sesamum (Til)
(*c*) Neem (*d*) Groundnut

207. Which one of the following organic manures has the narrowest C/N ratio–

(*a*) Biogass slurry (*b*) Groundnut cake
(*c*) Farm yard manure (*d*) Compost

208. Biofertilizer is a–

(*a*) Mixture of inorganic fertilizer and microorganisms
(*b*) Mixture of organic manure and microorganisms
(*c*) Culture having he desired strain of microorganisms
(*d*) Decomposed compost enrichedwith mineral solubilizing bacteria.

209. Super digested compost is called so because–

(*a*) It contains plant nutrients more than that present in ordinary compost.
(*b*) Superphosphate is added to he compost during its preparation.
(*c*) It is prepared by allowing it to decompose beyond the normal process of decomposition.
(*d*) Its P_2O_5 content is more than that present in the ordinary compost.

210. The mineral chlorite has an extra layer of–

(*a*) Brucite (*b*) Gibbsite
(*c*) Montomorillonite (*d*) Illite

211. Which one of the following minerals is the main source of boron in soil–

(*a*) Tourmaline (*b*) Hemimorphite
(*c*) Haematite (*d*) Pyrolusite

212. Criteria of essentiality of nutrients or plants were given by–

(*a*) Among (*b*) Russed
(*c*) Arnon & Staut (*d*) Liebig

213. Appetite is a group of minerals which mainly contains–

(*a*) Sulphur (*b*) Titanium
(*c*) Nitrogen (*d*) Phosphorus

214. The diagnostic horizon in Alfisol is termed–

(*a*) Spodic (*b*) Oxic
(*c*) Argillic (*d*) Mollic

215. Which of the following soils has got the highest bulk density–

(*a*) Clay Soil (*b*) Silty clay
(*c*) Loam (*d*) Sandy soil

216. The equation of soil formation, S = f(Cl, o, r, p, t) was given by–

(*a*) Glinka (*b*) Jenny
(*c*) Kellog (*d*) Dokuchaev

217. The structural rigidity of kaolinite is due to–

(*a*) K-bridge (*b*) H-bond

(*c*) O-O bond (*d*) Internal absorbed water

218. A soil formation process in which humus and sesquioxides become mobile and remain behind–

(*a*) Calcification (*b*) Podsolization

(*c*) Pedoturbation (*d*) Calcification

219. Attraction of slid surface for water molecule is called–

(*a*) Adsorption (*b*) Adhesion

(*c*) Cohesion (*d*) Absorption

220. Erosion caused by spattering of soil particles by the impact of rain drops is known as–

(*a*) Sheet erosion (*b*) Gully erosion

(*c*) Rill erosion (*d*) Splash erosion

221. Which of the following is not a sedimentary rock–

(*a*) Gneiss (*b*) Sand stone

(*c*) Limestone (*d*) Conglomerate

222. Chlorite belongs to the–

(*a*) 2 : 2 type (*b*) 2 : 1 type

(*c*) 1 : 1 type (*d*) Amorphous type

223. The soil layer of maximum leaching is indicated by the symbol–

(*a*) A_1. (*b*) A_2

(*c*) B_1 (*d*) B_2

225. The horizons which make up the profile of a lowest soil would include–

(*a*) A, C, & O (*b*) A, B, C & O

(*c*) A, B & C (*d*) B & O

226. National Remote Sensing Agency was established in–

(*a*) 1968 (*b*) 1977

(*c*) 1970 (*d*) 1974

227. The head quarter of NRSA is at–

(*a*) New Delhi (*b*) Secunderabad (Hyderabad)

(*c*) Mumbai (*d*) Banglore

228. National Bureau of Soil Survey and Land Use Planning Head Quarter is at–

(*a*) Culcutta (*b*) Nagpur

(*c*) Dehradun (*d*) Mumbai

229. The diameter of the silt practicles is–

(*a*) 0.0005-0.0002 (*b*) 0.5 to 0.2 mm

(*c*) Less than 0.002 (*d*) 0.05-0.002

230. Different soil separate may be determined with the help of–

(*a*) Yet's chart (*b*) Munsell chart

(*c*) International pipette method (*d*) None of the above

231. The arrangement of small, medium and large soil particles in a set patterns is known as–

(*a*) Mean weight diameter (*b*) Particle density

(*c*) Soil texture (*d*) Soil structure

232. The natural soil aggregates are called as–

(*a*) Soil separates (*b*) Mottling

(*c*) Peds (*d*) Concretion

233. The average soil bulk density of cultivated loamy soil is approximately–

(*a*) 1.5-1.65 gm cm^{-3} (*b*) 1.5-1.4 gm cm^{-3}

(*c*) 1.5-1.0 gm cm^{-3} (*d*) None of the above

234. The mass per unit volume of the solid mass of the soil excluding pore space is known as–

(*a*) True density (*b*) Bulk density

(*c*) (*a*) and (*b*) both (*d*) None of these

235. A combination of many taxonomic unit like soil series, phase or types is called–

(*a*) Soil series (*b*) Soil complex

(*c*) Soil variant (*d*) Soil association

236. The patterns of occurrence of various soil taxonomic units on the detailed map is called–

(*a*) Soil phase (*b*) Soil association

(*c*) Soil variant (*d*) Soil complex

237. The texture of surface soil of surface horizon is called–

(*a*) Soil association (*b*) Soil variant

(*c*) Soil complex (*d*) Soil catina

238. The characteristics of surface soil which have important bearing in soil management and crop production, is known as–

(*a*) Soil phase (*b*) Soil series

(*c*) Soil variant (*d*) None of these

239. The representation of surface feature on map and heir identification, is called–

(*a*) Soil variant (*b*) Soil map

(*c*) Soil lenged (*d*) None of these

240. An abrupt change in texture class of no continuity found between B and C horizon, is termed as–

(*a*) Lithological discontinuity (*b*) Regolith discontinuity

(*c*) Textural change (*d*) None of the above

241. How many times the soil organic matter hold the water of it is weight–

(*a*) 20 times (*b*) 15 times

(*c*) 10 times (*d*) 25 times

242. Water drains by gravitational force from pores larger than–

(*a*) About 30-60 microns (*b*) About 10-20 microns

(*c*) About 20-30 microns (*d*) None of the above

243. Soils with high pH are generally deficient in–

(*a*) Zn & Mn (*b*) Ca & Mg

(*c*) B & E (*d*) Cu & Mo

244. Which one of the following plant nutrients is useful in increasing resistance to diseases and insect-pests–

(*a*) Calcium (*b*) Potassium

(*c*) Phosphorus (*d*) Nitrogen

245. Use of materials like sulphur, polyform UF, isobutylidene diurea etc. improves fertilizer use efficiency. When such additives are used, the N-fertilizers are termed as–

(*a*) Prillede (*b*) Controlled release nitrogenous fertilizer

(*c*) Slow nitrifying N-fertilizer (*d*) Complex fertilizer

246 Essential elements are those–

(*a*) Which could be replaced by other elements with similar properties.

(*b*) Which are required in large quantities.

(*c*) Whose deficiency would prevent the completion of plant's life cycle.

(*d*) Which would promote plant growth.

247. Molybdenum is required by plants because it is a cofactor–

(*a*) Cytohrome oxidase (*b*) Phosphatase

(*c*) Nitrite reductase (*d*) Nitrate reductase

248. Organic matter content of histosols' and hydromorphic soil is–

(*a*) 30-40% (*b*) 2-18%

(*c*) 50-57% (*d*) 60-70%

249. The relative amounts of air and water in the pore spaces:

(*a*) Half filled and half empty (*b*) Always remain constant

(*c*) Fluctuate continuously (*d*) All of the above

250. Moisture content from lower to upper plastic limit is known as–

(*a*) Sticky point (*b*) Plastic number

(*c*) Field capacity (*d*) All the above

251. Soil colour determination is standardized and determined by the comparison of the soil colour to–

(*a*) Tensio meter (*b*) Munsell chart

(*c*) Gypsum block (*d*) None of these

252. 'Hue' is the term which is used for the determination of–

(*a*) Dominant spectral or rainbow (*b*) Relative thickness of whiteness

(*c*) Purity of the colour (*d*) All of the above.

253. The main source of heat energy for soil is–

(*a*) Intra red radiation (*b*) Solar radiation

(*c*) Altra violet radiation (*d*) None of the above

254. Specific heat of the mineral matter is–

(*a*) 1.0 cal gm^{-1} (*b*) 24.0 cal gm^{-1}

(*c*) 0.462 cal gm^{-1} (*d*) 0.18 Cal gm^{-1}

255. Example of cumulous material are–
(*a*) Gneiss (*b*) Till plain
(*c*) Peat and Muck (*d*) Colluvial

256. Aeoline deposits are formed by the transportation of materials through–
(*a*) Wind (*b*) Sea
(*c*) Running water (*d*) Ice

257. Solum is made up of
(*a*) 'C' horizon (*b*) 'C+D' horizon
(*c*) 'A+B' horizon (*d*) 'C' horizon

258. Identify which of the following is a passive soil forming factors–
(*a*) Relief (*b*) Climate
(*c*) Biosphere (*d*) None of the these

259. Aridisol soils are found in the region of–
(*a*) Humid (*b*) Submerged
(*c*) Arid (*d*) None of these

260. The dominant colour of spectral (rainbow) in soil indicates–
(*a*) Kaoline type of clay mineral (*b*) Value
(*c*) Hue (*d*) Chroma

261. Montmorillonite is following type of clay mineral–
(*a*) 2 : 2 (*b*) 3 : 1
(*c*) 1 : 1 (*d*) None of these

262. Soils are acidic for one of the reason–
(*a*) Acidic parent material (*b*) Basic slag
(*c*) Low rainfall (*d*) None of these

263. A soil having pH 8.5 ; ESP 15 and CE < 4 dSm^{-1} at 25°C is known as–
(*a*) Saline soil (*b*) Alkali soil
(*c*) Recent alluvium (*d*) Saline alkali soil

264. A soil having pH 6.0 is called–
(*a*) Acidic soil (*b*) Saline soil
(*c*) Alkaline soil (*d*) Normal soil

265 The diameter of water molecule is approximately
(*a*) 2.64 Å (*b*) 2.54 Å
(*c*) 1.33 Å (*d*) 2.94 Å

266. How many order are included in the 7th approximation system of soil classification–
(*a*) 8 (*b*) 10
(*c*) 12 (*d*) 15

267. Clay are classified as–
(*a*) Primary minerals (*b*) Hydroxy minerals
(*c*) Secondary minerals (*d*) Tertiary minerals

268. Soils formed under impeded drainage condition where movement of air and water is restricted is known as–
(*a*) Acid soil (*b*) Podzol
(*c*) Gley Soil (*d*) Cherozem

269. Physical weathering causes–

(*a*) Alternation of rocks and minerals
(*b*) Decomposition of rocks and minerals
(*c*) Disintegration of rocks and minerals
(*d*) Synthesis of rocks and minerals.

270. Consider the following statements regarding the causes of low crop productivity of sandy soils–

1. **Sandy soils have very low water retention capacity**
2. **Applied plant nutrients easily leach out through drainage**
3. **Sandy soils have very low organic matter content**
4. **Sandy soil easily fix applied P. of these statements**

(*a*) 1, 2 & 3 are correct
(*b*) 2, 3 & 4 are correct
(*c*) 1, 2 & 4 are correct
(*d*) 1, 3 & 4 correct

271. The phosphorus content as P in plough layer of one hectare of soil containing 0.1% P_2O_5 is–

(*a*) 430 kg
(*b*) 980 kg
(*c*) 1290 kg
(*d*) 1500 kg

272. If the C : N ratio of crop residues is 20-30 than–

(*a*) Mineralization may not take place
(*b*) Immobilization may not take place
(*c*) Immobilizion may take place
(*d*) Not known

273. If the C : N ratio of crop residue is more than 30 than

(*a*) Partial mineralization will take place
(*b*) Immobilization will take place
(*c*) Mineralization will take place
(*d*) All of these

274. If the C : N ratio of crop residues is less than 22, than

(*a*) Mineralization will take place
(*b*) Immobilization will take place.
(*c*) Both of these
(*d*) None of these

275. The organism which can survive at the temperature 10-15°C is called–

(*a*) Psychrophylic
(*b*) Mesophylic
(*c*) Thremophilic
(*d*) Thermiduric

276. The microbes which can survive at the temperature 25-30°C is called–

(*a*) Thermoduric
(*b*) Thermophilic
(*c*) Mesophylic
(*d*) Psychrophyfic

277. Which nitrogenous fertilizer will you recommend for paddy crop–

(*a*) Nitrate fertilizer
(*b*) Nitrate ammonical fertilizer
(*c*) Amide fertilizer
(*d*) All of the above

278. The common chemical preservatives are–

(*a*) Calcium chloride
(*b*) Calcium sulphate
(*c*) Mangnesium sulphate
(*d*) None of the above

279. The average chemical composition of NPK percentage of night soil is–

(*a*) 0.5-06-0.5
(*b*) 3.7-4.0-2.0
(*c*) 2.0-2.6-0.5
(*d*) 5.5-4.0-2.0

280. The residual effect of ammonical nitrogenous fertilizer in soil as–

(*a*) Alkaline
(*b*) Acidic
(*c*) Neutral
(*d*) None of these

281. Urea is mineralized in the presence of enzyme

(*a*) Peptase (*b*) Urease
(*c*) Co-enzyme (*d*) All the above

282. When you apply 80 kg N/ha to wheat crop how many kg of urea would be required–

(*a*) 120.00 kg (*b*) 80.00 kg
(*c*) 173.91 kg (*d*) 100.25 kg

283. Single super phosphate (SSP) is manufactured from–

(*a*) Rock phosphate (*b*) Bone meal
(*c*) Di-calcium phosphate (*d*) None of the above

284. *Rhizobium leguminoserum* can fix the nitrogen in the roots of–

(*a*) Pea, sweet pea, lentil (*b*) Alfalfa,Sweet clover
(*c*) Clovers (*d*) Beans

285. *Rhizobium trifoli* can fix the nitrogen in the roots of

(*a*) Sweet colour (*b*) Clover
(*c*) Soyabean (*d*) Lupines

286. *Rhizobium species* and the legume is called–

(*a*) Non symbiotic N_2 fixation (*b*) Symbiotic N_2 fixation
(*c*) Both of these (*d*) None of the above

287. *Rhizobium phaseoli* can fix the nitrogen in the roots of–

(*a*) Soybean (*b*) Pea
(*c*) Beans (*d*) Lentil

288. *Rhizobium japonicum* can fix the nitrogen in the roots of–

(*a*) Soybean (*b*) Cowpea
(*c*) Lentil (*d*) Beans

289. The N_2 fixation b Azotobacter and Azospirillum in the cereals in called–

(*a*) Non symbiotic N_2 fixation (*b*) Symbiotic N_2 fixation
(*c*) Both of these (*d*) None of above

290. Temperature has not significant effects on–

(*a*) Structure (*b*) Weathering of rocks and minerals
(*c*) Biologicl acitivity (*d*) All of the above

291. Heterotrophic organic obtain energy from the biological oxidation of–

(*a*) SO_4^{-2} (*b*) CO_2
(*c*) NH_4^+ (*d*) Organic carbon

292. Percentage of soil solids in soil is–

(*a*) 50% (*b*) 40%
(*c*) 30% (*d*) 60%

293. Which of he following is known as father of pedology–

(*a*) V.V. Dokuchaiev (*b*) D.G. Vilensky
(*c*) K.D. Glinka (*d*) C.F. Marbut

294. The average arable surface soil may be considered to havea particle density of about–

(*a*) 3.00 gms/cc (*b*) 2.64 gms/cc
(*c*) 2.70 gms/cc (*d*) 3.00 gms/cc

295. The illuviation is zone of–
(*a*) Hard crust (*b*) Leaching
(*c*) Accumulation (*d*) None of these

296. The maximum moisture is available to plant at–
(*a*) Wilting point (*b*) Hygroscopic coefficient
(*c*) Saturation (*d*) Field capacity

297. The method of survey adopted or intensive cultivation is–
(*a*) Detailed survey (*b*) Reonnaissance survey
(*c*) Detailed and reconnaissance survey (*d*) All of the above

298. Soil air contain–
(*a*) 2.5% CO_2 (*b*) 0.02% CO_2
(*c*) 3.0% CO_2 (*d*) 0.25% CO_2

299. The diagnostic surface horizons are called–
(*a*) Polypedon (*b*) Pedon
(*c*) Epipedon (*d*) All of them

300. A thick dark coloured horizon which have high base saturation (50% or more) high organic matter content and with strong soil-structure, is called–
(*a*) Ochric epipedon (*b*) Histic epipedon
(*c*) Umbric epipedon (*d*) All of them

301. An epipedon which has dark colour low in base saturation is called–
(*a*) Ochric epipedon (*b*) Umbric epipedon
(*c*) Histric epipedon (*d*) Mollic epipiedon

302. A man made epipedon which is similar to molic epipedon in many characters expect P_2O_5 content (more than 250 ppm) is–
(*a*) Umbric epipedon (*b*) Anthtropic epipedon
(*c*) Ochric epipedon (*d*) Hstic epipedon

303. Geological weathering takes place in–
(*a*) Upper layers of soil (*b*) Lower layers of soil
(*c*) On earth crust (*d*) None of the above

304. Bone meal is well suited for–
(*a*) Alkaline soil (*b*) Neutral soil
(*c*) Acidic Soil (*d*) All of these

305. All potassium fertilizer's are physiologically alkaline, their reaction with soil is–
(*a*) Acidic (*b*) Alkaline
(*c*) Neutral (*d*) None of these

306 If the nitrogen content in crop residues is less than 2% than
(*a*) Net immobilization will take place (*b*) Partial mineralization will take place
(*c*) Net mineralization will take place (*d*) None of the above

307. 'Whiptail' symptom in caulifower is due to the deficiency of–
(*a*) Iron (*b*) Molybdenum
(*c*) Zinc (*d*) Copper

308. The number of essential elements required for the growth of most higher plant is–

(*a*) 17
(*b*) 16
(*c*) 18
(*d*) 3

309. Which one of the following is not a component of the moisture potential in soils–

(*a*) Turgor potential
(*b*) Osmotic potential
(*c*) Gravity potential
(*d*) Metric potential

310. Crop logging is the method of

(*a*) Soil fertility evaluation
(*b*) Assessing crop damage
(*c*) Testing suitability of fertilizer
(*d*) Plant analysis of assessing requirement of nutrients for crop production

311. In a composed pit, the heat of combustion of organic matter raises the temperature when decay is occurring rapidly, during decay, the temperature rise by–

(*a*) 75-90°C
(*b*) 40-60°C
(*c*) 60-80°C
(*d*) 50-72°C

312. The maximum irrigation efficiency percent age is found in which class of soil?

(*a*) Sandy soil
(*b*) Loamy soil
(*c*) Clay loam
(*d*) Heavy clay

313. The biofertilizer like blue-green algae recommended for cultivation of 1ha paddy crop is

(*a*) 5-10
(*b*) 10-15
(*c*) 25-30
(*d*) 15-20

314. The total and area on a water way that contributes run off water to the flow at the point is known as–

(*a*) Water Conservation
(*b*) Watershed
(*c*) Soil Conservation
(*d*) All of these

315. Mixed cropping provides–

(*a*) Almost a complete protection against soil erosion
(*b*) Better and continuous cover of land
(*c*) Good protection against the beating action of the rain
(*d*) Assurance of one or more crops to the form

316. Which of the following grasses can be used for preventing soil erosion by intercropping–

(*a*) *Cynodon dactylon*
(*b*) *Dianthuim annulatum*
(*c*) *Cenchrus ciliaris*
(*d*) All of these

317. Which of the following examples of erosion permitting crop?

(*a*) Pearlmillet
(*b*) Sorghum
(*c*) Maize
(*d*) all of these

318. Contour bunding is useful as it–

(*a*) Increase utter level's in the wells
(*b*) increases yield of crops in dry farming areas in Maharashtra
(*c*) Increases employment opportunities
(*d*) All of the above

319. Rhizobium culture is generally used for–

(*a*) Cash crops (*b*) Cereals
(*c*) Legume crop (*d*) All of these

320. The first entry and movement of water through the soil surface is known as–

(*a*) Gravitational law (*b*) Percolation
(*c*) infiltration (*d*) None of these

321. The most important strip cropping practices in controlling erosion and conserving water is (are)–

(*a*) Field strip cropping (*b*) Contour strip cropping
(*c*) Wind strip cropping (*d*) All of these

322. Poor nitrification rate of non-edible mahua (*Madhucal latifolia*) cake is due to–

(*a*) Wide C : N ratio (*b*) The presence of oil
(*c*) Low nitrogen content (*d*) The presence of certain alkaloids

323. Which of the following pairs is correctly matched–

(*a*) Urea 42.0(%N) (*b*) Diammonium phosphate 20.2(%P)
(*c*) Muriate of potash 47.5(%K) (*d*) Ammonium sulphate 21.5(%N)

324. The neutralizing values of the following liming materials are such that–

(*a*) $CaCO_3 > CaO > Ca(OH)_2CaMg(CO_3)_2$
(*b*) $CaO > Ca(OH)_2 > CaCO_3 > CaMg(CO_3)_2$
(*c*) $Ca(OH)_2 > CaO > CaMg(CO_3)_2 > CaCO_3$
(*d*) $CaO > Ca(OH)_2 > CaMg(CO_3)_2 > CaCO_3$

325. The nitrogenous fertilizer of choice for tea is–

(*a*) Urea (*b*) Calcium ammonium nitrate
(*c*) Ammonium sulphate (*d*) Ammonium nitrate

326. Transport of phosphate from the cytosol (pH about 7.0) into vacuoles (pH nearly 5.5) involves–

(*a*) (H_2PO_4) alone (*b*) (HPO_4) and $(HPO_4)^{2-}$
(*c*) $(HPO_4)^{2-}$ alone (*d*) $(PO_4)^{3-}$ lone

327. If the slope of the land is increased 4 times the velocity of water flowing over it is approximately double and capacity of water is increased about–

(*a*) 2-time (*b*) 8-time
(*c*) 4-time (*d*) 6-time

328. The nitrogen fixing bacteria are–

(*a*) Azospirillum (*b*) Rhizobium
(*c*) Azotobacter (*d*) All of the above

329. Magnesium is necessary for–

(*a*) Chlorophyll (*b*) Plasma
(*c*) Plastids (*d*) None of these

330. Biofertilizer is a–

(*a*) Mixture of inorganic fertilizer and microorganism
(*b*) Decomposed compost enriched with mineral solubilising bacteria
(*c*) Mixture of inorganic matter and microorganism
(*d*) Culture having the desired strain of microorganism

331. The mechanisms of the crop plants in operation in the soil water plant system is/as follows–

(*a*) Diffusion
(*b*) The constant exchange and root interception
(*c*) The mass flow or convection
(*d*) All of the above

332. Diminished carbohydrate status of the placed under high nitrogen supply is due to–

(*a*) Lower photosynthetic activity
(*b*) Increased transpiration ratio
(*c*) Increased vegetative growth
(*d*) Vigorous protein synthesis

333. Consider the following symptoms–

1. Effect more pronounced on shoots when compared to roots and cruciferious plants develop narrow leaf lamina

2. Blockage of the synthasis of cystine, methionine etc.

3. Younger leaves shows signs of deficiency first

4. High amide and nitrate nitrogen

Development of the above mentioned symptoms is attributable to the deficiency of–

(*a*) Calcium
(*b*) Magnesium
(*c*) Sulphur
(*d*) Nitrogen

334. Gully-erosion affects 2.3 million ha in India which occurs because of–

(*a*) Carrying out mechanical measures
(*b*) Bad management of land resources
(*c*) Designing of various structures
(*d*) All of the above

335. The vegetative development of plants by imparting a healthy green colour to leave is done by–

(*a*) Nitrogen
(*b*) Potassium
(*c*) Phosphorus
(*d*) None of these

336. The influence on vigour of plants and formation of meacells etc. is done by the–

(*a*) Phosphorus
(*b*) Potassium
(*c*) Nitrogen
(*d*) None of these

337. In saline soil exchangeable sodium percentage is less than–

(*a*) 11
(*b*) 17
(*c*) 15
(*d*) 23

338. The length of spillway is determined by the formula of–

(*a*) Q = 1.70 LH 3x2
(*b*) Q = 17.0 LH_3x2
(*c*) Q = 1.70LH3
(*d*) None of these

Here Q = run-off in cubic meters/sec; L = Length in m of water flow above the spillway level

339. The tolerant spp. able to grow over 5000 ppm salts is–

(*a*) Barley
(*b*) Sugarcane
(*c*) Datepalm
(*d*) All of the above

340. In non-saline alkali or sodic soils the Electrical Conductivity (EC) is less than–

(*a*) 2 dSm^{-1}
(*b*) 8 dSm^{-1}
(*c*) 6 dSm^{-1}
(*d*) 4 dSm^{-1}

341. Any system of gullies an independent catchment with a regular stream which is called–

(*a*) Nomenclature
(*b*) Irrigation
(*c*) Drainage system
(*d*) None of these

342. For preparing a mixed fertilizer, 100 kg of ammonium sulphateand 125 kg of single super phosphate were mixed and 25 kg of filler was added to this mixture. In terms of N-P_2O_5-K_2O, the fertilizer grade of this mixture will be–

(*a*) 10-10-0
(*b*) 5-10-0
(*c*) 8-8-0
(*d*) 5-5-0

343. In respect of sugarcane crop to be grown in an acidic soil having high P fixing capacity, the fertilizer of choice would be–

(*a*) Triple super phosphate
(*b*) Finely ground rock phosphate
(*c*) Coarse rock phosphate
(*d*) Super phosphate

344. A soil with 20 me/100g CEC and 5 me/100g exchangeable H will have a base saturation of–

(*a*) 25.0%
(*b*) 133.3%
(*c*) 80.0%
(*d*) 75.0%

345. What would be the concentration of nutrients in plants when they are suffering from hidden hunger–

1. Above deficiency symptom zone
2. Below deficiency symptom zone
3. Above profitable yield zone
4. Below profitable yield zone

Select the correct answer using the codes given below:

(*a*) 1 & 3
(*b*) 2 & 3
(*c*) 1 & 2
(*d*) 3 & 4

346. High R.S.C. of irrigation water results in

(*a*) Precipitation of Na
(*b*) Precipitation of Ca and Mg
(*c*) Precipitation of K
(*d*) None of the above

347. Mg and S are termed as–

(*a*) Primary nutrients
(*b*) Secondary nutrients
(*c*) Micronutrients
(*d*) None of the above

348. Nitrogen is absorbed by the plants in the from–

(*a*) NO_3^{-1} and NH_4^{1+}
(*b*) Only as NO_3^{1-}
(*c*) Only as NH_4^{1+}
(*d*) None of the above

349. Chlorosis refers to the

(*a*) Burning of the leaf tissues
(*b*) Development of brown colour on the leaves
(*c*) Death of the leaf tissues
(*d*) Yellowing of the leaf tissues

350. Nitrogen is an essential nutrient elements for the plants because–

(*a*) It strengthens straw and prevent lodging
(*b*) It imparts early green colour
(*c*) It imparts early vegetative growth and dark green colour
(*d*) It stimulates seed formation

351. Deficiency of iron result in typical intervainal chlorosis in which–

(*a*) Younger leaves are first affected
(*b*) Necrotic spots in the interveinal areas develops

(c) Interveinal areas of the older leaves are first affected
(d) None of the above

352. Non-symbiotic bacteria fixes ________ amount of N_2 than symbiotic N_2 fixers–
(a) Less (b) More
(c) Equal (d) Not Known

353. $NaAlSi_2O_8$ is the formula of
(a) Anorhite (b) Albite
(c) Mica (d) Ilite

354. $CaAl_2Si_3 \cdot O_8$ is the formula of–
(a) Anorhite (b) Albite
(c) Montmorillinite (d) Ilite

355. 0.5 $NaHCO_3$ (pH 8.5) is–
(a) Brays No. 2 extractant (b) Brays No. 1 extractant
(c) Olsen extractant (d) None of the above

356. S. M. P. buffer is used in ________ determination–
(a) Nitrogen (b) Potassium
(c) Calcium (d) Lime

357. Saline soils are reclaimed/managed by–
(a) Addition of pyrite (b) Addition of gypsum
(c) Leaching the soluble salts (d) addition of lime

358. Which of the following soil has higher buffering capacity–
(a) Sandy soils (b) Loamy soils
(c) Clay soils (d) Loamy sand soils

359. Gypsum is an important amendment for problematic soil. It widely occurs in the state of–
(a) U.P. (b) Rajasthan
(c) Gujarat (d) M.P.

360. While classifying the soil according to textural class in equilarate triangle suggested by the USDA, the % of clay is plotted parallel to–
(a) Sand (b) Silt
(c) Clay (d) Loam

361. The pH of solution, containing 1x10 g H ion/ ml will be–
(a) 7 (b) 6
(c) 9 (d) 8

362. The science which deals with the fundamental studies of soils is known as–
(a) Neurology (b) Pedology
(c) Limnology (d) Embryology

363. Mass flow of gases into the soil occurs due to the difference of–
(a) Surface tension (b) Pressure gradient
(c) Both of above (d) None of the above

364. The molecular transfer of gases due to concentration of partial pressure gradient in the soil, is termed as–

(*a*) Mass flow (*b*) Diffusion
(*c*) Both a and b (*d*) None of these

365. A property of fluids by virtue of which it reduces the relative motion among different layers of fluid, is termed as–

(*a*) Viscosity (*b*) Soil spericity
(*c*) Soil consistency (*d*) None of these

366. The manifestation of the physical forces of cohesion and adhesion acting within soil at various moisture contents, is called–

(*a*) Soil elasticity (*b*) Soil consistency
(*c*) Soil plasticity (*d*) All of these

367. Upper plastic limit is also known as–

(*a*) Lower limit (*b*) Liquid limit
(*c*) Index of plasticity (*d*) None of the above

368. Which of the following not a method of soil moisture measurement–

(*a*) Gravitational (*b*) Gypsum block method
(*c*) Tensiometer (*d*) None of the above

369. The acidic igneous rocks contains silica–

(*a*) $>65\%$ (*b*) 60-65%
(*c*) $<65\%$ (*d*) None of these

370. The foliated metamorphic rocks are formed due to–

(*a*) Heat-metamorphism (*b*) Pressure-metamorphism
(*c*) Hydro-metamorphism (*d*) None of these

371. A surface horizon which has very high organic matter is–

(*a*) Histic epiepdon (*b*) Umbric epiepdon
(*c*) Ochric epiepdon (*d*) None of the above

372. An agrillic sub-surface horozon with high E.S.P. (more than 15) is called–

(*a*) Cambic horizon (*b*) Oxic horizon
(*c*) Natric horizon (*d*) Agric horizon

373. A sub- surface horizon with highly oxidized material and 1 : 1 type clay minerals is known as–

(*a*) Cambic horizon (*b*) Sodic horizon
(*c*) Agric horizon (*d*) Oxic horizon

374. A surface horizon in which the accumulation of organic matter and clay occurs just below the plough layer is–

(*a*) A horizon (*b*) C horizon
(*c*) B horizon (*d*) None of these

375. Volumetric heat capacity can be calculated by multiplying specific heat with the corresponding–

(*a*) Volume (*b*) Density
(*c*) Mass (*d*) Thermal conductivity

376. The causes of deforestation are–

(*a*) Overgrazing by cattle, sheep and goats

(*b*) Extensive deforestation owing to increased demand for fuel and timber

(*c*) Both of the above

(*d*) None of the above

377. Who discovered that plant take nutrients form soil–

(*a*) Nicholas (*b*) Liebig

(*c*) J C Bose (*d*) Both (*a*) and (*b*)

378. Boruyoucos and Mick (1946) invented a method for the measurement of soil moisture in-situ. It is called–

(*a*) Gypsum blocks (*b*) Tensiometer

(*c*) Neutron scattering method (*d*) None of these

379. Which of the examples are erosion resisting crops–

(*a*) Horesegram (*b*) Chickpea

(*c*) Soyabean (*d*) All of these

380. Howard and wad (1931) developed a method for the preparation of farm compost is called–

(*a*) PWP method (*b*) Kjeldahl method

(*c*) INDORE method (*d*) None of these

381. The small interrupted basins along the crinter with a special impalement is called–

(*a*) Contour bunding (*b*) Basin listing

(*c*) Bench terracing (*d*) Sub soiling

382. Richard and Grander (1936) invented an instrument for the measurement of soil moisture–

(*a*) Hydrometer (*b*) Neutron scattering method

(*c*) Hygrometer (*d*) Tensiometer

383. Irrigation efficiency is very low in India mainly because–

(*a*) A major part of the soil types is not suitable for irrigation

(*b*) Large irrigated area is under canal irrigation system

(*c*) Of the adverse climatic condition

(*d*) Of the poor quality of irrigation water

384. Which one of the following is not a component of the moisture potential in soils–

(*a*) Turgor potential (*b*) Osmotic potential

(*c*) Gravity potential (*d*) Metric potential

385. The crops suitable for cultivation in saline sodic soil would include–

(*a*) Sugarbeat and rice (*b*) Soybean and Sugarbeat

(*c*) Soybean and rice (*d*) Rice and maize

386. The unconsolidated material on the underlying rock is called–

(*a*) Regolith (*b*) Soil

(*c*) Solum (*d*) Earth

387. If a soil has a bulk density of 1.50 mg/m^3 and a particle density of 2.65 mg/m^3, than the percentage pre space of that soil will be–

(*a*) 43.4 (*b*) 38.5
(*c*) 48.5 (*d*) 35.0

388. Active soil forming factors would include–

(*a*) Vegetation and topography (*b*) Time and vegetation
(*c*) Vegetation and climate (*d*) Vegetation and topography

389. The black cotton soils of central India have been derived from–

(*a*) Granodiorites (*b*) Rhyolite
(*c*) Basalt (*d*) Granites

390. The best estimate of the available P in phosphatic fertilizer is obtained from the–

(*a*) Citrate insoluble fraction (*b*) Water soluble and citrate soluble fractions
(*c*) Citrate soluble fraction (*d*) Water soluble fraction

391. Thermal conductivity of different textural classes of the soils follows the following order–

(*a*) Sand < loam < clay < peat (*b*) Peat = clay = loam = sand
(*c*) Sand > loam > clay > peat (*d*) None of the above

392. Hygroscopic moisture is held at–

(*a*) 31 atm (*b*) 99 atm
(*c*) 1000 atm (*d*) 200 atm

393. Land capability classes have–

(*a*) 4 class (*b*) 8 class
(*c*) 5 class (*d*) 3 class

394. The maximum size limit of clay fraction is considered to be–

(*a*) 0.02 mm (*b*) 0.0002 mm
(*c*) 0.002 mm (*d*) None of the above

395. Cation exchange capacity is expressed as–

(*a*) Mole/litre (*b*) Meq/100g
(*c*) Meq/litre (*d*) Per cent

396. Montmorilionite is a–

(*a*) 1 : 1 type clay (*b*) 2 : 1 type clay
(*c*) 2 : 2 type clay (*d*) None of these

397. Cation exchange capacity is highest in–

(*a*) Kaolinite (*b*) Humus
(*c*) Illite (*d*) Montmorillonite

398. For managing acid soils following chemical amendment is quite essential–

(*a*) CuO (*b*) $ZnSO_4$
(*c*) CaO (*d*) $CaSO_4$ $7H_2O$

399. Absorbed H and Al are largely responsible for–

(*a*) Soil alkalinity (*b*) Soil acidity
(*c*) Neutrality (*d*) None of the above

400. Buffering capacity of soil means resistance to a change in–

(*a*) Soil acidity (*b*) Soil pH
(*c*) Soil microbial activity (*d*) Base saturation

401. The concentration of CO_2 in the soil increases after the rains, probably because of–

(*a*) Increase nitrification and decomposition of organic matter
(*b*) Increased leaching of nitrogen and CO_2
(*c*) Increase de-nitrification
(*d*) None of the above

402. The gaseous exchange between soil and atmosphere is the–

(*a*) Natural process (*b*) Change in soil structure
(*c*) Field capacity (*d*) None of the above

403. The water held with a water potential greater than–1/3 bar is known as–

(*a*) Field capacity (*b*) Available water
(*c*) Gravitation water (*d*) Unavailable water

404. General soil productivity index (GSPI) can be calculated by–

(*a*) Sum of PRI's of major crops/number of crops × 100
(*b*) Sum of PRI's of major crops/number of crops
(*c*) Number of crops/Sum of PRI's of major crop
(*d*) None of above

405. A = RKLSCP denote universal soil loss equation in which K is equal to–

(*a*) Soil productivity (*b*) Soil leaching factor
(*c*) Soil erodibility factor (*d*) Crop management factor

406. A soil which have pH less than 8.5, ESP less than 15 and EC more than 4 mmhos/cm at 25°C is called–

(*a*) Alkali soil (*b*) Saline-alkali soil
(*c*) Saline soil (*d*) All of the above

407. The porosity will be more in soil having particle size of–

(*a*) 0.02 mm (*b*) 0.002 mm
(*c*) 2.0 mm (*d*) 0.005 mm

ANSWERS

1.	d	2.	b	3.	a	4.	b	5.	c	6.	c	7.	d	8.	c	9.	c	10.	a
11.	a	12.	b	13.	b	14.	b	15.	c	16.	a	17.	d	18.	d	19.	d	20.	b
21.	d	22.	a	23.	c	24.	d	25.	b	26.	c	27.	c	28.	a	29.	a	30.	d
31.	c	32.	d	33.	b	34.	b	35.	b	36.	b	37.	b	38.	c	39.	a	40.	d
41.	c	42.	c	43.	b	44.	c	45.	a	46.	d	47.	c	48.	c	49.	c	50.	d
51.	c	52.	d	53.	c	54.	d	55.	b	56.	c	57.	c	58.	c	59.	b	60.	d
61.	b	62.	a	63.	d	64.	a	65.	b	66.	b	67.	b	68.	d	69.	b	70.	c
71.	a	72.	a	73.	c	74.	b	75.	b	76.	c	77.	b	78.	b	79.	b	80.	c
81.	a	82.	c	83.	c	84.	b	85.	c	86.	b	87.	b	88.	c	89.	c	90.	d

91.	b	92.	b	93.	c	94.	c	95.	c	96.	c	97.	a	98.	b	99.	a	100.	a
101.	d	102.	b	103.	d	104.	a	105.	a	106.	c	107.	b	108.	b	109.	a	110.	b
111.	a	112.	a	113.	b	114.	a	115.	c	116.	a	117.	d	118.	d	119.	d	120.	a
121.	d	122.	d	123.	c	124.	b	125.	a	126.	d	127.	b	128.	b	129.	d	130.	d
131.	a	132.	a	133.	b	134.	b	135.	c	136.	c	137.	?	138.	b	139.	a	140.	b
141.	c	142.	c	143.	a	144.	a	145.	a	146.	b	147.	c	148.	c	149.	d	150.	d
151.	c	152.	a	153.	d	154.	d	155.	a	156.	d	157.	a	158.	c	159.	d	160.	a
161.	b	162.	n	163.	n	164.	d	165.	?	166.	d	167.	?	168.	?	169.	?	170.	?
171.	a	172.	c	173.	b	174.	a	175.	b	176.	a	177.	b	178.	c	179.	b	180.	a
181.	c	182.	a	183.	a	184.	b	185.	c	186.	a	187.	c	188.	d	189.	c	190.	d
191.	d	192.	d	193.	a	194.	a	195.	b	196.	c	197.	a	198.	a	199.	d	200.	a
201.	d	202.	c	203.	a	204.	b	205.	c	206.	c	207.	d	208.	c	209.	b	210.	a
211.	a	212.	c	213.	d	214.	d	215.	d	216.	d	217.	b	218.	b	219.	b	220.	d
221.	a	222.	a	223.	d	224.	?	225.	c	226.	d	227.	b	228.	b	229.	d	230.	c
231.	d	232.	c	233.	b	234.	a	235.	d	236.	d	237.	b	238.	a	239.	c	240.	a
241.	c	242.	a	243.	a	244.	b	245.	b	246.	c	247.	d	248.	b	249.	d	250.	b
251.	b	252.	a	253.	a	254.	d	255.	c	256.	a	257.	c	258.	a	259.	c	260.	c
261.	a	262.	a	263.	b	264.	a	265.	a	266.	c	267.	c	268.	c	269.	c	270.	a
271.	b	272.	c	273.	b	274.	c	275.	b	276.	c	277.	c	278.	b	279.	d	280.	b
281.	b	282.	c	283.	a	284.	a	285.	b	286.	b	287.	c	288.	a	289.	a	290.	?
291.	d	292.	a	293.	a	294.	b	295.	c	296.	d	297.	b	298.	d	299.	c	300.	b
301.	b	302.	b	303.	c	304.	c	305.	c	306.	a	307.	b	308.	a	309.	a	310.	d
311.	c	312.	c	313.	c	314.	c	315.	b	316.	b	317.	c	318.	d	319.	c	320.	c
321.	d	322.	d	323.	d	324.	d	325.	d	326.	b	327.	b	328.	d	329.	c	330.	d
331.	d	332.	d	333.	c	334.	c	335.	a	336.	c	337.	c	338.	c	339.	c	340.	d
341.	a	342.	c	343.	b	344.	a	345.	a	346.	b	347.	a	348.	a	349.	d	350.	c
351.	a	352.	a	353.	b	354.	b	355.	c	356.	d	357.	c	358.	c	359.	b	360.	b
361.	a	362.	b	363.	c	364.	b	365.	a	366.	b	367.	b	368.	d	369.	a	370.	b
371.	a	372.	c	373.	d	374.	c	375.	d	376.	c	377.	b	378.	b	379.	c	380.	c
381.	c	382.	?	383.	b	384.	a	385.	a	386.	a	387.	a	388.	c	389.	c	390.	b
391.	c	392.	a	393.	b	394.	c	395.	b	396.	b	397.	b	398.	c	399.	b	400.	b
401.	a	402.	a	403.	c	404.	a	405.	c	406.	c	407.	d						

Appendices

APPENDIX-I

Indian Council of Agricultural Research (ICAR)

The Indian Council of Agricultural Research (ICAR) is an autonomous organisation under the Department of Agricultural Research and Education (DARE), Ministry of Agriculture and Farmers Welfare, Government of India. Formerly known as Imperial Council of Agricultural Research, it was established on 16 July 1929 as a registered society under the Societies Registration Act, 1860 in pursuance of the report of the Royal Commission on Agriculture. The ICAR has its headquarters at New Delhi. The Council is the apex body for co-ordinating, guiding and managing research and education in agriculture including horticulture, fisheries and animal sciences in the entire country. With 101 ICAR institutes and 71 agricultural universities spread across the country this is one of the largest national agricultural systems in the world. The ICAR has played a pioneering role in ushering Green Revolution and subsequent developments in agriculture in India through its research and technology development that has enabled the country to increase the production of foodgrains by 5.6 times, horticultural crops by 10.5 times, fish by 16.8 times, milk by 10.4 times and eggs by 52.9 times since 1950-51 to 2017-18, thus making a visible impact on the national food and nutritional security. It has played a major role in promoting excellence in higher education in agriculture. It is engaged in cutting edge areas of science and technology development and its scientists are internationally acknowledged in their fields.

1. The Mandate

2. Milestone

3. Organization

4. ICAR institutions

- **4.1.** ICAR Institute
- **4.2.** National Research Centre
- **4.3.** Bureau
- **4.4.** Project Directorate
- **4.5.** AICRP
- **4.6.** Network Project
- **4.7.** Others Project

5. ICAR Headquarters

6. All India Agriculture Entrance Examination
7. ICAR Merits & Awards
8. External links

1. THE MANDATE

To plan, undertake, aid, promote and co-ordinate education, research and its application in agriculture, agroforestry, animal husbandry, fisheries, home science and allied sciences.

To act as clearing house of research and general information relating to agriculture, animal husbandry, home science and fisheries through its publications and information system, and instituting and promoting transfer of technology programmes.

To provide, undertake and promote consultancy services in the fields of education, research, training and dissemination of information in agriculture, agroforestry, animal husbandry, fisheries, home science and allied sciences.

To look into problems relating to broader areas of rural development concerning agriculture, including post-harvest technology, by developing co-operative programmes with other organizations such as the Indian Council of Social Sciences Research, Council of Scientific and Industrial Research, Bhabha Atomic Research Centre, and universities.

To do other things considered necessary to attain objectives of the Society.

The 'Committee to Advise on Renovation and Rejuvenation of Higher Education' (Yashpal Committee, 2009) has recommended setting up of a constitutional body-The National Commission for Higher Education and Research, which would be a unified supreme body to regulate all branches of higher education including agricultural education. Presently, regulation of agricultural education is the mandate of ICAR, Veterinary Council of India (Veterinary sub-discipline) and Indian Council of Forestry Research and Education (Forestry sub-discipline). The UPA government has included Yashpal Committee recommendations in its '100 days agenda'.

Current Mandate:

- Plan, Undertake, Coordinate and Promote Research and Technology Development for Sustainable Agriculture.
- Aid, Impart and Coordinate Agricultural Education to enable Quality Human Resource Development.
- Frontline Extension for technology application, adoption, knowledge management and capacity development for agri-based rural development.
- Policy, Cooperation and Consultancy in Agricultural Research, Education & Extension.

2. ORGANIZATION

- ICAR has following organizational structure:
- Union Minister of Agriculture is the ex-officio President of the ICAR Society.
- Secretary, Department of Agricultural Research & Education Ministry of Agriculture, Govt. of India & Director-General, ICAR – the Principal Executive Officer of the Council.
- Governing Body is the policy-making authority
- Agricultural Scientists' Recruitment Board
- Deputy Directors-General (8)
- Additional Secretary (DARE) and Secretary (ICAR)

- Additional Secretary and Financial Advisor
- 24 Assistant Directors-General
- National Director, National Agricultural Innovation Project
- Directorate of Information and Publications of Agriculture

ICAR has two bodies:

- The General Body, the supreme authority of the ICAR, is headed by the Minister of Agriculture, Government of India
- The Governing Body which is the chief executive and decision making authority of the ICAR. It is headed by the Director-General.

4. ICAR INSTITUTIONS

As on 22 October 2020 ICAR has following number of institutions:

- 4 Deemed Universities
- 65 ICAR Institutions
- 14 National Research Centres
- 6 National Bureaux
- 13 Directorate/Project Directorates
- 15 National Research Centres
- 60 AICRPs (All India Coordinated Research Projects)
- 19 Network Projects
- 10 Other Projects
- 11 Agricultural Technology Application Research Institutes (ATARI)
- 721 Krishi Vigyan Kendras (KVKs)
  - ATARI, Zone I, Ludhiana – 69 KVKs
  - ATARI, Zone II, Jodhpur– 63 KVKs
  - ATARI, Zone III, Kanpur– 86 KVKs
  - ATARI, Zone IV, Patna– 68 KVKs
  - ATARI, Zone V, Kolkata– 59 KVKs
  - ATARI, Zone VI, Guwahati- 47 KVKs
  - ATARI, Zone VII, Barapani– 43 KVKs
  - ATARI, Zone VIII, Pune– 81 KVKs
  - ATARI, Zone IX, Jabalpur– 82 KVKs
  - ATARI, Zone X, Hyderabad– 75 KVKs
  - ATARI, Zone XI, Bengaluru– 48 KVKs
- 64 State Agricultural Universities (SAUs)
- 3 Central Agricultural University
- 4 Deemed Universities
- 4 Central Universities having faculty of agriculture

4.1. ICAR Institute

1. ICAR-Central Island Agricultural Research Institute, Port Blair
2. ICAR-Central Arid Zone Research Institute, Jodhpur
3. ICAR-Central Avian Research Institute, Izatnagar
4. ICAR-Central Inland Fisheries Research Institute, Barrackpore
5. ICAR-Central Institute Brackishwater Aquaculture, Chennai
6. ICAR-Central Institute for Research on Buffaloès, Hissar
7. ICAR-Central Institute for Research on Goats, Makhdoom
8. ICAR-Central Institute of Agricultural Engineering, Bhopal
9. ICAR-Central Institute for Arid Horticulture, Bikaner
10. ICAR-Central Institute of Cotton Research, Nagpur
11. ICAR-Central Institute of Fisheries Technology, Cochin
12. ICAR-Central Institute of Freshwater Aquaculture, Bhubneshwar
13. ICAR-Central Institute of Research on Cotton Technology, Mumbai
14. ICAR-Central Institute of Sub Tropical Horticulture, Lucknow
15. ICAR-Central Institute of Temperate Horticulture, Srinagar
16. ICAR-Central Institute on Post harvest Engineering and Technology, Ludhiana
17. ICAR-Central Marine Fisheries Research Institute, Kochi
18. ICAR-Central Plantation Crops Research Institute, Kasargod
19. ICAR-Central Potato Research Institute, Shimla
20. ICAR-Central Research Institute for Jute and Allied Fibres, Barrackpore
21. ICAR-Central Research Institute of Dryland Agriculture, Hyderabad
22. ICAR-National Rice Research Institute, Cuttack
23. ICAR-Central Sheep and Wool Research Institute, Avikanagar, Rajasthan
24. ICAR- Indian Institute of Soil and Water Conservation, Dehradun
25. ICAR-Central Soil Salinity Research Institute, Karnal
26. ICAR-Central Tobacco Research Institute, Rajahmundry
27. ICAR-Central Tuber Crops Research Institute, Trivandrum
28. ICAR-ICAR Research Complex for Eastern Region, Patna
29. ICAR-ICAR Research Complex for NEH Region, Barapani
30. ICAR-Central Coastal Agricultural Research Institute, Ela, Old Goa, Goa
31. ICAR-Indian Agricultural Statistics Research Institute, New Delhi
32. ICAR-Indian Grassland and Fodder Research Institute, Jhansi
33. ICAR-Indian Institute of Agricultural Biotechnology, Ranchi
34. ICAR-Indian Institute of Horticultural Research, Bengaluru
35. ICAR-Indian Institute of Natural Resins and Gums, Ranchi
36. ICAR-Indian Institute of Pulses Research, Kanpur
37. ICAR-Indian Institute of Soil Sciences, Bhopal
38. ICAR-Indian Institute of Spices Research, Calicut
39. ICAR-Indian Institute of Sugarcane Research, Lucknow

40. ICAR-Indian Institute of Vegetable Research, Varanasi
41. ICAR-National Academy of Agricultural Research & Management, Hyderabad
42. ICAR-National Institute of Biotic Stresses Management, Raipur
43. ICAR-National Institue of Abiotic Stress Management, Malegaon, Maharashtra
44. ICAR-National Institute of Animal Nutrition and Physiology, Bengaluru
45. ICAR-ICAR-National Institute of Natural Fibre Engineering and Technology, Kolkata, Kolkata
46. ICAR-National Institute of Veterinary Epidemiology and Disease Informatics, Hebbal, Bengaluru
47. ICAR-Sugarcane Breeding Institute, Coimbatore
48. ICAR-Vivekananda Parvatiya Krishi Anusandhan Sansthan, Almora
49. ICAR-Central Institute for Research on Cattle, Meerut, Uttar Pradesh
50. ICAR-National Institute of High Security Animal Diseases, Bhopal
51. ICAR-Indian Institute of Maize Research,New Delhi
52. ICAR- Central Agroforestry Research Institute , Jhansi
53. ICAR-National Institute of Agricultural Economics and Policy Research, New Delhi
54. ICAR- Indian Institute of Wheat and Barley Research, Karnal
55. ICAR- Indian Institute of Farming Systems Research, Modipuram
56. ICAR- Indian Institute of Millets Research, Hyderabad
57. ICAR- Indian Institute of Oilseeds Research, Hyderabad
58. ICAR- Indian Institute of Oil Palm Research, Pedavegi, West Godawari
59. ICAR- Indian Institute of Water Management, Bhubaneshwar
60. ICAR-Indian Institute of Rice Research, Hyderabad
61. ICAR- Central Institute for Women in Agriculture, Bhubaneshwar
62. ICAR-Central Citrus Research Institute, Nagpur
63. ICAR-Indian Institute of Seed Research, Mau
64. ICAR-Indian Agricultural Research Institute, Post Box No. 48, Hazaribag 825 301, Jharkhand
65. ICAR-National Institute for Plant Biotechnology, New Delhi

4.2. National Research Centres

1. ICAR-National Research Centre for Banana, Trichi
2. ICAR-National Research Centre for Grapes, Pune
3. ICAR-National Research Centre for Litchi, Muzaffarpur
4. ICAR-National Research Centre for Pomegranate, Solapur
5. ICAR-National Research Centre on Camel, Bikaner
6. ICAR-National Research Centre on Equines, Hisar
7. ICAR-National Research Centre on Meat, Hyderabad
8. ICAR-National Research Centre on Mithun, Medziphema, Nagaland
9. ICAR-National Research Centre on Orchids, Pakyong, Sikkim
10. ICAR-National Research Centre on Pig, Guwahati
11. ICAR-National Research Centre on Seed Spices, Ajmer
12. ICAR-National Research Centre on Yak, West Kemang
13. ICAR-National Centre for Integrated Pest Management, New Delhi
14. Mahatma Gandhi Integrated Farming Research Institute, Motihari

4.3. Bureau

1. ICAR-National Bureau of Plant Genetics Resources, New Delhi
2. ICAR-National Bureau of Agriculturally Important Micro-organisms, Mau, Uttar Pradesh
3. ICAR-National Bureau of Agricultural Insect Resources, Bengaluru
4. ICAR-National Bureau of Soil Survey and Land Use Planning, Nagpur
5. ICAR-National Bureau of Animal Genetic Resources, Karnal
6. ICAR-National Bureau of Fish Genetic Resources, Lucknow

4.4. Directorates/Project Directorate

1. ICAR-Directorate of Groundnut Research, Junagarh
2. ICAR-Directorate of Soybean Research, Indore
3. ICAR-Directorate of Rapeseed & Mustard Research, Bharatpur
4. ICAR-Directorate of Mushroom Research, Solan
5. ICAR-Directorate on Onion and Garlic Research, Pune
6. ICAR-Directorate of Cashew Research, Puttur
7. ICAR-Directorate of Medicinal and Aromatic Plants Research, Anand
8. ICAR-Directorate of Floricultural Research, Pune, Maharashtra
9. ICAR-Directorate of Weed Research, Jabalpur
10. ICAR-Project Directorate on Foot & Mouth Disease, Mukteshwar
11. ICAR-Directorate of Poultry Research, Hyderabad
12. ICAR-Directorate of Knowledge Management in Agriculture (DKMA), New Delhi
13. ICAR-Directorate of Cold Water Fisheries Research, Bhimtal, Nainital

4.5. All India Coordinated Research Project

1. AICRP on Nematodes, New Delhi
2. AICRP on Maize, New Delhi
3. AICRP Rice, Hyderabad
4. AICRP on Chickpea, Kanpur
5. AICRP on MULLARP, Kanpur
6. AICRP on Pigeon Pea, Kanpur
7. AICRP on Arid Legumes, Kanpur
8. AICRP on Wheat & Barley Improvement Project, Karnal
9. AICRP Sorghum, Hyderabad
10. AICRP on Pearl Millets, Jodhpur
11. AICRP on Small Millets, Bangalore
12. AICRP on Sugarcane, Lucknow
13. AICRP on Cotton, Coimbatore
14. AICRP on Groundnut, Junagarh
15. AICRP on Soybean, Indore
16. AICRP on Rapeseed & Mustard, Bharatpur
17. AICRP on Sunflower, Safflower, Castor, Hyderabad
18. AICRP on Linseed, Kanpur

19. AICRP on Sesame and Niger, Jabalpur
20. AICRP on IPM and Biocontrol, Bangalore
21. AICRP on Honey Bee Research & Training, Hisar
22. AICRP -NSP(Crops), Mau
23. AICRP on Forage Crops, Jhansi
24. AICRP on Fruits, Bangaluru
25. AICRP Arid Zone Fruits, Bikaner
26. AICRP Mushroom, Solan
27. AICRP Vegetables including NSP vegetable, Varanasi
28. AICRP Potato, Shimla
29. AICRP Tuber Crops, Thiruvananthapuram
30. AICRP Palms, Kasaragod
31. AICRP Cashew, Puttur
32. AICRP Spices, Calicut
33. AICRP on Medicinal and Aromatic Plants including Betelvine, Anand
34. AICRP on Floriculture, New Delhi
35. AICRP in Micro Secondary & Pollutant Elements in Soils and Plants, Bhopal
36. IAICRP on Soil Test with Crop Response, Bhopal
37. AICRP on Long Term Fertilizer Experiments, Bhopal
38. AICRP on Salt Affected Soils & Use of Saline Water in Agriculture, Karnal
39. AICRP on Water Management Research, Bhubaneshwar
40. AICRP on Ground Water Utilisation, Bhubaneshwar
41. AICRP Dryland Agriculture, Hyderabad
42. AICRP on Agrometeorology, Hyderabad including Network on Impact adaptation & Vulnerability of Indian Agri. to Climate Change
43. AICRP Integrated Farming System Research, Modipuram including Network Organic Farming
44. AICRP Weed Control, Jabalpur
45. AICRP on Agroforestry, Jhansi
46. AICRP on Farm Implements & Machinery, Bhopal
47. All India Coordinated Research Project on Ergonomics and Safety in Agriculture
48. AICRP on Energy in Agriculture and Agro Based Indus.,Bhopal
49. AICRP on Utilization of Animal Energy (UAE), Bhopal
50. AICRP on Plasticulture Engineering and Technologies, Ludhiana
51. AICRP on Post Harvest Technology, Ludhiana
52. AICRP on Goat Improvement, Mathura
53. AICRP- Improvement of Feed Sources & Nutrient Utilisation for raising animal production, Bangalore
54. AICRP on Cattle Research, Meerut
55. AICRP on Poultry, Hyderabad

56. AICRP-Pig, Izzatnagar
57. AICRP Foot and Mouth Disease, Mukteshwar
58. AICRP ADMAS, Bangalore
59. AICRP on Home Science, Bhubaneshwar

4.6. Network Projects – 19

1. All India Network Project on Pesticides Residues, New Delhi
2. All India Network Project on Underutilised Crops, New Delhi
3. All India Network Project on Tobacco, Rajahmundry
4. All India Network Project on Soil Arthropod Pests, Durgapura
5. Network on Agricultural Acarology, Bangalore
6. Network on Economic Ornithology, Hyderabad
7. All India Network Project on Rodent Control, Jodhpur
8. All India Network Project on Jute and Allied Fibres, Barrackpore
9. Network project on Improvement of Onion & Garlic, Pune
10. Network Bio-fertilizers, Bhopal
11. Network Project on Harvest & Post Harvest and Value Addition to Natural Resins & Gums, Ranchi
12. Network project on Animal Genetic Resources, Karnal
13. Network Project on R&D Support for Process Upgradation of Indigenous Milk products for industrial application Karnal
14. Network Programme on Sheep Improvement, Avikanagar
15. Network Project on Buffaloes Improvement, Hisar
16. Network on Gastro Intestinal Parasitism, Izatnagar
17. Network on Haemorrhagic Septicaemia, Izatnagar
18. Network Programme Blue Tongue Disease, Izatnagar
19. Network Project on Conservation of Lac Insect Genetic Resources, Ranchi
20. Network Project on Agricultural Bioinformatics and Computational Biology, New Delhi

4.7. Other Project

1. Technology Mission on Cotton (CICR, Nagpur)
2. Technology Mission on Jute (CRIJAF, Barrackpore)
3. Continuation, Strengthening and Establishment of Krishi Vigyan Kendras
4. Strengthening & Development of Higher Agricultural Education in India, New Delhi
5. Central Agricultutral University, Imphal
6. Strengthening and Modernization of ICAR Headquarters
7. Intellectual Property Management & Transfer/Commercialisation of Agricultural Technology (Upscaling of existing component IPR HQ)
8. Indo US Knowledge Initiative
9. National Agricultural Innovative Project, New Delhi
10. National Fund for Basic and Strategic Research, New Delhi

5. ICAR HEADQUARTER ADDRESS

ICAR,
Krishi Bhavan,
Dr Rajendra Prasad Road,
New Delhi – 110114
91-11-25842787, 23388842
www.icar.org.in [www.icar.org.in]

6. ALL INDIA AGRICULTURE ENTRANCE EXAMINATION

The ICAR conducts an entrance test for a reserved pool of 15% seats in all undergraduate courses in agriculture and allied fields in all agriculture universities of India. The syllabus is parallel to various PMTs especially AIPMT There is a rule aimed at increasing admissions from more number of states by allowing only 40% seats from a state.

7. ICAR MERITS AND AWARDS

- Choudhary Devi Lal Outstanding All-India Coordinated Research Project Award
- Rafi Ahmed Kidwai Award
- Fakhruddin Ali Ahmed Award for Tribal Areas
- Hari Om Ashram Trust Award
- Jawaharlal Nehru Award
- Vasantrao Naik Award
- Lal Bahadur Shastri Young Scientist Award
- Bharat Ratna Dr C Subramaniam Outstanding Teacher Award
- Punjab Rao Deshmukh Woman Agricultural Scientist Award
- Chaudhary Charan Singh Award for Excellence in Journalism in Agricultural Research and Development
- N.G. Ranga Farmer Award for Diversified Agriculture
- Jagjivan Ram Kisan Puruskar
- Swamy Sahajanand Saraswati Extension Scientist/ Worker Award
- ICAR Award for Outstanding Multidisciplinary Team Research in Agriculture and Allied Sciences
- National Krishi Vigyan Kendra Award
- Dr Rajendra Prasad Puruskar for Technical Books in Hindi in the Field of Agriculture and Allied Sciences

8. EXTERNAL LINKS

Electronic journals published by the ICAR
ICAR.org
http://www.icar.org.in/dipa/events/ICAR-REPORTER/july-sept2005.pdf
http://www.ias.ac.in/currsci/jun252008/1547.pdf
http://www.icar.org.in/merits.html

❑❑❑

APPENDIX-II

International Agricultural Centre

CONSORTIUM OF INTERNATIONAL AGRICULTURAL RESEARCH CENTERS

CGIAR (formerly the **Consultative Group for International Agricultural Research**) is a global partnership that unites international organizations engaged in research about food security. CGIAR research aims to reduce rural poverty, increase food security, improve human health and nutrition, and sustainable management of natural resources. It is carried out at 15 centers (CGIAR Consortium of International Agricultural Research Centers) that collaborate with partners from national and regional research institutes, civil society organizations, academia, development organizations, and the private sector. These research centers are around the globe, with most in the Global South and Vavilov Centers of agricultural crop genetic diversity.

CGIAR is an ad-hoc organization funded by its members. Members include the USA, Canada, the UK, Germany, Switzerland, and Japan, the Ford Foundation, the Food and Agriculture Organization of the United Nations (FAO), the International Fund for Agricultural Development (IFAD), the United Nations Development Programme (UNDP), the World Bank, the European Commission, the Asian Development Bank, the African Development Bank, and the Fund of the Organization of the Petroleum Exporting Countries (OPEC Fund). In 2009 CGIAR had revenues of US$629 million.

(***Previously,*** The Consultative Group on International Agriculture (CGIAR) is an association of 46 countries including India, international and regional organizations, and private foundations devoted to improve global food production. It was established in 1971 and is now located in Washington, D.C. The CGIAR supports a network of 16 IARC's distributed throughout the world. The World Bank, the UNDP and FAO are co-support of this network in the the 16 IARCs)

At Present:

Formation: 1971; 50 years ago

Type: Partnership of funders and international agricultural research centers; Intergovernmental Organization

Purpose: To reduce poverty and hunger, improve human health and nutrition, and enhance ecosystem resilience through high-quality international agricultural research, partnership and leadership.

Headquarters: Montpellier, France (CGIAR Consortium of International Agricultural Research Centers)

Key people: Juergen Voegele Chair, CGIAR System Council;

Main organ: CGIAR Fund, CGIAR Consortium of International Agricultural Research Centers, Independent Science and Partnership Council.

MEMBERS OF THE CGIAR CONSORTIUM OF INTERNATIONAL AGRICULTURAL RESEARCH CENTERS

Active CGIAR Centers Headquarters Location

- Africa Rice Center (West Africa Rice Development Association, Warda) Bouaké, Côte D'ivoire / Cotonou, Benin
- Bioversity International (International Plant Genetics Resources Institute, IPGRI) Maccarese, Rome, Italy

- Center for International Forestry Research (CIFOR) Bogor, Indonesia
- International Center for Tropical Agriculture (CIAT) Cali, Colombia
- International Center for Agricultural Research in the Dry Areas (ICARDA) Beirut, Lebanon
- International Crops Research Institute for the Semi-Arid Tropics (ICRISAT) Hyderabad (Patancheru), India
- International Food Policy Research Institute (IFPRI) Washington, D.C., United States
- International Institute of Tropical Agriculture (IITA) Ibadan, Nigeria
- International Livestock Research Institute (ILRI) Nairobi, Kenya
- International Maize and Wheat Improvement Center (CIMMYT) Texcoco, Mexico State, Mexico
- International Potato Center (CIP) Lima, Peru
- International Rice Research Institute (IRRI) Los Baños, Laguna, Philippines
- International Water Management Institute (IWMI) Battaramulla, Sri Lanka
- World Agroforestry Centre (International Centre for Research in Agroforestry, ICRAF) Nairobi, Kenya
- Worldfish Center (International Center for Living Aquatic Resources Management, ICLARM) Penang, Malaysia

Centers No Longer Active

- International Laboratory for Research on Animal Diseases (ILRAD) Nairobi, Kenya; 1994: Merged With ILCA to Become ILRI
- International Livestock Centre For Africa (ILCA) Addis Ababa, Ethiopia; 1994: Merged With ILRAD To Become ILRI
- International Network for the Improvement of Banana and Plantain (INIBAP) Montpellier, France; 1994: Became A Programme of Bioversity International
- International Service For National Agricultural Research (ISNAR) The Hague, Netherlands; 2004: Dissolved, Main Programmes Moved To Ifpri Non–Icgar Institutions

Country Based Institutions

CIDA	:	Canadian International Development Agency, Canada
DANIDA	:	Danish Development Agency, Denmark
FINNIDA	:	Finish Development Agency, Finland
IDRC	:	International Development Research Center, Canada
IDS	:	International Service for the Acquisition of Agri-Biotechnology Application, U.S.A.
JIRCAS	:	Japanese International Research Centre for Agricultural Science, Japan
ODA	:	Overseas Development Administration, UK
SIDA	:	Swedish International Development Agency, Sweden
USAID	:	United State Agency for International Development, U.S.A.
USDA	:	United State Department of Agriculture, U.S.A.

Institutions for South–South Co-operation (Third World Countries)

- Third World Academy of Science -TWAS: Trieste (Italy)

❑❑❑

APPENDIX-III

Agriculture Scientist Recruitment Board (A.S.R.B.)

ARS MAINS EXAMINATION-2011
DICIPLINE : SOIL SCIENCE—Soil Chemistry/Fertility/Microbiology

Time Allowed : 3 Hours *Max. Marks : 240*

1. (*i*) Explain the double layer theory of ion distribution in soils

(*ii*) What is its important for plant nutrition ?

(*iii*) Enlist the factor that influences the thickness of diffuse double layer.

2. Write shot notes on :

(*a*) Ion adsorption

(*b*) Electrophoresis

(*c*) Electroosmosis

3. (*i*) Out line the fractionation scheme for soil humus.

(*ii*) How clay humus complex is formed ?

(*iii*) How are negative charges developed on the surface of humus colloid ?

(*iv*) Explain polyphenol theory.

4. (*i*) What is soil carbon sequestration ?

(*ii*) What are the common recommended management practices to sequester soil carbon ?

(*iii*) What is the potential of soil carbon sequestration to effect CO_2 emission ?

(*iv*) Mention different fractions of soil carbon.

5. (*i*) Explain the fate of single super phosphate in soils.

(*ii*) Discuss the interaction of suphur with nitrogen and phosphorus.

6. (*i*) What do you understand by site specific nutrient management ?

(*ii*) Briefly describe the various components of a site specific nutrient management.

(*iii*) How to curve N loss from submerged rise field ?

7. (*i*) What are micro nutrients and write their available forms in soils ?

(*ii*) Write the critical limits of micronutrient in soil system.

(*iii*) Mention the deficiency symptoms of zinc, iron, manganese and boron in cereal crops.

(*iv*) Mention the toxicity symptoms of iron and manganese under submerged soil condition in rice.

8. What are acid sulphate soils, how do they form, and how can they best be managed ?

9. (*i*) Defines soil quality.

(*ii*) What are the indicators for assessment of soil quality ?

(*iii*) State the scientific principles involved in selecting the indicators.

(*iv*) Different between organic agriculture and inorganic agriculture and justify their sustainability.

10. What are heavy metals ? What are the possible consequences of heavy metal contamination in soil ?

11. (*i*) What is green house effect ?
   (*ii*) List the green house gasses with their concentration at present in the atmosphere.
   (*iii*) Mention the measure to mitigate green house gasses from agriculture point of view.
   (*iv*) How methane emission can be mitigated in rice cultivation ?
12. Describe the advantages and disadvantages of applying fertilizer via broghdcast, bending ad foliar application.
13. Describe in brief the importance of biological nitrogen fixation by rhizobia in legumes, the process of infection, the steps involved in nitrogen fixation and assimilation and the underline biochemical reaction.
14. (*i*) What is mycorrhiza ? Describe briefly their role in plant nutrition with few examples of important species.
   (*ii*) What are phosphate solublizing bacteria ? Name a few species and the mechanism in solublization.
15. State the working principle of spectrophotometer. A student fits spectrophotometer and 620 nm instead of 720 nm during estimation of phosphorus. How does it affect phosphorus estimation? What is the chemistry behind blue colour formation during phosphorus estimation ?

■■■

ARS MAINS EXAMINATION-2011

DICIPLINE: SOIL SCIENCE—PEDOLOGY

Time Allowed : 3 Hours *Max. Marks : 240*

1. Name the soil forming factors and describe how they influence soil formation and development. Briefly explain the role of climate as a factor of soil formation.
2. Classify the rocks and describe their characteristics in brief. Bring out the differences between gneiss and schist rocks and mansion the properties of soil derived from the weathering of these rocks.
3. What are different kinds of wethering of rocks and minerals ? Briefly discuss the weathering of granite and basalt and the kind of soils formed by weathering of their rocks.
4. Describe genesis and classification of vertisols and discuss their production constraints, potential and management for land use.
5. Mention silent criteria of different categories of USDA soil taxonomy. What are the diagnostic criteria of mollic epipedon and natric horizon?
6. What is geomorphology ? Describe the role of soil landscape relationship in soil mapping. How the toposequence influences soil formation ?
7. Differentiate between the following (any four) :
   (*a*) Lithic contact and paralithic contact
   (*b*) Soil taxonomic unit and soil mapping unit
   (*c*) Epipedon and diagnostic horizon
   (*d*) Soil macro-monolith and micro-monolith
   (*e*) Acid soil and acid sulphate soils
   (*f*) Land capability and land irrigability
8. Mension the differentiating soil characteristics of the following (any four) :
   (*a*) Alfisols and vertisols
   (*b*) Entisols and inceptisols
   (*c*) Ultisols and oxisols
   (*d*) Mollic epipedon and argillic epipedon
   (*e*) Gypsi horizon and salic horizon
   (*f*) Pedocals and pedolfer

9. Differentiate between the following (any four) :
   (*a*) Lithosequence and toposequence
   (*b*) Soil association and catina
   (*c*) GIS and GPS
   (*d*) Alluvium and colluvium
   (*e*) Flood plain and deltec deposite
   (*f*) Loess and sand duns
10. Explain the utility of soil survey. Briefly state the steps involved in detailed and reconnaissance soil survey.
11. List the characteristics of detail and reconnaissance soil maps in relation to kind and scale of base maps, mapping unit, frequency of observations and accuracy of soil boundaries.
12. Write short note on the following (any four) :
   (*a*) Base maps
   (*b*) Soil micro morphology
   (*c*) Soil temperature regime
   (*d*) Soil moisture regime
   (*e*) Soil correlation
   (*f*) Cartography
13. (*a*) What do you understand by agro-ecological region (AERs), and sub regions (AESRs) ? How many AERs and AESRs is their in India ?
   (*b*) What do you under stand by redoximorphic features, mottles, gleiying and variegated soil colours ?
14. What is geographic information system ? Describe is concept, components and application and natural resource mapping.
15. What is land capability ? List the criteria used and the factors determining land capability. Give the structure of land capability classification.

■■■

ARS MAINS EXAMINATION-2010

DICIPLINE : SOIL SCIENCE—Soil Chemistry/Fertility/Microbiology

Time Allowed : 3 Hours *Max. Marks : 240*

1. Give reasons :
   (*i*) Why negative charge per unit cell of vermiculite is less than that of mica ?
   (*ii*) Why submerged soils are not ideal sites for testing of response of P fertilizer ?
   (*iii*) Why does S-coated urea perform better than normal urea for submerged rice ?
   (*iv*) Why does bio-fertilization (*Azatobactor, Azospirillum* etc.) to red and lateritic soils hardly respond ?
   (*v*) While estimated oxidizable organic carbon by wet oxidation method, sometimes green colour appears even before titration on addition of $K_2Cr_2O_7$ and H_2SO_4 into soil. Why does it happen and how do you overcome it ?
2. How do negative charges originate on soil colloids ? Cation exchange capacity in soils is next photosynthesis. Explain.
3. What is heavy metal ? How do Cd, Pb and As affect living organism ? Give the scientific principle of bio-remediation of contaminated soils.
4. What do you know about Integrated Nutrient Management? Discuss the role of green manure and farm yard manure for maintaining soil fertility and crop productivity.
5. (*i*) What is the carbon sequestration (*ii*) What are the common recommended management of practice to sequestration soil carbon ? (*iii*) What is the potential of soil carbon sequestration to offset of CO_2 emission ?

6. (i) What are the function of deficiency symptoms of B and Mo in plants ? (ii) How do Fe and Al-oxides influences their (B &Mo) availability in soils ? (iii) Suggestion some measures for correcting their deficiencies.

7. What is rhizospheric ? How does the rhizospheric soil differ from the non rhizospheric soils ? What do you understand by rhizospheric competence of microbes ?

8. Differentiate between (any four) :

   (i) Nitrification and denitrification
   (ii) Commesalism and parasitism
   (iii) Nitrogenage and dehydrogenase
   (iv) Autotrophs and htrotrophs
   (v) Aminization and ammonification
   (vi) Bacteria and actinomycetes

9. What is the role of devardas's alloy for nitrogen estimation? Mention the type of soils for which the DTPA of micronutrient (Zn, Cu, Fe and Mn) estimate was originally developed ? Why B and Mo can not be analyzed accurately through atomic absorption spectrophotometer. Why do we prefer Nephlometer not spectrometer for estimation of which of the essential elements for plants ?

10. Mention the soil conditions cause B and Mo deficiency. What are their typical deficiency symptoms ? How do we measure their availability in soils ? Name two zinc containing fertilizers and their amounts required for applying say10 kg zinc per hectare.

11. Are soil quality and soil health synonymous ? What is the basic difference between our age-old soil testing and current soil quality concept? Mention a few (5) most important soil quality indicator differ for soil growing paddy and potato-if yes why ?

12. (1) What is zero point of charge (ZPC) in soil ? (2) How does differ from iso-electric point (IEP), (3) how does ZPC influence p-fertilizer application in acid soil ? (4) What is limitation of Donnan equilibrium ?

13. (A) What is significance of organo-metallic complex and clay organic complex in soil for plant nutrition ?

    (B) What is the role of organic matter in up keeping soil productivity ?

14. Make a suitable prescription for balanced fertilizer through INM for transplanted rice.

15. (1) Explain the diffuse double layer theory of ion distribution in soil, (2) What is its importance for plant nutrition ? and (3) Enlist the factors that influence the thickness of the diffuse double layer.

16. State various type of soil erosion caused by water and wind. What is the impact of water erosion on loss of soil nutrients ? How can we control water erosion ?

17. Explain the fundamental principles of an experimental design. Make comparison between CRD and RBD.

18. (1) Write down the principle involved in the manufacturing process of ammonia.(2) How does ammonium polyphosphate influence Zn availability to plants and (3) How does ammonium polyphosphate differ from ammonium orthophosphate.

19. (1) Discuss in brief the reaction that take place when single super phosphate is added to soil and (2) Enlist the approach that are employed for increasing the use efficiency of prophetic fertilizer in red and lateritic soils.

20. What electrochemica! and biological change occurs in rice soil upon submergence ? How to increase the use efficiency of nitrogenous fertilizers in submerged rice ?

■■■

ARS MAINS EXAMINATION-2010

DICIPLINE: SOIL SCIENCE—PEDOLOGY

Time Allowed : 3 Hours *Max. Marks : 240*

1. Describe soil survey-types, soil mapping-application and its importance in agriculture.
2. Differentiate between :
   (*i*) Ultisols and Alfisols
   (*ii*) Antisols and Inceptisols
   (*iii*) Acid soils and Acid sulphate soils
   (*iv*) Sloe release N fertilizer and Nitrification inhibitor
3. What do you mean by diagnostic horizons and their uses ? Explain the differences between a diagnostic horizon and genetic horizon.
4. Differential between :
   (*i*) Lithosequence and toposequence
   (*ii*) Soil association and catena
   (*iii*) GIS and GPS
5. What is land capability classification ? What is the basis of this classification ? Describe the features of class IV type land.
6. How do aluminosilicates develop soil acidity ? Compare saline, sodic and saline sodic soils with respect to pH, SAR and ESP values. Assume that a soil test report recommends the application of 1.0 t/ha of burnt lime with a CaO equivalent of 98%. Incidentally this liming material is not available in the market. Instead, lime stone with $CaCO_3$ equivalent of 90% is available. How much of the lime stone you will recommend.
7. What do you mean by carbon sequestration in soils ? How do soil factor influenced such sequestration ? Mention a few (3) agricultural practices contribute significantly to emission of green house gasses. What is carbon trading ?
8. Write short note on :
   (*a*) Thin layer chromatography
   (*b*) Mass separator
   (*c*) Isotopes dilution technique
   (*d*) Electron capture detector
9. (*a*) Describe the limitation in genetic system of classification.
   (*b*) Classify alluvial and red soils according to soil taxonomy.
10. Describe how geomorphology is important study of soils ? Explain the different ways in which topography influences soil formation.
11. Describe the genesis, distribution, soil orders and important characteristics of black soils. State its production constraint and management options for increasing productivity.
12. Distinguish between the soil taxonomic unit and soil mapping unit. Discuss the important features of four different orders on taxonomy.
13. Classify rocks and describe their characteristics in brief. Discuss biogeochemical weathering of rocks and minerals.
14. Write short note on :
   (*a*) Colluviums
   (*b*) Flood plains
   (*c*) Alluvial
   (*d*) Delta deposits
   (*e*) Bunes
15. Explain the principle of atomic absorption spectroscopy. How does it differ from flame photometry ?
16. Explain the fundamental principle of an experimental design. Make comparison between CRD and RBD.

17. Differentiate between the following :
    (*a*) Loess and sand duns
    (*b*) Gneiss and schist
    (*c*) Grid survey and free survey
    (*d*) Pedocals and pedalfer
18. Mention the silent criteria of different categories of USDA soil taxonomy. What are diagnostic criteria of mollic epipedon and natric horizon ? How inceptisols differ from entisols ?
19. Differentiate between :
    (*a*) Fine and coarse drainage texture shown on soil maps
    (*b*) Macro monolith and micro monolith used in soil studies
    (*c*) Land capability and incapability classification
20. Differentiate between saline and alkaline soils. Discuss their production constraint, and management option for increasing productivity.

■■■

ARS MAINS EXAMINATION-2010

DICIPLINE : SOIL SCIENCE—Soil Science-Soil Physics/Soil and Water Conservation

Time Allowed : 3 Hours *Max. Marks : 240*

1. (*a*) How does the muddy water affect the intake rate of soils ?
   (*b*) What are the consequences of reservoir sedimentation ?
2. States various type of soil erosion caused by water. What is its impact of soil nutrients? How can you control gully erosion ?
3. Do you expect the percolation rate in a soil with similar cultural practices in two different sessions to be similar ? Explain in details.
4. Show graphically:
   (*a*) Relation between terminal velocity and raindrop size
   (*b*) Soil erosion and degree of slop, and
   (*c*) Rain intensity and medium drop size
5. Discuss the following :
   (*a*) Soil water movement in saturated and unsaturated condition, and
   (*b*) Energy concept of soil moisture retention
6. What do you mean by carbon sequestration soils ? How do soil factors influence such sequestration ? Mansion a few (3) agricultural practices contribute significantly to emission of green house gasses. What is carbon trading ?
7. Are soil quality and soil health synonymous ? What is the basic difference between over old soil testing and current soil quality concept ? Mention a few (5) most important soil quality indicators. Do soil quality indicators differ for soil growing paddy and potato; if yes, why ?
8. (*i*) What zero point of charge (ZPC) in soil ?
   (*ii*) How does it differ from isoelectric point (IEP) ?
   (*iii*) How does ZPC influence P fertilizer application in acid soils ?
   (*iv*) What is the limitation of donnan equilibrium ?
9. Define the following :
   (*a*) Chemisorptions
   (*b*) Darcy's law
   (*c*) Thermal diffusivity
   (*d*) Hydraulic gradient

10. (*a*) Describe the condition conductive for surface crusting.
    (*b*) Explain how tillage practices affect soil bulk density and pore space.
11. Define soil water infiltrabitlity ? How initial soil watering influence infilterability ? State Phillip's equation for sorptivity of soil.
12. (*a*) The code of watershed map id 4G 4D 3B. Reveal the details of the watershed,
    (*b*) Write about the concept and methods of precision farming in watershed management.
13. Show diagrammatically :
    (*a*) Effect of soil texture and structure on soil moisture characteristics.
    (*b*) Relation between flux, section gradient and K.
    (*c*) Variation of K from saturation to unsaturation with reference to soil texture.
14. Explain the use remote sensing for resource management and land use planning.
15. (*a*) Discuss the agro-ecological region of India.
    (*b*) What do you mean by GIS ? Give its important for agriculture.
16. Using the term: adhesion, cohesion, meniscus, surface tension atmospheric pressure and hydrophilic surface, write a brief assay to explain why water rises up from the water table in mineral soil.
17. (*a*) what is hysteresis in soil moisture retention ?
    (*b*) What is the different factor responsible for it ?
    (*c*) Why friable consistence is optimum condition for tillage ?
    (*d*) Why do soil puddle at plastic consistence ?
18. How do aluminosilicates develop soil acidity ? Compare saline, sodic and saline sodic soils with respect to pH, SAR and ESP values. Assume that a soil test report recommends the application of 1.0 t/ha of burnt lime with a CaO equivalent of 98%. Incidentally this liming material is not available in the market. Instead, lime stone with $CaCO_3$ equivalent of 90% is available. How much of the lime stone you will recommend.
19. What is the principle behind mechanical analysis of soil by international pipette method. How does the method differ from hydrometer method in respect to accuracy ? What are the limitations in both the methods ?
20. (*i*) Differentiate between saturated and unsaturated flow.
    (*ii*) What is the significance of Reynold number ?
    (*iii*) Why does tensiometer reading fail to read beyond 0.8 bar ?
    (*iv*) Establish a relationship between porosity and void ratio, using mass volume relationship.

■■■

ARS MAINS EXAMINATION-2009

Paper II (Professional)

DICIPLINE : SOIL SCIENCE

Time Allowed: 3 Hours *Max. Marks : 240*

SECTION 'A'

1. What do you mean by weathering of rocks and minerals ? Classify the different weathering process ? Describe the weathering processes through enrolment of water, oxygen CO_2.
2. Describe the following pedogenic process and mention the related typical soil order:
   (*i*) Podzolization (*ii*) Gliezation (*iii*) Letrization

3. What do you mean by red soil? Discuss the silent features, land use pattern and soil orders of red soil in India.
4. How would you utilize the remote sensing techniques for characterization of soil, water bodies and natural vegetation ?
5. What are the main forms of soil erosion caused by water ? Discuss it impacts on soil nutrient and plant growth.
6. What do you understand by soil conservation? How it can be practiced for non arable lands ?
7. What are the policies for soil scientists and national land use policy (NLUP) and how it can be implements ?
8. Describe the classification of salt affected soils. Discuss their characteristics, constraints and potential plant growth.
9. Describe soil survey interpolation according to scientific principle. How it can be different for agricultural and non agricultural uses ?
10. Describe in brief the tools and techniques required for modern soil survey and mapping.
11. Describe relevance of agro-ecological regions of India for suitable land resource management.
12. Define various soil structural indices. How soil structural improvements are carried out for slowly and highly permeable soils ?
13. Discuss the genesis, classification and land use of mollisols in the India context.
14. Explain the role of parent materials in formation of soils.
15. Differentiate between :
    (*a*) Inceptisol and entisol
    (*b*) Masic and thermic soil temperature regime
    (*c*) Calcic horizon and petrocalcic horizons

SECTION 'B'

16. What is soil water potential and how could you measure it ?
17. Explain soil water atmospheric continuum (SPAC).
18. Derive equation of Darcy's flow and explain its applicability in soil water movement.
19. What is the classical and newer concept of soil water availability ?
20. What is the composition of soil air ? Discuss the responsible factors affecting the compositional difference in soil air and atmospheric air.
21. What are the physical factor affecting radiation and soil heat balance ?
22. What are the different tillage practices in India ? What are the impacts of tillage on soil physical environment for plant growth?
23. Briefly describe the composition of soil colloidal system. Discuss the Stern's theory of diffuse double layer of ions on soil colloidal dispersed phase.
24. Describe the processes of loss of applied nitrogen fertilizer in soil. How could you improve the efficiency of nitrogen fertilizer use in soil ?
25. How would you fractionate (scheme) humic substances in soil ? Briefly describe the biogenesis of humic substances formation.
26. What is Donnan equilibrium and how it is applicable in soil system.
27. Describe the various techniques for management of heavy metals pollution in soil.

28. What are the green house gasses? How nitrous oxide and methane gasses are produced from cultivated soils ?

29. What is quantity-intensity (Q/I) relationship of K-Ca exchange in soil ? Draw theoretical Q/I K-Ca curve and indicate measurement of different parameters from it.

30. What is ligand exchange of an anion? Write the characteristics features of legend exchange reaction of an anion with the help of an equation.

SECTION 'C'

31. What is humus ? How humus substances are classified ? Explain the nature and properties of humic substances.

32. What is the diffuse double layer ? Explain the briefly the Donnan equilibrium. How does it explain ionic distribution on colloids and soil solution ?

33. What do you mean by essential and beneficial plant nutrients ? With the criteria as proposed by Arnon and Stout (1939). Give the list of essential nutrients recognized so for.

34. What are (*a*) nitrification inhibitor and (*b*) slow release fertilizers ? Give examples and mention how they help in arresting fertilizer nitrogen losses from the soil.

35. Write in brief the fertilizer P rejection products in soil.

36. Describe the Mitcherlich equation along with its modification made by Bray.

37. Enlist different techniques used for assessment of soil fertility. Discuss any two of them.

38. What are soil enzymes ? Give examples of various types of soil enzymes. How are soil enzyme protected from microbial degradation ?

39. Write a short note on rhizosphere and other areas around plant roots in relation to microbial activity.

40. Write a short note on soil microbial biomass, its measurement and significance.

41. Write a short note on plant growth promoting rhizobacteria (PGPR).

42. Write short note on the microbiological and biochemical process that occur during various phases of composting.

43. Explain the principle of determination of (*a*) organic carbon by wet digestion method (*b*) available P by Olson's methods.

44. Differentiate between atomic absorption spectroscopy and flam emission spectroscopy.

45. Explain simple correlation and regressions. What are the different types of regression and correlation analysis ?

❑❑❑

APPENDIX-IV

Conversion Factor

SOME IMPORTANT CONVERSION FACTOR USED IN SOIL SCIENCE

%O.M.	=	%O.C. × 1.724	%Mg	=	%MgO × 0.60
%O.C.	=	O.M./1.724	%MgO	=	%Mg × 1.67
O.M.	=	%N × 20	1%	=	10,000 ppm
%N	=	O.M. × 0.05	1 ppm	=	0.0001%
%N	=	%O.C. × 0.086	1 dS m^{-1}	=	640 ppm
%P	=	% P_2O_5 × 0.43	1 mmhos cm^{-1}	=	dS m^{-1}
%P_2O_5	=	%P × 2.29	1mg	=	10^6 g
%K	=	%K_2O × 0.83	1 ha	=	Acre × 2.471
% K_2O	=	%K × 1.21	1 Acre	=	ha × 0.405
NH_4^+	=	%N × 1.286	1 ml	=	20 drops
NO_3^-	=	%N × 4.43	1km^2	=	100 ha
%S	=	SO_4 × 0.33	10 km^2	=	1000 ha
% SO_4	=	%S × 3	1 meter	=	100 cm or 39.37″ or 3.286′
%Ca	=	%CaO × 0.72	1 inch	=	2.54 cm or 25.4 mm
%CaO	=	%Ca × 1.40	1 cm	=	10 mm or 0.3937″

APPENDIX–V

SOME IMPORTANT CONCEPT, CONTRIBUTOR AND DISCOVERIES

- Father of Soil Science and Soil Pedology –**V.V. Dokuchaiev (1886)**
- Father of Indian Soil Science –**J.W. Leather**
- Father of Soil Physics –**Hillel**
- Father of Soil Chemistry –**J. Thamus**
- Father of Agricultural Chemistry –**Van Liebig**
- Father of Soil Conservation –**H.N. Bunett**
- Father of Soil Conservation (UP) –**Azidulla Khan**
- Father of Soil Testing Programme –**G.S. Troug**
- 'A' value –**Fried and Dean**
- 'E' value –**Russell**
- 'Y' or 'L' value –**Larsen**
- pH concept –**Sorenson**
- pE concept –**Silen**
- Law of limiting factor –**Blakman**
- Law of minimum/Law of limiting nutrient –**Lievig**
- Water-essential for plant –**Van Helment**
- Water-transpiration –**Woodward**
- Salt index –**Puri**
- DRIS concept –**Beaufils**
- Q/I concept –**Beckett**
- DTPA/Extractable micronutrients –**Lindsey and Norvell**
- Polyphenol theory of organic matter –**Stevenson**
- Phenomenon of radioactivity –**Becquerel**
- Soil catena –**Milne**
- Integrated soil test approach –**Colwell**
- CEC –**Thampson and Way**
- Nutrient sufficiency concept –**Baule**
- Lignin theory –**Waksman**
- Ultra micronutrient concept –**Nicholas**
- Per cent yield concept –**Baule**
- Root CEC –**Devaux**
- Target yield concept –**Ramamoorthi *et al.***
- Electrochemical theory of nutrient –**Lundegardh**
- Theory of relativity –**Lundegardh**
- Nutrient mobility and per cent sufficiency concept –**Bray**
- Benchmark soils of India –**Murthi *et al.***
- Biogas –**S.V. Desai and S.C. Biswas**
- Electroultrafilteration theory –**Lundergardh**
- Soil as an inexhaustible source of nutrients –**Cameroon**
- C.E.C is next to photosynthesis –**Marshall**
- Root exchange contact –**Jenny & Overstreet**

IMPORTANT JOURNALS AND MAGAZINE OF THE SOIL SCIENCE AND RELATED FIELD IN INDIA AND ABROAD

Name	***Published from***
Journals	
In India	
Journal of the Indian Society of Soil Science	National Agricultural Science Center Complex, Dev Prakash Shashtri Marg, Pusa, New Delhi-110012
The Indian Journal of Agricultural Sciences	Indian Council of Agricultural Research (ICAR), Krishi Bhavan, New Delhi-110001
Indian Journal of Agricultural Chemistry	Indian Society of Agricultural Chemist, Sheila Dhar Institute of Soil Science, University of Allahabad, Allahabad-211002
Journal of the Indian Society of Coastal Agricultural	Central Soil Salinity Research Station, Regional Research

Research	Institute, P.O. Canning Town-743329.
Indian Journal of Soil Conservation	India association of soil water conservation, 218 Kaulagarh Road, Dehradun (Uttrakhand)
Journal of Soil and Water Conservation	Soil Conservation Society of India, All India Soil and Land Use Survey Organization, NASC Complex, New Delhi
Journal of Indian Water Resources Society	Water Resource Development and Training Center, Indian Institute of Technology, Roorkee. (Uttrakhand)
In Abroad	
Soil Science Society of America Journal	677, South Segoe Road, Madison, WI 53711, USA
European Journal of Soil Science	Rutgers University, New Brunswick, New Jersey-08903, USA
Agrochimica	Agro-Chimica- Industrie Lit. Grafiche V. Lischi & Figil P.Za Castelltto-7, 56100, PISA Italy
Plant and Soil	Institute Of Soil Fertility P.O.B. 30003, 9750RA Haren (Gr) The Netherlands
Fertilizer Research	Martinus Nijhoff/Dr. W. Junk Publishers, P.O.Box 566,2501 CN, The Hegu The Netherland
Advances in Soil Science	Springer-Verlag, New York Inc 175 5th Avenue, New York NY-10010, USA
Soil Science and Plant Nutrition	Japanise Society of Soil Science and Plant Nutrition, Center for Academic Publications, Japan
Biology and Fertility of Soils	Germany
The Journal of Agricultural Science	Deptt of Applied Biology Pemborke Street, Cambridge, CB 2 3DX
Water, Air and Soil Pollution	Kluwer Academic Publishers P.O. Box 17,3300, AA Dordrecht, The Nietherlands
Magazine	
Bhagirath (Hindi/English)	Kandriya Jal Ayog, Taknik Pralekhan Nidesalaya, 511, Seva Bhawan, R.K.Puram, New Delhi.
Farmer and Parliament (Hindi/English)	Farmer and Parliyament Forum, 215 Rouse Avenue, Deen Dyal Upadhyay Marge, New Delhi.
Krashi Chayanika (International)	ICAR, Krishi Anusandhan Bhawan, Pusa Gate New Delhi.
Kheti	ICAR, Krishi Anusandhan Bhawan, Pusa Gate New Delhi.
Fertilizer News (Hindi/English)	The Fertilizer Association of India, 10, Sahid Jeet Singh Marge, New Delhi
Mausum (Hindi/English)	Indian Meteorological Department, New Delhi.
Intensive agriculture/Unnat Kheti	Ministry of Agriculture, New Delhi.
Krishi Vistar Samiksha	Ministry of Agriculture, New Delhi.
Agriculture Situation in India	Ministry of Agriculture, New Delhi.
Kurukshetra (Hindi/English)	Ministry of Rural Development, New Delhi.
Yojana (Hindi/English)	Ministry of Information and Broadcasting, New Delhi.